Publish

THE
AIR FORCE
LIST

2003

DAN	14·1·03
D 3584	21/1/03
AIR	

ISBN 0 11 772990 6

ISSN 0266 8610

Published by TSO (The Stationery Office) and available from:

Online
www.tso.co.uk/bookshop

Mail, Telephone, Fax & E-mail
TSO
PO Box 29, Norwich NR3 1GN
Telephone orders/General enquiries 0870 600 5522
Fax orders: 0870 600 5533
E-mail: book.orders@tso.co.uk
Textphone 0870 240 3701

TSO Shops
123 Kingsway, London WC2B 6PQ
020 7242 6393 Fax 020 7242 6394
68-69 Bull Street, Birmingham B4 6AD
0121 236 9696 Fax 0121 236 9699
9-21 Princess Street, Manchester M60 8AS
0161 834 7201 Fax 0161 833 0634
16 Arthur Street, Belfast BT1 4GD
028 9023 8451 Fax 028 9023 5401
18-19 High Street, Cardiff CF10 1PT
029 2039 5548 Fax 029 2038 4347
71 Lothian Road, Edinburgh EH3 9AZ
0870 606 5566 Fax 0870 606 5588

TSO Accredited Agents
(see Yellow Pages)

and through good booksellers

CONTENTS

NOTES

The Air Force List is published annually. The Royal Air Force Retired List is published separately and biennially. Both Lists are on sale to the public.

This edition of the Air Force List is corrected to include details of officers serving in the Ministry of Defence, Command Headquarters, etc showing the position generally as at 2 July 2002, the date against names being date of postings to the appointments. Later appointments, where known, are also included. The ranks shown are either substantive or acting.

The Gradation Lists show seniority in existing substantive ranks to include changes published in London Gazette supplements up to that dated 2 July 2002. All officers with a common seniority date are shown in alphabetical order. Acting rank is shown only for Air Officers. In addition, most Air Rank Officers are shown under a separate list rather than the Branch Gradation Lists.

With effect from 1 August 2002 officers of the Provost and Security Branch moved from the Administrative Branch to the Operations Support Branch. However, for this edition entries remain under the Administrative Branch and are indicated by the (ProvSy) specialisation.

Officers who succeed to peerages, baronetcies or courtesy titles, are required to notify the Editor immediately requesting their inclusion in the Air Force List and records of the Ministry of Defence. Such communications should be submitted through the normal channels in order that unit, command and computer records may also be suitably amended. In the case of officers serving at MOD, or on other than a normal RAF administered unit, notification is to be made through the parenting unit.

Entries include honours and awards (as shown on Pages v-vi) and symbols relating to certain courses (as shown on Pages vii-viii). In addition, certain academic and professional qualifications are shown, although not necessarily a complete list of those held on official records. When notifying academic and professional qualifications, attention is drawn to GAI 5094 (The Air Force List—Insertion of Academic and Professional Qualifications) and the need for supporting documentary evidence.

Readers who may notice errors or omissions are invited to notify the Editor quoting the relevant page. Where applicable the procedures detailed in the above paragraphs should be followed. To enable correction of entries for the next edition, all notifications should reach the Editor by 23 June 2003. Such communications should not be sent to the printers or publishers.

The master Distribution List for the free issue of the Air Force List is controlled by the Editor. Defence Storage and Distribution Centre (DSDC) at Llangennech is responsible for the issue of the publication strictly in accordance with the Distribution List. Units are asked to ensure the Editor and DSDC are informed of any reduction in requirements. Unit requests for additional copies and amendment to the master Distribution List should be addressed to DSDC at Llangennech (normally using form MOD 999—Demand for Forms and Publications) and include a clear supporting case for the increase.

Correspondence for the Editor should be addressed to:

> Editor of The Air Force Lists
> PMA(Sec)1M1a1
> RAF Personnel Management Agency
> Room 5, Building 248A
> RAF Innsworth
> Gloucester
> GL3 1EZ

LETTERS DENOTING HONOURS AND AWARDS IN ORDER OF PRECEDENCE

VC............. Victoria Cross.

GC .... George Cross.

KG .... Knight of the Garter.

KT............. Knight of the Thistle.

KP............. Knight of the St. Patrick.

GCB .... Knight Grand Cross or Dame Grand Cross of the Order of the Bath.

OM............ Member of the Order of Merit.

GCSI.......... Knight Grand Commander of the Star of India.

CI .... Order of the Crown of India.

GCMG .... Knight Grand Cross or Dame Grand Cross of the Order of St. Michael and St. George.

GCIE.......... Knight Grand Commander of the Order of the Indian Empire.

GCVO......... Knight Grand Cross or Dame Grand Cross of the Royal Victorian Order.

GBE .... Knight Grand Cross or Dame Grand Cross of the Order of the British Empire.

CH............. Member of the Order of the Companion of Honour.

KCB .... Knight Commander ⎱ of the
DCB .... Dame Commander ⎰ Order of the Bath.

KCSI.......... Knight Commander of the Order of Star of India.

KCMG .... Knight Commander ⎱ of the Order
DCMG .... Dame Commander ⎰ of St. Michael and St. George.

KCIE.......... Knight Commander of the Order of the Indian Empire.

KCVO......... Knight Commander ⎱ of the
DCVO......... Dame Commander ⎰ Royal Victorian Order.

KBE .... Knight Commander ⎱ of the
DBE .... Dame Commander ⎰ Order of the British Empire.

CB............. Companion of the Order of the Bath.

CSI .... Companion of the Order of the Star of India.

CMG.......... Companion of the Order of St. Michael and St. George.

CIE .... Companion of the Order of the Indian Empire.

CVO .... Commander of the Royal Victorian Order.

CBE .... Commander of the Order of the British Empire.

DSO .... Companion of the Distinguished Service Order.

LVO .... Lieutenant of the Royal Victorian Order.

OBE .... Officer of the Order of the British Empire.

ISO .... Companion of the Imperial Service Order.

MVO.......... Member of the Royal Victorian Order.

MBE.......... Member of the Order of the British Empire.

RRC .... Member of the Royal Red Cross.

DSC .... Distinguished Service Cross.

MC .... Military Cross.

DFC .... Distinguished Flying Cross.

AFC .... Air Force Cross.

ARRC .... Associate of the Royal Red Cross.

DCM.......... Distinguished Conduct Medal.

CGM.......... Conspicuous Gallantry Medal.

GM .... George Medal.

DSM.......... Distinguished Service Medal.

MM........... Military Medal.

DFM.......... Distinguished Flying Medal.

QGM .... Queen's Gallantry Medal.

BEM.......... British Empire Medal.

RVM.......... Royal Victorian Medal.

QVRM .... Queens Volunteer Reserves Medal

ERD .... Army Emergency Reserve Decoration.

TD............. Territorial Decoration or Efficiency Decoration.

RD............. Royal Naval Reserve Officer's Decoration.

AE............. Air Efficiency Award.

* .... Denotes the award of a bar to a decoration or medal for gallantry. The award of an additional bar is indicated by the addition of a further star for each award.

NOTE—When the recipient of an Order of Knighthood is promoted to a higher rank within the same Order, the lower rank is absorbed in the higher and therefore the designation of the lower rank is omitted after the name.

OTHER HONOURS AND AWARDS

AK..Knight of Australia
QSO ....Queen's Service Order (New Zealand)

LETTER DENOTING APPOINTMENTS TO THE QUEEN

ADC............................... Aide-de Camp   QHDS............... Honorary Dental Surgeon
QHS........................... Honorary Surgeon   QHP........................Honorary Physician
QHC...........................Honorary Chaplain   QHNS .... Honorary Nursing Sister

EXPLANATIONS OF ABBREVIATIONS AND SYMBOLS
SHOWN IN GRADATION LISTS

a .... Qualified at Specialist Armament Course.

ac .... Qualified in Aircraft Control.

adp .... Qualified Advanced Automatic Date Processing Course.

ae .... Qualified Aero-Systems Engineering Course.

amec............... Qualified Advanced Maintenance Engineering Course. (from Course 8).

asq .... Qualified GD Aero-Systems Course.

awcc .... Graduates of the Air Warfare Commanders' Course, at the Department of Air Warfare. Royal Air Force College Cranwell (including graduates of the Royal Air Force College of Air Warfare Course at the Royal Air Force Flying College).

aws................ Graduates of the Air Warfare Course, at the Department of Air Warfare. Royal Air Force College Cranwell (including graduates of the Royal Air Force College of Air Warfare and graduates of the Air Warfare Course at the Royal Air Force Flying College).

ax .... Qualified at Advanced Armament Course.

cfs* .... General Duties Officers and Master Pilots who have qualified as flying instructors and who hold a Central Flying School A1 instructor category.

cfs .... General Duties Officers and Master Pilots who have qualified as flying instructors and who hold a Central Flying School A2 instructor category.

cfs(ae)............. Qualified Air Electronic Operator Instructors of A2 instructor category.

cfs(c)*............. General Duties Officers and Master Aircrew who have qualified as crewman instructors and who hold a Central Flying School A1 instructor category.

cfs(c).............. General Duties Officers and Master Aircrew who have qualified as crewman instructors and who hold a Central Flying School A2 instructor category.

cfs(n)*............. General Duties Officers who have qualified as navigation instructors and who hold a Central Flying School A1 instructor category.

cfs(n).............. General Duties Officers who have qualified as navigation instructors and who hold a Central Flying School A2 instructor category.

cfs(t) .... Qualified Tactics instructor of A2 instructor category.

df* .... Officers who have completed a Royal Air Force Diamond Jubilee Fellowship.

df.................. Officers who have completed Defence Fellowships.

e .... Qualified at Specialist Engineering Course.

e(t) .... Qualified at Specialist Engineering followed by Torpedo Course.

etps................ Graduate of the Empire Test Pilot's School.

ex .... Qualified at University Course in Engineering in addition to qualifying e.

fc.................. Qualified in Fighter Control.

G† .... Qualified at Army Long Gunnery Staff Course (AA).

G(a)............... Qualified at the Army Gunnery Staff Course, Air Defence.

gw................. Qualified at Advanced Guided Weapons Course or Advanced Weapons Course at the Royal Air Force Technical College or the Guided Weapons Course at the Royal Military College of Science or the Graduate Astronautics Course at the United States Air Force Institute of Technology, Dayton, Ohio.

hcsc .... Qualified at Higher Command & Staff course.

i* .... Qualified as 1st class interpreter/ Diploma 1st class pass.

i.................. Qualified as 2nd class interpreter/ Diploma 2nd class pass.

icc .... Graduate of the Police Staff College (Bramshill) Intermediate Command Course.

idc................. Graduate of the Imperial Defence College, prior to 17 January 1971; or has held an appointment as Commandant or Instructor at the college for a period of one year.

ifp .... International Fellows Programme at the National Defence University in Washington DC.

im .... Supply Officers qualified at an Industrial Management/Management Science Course at Manchester University.

jsdc................ Graduate of the Joint Service Defence College.

jssc .... Graduate of the— Joint Services Staff College, prior to 6 August 1971.

met................ Qualified at University Course in Meteorology.

n .... Qualified at Specialists Navigation Course.

nadc .... Graduate of the NATO Defence College.

ndc .... Graduate of the— National Defence College.

nx .... Qualified at Advanced Specialists Navigation Course. Graduate of the—

oaws(US)........... United States Air War College.

ocds(Can)........... Canadian National Defence College.

ocds(Ind) .... Indian National Defence College.

odc(Aus)........... Australian Joint Service Staff College.

odc(US) .... { United States Armed Forces Staff College.
{ United States Navy War College.

odc(Fr) } .... Cours Superieure Interarmes.
osc(Fr) } (to include French Ecole Superieure de Geurre).

odc(Ge) } .... Command and General Staff
osc(Ge) } College of the Federal German Armed Forces.

osc(Ku)............. Graduate of the Kuwaiti Staff Course.

vii

osc(US)	United States Air Command and Staff College.	qs	Qualified Staff.
pfc	Graduate of the RAPC Long Finance and Accountancy Course.	qss*	Qualified Staff Studies. (2 year course).
ph	Qualified at Specialist Photographic Course.	qss	Qualified Staff Studies. (18 months course).
pi	Qualified in Photographic Interpretation duties.	qss2	Qualified Staff Studies Module 2.
		qss1	Qualified Staff Studies Module 1.
pji	Qualified as a parachutist Instructor.	qtm	Qualified Targeting and Mission Support Course.
ppetc	Long Petroleum Course.		
psc	Royal Air Force Graduates of the Royal Air Force Staff College and Foreign and Commonwealth Staff Colleges approved by the Director General of RAF Training.	qwi	Qualified Weapons Instructor.
		qwi(AD)	Qualified Weapons Instructor (Air Defence).
		qwi(SAW)	Qualified Weapons Instructor (Surface-to-Air Weapons).
psc(a)	Royal Navy and Army graduates of Royal Air Force Staff College.	qwi(T)	Qualified Weapons Instructor (Tornado).
psc(Aus)	RAAF Staff College, Canberra.	rcds	Graduate of the Royal College of Defence Studies.
psc(Aus)	Australian Joint Service Staff College, Canberra.	s	Qualified at Specialist Signals Course.
psc(Can)	Canadian Forces Command and Staff College, Toronto.	scc	Graduate of the Police Staff College (Bramshill) Strategic Command Course.
psc(Fr)	College Interarmees de Defense, Paris.	semc	Qualified Senior Engineering Management Course.
psc(Ge)	Fuhrungsakademie der Bundeswehr, Hamburg.	slmc	Senior Logistics Management Course.
psc(Ind)	Indian Defence Services Staff College, Wellington.	snc	Qualified Staff Navigation Course. (Series beginning April, 1957).
psc(j)	Graduate of Joint Services Command & Staff College.	sowc	Qualified at Senior Officers War Course. Royal Naval War College.
psc(m)	Royal Air Force graduates of the Army Staff College.	ssc	Senior Supply Course.
psc(n)	Royal Air Force graduates of the Royal Naval Staff College.	sx	Qualified at University Course in Electrical Engineering and Wireless Telegraphy in addition to qualifying s.
psc(Spa)	Escuela Superior del Air, Madrid.	TIG(a)	Trained in Gunnery (Air Defence).
psc(US)	United States Command and Staff College, Maxwell AFB.	tp	Pilot graduate of the Empire Test Pilots' School (ETPS). United States Air Force Test Pilots' School (USAFtps), United States Navy Test Pilots' School (USNtps), or French Ecole du Personnel Navigant d'Essais et de Reception (EPNER).
psm	Advanced Certificates of the Royal Military School of Music.		
ptsc	Graduate of the Royal Military College of Science.		
qab	Qualified Air Battle.	ts	Supply Officers who have completed the Cranfield Institute of Technology MSc course in Transport Studies.
qcc	Qualified at Officers Command Courses.		
qhti	Qualified Helicopter Tactics Instructor.	w	Qualified at the Senior Weapons Course.
qsb	Qualified Support Battlestaff Course.		

SYMBOLS DENOTING AIRCREW CATEGORY AND SPECIALIZATION WITHIN BRANCHES

(P)	Pilot		
(N)	Navigator		
(AEO)	Air Electronics Officer		General Duties Branch
(Sig)	Signaller		
(ENG)	Engineer		
(ALM)	Air Loadmaster		
(AG)	Air Gunner		
(ATC)	Air Traffic Control		
(FC)	Fighter Control		Operations Support Branch
(INT)	Intelligence		
(FLTOPS)	Flight Operations		
(REGT)	Regiments		

(A)	Armament	
(E)	Engineer	
(EI)	Electrical Engineer	
(GS)	Ground Support	
(LA)	Electronic Air	Engineer Branch
(LG)	Electronic Ground	
(M)	Mechanical Engineer	
(MC)	Marine Craft	
(Ph)	Photography	
(S)	Signals	
(Sec)	Secretarial	*Administrative Branch
(Trg)	Training	
(Cat)	Catering	
(P.Ed)	Physical Education	
(ProvSy)	Provost Security	
(F)	Medical Officers qualified as Flight Medical Officer.	

* Symbol denotes former specialization for group captains and wing commanders and current specialization for other officers.

ROYAL AIR FORCE
"Per Ardua ad Astra"

THE QUEEN

Air Commodore-in-Chief. . . . . Royal Auxiliary Air Force (1.6.53)

Air Commodore-in-Chief. . . . . Royal Air Force Regiment (1.6.53)

Commandant-in-Chief . . . . Royal Air Force College, Cranwell (27.5.60)

Honorary Air Commodore . . . . Royal Air Force Marham (11.6.77)

Commonwealth Forces

Air Commodore-in-Chief. . . . . Air Reserve (of Canada), Royal Australian Air Force Reserve, Territorial Air Force (of New Zealand)

MEMBERS OF THE ROYAL FAMILY

His Royal Highness The Prince Philip, Duke of Edinburgh, KG KT OM GBE AC QSO

Marshal of the Royal Air Force . . . . (15.1.53)

Air Commodore-in-Chief. . . . . Air Training Corps (15.1.53)

Honorary Air Commodore . . . . Royal Air Force Kinloss (11.6.77)

Commonwealth Forces

Marshal of the Royal Australian Air Force

Marshal of the Royal New Zealand Air Force

Air Commodore-in-Chief Royal Canadian Air Cadets

His Royal Highness The Prince of Wales, KG KT GCB AK QSO ADC

Air Vice-Marshal . . . . (14.11.98)

Honorary Air Commodore . . . . Royal Air Force Valley (1.4.93)

Commonwealth Forces

Air Commodore-in-Chief. . . . . Royal New Zealand Air Force

Colonel-in-Chief . . . . Air Reserve Group of Air Command (of Canada)

His Royal Highness The Duke of York, CVO ADC

Honorary Air Commodore . . . . Royal Air Force Lossiemouth (15.9.96)

Her Royal Highness The Princess Royal, KG KT GCVO QSO

Honorary Air Commodore . . . . Royal Air Force Lyneham (11.6.77)

Honorary Air Commodore . . . . University of London Air Squadron (2.9.93)

Her Royal Highness Princess Alice
Duchess of Gloucester, GCB CI GCVO GBE

Air Chief Marshal . . . . (23.2.90)

Air Chief Commandant . . . . Women, Royal Air Force (1.4.94)

1

His Royal Highness The Duke of Gloucester GCVO

Honorary Air Marshal. . . . . Royal Air Force (1.9.96)

Honorary Air Commodore . . . . Royal Air Force Odiham (1.4.93)

Honorary Air Commodore . . . . 501 (County of Gloucester) Squadron Royal Auxiliary Air Force

His Royal Highness The Duke of Kent, KG GCMG GCVO ADC

Honorary Air Chief Marshal . . . . Royal Air Force (1.7.96)

Honorary Air Commodore . . . . Royal Air Force Leuchars (1.4.93)

Her Royal Highness Princess Alexandra, The Hon. Lady Ogilvy, GCVO

Patron and Air Chief Commandant . . . . Princess Mary's Royal Air Force Nursing Service (1.11.66)

Honorary Air Commodore . . . . Royal Air Force Cottesmore (15.9.00)

Air Aides-de-Camp to The Queen

Air Chief Marshal Sir Peter Squire, GCB DFC AFC ADC DSc FRAeS

Air Chief Marshal Sir John Day, KCB OBE ADC BSc

Aides-de-Camp to The Queen

Air Commodore M. J. Good, ADC MIDPM MCMI

Air Commodore M. J. Routledge, ADC BSc

Group Captain M. A. Sharpe, OBE ADC

Group Captain P. W. Rycroft, OBE ADC

Group Captain L. J. Burrell, ADC BEng CEng FRAes

Group Captain R. F. Garwood, DFC ADC MA

Group Captain P. C. Goodman, MBE ADC BSc

Group Captain F. F. Amroliwala, OBE ADC MA MBA

Group Captain A. J. Pollock, ADC

Group Captain B. L. Bates, ADC BA

Group Captain R. G. Kemp, QVRM AE ADC FRIN RAuxAF

Director of Royal Travel

Group Captain T. C. Hewlett, OBE

Extra Equerries to The Queen

Air Commodore the Hon. Timothy Elworthy, CVO CBE

Group Captain T. C. Hewlett, OBE

Air Vice-Marshal Sir John Severne, KCVO OBE AFC DL

Air Commodore Sir Archie Winskill, KCVO CBE DFC* AE MRAeS

Honorary Physicians to The Queen

Air Vice-Marshal W. J. Pike, QHP MSc MB BS MRCGP MRCS MFOM DRCOG DAvMed LRCP

Air Commodore S. R. C. Dougherty, QHP MSc MB BS FFOM FCMI FRAeS DRCGO DAvMed

Air Commodore B. T. Morgans, QHP MB BCh FRCS (Glas.)

Air Commodore E. J. Thornton, QHP MB ChB FCMI MFOM DAvMed

Honorary Surgeons to The Queen

Air Commodore S. A. Cullen, QHS MB ChB FRCPath FRAeS DCP

Air Commodore I. D. Mitchell, QHS MDA BSc MB BS FRAeS MRCGP MHSM DRCOG DAvMed AFOM

Air Commodore M. Ranger, QHS MB BS DAvMed AFOM MRAeS

Group Captain A. J. Batchelor, CBE QHS BSc MB BS FRCP DRCOG DAvMed

Honorary Dental Surgeons to The Queen

Air Commodore J. Reid, QHDS BDS MGDSRCPS (Glas)

Group Captain P. M. Gallagher, QHDS BDS BA MGDSRCS(Ed)

Honorary Chaplains to The Queen

The Venerable R. D. Hesketh, QHC BA

The Reverend Monsignor T. J. Devany, QHC GV

The Reverend S. J. Ware, QHC BA

The Reverend P. W. Mills, QHC BD CPS

FOREIGN SOVEREIGNS
AND
MEMBERS OF FOREIGN ROYAL FAMILIES
who hold Honorary Commissions in the Royal Air Force

Air Chief Marshal

HM The Sultan of Brunei Darussalam GCB, GCMG 5.11.92

Air Marshal

H.R.H. Prince Bernhard of the Netherlands, GCB GCVO GBE 15.9.64

DEFENCE COUNCIL

AIR FORCE BOARD OF THE DEFENCE COUNCIL

The Right HONOURABLE

GEOFFREY HOON, MP
Secretary of State for Defence
(Chairman of the Defence Council and Chairman of the Air Force Board of the Defence Council)

The Right HONOURABLE ADAM INGRAM, JP MP
Minister of State for the Armed Forces

The LORD BACH of Lutterworth
Parliamentary Under Secretary of State and Minister for Defence Procurement

Dr LEWIS MOONIE, MP
Parliamentary Under Secretary of State for Defence and Minister for Veterans Affairs

Air Chief Marshal Sir PETER SQUIRE, GCB DFC AFC ADC DSc FRAeS RAF
Chief of the Air Staff

Mr IAN ANDREWS, CBE TD
Second Permanent Under Secretary of State

Air Chief Marshal Sir JOHN DAY, KCB OBE ADC BSc RAF
Commander-in-Chief Strike Command

Air Marshal Sir CHRISTOPHER COVILLE, KCB BA FCIPD FRAeS RAF
Air Member for Personnel
Commander-in-Chief Personnel and Training Command

Air Vice-Marshal P. O. STURLEY, CB MBE BSc FRAeS RAF
Assistant Chief of the Air Staff

Air Vice-Marshal B. M. THORNTON, MSc BSc CEng FIMechE FCMI, RAF
Controller Aircraft & Executive Director 3

Air Vice-Marshal P. LIDDELL, CB BSc CEng FIEE FRAeS RAF
Director General Equipment Support (Air)

DEFENCE STAFF

SECRETARY OF STATE FOR DEFENCE
The Right HONOURABLE GEOFFREY HOON, MP

Private Secretary
Mr J. Miller

MINISTER OF STATE FOR THE ARMED FORCES
The Right HONOURABLE ADAM INGRAM, JP MP

Private Secretary
Mr D. Applegate

PARLIAMENTARY UNDER SECRETARY OF STATE AND MINISTER FOR DEFENCE PROCUREMENT
The LORD BACH of Lutterworth

Private Secretary
Mr D. Hatcher

PARLIAMENTARY UNDER SECRETARY OF STATE FOR DEFENCE AND MINISTER FOR VETERANS AFFAIRS
Dr LEWIS MOONIE, MP

Private Secretary
Miss K. Stevens

Military Assistant
Lieutenant Commander D. Radakin, RN

CHIEF OF THE DEFENCE STAFF
Admiral Sir MICHAEL BOYCE, GCB OBE ADC

Principal Staff Officer
Brigadier A. R. D. SHIRREFF, CBE

Deputy Principal Staff Officer
Group Captain J. Stinton, MA BA RAF

Military Assistants
Commander H. Parker, RN
Captain O. Lee, RM

PERMANENT UNDER SECRETARY OF STATE
Sir KEVIN TEBBIT, KCB CMG

Private Secretary
Mr D. Wilson

VICE CHIEF OF THE DEFENCE STAFF
Air Chief Marshal Sir ANTHONY BAGNALL, KCB OBE FRAeS RAF

Private Secretary
Mr R. Hayes

Military Assistant
Lieutenant Colonel A. P. Bristow

Assistant Military Assistant
Flight Lieutenant J. S. Casebury, BA

DEFENCE SERVICES SECRETARY
Major General C. H. ELLIOTT

Military Assistant
Wing Commander C. J. Oxland, OBE ACIS

DIRECTORATE GENERAL CORPORATE COMMUNICATION
Director News
   Mr M. HOWARD
Private Secretary
   Mrs A. Southwell

DIRECTOR OF CORPORATE COMMUNICATION (RAF)
   Air Commodore P. R. THOMAS, MBE BSc RAF
Personal Assistant
   Mrs B. Caton

CHIEFS OF STAFF SECRETARIAT
SECRETARY CHIEFS OF STAFF COMMITTEE
   Group Captain M. Swan, LLB RAF
Assistant Secretaries
   Wing Commander A. S. Barmby, BSc RAF
   Commander E. A. Spencer, BEd MA FRMets RN

DEPUTY CHIEF OF THE DEFENCE STAFF (COMMITMENTS)
   Lieutenant General Sir ANTHONY PIGOTT, KCB CBE
Military Assistant 1
   Wing Commander M. N. Driver, BSc(Eng) MRAeS RAF
Military Assistant 2
   Major D. L. Kassapian, MA BA RM
ASSISTANT CHIEF OF THE DEFENCE STAFF (OPERATIONS)
   Air Vice-Marshal P. B. WALKER, CBE BA RAF
Military Assistant
   Lieutenant Commander J. E. Thomas, RN
DIRECTOR GENERAL OPERATIONAL POLICY
   Mr D. BOWEN
DIRECTOR OF NAVAL OPERATIONS
   Commodore A. P. DICKINSON, RN
DIRECTOR OF MILITARY OPERATIONS
   Brigadier J. N. R. HOUGHTON, CBE Late GREEN HOWARDS
DIRECTOR OF AIR OPERATIONS
   Air Commodore S. G. G. DALTON, BSc FRAeS MCMI
DIRECTOR OF JOINT WARFARE
   Commodore A. R. NANCE, OBE BSc RN
DIRECTOR OF OPERATIONAL CAPABILITY
   Commodore C. J. PARRY, MA RN
DIRECTOR OF SPECIAL FORCES
   Brigadier G. C. M. LAMB, OBE
DIRECTOR OF OVERSEAS MILITARY ACTIVITY
   Brigadier A. STEWART, CBE
DIRECTOR BALKANS
   Mr J. TESH
HEAD OF SECRETARIAT (OVERSEAS)
   Mr S. J. POLLARD, MA MPhil
HOME AND SPECIAL FORCES SECRETARIAT
   Mr C. DAVENPORT
HEAD OF ATTACHÉ AND ADVISOR ADMINISTRATION AND LIAISON
   Captain M. A. Johnson, RN

JOINT ARMS CONTROL IMPLEMENTATION GROUP
Colonel J. R. M. Hackett, CBE Late WFR

GULF VETERANS ILLNESS UNIT
Mr D. J. S. APPLEGATE

Group Captains

T. Almond, MBE MA BA FRIN MCMI
A. G. O. Dee
J. N. Fradgley, OBE AFC BSc FRAeS
P. W. Gray, MPhil BSc LLB
K. J. Pellatt FCMI
N. C. Randle, BSc MRAeS MRIN
C. A. Suckling, MBE BSc CEng MIEE
G. A. Wright, OBE BSc

Wing Commanders

C. J. Abbott
A. M. Bone, AFC
N. Bray
D. Burley
I. D. Chalmers, MA
R. J. Chatterton
J. M. Clifford, MSc BSc
J. E. Coote, MBE
B. A. Cornwell, BSc ARCS
P. A. Davies
N. J. Goodenough, MA BSc
A. K. Groves
A. Monkman, BA
R. W. Munday
D. R. Paton, OBE BA
L. E. F. Pearce
J. V. Plumb
M. G. Richardson, OBE
I. M. Robertson, RAFR
C. M. Scott, AFC MPhil BA
D. M. Shaw
A. D. Stevenson, OBE
K. N. Strickland
D. T. Turnbull BSc
A. M. Turner, MSc
R. J. R. Ward, MSc BSc
J. P. White, BSc
D. A Wilson, MA BSc
S. J. Wilson, BA
C. D. L. Winwood, BSc CEng MIEE

Principals and Equivalent Grades

N. F. W. Blatchley, BSc
Dr S. Cholerton
J. Chorley
M. J. Davis
G. N. Dean
A. J. B. Elford
M. House
B. Merrick
Mr P. Rimmer
Mrs B. M. E. Rodgers
S. D. Trout, MCIPS
Mrs T. Vennai

DEPUTY CHIEF OF THE DEFENCE STAFF (EQUIPMENT CAPABILITY)
Air Marshal Sir JOCK STIRRUP, KCB AFC FRAeS FCMI

Military Assistants
Lieutenant Colonel R. J. Cripwell, MSc FRGS RE
Captain B. J. Warrack, BA LD

CAPABILITY MANAGER (STRIKE)
Air Vice-Marshal N. J. DAY, CBE BSc(Eng) ACGI

CAPABILITY MANAGER (MANOEUVRE)
Major General A. C. FIGGURES, CBE MA

CAPABILITY MANAGER (STRATEGIC DEPLOYMENT)
Rear Admiral C. R. STYLE, RN

CAPABILITY MANAGER (INFORMATION SUPERIORITY)
Major General R. H. G. FULTON, RM

DIRECTOR EQUIPMENT CAPABILITY (THEATRE AIRSPACE)
Air Commodore A. D. SWEETMAN, OBE BA RAF

DIRECTOR EQUIPMENT CAPABILITY (DEEP STRIKE)
Air Commodore A. T. HUDSON, OBE BSc RAF

Group Captains
T. Almond, MBE MA BA FRIN MCMI
T. M. Anderson, DSO MA MRAeS
J. A. Ball, AFC
L. J. F. Barnes, MSc
S. J. Bollom, BSc CEng MIMechE
S. D. Butler
C. H. Green, MA BSc CEng MRAeS
S. L. Parkinson
A. J. Sudlow, MBE BSc

Wing Commanders
R. J. Atkinson
N. P. Ayres, BSc
M. Barley, BA
T. Bennington, BSc
B. A. J. Bray, BSc
Q. L. Dixon, MA MSc BSc CEng MIEE
I. M. Draper, BA
D. B. Fares, MInstAM MHSM MCMI RAFR
M. C. Fenlon, BSc(Eng) CEng MRAeS
C. M. H. Hawes, BA
P. C. Jacobs
J. K. Jenkins
D. J. Keenan, OBE
N. W. G. Laird, BA
D. W. Leech, MSc BA BEng CEng MIEE
N. G. Millington, IEng FIIE
I. Mowat
T. Newby
J. H. Scholtens, BA
N. D. Sharpe, BA
M. K. Small, MSc BSc
G. D. Soul
R. D. Todd, BSc(Econ)
J. G. Wheatcroft, MSc BSc(Eng) CEng MIEE
J. Wiltshire

POLICY DIRECTOR
S. WEBB, CBE

Private Secretary
J. Horner

DIRECTOR GENERAL JOINT DOCTRINE AND CONCEPTS CENTRE
Air Vice-Marshal I. W. McNICOLL, CBE BSc FRAeS RAF

HEAD OF BDS(W)
Air Vice-Marshal J. H. THOMPSON, CB RAF

ASSISTANT CHIEF OF DEFENCE STAFF (POLICY)
Air Vice-Marshal D. A. HOBART, MPhil MCMI RAF

Military Assistant
Lieutenant Commander P. Green, RN

DIRECTOR OF POLICY PLANNING
P. TURNER

DIRECTOR OF FORCE DEVELOPMENT
Commodore A. RICHARDS, RN

DIRECTOR OF NUCLEAR POLICY
Commodore M. FITZGERALD, OBE, RN

DEFENCE DIPLOMACY STAFF
Captain C. PEACH, RN

DIRECTOR GENERAL INTERNATIONAL SECURITY POLICY
B. R. HAWTIN, CB

DIRECTOR EUROPE
I. R. LEE

DIRECTOR NATO
Air Commodore R. H. LACEY, MA BA RAF

DIRECTOR OF CENTRAL AND EASTERN EUROPE
M. HAWORTH

DIRECTOR OF PROLIFERATION AND ARMS CONTROL SECRETARIAT
P. G. SHULTE

DIRECTOR OF CHEMICAL AND BIOLOGICAL WEAPONS POLICY
C. GORDON

HEAD OF PROTOCOL
Colonel M. Corbet Burcher, Retd

DIRECTOR GENERAL OF CORPORATE COMMUNICATIONS
M. HOWARD

DIRECTOR NEWS
D. PLEWS

DIRECTOR OF CORPORATE COMMUNICATIONS SERVICES
Mr C. WILLIAMS

DIRECTOR OF CORPORATE COMMUNICATIONS (RAF)
Air Commodore P. R. THOMAS, MBE BSc RAF

DIRECTOR OF CORPORATE COMMUNICATIONS (NAVY)
Commodore R. LEAMAN

DIRECTOR OF CORPORATE COMMUNICATIONS (ARMY)
Brigadier M. SYKES

POLICY AND COMMITMENTS MANAGEMENT UNIT
P. S. O'BRIEN

Wing Commanders
J. J. Byard
A. J. Byford, MA MA
A. I. Ferries, BSc
J. D. Spencer, BSc
J. Taylor, MCMI

I. R. Tolfts
N. E Wharmby, OBE MA BSc

Retired Officer
Wing Commander G. Clark

Senior Principals
R. Cockram
J. P. Harrison
R. Holderness
D. Howard
D. Murtagh

Principals
J. Babbage
P. Balmer
T. Bonney
S. Elwell
G. Hicks
C. McCafferty
A. P. Nicholson
M. J. Shaps
T. Tichmarsh
R. Vincent
A. Willis
B. Wilson
A. Wood

DEPUTY CHIEF OF THE DEFENCE STAFF (PERSONNEL)
Lieutenant General A. M. D. PALMER, CBE BSc Late RGJ

Military Assistant
Commander S. N. White, BA RN
Assistant Military Assistant
Flight Lieutenant M. V. Taylor, MSc BSc

DEFENCE SERVICES SECRETARY & DIRECTOR GENERAL RESERVE FORCES AND CADETS
Major General C. H. ELLIOTT, CBE

Staff Officer
Wing Commander C. J. Oxland, OBE ACIS RAF

Staff Officer/Honours & Awards
Lieutenant Colonel S. J. Cadec, AGC (SPS)

DIRECTOR OF RESERVE FORCES AND CADETS
Brigadier T. H. LANG, TD TA

DIRECTOR OF MILITARY OUTPLACEMENT SERVICES
Brigadier D. H. GODSAL, MBE BA

DIRECTOR GENERAL SERVICE PERSONNEL POLICY
Ms E. McLAUGHLIN

DIRECTOR SERVICE PERSONNEL POLICY PAY & ALLOWANCES
Air Commodore D. J. POCOCK, BA RAF

DIRECTOR SERVICE PERSONNEL POLICY SERVICE CONDITIONS
Mr M. FULLER

DIRECTOR SERVICE PERSONNEL POLICY MANNING AND WELFARE
Commodore N. C. PRESTON-JONES

DIRECTOR SERVICE PERSONNEL POLICY PENSIONS & VETERANS
Mr J. IREMONGER

DIRECTOR JOINT PERSONNEL ADMINISTRATION STRATEGY STUDY
Air Commodore J. D. TONKS, BSc RAF

DIRECTOR GENERAL TRAINING & EDUCATION
Major General A. P. RIDGWAY

DIRECTOR DEFENCE TRAINING & EDUCATION
Commodore W. D. M. FAIRBAIRN

DIRECTOR DEFENCE TRAINING REVIEW IMPLEMENTATION
Mr C. KERR

DIRECTOR PAY-AS-YOU-DINE
Brigadier P. J. T. MAGGS, CBE

CHIEF EXECUTIVE DEFENCE HOUSING EXECUTIVE
Mr J. R. WILSON

DIRECTOR OF SERVICE LIAISON DEFENCE HOUSING EXECUTIVE
Brigadier C. D. LUNN

DIRECTOR OF HOUSING, DEFENCE HOUSING EXECUTIVE
Mrs W. JARVIS

DIRECTOR OF FINANCE & SECRETARIAT, DEFENCE HOUSING EXECUTIVE
Mr A. ADAMS

CHIEF EXECUTIVE ARMED FORCES PERSONNEL ADMINISTRATION AGENCY
Mr T. S. LORD, FCMA

DEPUTY CHIEF EXECUTIVE AFPAA & DIRECTOR OPERATIONS
Commodore T. A. SPIRES, BSc CDipAF FCIPD MINucE

DIRECTOR STRATEGY
Air Commodore B. J. JERSTICE, CBE, BA FCIPD RAF

DIRECTOR DEVELOPMENT
Brigadier R. LEIGHTON, BSc FCMA

DIRECTOR PERSONNEL & FINANCE
Mrs L. D. KYLE

Group Captains
I. Harvey, BSc
P. G. H. Hodcroft, BSc MBCS
S. C. Knight, MA FCIPD
M. T. Leatt, BSc
R. Paterson, OBE BSc
F. L Turner

Wing Commanders
L. Carver, BA
S. A. Gracie, MA BA
A. R. Mitra
C. J. Hill, FISM MCMI
I. Melvin, BSc
D. StJ. Salisbury
M. J. Shackleton, BSc
I. R. Tench, PhD MA

Principals and Equivalent Grades
Ms A. J. Ashbolt
P. Aylott
Mrs S. Bampton
K. R. Banner
M. Bennett
M. Bevis
K. Bissex
Dr R. Bratt
Ms D. Brothers
P. Buckley
Ms P. Dean
P. Donaldson
A. S. French
I. Gibson
P. Hancock
Mrs S. Holroyd
I. S. Manson
S. McDonald
Mrs. G. Monaghan
Mrs A. Miller
R. Mitchell
D. P. Pope
K. Robinson
S. Robinson
M. Sands
R. Sharpe
J. R. E. Sinfield
D. Sivers
J. H. Spiers
A. P. Suggitt
J. W. Sutherland
I. Swann
J. Thrower
Ms A. M. Wilsdon
D. Woodhead

CIVILIAN STAFF

PERMANENT UNDER SECRETARY OF STATE
Sir KEVIN TEBBIT, KCB CMG

Private Secretary
D. Wilson

SECOND PERMANENT UNDER SECRETARY OF STATE
  Mr IAN ANDREWS, CBE TD

Private Secretary
  Ms A. Forsyth

FINANCE DIRECTOR
  C. V. BALMER, CB

Private Secretary
  S. P. Shelley

PERSONNEL DIRECTOR
  R. P. HATFIELD, CBE

Private Secretary
  C. V. Bruce

POLICY DIRECTOR
  S. WEBB, CBE

Private Secretary
  M. Crabtree

DIRECTOR GENERAL SERVICE PERSONNEL POLICY
  Mrs E. M. McLOUGHLIN, CBE

Personal Secretary
  Mrs J. M. Amdur

COMMAND SECRETARY RAF STRIKE COMMAND
  I. G. McEWEN

Personal Secretary
  Mrs D. Cole

COMMAND SECRETARY RAF PERSONNEL AND TRAINING COMMAND
  R. J. ROOKS

Personal Secretary
  Mrs J. Coker

DEFENCE SCIENTIFIC STAFF

CHIEF SCIENTIFIC ADVISER
  Professor Sir KEITH O'NIONS, FRS

PRIVATE SECRETARY
  Dr R. Freer

SCIENCE & TECHNOLOGY DIRECTOR
  Mr G. H. B. JORDAN

PRIVATE SECRETARY
  Dr H. McNaughton

DIRECTOR GENERAL (RESEARCH AND TECHNOLOGY)
  Mr M. MARKIN

DIRECTOR GENERAL (SCRUTINY AND ANALYSIS)
  Mr N. BENNET

DIRECTOR STRATEGIC TECHNOLOGIES
  Mr P. ROPER

DIRECTOR TECHNOLOGY DEVELOPMENT
  Professor P. SUTTON

DIRECTOR (SCRUTINY & ANALYSIS) LAND/AIR (D (S & A) LAND/AIR)
  Mr N. Barnet

DIRECTOR (SCRUTINY & ANALYSIS) SEA/CIS (D (S & A) SEA/CIS)
  Dr A. SINDEN

DIRECTOR (SCRUTINY & ANALYSIS) P & P (D (S & A) P & P)
  Mr A. EVERETT

DIRECTOR SCIENCE & TECHNOLOGY POLICY
  Ms F. STRENS

MET OFFICE EXECUTIVE AGENCY

CHIEF EXECUTIVE
Mr P. D. EWINS, CB FREng FRAeS

SENIOR PERSONAL SECRETARY
Mrs M. J. Daubney

DEFENCE PROCUREMENT AGENCY

CHIEF OF DEFENCE PROCUREMENT AND CHIEF EXECUTIVE
Sir ROBERT WALMSLEY, KCB FREng

Military Assistant
Captain C. Hockley, RN

Private Secretary
Mr J. Palmer

DEPUTY CHIEF EXECUTIVE
Mr D. J. GOULD

Private Secretary
Ms P. Burton

EXECUTIVE BOARD DIRECTORS

Executive Director 1
Mr I. D. FAUSET, CB

Staff Officer
Mr I. N. Webb, BSc CDipAF

Executive Director 2/Master General of the Ordnance
Major General P. GILCHRIST

Military Assistant
Lieutenant Colonel S. Wilson, RTR

Executive Director 3/CONTROLLER AIRCRAFT
Air Vice-Marshal B. M. THORNTON, MSc BSc CEng FIMechE FCMI FRAeS RAF

Military Assistant
Commander A. Martin, RN

Controller Aircraft Co-Ordinator
Wing Commander J. Faulkes, MA RAF

Executive Director 4/CONTROLLER OF THE NAVY
Rear Admiral N. C. F. GUILD, BA PhD MIEE MIMA

Military Assistant
Commander A. G. Finlayson, MA RN

Executive Director 5/ AND DIRECTOR GENERAL COMMERCIAL MOD
Mr S. L. PORTER, MCIPS FRAeS

Military Assistant
Major R. Bruce

Executive Director 6
Ms S. M. SCHOLEFIELD, CMG

Senior Personal Secretary
Mrs S. Harvey

INTEGRATED PROJECT TEAMS

Air Command & Control Systems
Mr T. Ashton, BSc AMIME MIME MIMgt
Wing Commander P. J. White, IEng FIIE RAF
Wing Commander H. A. Whiteway, RAF

Airborne Stand Off Radar
Mr W. CHRISPIN
Wing Commander S. A. Moss, MBE MSc BSc CEng MIEE MRAeS RAF

Advanced Short Range Air-to-Air Missile
Mr E. O'Donnell, MInstP

Aerial Target Systems
Mr. T. A. Jones

Attack Helicopters
Captain D. Reid, RN

A400M
Mr S. MOFFATT
Wing Commander G. C. Martin, RAF

Beyond Visual Range Air-to-Air Missile
Mr M. A. Smith

Brimstone
Mr P. Gates, CEng MRAeS

Conventionally Armed Stand Off Missile
Commander P. Hammond, BEng MSc CEng MIEE RN

Combat Support Vehicle Heavy
Mr P. G. Jennings, BSc MSc CEng MIMechE MAPM

Combat Support Vehicle Light
Colonel J. J. Little, OBE MBA MILT

Command Support and Information Systems
Mr P. D. BEAZLEY, MA(Cantab) CEng MIMechE

Communications Messaging
Wing Commander M. P. Aleandri, BSc RAF

Cryptographic and Secure Systems
Mr S. R. Jackson, OBE BSc CEng MIMechE MAPM

Eurofighter
Air Commodore D. N. WILLIAMS, OBE BSc CEng FRAeS RAF
Group Captain G. E. McElroy, MDA BSc CEng MRAeS RAF
Wing Commander R. M. Allchorne, RAF
Wing Commander R. Betteridge, MSc BSc ARCS RAF
Wing Commander C. A. R. Burgess, MSc RAF
Wing Commander J. G. Chapman, MA MSc BA BSc RAF
Wing Commander R. J. Hargrave, BSc CEng MRAeS RAF
Wing Commander J. J. Hitchcock, RAF
Wing Commander D. J. M. Honeyman, BSc RAF
Wing Commander G. J. Kevan, RAF
Wing Commander P. Martin, MSc BSc CEng MIEE RAF
Wing Commander N. J. Scotchmer, BSc RAF

Flight Simulation and Synthetic Trainers
Group Captain V. Smith, MSc MBA BEd MCIPD MCMI AMBCS RAF

Joint Combat Aircraft
Commodore S. M. HENLEY, MBE BSc CEng FRAeS RN
Wing Commander S. M. Bell, BSc(Eng) RAF

Future Offensive Air System
Mr J. H. LYLE, MSc CEng MIEE RCNC
Wing Commander R. T. Johnston, MA RAF

Future Strategic Tanker Aircraft
Mr L. M. DOWN, MSc BEng CEng MIMechE
Group Captain P. A Atherton, RAF
Wing Commander R. J. Barwell, BSc CEng MRAeS RAF
Wing Commander P. F. Lindsay, MBE RAF

Group Based Air Defence
Air Commodore R. C. MOORE, MBE BSc RAF
Wing Commander N. W. Mullings, BSc RAF

Imagery & Geospatial Systems
Dr J. Bishop
Wing Commander I. R. Tyrrell, MSc BEng RAF

Infra Red Counter Measures
Mr T. Watts, BSc (Hons)

Military Airborne Communications and Homing Systems
Mr T. McKinley, IEng MIIE

Nimrod MRA4
Mr D. King
Group Captain A. J. Goody, MA BSc(Eng) CEng FRAeS ACGI RAF
Wing Commander S. J. Parkinson, RAF
Wing Commander C. R. Purser, RAF

Nuclear Biological and Chemical
Colonel A. Pedder

Precision Guided Bombs
Wing Commander P. Barker, RAF

Satellite Communication Acquisition Team
Mr S. KERSHAW
Wing Commander A. J. Barnes, BSc RAF

Sensors, Avionics and Navigation Systems
Mr D. LASCELLES

Strategic Terrestrial Radio Systems
Mr I. H. WAKELING, MSc CEng MRINA APMP RCNC
Wing Commander D. A. R. Ward, BSc CEng MIEE RAF

Support Amphibious Battlefield Rotorcraft
Mr C. D. Trout, MSc BSc CEng MIEE RCNC
Wing Commander G. M. Horwood, RAF

Tactical Datalinks
Mr P. Blakiston

United Kingdom Military Flying Training System
Air Commodore P. A. COKER, OBE FRAeS FCMI RAF
Wing Commander T. W. Jones, RAF

SUPPORT GROUPS

Air/Land Technology Group
Mr C. DALLIMORE, CEng BSc MRAeS
Group Captain A. A. YOUNG, MA MRAeS RAF
Wing Commander R. D. Jenkins, RAF
Wing Commander C. J. Woods, MSc BSc(Eng) CEng MIMechE MRAeS RAF

Defence Ordnance Group
Mr J. J. McLAY, BSc CEng MIEE RCNC
Wing Commander L. A. Tilbrook, MSc BEng RAAF

Integration Authority
Professor P. BROOK, FREng FIEE
Wing Commander J. D. Wilmshurst-Smith, RAF

DEFENCE ORDNANCE SAFETY GROUP MANAGEMENT BOARD

Postal Address—Defence Ordnance Safety Group,
Ash 2b, MOD Abbey Wood, # 3212
Bristol BS34 8JH
Telephone No 0117-91-35500

Director

J. J. McLAY, BSc CEng MIEE RCNC 30.7.01

Members

Dr G. D. West, BSc PhD 2.10.00
Colonel A. Amber, MBE BSc(Eng) MSc 8.4.02
J. A. Weldon, OBE BSc CEng MIMechE RCNC 2.10.00
D. McDonald, BEng MSc AMIEE RCNC 2.10.00
R. Wallace 2.10.00

Secretary

A. M. Jenkins, BEng AMIEE 3.10.01

PERMANENT JOINT HEADQUARTERS (UK)

Postal Address—NORTHWOOD, MIDDLESEX, HA6 3TJ
Telephone No 01923 826161

Chief of Joint Operations
Lieutenant General J. G. REITH, CB CBE 6.8.01

Military Assistant
Wing Commander K. B. McCann 23.4.01

Deputy Chief of Joint Operations (Operations)
Major General R. A. FRY, CBE RM 30.5.02

Military Assistant
Major P. A. Harkness 10.1.02

Deputy Chief of Joint Operations (Operational Support)
Air Vice-Marshall P. A ROBINSON, OBE FRAes 17.12.01

Military Assistant
Major J. A. J. Morris, RM 27.8.02

Staff Duties Branch
Wing Commander C. M. West, BSc 19.11.01

Assistant Chief of Staff J1/J4
Brigadier M. KERLEY, CBE QGM 18.12.00
Group Captain N. P. Beet, MA BA 2.9.02
Wing Commander J. D. Bleeker, MBA BA BSc MCIPS 23.11.01
Wing Commander R. J. M. Broadbridge, MB BS MRCGP DRGOG DAvMed DOccMed 3.9.01

Assistant Chilef of Staff J2
Commodore C. R. MUNNS 16.4.02

Assistant Chief of Staff J3
Air Commodore C. R. LOADER, OBE 29.10.01
Group Captain J. R. Jones, CBE 10.12.01
Wing Commander A. D. Green, OBE BA 11.2.02
Wing Commander P. O. Lloyd, MBE MBA 29.10.01
Wing Commander P. A. Round, MA BSc MRAeS 23.3.02
Wing Commander W. S. Taylor, MBE MSc BSc MCMI 9.1.02

Assistant Chief of Staff J5
Brigadier N. H. ROLLO 11.12.01
Group Captain M. A. J. Barnes, BSc 22.6.02
Wing Commander D. J. Hayward 13.11.00

Assistant Chief of Staff J6
Air Commodore B. M. WYNN, OBE, BSc 6.12.01
Wing Commander M. Greatorex 28.11.00
Wing Commander S. R. Wilkinson, MDA BSc CEng MRAeS MCMI 13.8.01

Assistant Chief of Staff J7
Brigadier A. R. FREER, OBE 11.12.00
Group Captain A. F. P. Dezonie, OBE 30.4.02
Wing Commander T. R. Barton 22.4.02
Wing Commander R. J. T. Hemsley, BA 1.4.01
Wing Commander D. H. John, LLB BA 20.8.01

Joint Force Headquarters
Brigadier P. A. WALL, CBE 2.4.01
Group Captain G. J. Howard, MA MCIT MILT MCMI 26.11.01
Wing Commander N. A. Chapman, MSc BA 21.8.00
Wing Commander G. S. Kelly, BSc 25.2.02

DEFENCE LOGISTICS ORGANISATION

CHIEF OF DEFENCE LOGISTICS
Air Chief Marshal Sir MALCOLM PLEDGER, KCB OBE AFC BSc FRAeS

Military Assistant
Captain P. Jones, RN

Military Assistant 2
Commander E. M. King, BSc MSc CDipAF CEng MIEE RN

DEPUTY CHIEF OF DEFENCE LOGISTICS
Mr J. R. C. OUGHTON

Private Secretary
Mrs I. Vaughan

DIRECTOR GENERAL STRATEGY & LOGISTIC DEVELOPMENT
Major General A. RAPER, CBE

Military Assistant
Wing Commander B. L. Craib, MBA BSc RAF

Director Strategy
Commodore R. A. MARK, RN

Director Logistic Strategy
Brigadier J. G. MORRISON, BCom MDA MIExpE MCIPF

Director Programmes
Mr G. Morris

DIRECTOR GENERAL OPERATIONS
Rear Admiral M. G. WOOD, CBE RN

Staff Officer
Commander K. A. Taylor, BSc RN

DMCBU
Air Commodore T. G. HOWSON, MSc BA RAF

Director Safety, Estates and Security
Mr P. D. NORTHEN

Director Operations, Secretariat and Communications
Brigadier D. R. JEFFREY, MDA MInstD MCIT MILog CGIA

PD COMMERCIAL
Mr M. PEDLINGHAM

DC C&C
Mr J. HARFORD

DIRECTOR GENERAL RESOURCES
Mr N. H. R. EVANS

SPS
Mrs J. Hazel

Director Human Resources Strategy
Brigadier J. DOWSON

Director Personnel Services Centre
Mr S. J. PENFOLD

Director Finance and Business Plans
Mr M. HUTCHINSON

DIRECTOR GENERAL EQUIPMENT SUPPORT(SEA) AND CE WARSHIP SUPPORT AGENCY
Mr. J. D. COLES, BSc MSc CEng MRINA RCNC

Military Assistant
Commander I. Shipperley

DCE
Rear Admiral J. REEVE

Military Assistant
Commander M. J. Atherton

FOSNNI
Rear Admiral D. J. ANTHONY, MBE

Military Assistant
Commander N. P. B. Morton

Director Naval Base Clyde
Commodore K. J. BORLEY

Director Operations
Mr M. J. FROWDE

Director Operations Eqiupment
Mr F. EDWARDS

Director Maritime Spt (D Tech)
Mr R. R. CUMMINGS

Director Commercial
Mr J. M. HALL

Director Finance and Communications
Mr J. CLAYTON

Director Support Chain/Chief Operations Waterfront
Commodore P. J. HORSTED

Director Non project Procurement Office (NPPO)
Mrs D. J. FORMBY

Director Human Resources
Mr R. BEETHAM

Director Business Development
Mr A. ROSSI

Naval Bases Command Portsmouth
Commodore R. P. BOISSIER, ADC

Naval Bases Command Devonport
Commodore R. F. CHEADLE, ADC

Submarine IPTL
Commodore T. C. CHITTENDEN

CSSE/Strategic Systems IPTL
Commodore M. J. HOLMES, ADC

Frigates IPTL
Mr N. J. WILCOX

DIRECTOR GENERAL EQUIPMENT SUPPORT (LAND)
Major General M. HUNTLEY

Military Assistant
Lieutenant Colonel J. R. Free

Director Business Development
Brigadier N. T. S. WILLIAMS, MBE

Director Commercial
Mr A. BEVAN

Director Support Operations
Brigadier K. E. FERGUSON

Director Resource Management
Mr K. L. BELLAMY

Director Technical
Brigadier P. C. CORT

DIRECTOR GENERAL EQUIPMENT SUPPORT (AIR)
Air-Vice Marshal P. LIDDELL, CB BSc CEng FIEE FRAeS RAF

Staff Officer
Wing Commander M. Quigley, RAF

Director Business Improvements (Air)
Air Commodore A. C. SPINKS, FRAeS FCIT FILT RAF

Director Commercial
Mr D. MACFARLANE

Director Support Operations (Fixed Wing)
Air Commodore J. J. WITTS, DSO FRAeS RAF

Director Resource Management
Mr D. HATCHER

Director Support Operations (Rotary Wing)
Commodore R. A. N. PALMER

Harrier IPTL
Air Commodore C. W. NESS, BEng CEng FRAeS RAF

Tornado IPTL
Air Commodore S. B. SCHOFIELD, MSc BSc CEng MRAeS RAF

DIRECTOR GENERAL COMMUNICATIONS AND INFORMATION SERVICES SUPPORT AND DEFENCE COMMUNICATIONS SERVICES AGENCY
Rear Admiral R. G. J. WARD, CB

Military Assistant
Lieutenant Colonel D. Warne, R SIGNALS

Director Operations
Air Commodore J. I. KANE, BSc CEng MIEE MCMI RAF

Director Engineering and Interoperability and Communications and Information Systems
Brigadier T. M. GREGORY, BA RM

Director Resources
Mr N. F. JARVIS

Director Strategy and Technical Development
Brigadier, J. E. THOMAS, MBE

Director Commercial
Mr L. A. SIGRIST, OBE

Defence Information Infrastructure IPTL
Mr R. H. QUICK, OBE

Logistics Application IPTL
Brigadier P. FLANAGAN

DIRECTOR GENERAL DEFENCE SUPPLY CHAIN
Major General T. CROSS, CBE

Military Assistant
Lieutenant Commander L. P. Notley, RN

Director Commercial
Mr T. LOGAN

Chief Executive Defence Storage and Distribution Agency
Mr P. FOXTON, CBE

Director Defence Catering Group
Air Commodore S. WOOD, MHCIMA RAF

Chief Executive British Forces Post Office
Brigadier P. J. T. MAGGS, CBE

Director Defence Fuels Group
Air Commodore D. P. HEDGES, RAF

Chief Executive Defence Transport and Movements Agency
Air Commodore P. WHALLEY

Director Corporate Technical Services
Mr H. W. PERKINS

Director Logistics Business Management
Mr S. W. WALLACE

Director Pay As You Dine
Brigadier A. C. MANTELL, OBE

Director Operations Supply Chain
Commodore N. D. SAVAGE

Director Defence Munitions
Mr A. BLAIR

DEFENCE SCIENCE & TECHNOLOGY LABORATORY (Dstl)

CHIEF EXECUTIVE
Mr M. EARWICKER

DSTL MAIN BOARD
Mr P. Starkey – Analysis and Systems
Mr M. Hone – Finance
Mr M. Jenden — Technology
Mr S. Mepham – Operations
Mr R. Scott – Science
Mr A. Baird – Technical
Mr N. Helbren – Programme Coordination

(Non Executive Directors)
Major General P. GILCHRIST
Mr R. BLACK

DIRECTOR FRONT LINE
Mr S. Ibbotson

DIRECTOR POLICY AND CAPABILITY STUDIES
Mr A. Pickup

DIRECTOR NAVAL SYSTEMS
Mr N. Stansfield

DIRECTOR LAND SYSTEMS
Mr K. Wagstaff

DIRECTOR AIR SYSTEMS
Mr G. Fluck

DIRECTOR INFORMATION MANAGEMENT
Mr P. James

DIRECTOR ENVIRONMENTAL SCIENCES
Mr J. Richards

DIRECTOR ENERGETICS
Mr D. Tisley

DIRECTOR MISSILES AND COUNTERMEASURES
Mr M. Taylor

DIRECTOR ELECTRONICS
Mr K. Brigden

DIRECTOR SENSORS
Mr A. Mckie

DIRECTOR DETECTION
Mr A. Hammer

DIRECTOR BIOMEDICAL SCIENCES DEPT
Dr M. Fulop

DIRECTOR PHYSICAL SCIENCES
Mrs S. HOLMES

DIRECTOR HUMAN RESOURCES
Mr R. Eade

DIRECTOR ESTATES
Mr C. Harding

DIRECTOR COMMERCIAL SERVICES
Mr R. Hunt

DIRECTOR SHEF
Mr P. Brooke

DIRECTOR INFORMATION SYSTEMS
Mr J. Day

DIRETOR KNOWLEDGE SERVICES
Mrs C. Stewart

DIRECTOR TECHNOLOGY TRANSFER AND INVESTMENTS
Mr T. Rubidge

DIRECTOR FINANCE
Mr S. Williams

DIRECTOR COMMUNICATIONS
Mr C. Imison

DIRECTOR PROGRAMME COORDINATION
Mr M. Hogwood

DIRECTOR SECURITY
Mr W. Charlseworth

DIRECTOR CORPORATE AFFAIRS
Mr R. Bexon

MILITARY CAPABILITY LEADERS
Captain I. Jarvis, RN
Colonel C. Nicholls
Group Captain A. J. Vincent, MA RAF

OFFICE OF THE
JUDGE ADVOCATE GENERAL OF THE FORCES

(LORD CHANCELLOR'S DEPARTMENT)

(Joint Service for the Army and Royal Air Force)

81 Chancery Lane, London, WC2A 1DD Tel. 0207-218 8089

Judge Advocate General
HIS HONOUR JUDGE J. W. RANT, CB QC

Senior Personal Secretary
Miss E. F. Ruddy

Vice Judge Advocate General
E. G. MOELWYN-HUGHES

Assistant Judge Advocates General (London Office and Overseas)
Judge Advocate M. A. HUNTER (DJAG BRITISH FORCES IN GERMANY)
Judge Advocate J. P. CAMP
Judge Advocate R. C. C. SEYMOUR
Judge Advocate I. H. PEARSON
Judge Advocate R. G. CHAPPLE
Judge Advocate J. F. T. BAYLISS
Judge Advocate C. R. BURN

Grade 6 Legal
T. S. G. Miller

Registrar
Miss J. Norris

SOVEREIGN BASE AREAS OF AKROTIRI
AND DHEKELIA ADMINISTRATION

Postal Address—HEADQUARTERS, SOVEREIGN BASE AREAS ADMINISTRATION, EPISKOPI.
BRITISH FORCES POST OFFICE 53

THE ADMINISTRATOR

Air Vice-Marshal T. W. RIMMER, CB OBE MA FRAeS 4.9.00

Military Assistant
Major B. Baldwin

Aide-de-Camp
Flight Lieutenant S. J. L. Lawrence 13.1.02

Chief Officer of Sovereign Base Areas
D. BONNER

Administrative Secretary
G. G. BARLOW

Judiciary
The Honourable Justice Mr G. H. M. DANIEL, DL . . . .   Senior Judge
His Honour Judge D. B. PAIN . . . .   Resident Judge

Legal
P. W. VISAGIE . . . .   Attorney General and Legal Adviser

Akrotiri Area Office
C. Athanasiai . . . .   Area Officer

Dhekelia Area Office
K. A. Demetriades . . . .   Area Officer

Sovereign Base Areas Police
E. Vallance, QPM LLB . . . .   Chief Constable

Sovereign Base Areas Customs
A. Livingstone. . . . .   Fiscal Officer

Administrator's Advisory Board
D. BONNER . . . .   Chief Officer
Brigadier D. E. RADCLIFFE, OBE . . . .   Chief of Staff, British Forces Cyprus
P. W. VISAGIE, ...   Attorney General and Legal Advisor
Colonel G. B. Grossmith . . . .   Garrison Commander, Dhekelia

DEFENCE AND AIR ATTACHES TO EMBASSIES

ABU DHABI (UAE)—(British Embassy, Abu Dhabi, c/o FCO, Outward Bag Room, King Charles Street, London SW1A 2AH)
Defence Attaché. . . . .   Colonel A. V. Malkin 11.00

AMMAN—(British Embassy, Amman, c/o FCO, Outward Bag Room, King Charles Street, London SW1A 2AH)
Defence, Naval and Military Attaché . . . .   Colonel C. R. Romberg 1.01
Air Attaché . . . .   Wing Commander S. J. Orwell, RAF 10.99

ANKARA—(British Embassy, Ankara. c/o FCO, Outward Bag Room, King Charles Street, London SW1A 2AH)
Defence and Military Attaché. . . . . . .   Brigadier K. O. WINFIELD 11.99
Naval and Air Attaché . . . .   Commander S. M. Pegg, RN 8.99

ATHENS—(British Embassy, Athens, c/o FCO, Outward Bag Room, King Charles Street, London SW1A 2AH)
Defence, Naval and Air Attaché . . . . . .   Commodore J. L. MILNES, RN 12.98
Defence and Military Attaché. . . . . .   Lieutenant Colonel S. W. L. Strickland, OBE. . . 11.00

BAHRAIN—(British Embassy, Bahrain, BFPO 632)
Defence Attaché. . . . .   Commander M. Dodds, RN 6.99

BANGKOK—(British Embassy, Bangkok, c/o FCO Outward Bag Room, King Charles Street, London SW1A 2AH)
Defence Attaché. . . . .   Colonel A. R. Singer, OBE 9.00

BEIRUT—(British Embassy, Beirut, c/o FCO, Outward Bag Room, King Charles Street, London SW1A 2AH)
Defence Attaché. . . . .   Lieutenant Colonel D. J. A. Bergin, OBE 7.99

BELGRADE—(British Embassy, Belgrade, c/o FCO, Outward Bag Room, King Charles Street, London SW1A 2AH)
Defence Attaché. . . . .   Colonel W. E. Nowosielski-Slepowron, ... 4.01

BERLIN—(British Embassy, BFPO 30)
Defence and Military Attaché. . . . . . .   Brigadier B. R. ISBELL 8.96
Air Attaché . . . .   Group Captain J. P. Moloney, MA BA 2.02

BERNE—(British Embassy, Thunstrasse 50, 3005 Berne, Switzerland)
Defence Attaché. . . . .   Lieutenant Colonel P. Bangham. 1.02

BOGOTA—(British Embassy, Bogota, c/o FCO, Outward Bag Room King Charles Street, London SW1A 2AH)
Defence Attaché. . . . .   Colonel M. E. Wilcox 6.02
   (also Defence Attaché Lima)

BRASILIA—(British Embassy, Brasilia, c/o FCO, Outward Bag Room, King Charles Street, London SW1A 2AH)
Defence, Military and Air Attaché . . . . .   Colonel J. M. Bowles, OBE 1.99

BRATISLAVA—(British Embassy, Bratislava c/o FCO Outward Bag Room, King Charles Street, London SW1A 2AH)
Defence Attaché. . . . .   Lieutenant Colenel N. S. Southward, OBE . . . 7.00

BRUSSELS—(British Embassy, BFPO 49)
Defence Attaché. . . . .   Group Captain J. D. Bullen, OBE RAF 7.01
   (also Defence Attaché Luxembourg)

BUCHAREST—(British Embassy, Bucharest, c/o FCO, Outward Bag Room, King Charles Street, London SW1A 2AH)
Defence, Attaché . . . .   Colonel A. T. Bruce, MBE 11.00
   (also Defence Attaché Kishinev)

BUDAPEST—(British Embassy, Budapest, c/o FCO, Outward Bag Room, King Charles Street, London SW1A 2AH)
Defence Attaché. . . . .   Colonel J. S. B. Frere, MBE 7.01

BUENOS AIRES—(British Embassy, Buenos Aires, c/o FCO Outward Bag Room, King Charles Street, London SW1A 2AH).
Defence, Naval and Military Attaché . . . .   Colonel P. A. Reynolds, RM 12.00
Air Attaché . . . .   Group Captain T. P. Brewer, OBE BSc RAF . . . 12.99
   (also Defence Attaché Asuncion and Montevideo)

CAIRO—(British Embassy, Cairo, c/o FCO, Outward Bag Room, King Charles Street, London SW1A 2AH)
Defence and Military Attaché. . . . . . .   Colonel P. Dennison, OBE RAF 11.99
Naval and Air Attaché . . . .   Commander P. Holihead 12.01

CARACAS—(British Embassy, Caracas, c/o FCO, Outward Bag Room, King Charles Street, London SW1A 2AH)
Defence, Naval, Military and Air Attaché . . . .   Colonel E. F. Searle, RN 8.00
   (also Defence Attaché Quito and Panama City)

COPENHAGEN—(British Embassy, 36/38/40 Kastelsvej, DK-2100 Copenhagen, Denmark)
Defence, Naval, Military and Air Attaché . . . . Commander R. P. B. Ayers, RN 5.01

DAMASCUS—(British Embassy, Damascus, c/o FCO Outward Bag Room, King Charles Street, London SW1A 2AH)
Defence Attaché. . . . . Colonel R. C. J. Martin, OBE 2.01

DOHA—(British Embassy, Doha, Qatar, c/o FCO Outward Bag Room, King Charles Street, London SW1A 2AH)
Defence Attaché. . . . . Wing Commander P. Cottell 2.02

DUBLIN—(British Embassy, Dublin, c/o FCO, Outward Bag Room, King Charles Street, London SW1A 2AH)
Defence Attaché. . . . . Colonel P. B. G. Cummings 3.01

GUATEMALA CITY—(British Embassy Guatemala City, Guatemala, c/o FCO Outward Bag Room, King Charles Street, London, SW1A 2AH)
Defence Attaché. . . . . Colonel C. D. Blair-Pilling 9.00
(also Defence Attaché San Salvador and Tegucigalpa, Managua and Mexico City)

THE HAGUE—(British Embassy, Lange Voorhout 10, 2514 ED, The Hague, Netherlands)
Defence and Naval Attaché . . . . Captain N. A. M. Butler, RN 3.01

HELSINKI—(British Embassy, Uudenmaankatu 16,20, 00120 Helsinki 12 Finland)
Defence, Naval, Military and Air Attaché . . . . Lieutenant Colonel P. W. Clarke. 5.01
(also Defence Attaché Tallinn)

JAKARTA—(British Embassy, Jakarta, c/o FCO, Outward Bag Room, King Charles Street, London SW1A 2AH)
Defence Attaché. . . . . Colonel A. R. Roberts. 12.00

KATHMANDU—(British Embassy, Kathmandu, BFPO 4)
Defence Attaché. . . . . Colonel M. Dowdle 10.98

KUWAIT CITY—(British Embassy, Kuwait City, c/o FCO Outward Bag Room, King Charles Street, London SW1A 2AH)
Defence Attaché. . . . . Colonel S. O. Thomas 1.02

KYIV—(British Embassy, KYIV, c/o FCO, Outward Bag Room, King Charles Street, London SW1A 2AH)
Defence Attaché. . . . . Captain M. N. Littleboy, RN 10.98

LISBON—(British Embassy, Lisbon, BFPO 6)
Defence Attaché. . . . . Commander A. J. Bull, RN 11.99

LJUBLANA—(British Embassy, Ljublana, c/o FCO, Outward Bag Room, King Charles Street, London SW1A 2AH)
Defence Attaché. . . . . Lieutenant Colonel L. Wilson 6.02

LUANDA—(British Embassy, Luanda, c/o FCO, Outward Bag Room, King Charles Street, London SW1A 2AH)
Defence Attaché. . . . . Lieutenant Colonel A. A. Gilbert 6.01

MADRID—(British Embassy, Madrid, c/o FCO, Outward Bag Room, King Charles Street, London SW1A 2AH)
Defence and Naval Attaché . . . . Captain A. Croke, RN 9.00
Military and Air Attaché . . . . Colonel R. J. Lawson 9.97

MANILA—(British Embassy, Manila, c/o FCO, Outward Bag Room, King Charles Street, London SW1A 2AH)
Defence Attaché. . . . . Colonel M. K. Stretch 7.01

MOSCOW—(British Embassy, Moscow, c/o FCO, Outward Bag Room, King Charles Street, London SW1A 2AH)
Defence and Air Attaché . . . . Air Commodore J. C. JARRON, RAF 8.99
Assistant Air Attaché . . . . Squadron Leader S. T. O'Brien, MA MSc. . . . 5.02
(also Assistant Defence Attaché Almaty and Bishkek)

MUSCAT—(British Embassy, Muscat, c/o FCO, Outward Bag Room, King Charles Street, London SW1A 2AH)
Defence and Military Attaché. . . . . . . Brigadier M. SMITH, CBE MC 8.99
Naval and Air Attaché . . . . Commander R. P. Thomas, RN 1.02

OSLO—(British Embassy, Thomas Heftyesgate 8, 0244 Oslo 2, Norway)
Defence and Naval Attaché . . . . . . Lieutenant Colonel S. J. Hughes, RM 11.01

PARIS—(British Embassy, 35 rue du Faubourg St. Honore, 75383 Paris Cedex 08, France)
Defence and Air Attaché . . . . Air Commodore C. J. BLENCOWE, MA BA . . . 7.01
Assistant Air Attaché . . . . Wing Commander G. I. August, BA RAF 7.99

PEKING—(British Embassy, Peking, c/o FCO. Outward Bag Room, King Charles Street, London SW1A 2AH)
Defence, Military and Air Attaché . . . . . Brigadier J. G. KERR, OBE QGM 6.98

PRAGUE—(British Embassy, Prague, c/o FCO, Outward Bag Room, King Charles Street, London SW1A 2AH)
Defence Attaché. . . . . Colonel D. A. Wynne-Davies 3.01

DEFENCE AND AIR ATTACHES

RABAT—(British Embassy, Rabat, c/o FCO Outward Bag Room, King Charles Street, London SW1A 2AH)
Defence Attaché. . . . . Lieutenant Colonel G. D. Duthoit 6.00
(also Defence Attaché Nouakchott and Dakar)

RIGA—(British Embassy, Riga, c/o FCO, Outward Bag Room, King Charles Street, London SW1A 2AH)
Defence Attaché. . . . . Lieutenant Colonel A. S. Tuggey 9.99

RIYADH—(British Embassy, Riyadh, c/o FCO, Outward Bag Room, King Charles Street, London SW1A 2AH)
Defence and Military Attaché. . . . . Brigadier J. D. DEVERELL, OBE. 9.98
(also Defence Attaché Sana'a)
Air Attaché . . . . Wing Commander J. A. Bartram, MSc MECI MIMgt RAF 2.00

ROME—(British Embassy, BFPO 8)
Defence and Military Attaché. . . . . Brigadier A. L. MALLINSON 7.00
Air Attaché . . . . Group Captain D. H White, RAF 9.01

SANTIAGO—(British Embassy Santiago, c/o FCO, Outward Bag Room, King Charles Street, London SW1A 2AH)
Defence Attaché. . . . . Colonel R. M. J. Rollo-Walker, OBE 8.00

SEOUL—(British Embassy, Seoul, c/o FCO, Outward Bag Room, King Charles Street, London SW1A 2AH)
Defence and Military Attaché. . . . . Brigadier J. C. L. KING, MBE 7.01
Naval and Air Attaché . . . . Group Captain K. R. C. Greaves, OBE RAF . . . 4.02

SKOPJE—(British Embassy, Skopje, c/o FCO, Outward Bag Room, King Charles Street, London SW1A 2AH)
Defence Attaché. . . . . Lieutenant Colonel M. S. Rees 1.02

SOFIA—(British Embassy, Sofia, c/o FCO, Outward Bag Room, King Charles Street, London SW1A 2AH)
Defence Attaché. . . . . Colonel R. Z. A. Ciaglinski 2.01

STOCKHOLM—(British Embassy, Box 27819-115-93 Stockholm, Sweden)
Defence and Air Attaché . . . . Wing Commander P. M. Leadbetter, MVO . . . 9.01

TBILISI—(British Embassy, Tbilisi, c/o FCO, Outward Bag Room, King Charles Street, London SW1A 2AH)
Defence Attaché. . . . . Wing Commander A. W. Kerr, BA AIL RAF . . . 6.99
(also Defence Attaché Baku and Yerevan)

TEL AVIV—(British Embassy, Tel Aviv, c/o FCO, Outward Bag Room, King Charles Street, London SW1A 2AH)
Defence and Military Attaché. . . . . Colonel T. M. Fitzalan Howard, OBE 11.00
Naval and Air Attaché . . . . Wing Commander S. Cummings, RAF 5.01

TOKYO—(British Embassy No. 1 Ichiban-cho. Chiyoda-ku, Tokyo 102, Japan)
Defence and Naval Attaché . . . . Captain J. A. Boyd, RN 10.99

VIENNA—(British Embassy, Jaucesgasse 12, 1030 Vienna, Austria)
Defence Attaché. . . . . Lieutenant Colonel J. A. Bourne 6.00

VILNIUS—(British Embassy, 2 Antakalnio 2055 Vilnios, Lithuania)
Defence Attaché. . . . . Lieutenant Colonel P. R. P. Swanson, MBE . . . 2.01

WARSAW—(British Embassy, Warsaw, c/o FCO, Outward Bag Room, King Charles Street, London SW1A 2AH)
Defence and Air Attaché . . . . Group Captain T. J. Williams, AFC RAF 10.01
Naval and Military Attaché . . . . Lieutenant Colonel I. F. Watts 11.00

WASHINGTON—(British Embassy, BFPO 2)
Defence Attaché. . . . . Air Vice-Marshal J. H. THOMPSON, CB RAF. . . 4.00
Air Attaché . . . . Air Commodore G. D. SIIMPSON, CBE AFC FRAeS RAF 11.99
Assistant Air Attaché . . . . Group Captain B. T. Dingle, RAF 3.99

ZAGREB—(British Embassy, Zagreb, c/o FCO, Outward Bag Room, King Charles Street, London SW1A 2AH)
Defence Attaché. . . . . Lieutenant Colonel R. M. Thornely. 5.01

DEFENCE AND AIR ADVISERS TO BRITISH HIGH COMMISSIONS

ABUJA—(British High Commission, Abuja, c/o FCO, Outward Bag Room, King Charles Street, London SW1A 2AH)
Defence Adviser. . . . . Colonel J. R. Lemon 6.01

ACCRA—(British High Commission, Accra, c/o FCO, Outward Bag Room, King Charles Street, London SW1A 2AH)
Defence Adviser. . . . . Lieutenant Colonel S. K. E. Clarke, OBE 1.01
(also Freetown and Defence Attaché Lome and Abidjan)

ALMATY—(British Embassy, c/o FCO, Outward Bag Room, King Charles Street, London SW1A 2AH)
Defence Attaché. . . . . Lieutenant Colonel G. J. Sheeley, AFC 7.01

BANDAR SERI BEGAWAN—(British High Commission, Bandar Seri Begawan, c/o FCO, Outward Bag Room, King Charles Street, London SW1A 2AH)
Defence Adviser. . . . . Captain P. H. Jones, RN 7.99

BRIDGETOWN—(British High Commission, Lower Collymore Rock, (PO Box 676), Bridgetown, Barbados
Defence Adviser. . . . . Captain S. C. Ramm, RN 4.01
Defence Adviser to States of Regional Security: Grenada, St Vincent, St Lucia, Dominica, Antigua & Barbuda, St Kitts.
Defence Adviser to British Dependant Territories: British Virgin Islands. Anquilla, Montserrat.
Defence Adviser to Trinidad & Tobago (Port of Spain)
Defence Adviser to Guyana (Georgetown)
Defence Attaché to Suriname (Paramaribo)
Defence Visiting Officer to Guadeloupe, Martinique, Curacao, US Virgin Islands, Puerto Rico.

CANBERRA—(British High Commission, Commonwealth Avenue, Canberra, Australia)
Defence and Naval Adviser . . . . Commodore G. J. WILTSHIRE, RN 5.01
Air Adviser . . . . Group Captain N. C. Rusling BA RAF 6.99

COLOMBO—(British High Commission, Colombo, c/o FCO, Outward Bag Room, King Charles Street, London SW1A 2AH)
Defence Adviser. . . . . Lieutenant Colonel M. H. D. Weldon 4.01

HARARE—(British High Commission. Harare, c/o FCO, Outward Bag Room, King Charles Street, London SW1A 2AH)
Defence Adviser. . . . . Colonel J. S. Field, CBE 8.99
(also Defence Adviser Gaborone, Lilongwe and Maputo)

ISLAMABAD—(British High Commission, Islamabad, c/o FCO, Outward Bag Room, King Charles Street, London SW1A 2AH)
Defence and Military Adviser. . . . . Brigadier B. D. WHEELWRIGHT. 6.97
Naval and Air Adviser . . . . Captain A. T. Welch, FNI RN. 6.00

KAMPALA—(British High Commission, Kampala, c/o FCO, Outward Bag Room, King Charles Street, London SW1A 2AH)
Defence Adviser. . . . . Lieutenant Colonel C. Wilton 1.02
(also Defence Attaché Bujumbura and Kigali)

KINGSTON—(British High Commission, Kingston, c/o FCO, Outward Bag Room, King Charles Street, London SW1A 2AH)
Defence Adviser. . . . . Colonel R. A. Hyde-Bales. 4.00
Defence Adviser to Bahamas (Nassau), Belize (Belmopan)
Defence Adviser to British Dependant Territories: Cayman Islands, Turks & Caicos.

KUALA LUMPUR—(185 Jalan Ampang 50450 Kuala Lumpur, Malaysia)
Defence Adviser. . . . . Colonel R. J. Little 10.99
(also Defence Attaché Hanoi)
Assistant Defence Adviser. . . . . Lieutenant Commander A. Joyner, RN 8.01

DEFENCE AND AIR ADVISERS

NAIROBI—(British High Commission, BFPO 10)
Defence and Military Adviser. . . . . Colonel J. R. Barnes 4.01
  Defence Attaché to Eritrea (Asmara)
  Defence Attaché to Ethiopia (Addis Ababa)
  Defence Adviser to Tanzania (Dar-es-Salaam)
  Defence Adviser to Mauritius (Port Louis)
  Defence Adviser to Seychelles (Victoria)

NEW DELHI—(British High Commission, New Delhi, c/o FCO, Outward Bag Room, King Charles Street, London SW1A 2AH)
Defence and Military Adviser. . . . . Brigadier S. M. A. LEE, OBE. 11.97
  (also Defence Adviser Dhaka)
Naval and Air Adviser . . . . Group Captain N. B. Spiller, RAF 1.01

NICOSIA—(British High Commission, BFPO 567)
Defence Adviser. . . . . Colonel J. Anderson 7.01

OTTAWA—(British High Commission, Ottawa BFPO 487)
Defence and Military Adviser. . . . . Brigadier C. J. R. DAY 3.01
Naval and Air Adviser . . . . Captain M. D. Booth, RN. 8.00

PRETORIA—(British High Commission, Pretoria, c/o Outward Bag Room, King Charles Street, London SW1A 2AH)
Defence and Military Adviser. . . . . Brigadier M. R. RAWORTH 4.99
  (also Defence Adviser Maseru and Mbabane)
Naval and Air Adviser . . . . Wing Commander T. A. Harper, RAF 2.01

SINGAPORE—(British High Commission, Naval Party 1022 BFPO Ships)
Defence Adviser. . . . . Group Captain M. D. Stringer, RAF 7.01
  (also Defence Adviser Bandar Seri Begawan)

TASHKENT—(British Embassy, Tashkent, Uzbekistan)
Defence Attaché. . . . . Lieutenant Colonel N. Ridout 3.02

WELLINGTON—(British High Commission, PO Box 1812, (44 Hill Street), Wellington, New Zealand)
Defence Adviser. . . . . Colonel A. A. Peebles. 10.01
  (also Defence Attaché Suva and Nuku'alofa)

BRITISH DEFENCE STAFF WASHINGTON

Postal Address BFPO 2

CENTRAL STAFF

Joint Staff

Wing Commander A. R. D. Welham 26.10.01

Communications Information Service

Wing Commander R. B. McTeague, BSc 7.4.00

ROYAL AIR FORCE STAFF

Air Attaché

Air Commodore G. D. SIMPSON, CBE AFC FRAeS 19.11.99

Group Captain

A. J. Barrett 26.7.02

Wing Commanders

G. R. Bond 1.6.01
D. C. Coombes, OBE GradDipMS FInstAM MBIFM MCMI 5.10.00
R. M. Harris, BSc CEng MIEE 23.7.99
W. D. Williams, BA 16.6.00

DEFENCE STAFF

DE/Air Armaments

Wing Commander J. W. C. Spencer, MSc BSc CEng MIMechE 11.8.00

DLO LIAISON OFFICER

Group Captain D. S. Belmore, MBE MCIPS 10.5.02

HEADQUARTERS IN THE UNITED KINGDOM OF THE AIR FORCES OF COMMONWEALTH COUNTRIES

AUSTRALIA. Australian Defence Staff

Address: Australia House, Strand, London, WC2B 4LA. Telephone: 020 7887 5264

Air Adviser
Group Captain T. F. Owen, RAAF

Assistant Air Adviser
Wing Commander E. J. Walsh, RAAF

CANADA. Canadian Forces, Canadian Defence Liaison Staff.

Address: 1 Grosvenor Square, London W1X 0AB. Telephone 0207-258 6424

Air Force Adviser
Colonel M. Legault, CD

Assistant Air Force Adviser
Lieutenant Colonel A. L. Smith, CD

NEW ZEALAND. New Zealand Defence Staff.

Address: New Zealand House, 80 Haymarket, London SW1Y 4TQ. Telephone 0207-930 8400

Head NZDS
Commodore A. J. Peck, ONZM RNZN

Air Adviser
Wing Commander S. A. V. James, RNZAF

INDIA. Air Adviser to the High Commissioner for India in the U.K.

Address: India House, Aldwych. London WC2B 4NA Telephone: 020 7240 1948

Air Adviser
Air Commodore M. SUNDARAM, AVSM

DEPARTMENT
OF THE
CHIEF OF THE AIR STAFF

CHIEF OF THE AIR STAFF
Air Chief Marshal Sir PETER SQUIRE, GCB DFC AFC ADC DSc FRAeS 19.4.00

Private Secretary
Dr M. J. Rutter

Personal Staff Officer
Wing Commander C. R. Bushell, MA BSc CEng MIMechE 12.12.00

Staff Officer
Flight Lieutenant C. J. Bellworthy 10.9.01

ASSISTANT CHIEF OF THE AIR STAFF
Air Vice-Marshal P. O. STURLEY, CB MBE BSc FRAeS 1.9.00

Personal Staff Officer
Wing Commander C. Basnett 15.4.02

Staff Officer
Squadron Leader T. H. P. Wood 10.8.01

DIRECTOR OF AIR STAFF
Air Commodore C. H. MORAN, OBE MVO MA BSc 18.9.00

HEAD OF AIR HISTORICAL BRANCH (RAF)
J. S. COX, BA MA

DEPUTY DIRECTOR OF AIR STAFF
R. HOWARD

DIRECTOR OF DEFENCE STUDIES (RAF)
Group Captain C. J. Finn, MPhil 10.6.02

Group Captains
S. H. Anderton, MSc Bsc FCMI 1.10.01
G. P. Dixon, BSc 14.6.02
S. D. Ottridge, BSc CEng MIEE MBCS 22.7.02

Wing Commanders
M. F. Baker 27.8.01
J. C. Ball 1.8.01
R. P. Caddick, MA 7.8.00
F. E. Fisher, MBE BSc CEng MRAeS 20.5.02
N. J. Furniss, MBE 23.4.93
M. A. Jeffery, OBE BSc ARCS 20.8.01
M. F. Killen, BSc 28.1.02
S. M. J. Macartney, BSc 1.11.99
A. W. Mawston, BSc 7.8.01
H. W. Nash 22.4.02
K. A. Revell, BA 26.7.99
J. G. Richardson, BSc 25.2.02
C. Taylor, BA 10.9.01
M. P. Tomany, BEd 27.8.01
R. A. Wilder, BSc 4.8.01

Principals and Equivalent Grades
M. Field
G. Rees

DIRECTORATE OF AIRSPACE POLICY

DIRECTOR AIRSPACE POLICY
J. R. D. ARSCOTT

Group Captain
I. S. Middleton, MBA BA 26.3.01

Wing Commanders
C. J. Peart 27.11.00
R. N. Williams 29.3.00

STRIKE COMMAND

Postal Address RAF HIGH WYCOMBE, BUCKINGHAMSHIRE, HP14 4UE

Telephone Nos—(01494) 461461 (VPN 95221)

COMMAND HEADQUARTERS

COMMANDER-IN-CHIEF
Air Chief Marshal Sir JOHN DAY, KCB OBE ADC BSc 5.4.01

Personal Staff Officer
Wing Commander P. N. Oborn 8.8.00

Deputy Personal Staff Officer
Squadron Leader R. A. Morin, BA DMS 19.3.01

Aide-de-Camp
Flight Lieutenant T. Flett 20.5.02

DEPUTY COMMANDER-IN-CHIEF
Air Marshal B. K. BURRIDGE, CBE MBA BSc FCMI. 4.2.02

Personal Staff Officer
Squadron Leader R. Bailey 24.9.01

DEPUTY CHIEF OF STAFF OPERATIONS
Air Vice-Marshal N. J. SUDBOROUGH, CB OBE FCIPD 8.5.00

Staff Officer
Squadron Leader M. Godsland, BEd 24.7.00

Air Commodore Operations (Assistant Chief of Staff A3 Operations)
Air Commodore R. COOK, CBE BTech 15.7.00

Air Commodore Operations Support (Assistant Chief of Staff A3 Operations Support)
Air Commodore N. WILLIAMS 4.3.02

Air Officer Security and Provost Marshal (RAF)(Assistant Chief of Staff A3 Security)
Air Commodore C. R. MORGAN 25.9.00

Air Commodore Test and Evaluation (Boscombe Down)
Air Commodore N. R. WOOD, BSc MRAeS 23.9.96

Commandant Air Warfare Centre (Waddington)
Air Commodore S. W. PEACH, CBE MPhil BA FRAeS MRIN 24.7.00

Executive Officer
Wing Commander J. Lawlor, BA 12.3.01

AIR OFFICER LOGISTICS AND COMMUNICATION INFORMATION SYSTEMS
Air Vice-Marshal P. J. SCOTT, MSc BSc CEng FIMechE FRAeS 24.8.98

Staff Officer
Squadron Leader A. Simmonite, BEng 24.7.00

Air Commodore Communications Information Systems (Assistant Chief of Staff A6)
Air Commodore A. E. WARNES, MA BSc CEng MIEE 1.2.02

Air Commodore Logistics Policy and Plans
Air Commodore N. S. MORRIS, MSc BA MIL MILT. 3.7.00

Air Commodore Logistics (Assistant Chief of Staff A4)
Air Commodore P. D. RAWSON, BA IEng FRAeS 1.3.02

Assistant Chief of Staff A1
Air Commodre S. CHISNALL, MPhil, BA CertEd 23.4.01

AIR OFFICER PLANS (ASSISTANT CHIEF OF STAFF A5)
Air Commodore A. D. WHITE, BTech 16.12.99

COMMAND SECRETARY
   Mr I. G. McEWEN

Personal Staff Officer
   Squadron Leader D. R. Salmon 4.3.02

Deputy Command Secretary (Assistant Chief of Staff A8/9)
   Mr G. Magnus

Group Captains
   R. Ashenhurst, MSc BSc CEng MRAes 21.8.00
   R. J. Allen 27.4.02
   S. Blackburn, MBE 18.3.01
   R. F. R. Carr, MBE 15.7.97
   A. J. R. Davenport 23.7.01
   A. Davie, OBE MA MBA 11.6.02
   I. L. Dugmore, BSc 16.12.00
   R. J. Dunsford, BSc 5.11.01
   R. I. Elliott, OBE BSc 22.4.02
   E. J. Faulconer, MA BSc 15.1.01
   S. D. Forward, BSc 1.3.02
   J. A. Goodbourn, BSc 7.1.02
   B. L. Gray, BSc IEng FIIE 1.2.02
   N. A. Gregory, BA ACII 22.2.99
   G. J. Harding, LLB 31.7.00
   R. A. Harding, MA MDA BA MCIPD 18.10.99
   B. T. Keatings, MMedSci MB ChB MFOM DAvMed 12.6.00
   T. Kirby, MBE 1.2.00
   A. C. Major, MSc BTech CEng MRAeS 5.10.01
   M. S. McGeown, MA 24.10.01
   I. A. McPhee 12.2.01
   N. D. Meyrick 18.6.01
   C. J. Morris, OBE FRIN 2.4.02
   P. S. Richardson, MSc BDS MGDSRCS(Eng) MGDSRCS(Ed) LDSRCS(Eng) DDPHRCS(EnG) 2.10.00
   J. P. Stenson, MBE BSc 1.4.02
   I. Travers Smith, DSO 25.3.96
   C. D. Turner, MSc BSc 8.3.02
   T. C. Wardill 24.1.00
   Rev S. J. Ware, QHC BA 14.8.00
   J. W. White, CBE FRAeS FCMI 12.12.96

Wing Commanders
   W. J. Alexander 28.8.01
   K. W. Anderson 25.3.02
   Lieutenant Colonel M. Andrews 26.3.02
   R. L. A. Atherton 11.6.02
   J. K. L. Babraff 18.2.93
   P. Bayer 11.1.93
   A. Bentham 14.4.98
   P. N. Birch, MBE 14.6.99
   J. B. Bishopp 24.6.02
   C. A. Britton, MCIPD 24.7.00
   B. E. Bunting 9.10.01
   J. Burr, DFC BSc 23.4.01
   D. P. Calvert, MBE BSc 3.5.00
   P. J. Chapman 2.10.99
   S. C. Cockbill, BSc 1.5.02
   Lieutenant Colonel D. Collard 1.3.02
   J. D. Cookson, BEM 14.2.02
   N. T. Cookson 23.2.02
   I. J. Craig, MBE 29.4.96

S. H. Crockatt	1.5.02
J. C. Davies, BSc DipAppSS	18.9.00
M. Dobson	1.4.96
S. J. Edmondson, BSc CEng MIEE	1.2.02
K. M. Erwich	24.1.02
G. J. Fletcher, MA MSc BSc CEng DMS MIEE	7.8.00
K. G. M. Flynn, BSc FCMA MCMI	14.8.00
D. J. Gale MBE MA MDA BSc CEng MIEE	18.3.02
Commander S. A. George	23.8.02
C. N. R. Gilbert, MSc BEng	6.8.01
B. C. Green	1.7.98
Rev I. F. Greenhalgh	3.6.02
Commander R. C. Hawkins	2.10.01
D. R. Herriot	2.6.02
R. A. Highmore	29.4.02
K. W. M. Hill, MSc BSc CEng MIMechE	9.4.02
T. J. Hill, BA	1.11.99
W. R. Hughes	20.8.01
L. J. Humphries, MSc BA CEng MRAeS	19.2.01
E. S. J. Hunt	22.4.02
R. D. Huxtable	27.9.99
C. B. Hyde, RAuxAF	1.12.99
R. M. Hyslop	2.3.00
A. Johnston	21.5.99
A. K. Johnstone, MSc BSc CEng MIMechE MRAeS	1.11.99
D. K. Jones	29.4.02
R. W. Judson	28.1.02
A. G. Kime	30.7.01
R. C. Knowles, BDS LDSRCS	3.4.02
A. Land, IEng MIIE	10.9.01
G. D. Liston, MSc BSc	12.11.01
N. G. Little, BSc CEng MIEE	13.11.00
A. J. M. Maddox	23.1.02
B. S. Mahaffey, BA	22.5.95
C. D. Malcolm	7.5.02
C. R. Markey	15.1.01
P. J. McLintic	13.2.02
S. C. Moody, MA BSc	9.8.99
I. A. Myers	1.10.01
J. G. Niven	28.4.02
R. C. Old	7.2.00
D. G. Orton, BSc CEng MIEE	11.2.02
J. M. Paige	16.1.02
J. E. Parker	11.10.99
C. R. Parkhurst	6.9.99
E. F. Partridge, OBE AE BEd RAuxAF	5.1.00
P. F. B. Paterson	15.11.99
C. R. Pitt, BSc	21.2.00
M. M. Pollitt, BSc	7.6.99
A. K. Quin	31.10.01
N. B. Randall	22.6.98
C. Reeves, MA BSc	2.2.00
A. J. Roberts	31.10.01
M. J. Roche	16.8.99
P. H. Rosentall	1.6.96
P. J. Rowney	22.5.00
R. S. Ryder, MSc BSc	4.9.00
J. S. B. Schollar, MDA MInstAM MCMI	30.5.00
N. I. M. Seward	12.7.02
I. D. L. Shore, MIMIS	10.11.97

P. Short, BSc 1.2.02
D. A. Simpson, BSc 1.4.02
D. M. Smith, BA 22.5.02
M. D. Smith 27.4.98
S. J. Spence 4.3.02
C. J. H. Stretton, MSc BSc 22.5.00
M. C. G. Strong 6.12.00
P. R. Sutton, MA MEAeS 30.9.01
A. J. Taylor, BSc CEng MRAeS 23.10.00
N. R. Tench, MBE 3.6.95
M. J. Tetlow, MA 24.8.99
G. D. Thomas 8.10.01
R. T. N. Thompson, MSc BSc 22.2.00
C. C. Trundle 7.2.02
G. A. J. Tull 13.10.97
R. D. A. Tulloch, MBE BSc 2.5.00
S. Tyrer 29.4.02
G. P. Underhill, BSc CEng MIEE 20.10.00
G. M. Viney, BSc 22.6.92
T. A. Wilkinson, MBE BSc 10.7.00
J. A. Worrall 30.10.00
B. Wroe, CertEd 23.4.01
R. A. Youngs, DMS 1.3.02

Retired Officers

Group Captain G. W. Gibson, CBE
Wing Commander N. G. Dixon, BA
Wing Commander P. R. Fennell
Wing Commander R. J. C. Green, MRIN MCMI

Civilians

Mr A. L. H. Bailey
Mr B. T. Brown
Mr T. Browne
Mr J. H. Evans
Mr J. M. Hurford-Potter
Mr E. Martin
Mr A. L. Maynard
Mr L. Milne
Mr M. Ollerenshaw
Mr R. E. Partridge
Mr K. Proctor
Mr. J. Rolfe
Mr I. Smelt
Mr G. Sullivan

ROYAL AIR FORCE PERSONNEL AND TRAINING COMMAND

Postal Address RAF INNSWORTH, GLOUCESTER GL3 1EZ
Telephone No—01452-712612

AIR MEMBER FOR PERSONNEL AND COMMANDER-IN-CHIEF PTC
Air Marshal Sir CHRISTOPHER COVILLE, KCB BAFCIPD FRAeS 20.3.01

Personal Staff Officer
Wing Commander C. R. Todd, BSc 20.8.01

Aide-de-Camp
Flight Lieutenant M. J. E. Senescall 22.4.02

CHIEF OF STAFF/AIR MEMBER FOR PERSONNEL
Air Vice-Marshal G. JONES, CBE BSc CEng MIEE 12.12.01

Staff Officer
Squadron Leader, N. J. Alcock, BSc 27.5.02

PLANS AND POLICY
Air Commodore Policy and Plans
Air Commodore D. N. CASE, MSc BSc CEng FRAeS 7.8.00

Chief Scientific Support Officer
Mr M. E. COURT, BSc. . . . .

AIR OFFICER ADMINISTRATION AND AIR OFFICER COMMANDING DIRECTLY ADMINISTERED UNITS
Air Vice-Marshal A. J. BURTON, OBE BSc FCIS FCIPD 1.5.01

Air Commodore (Support)
Air Commodore M. J. GOOD, ADC MIDPM MCMI 7.8.00

Air Commodore Infrastructure (Benson)
Air Commodore J. A. McLOUGHLIN, MBE MA 2.5.00

AIR OFFICER COMMANDING TRAINING GROUP CHIEF EXECUTIVE TRAINING GROUP DEFENCE AGENCY
Air Vice-Marshal G. A. MILLER 4.4.02

Staff Officer
Squadron Leader S. Knott, BSc. 20.8.01

TRAINING STAFF
Director of Training
Air Commodore J. A. CLIFFE, OBE FRAeS 7.1.02

Director of Corporate Development
Air Commodore P. J. DYE, OBE BSc (Eng) CEng MRAeS ACGI 4.8.01

Director RAF Sports Board
Air Vice-Marshal C. DAVISON, (Retd), MBE FCMI DPhysEd 1.6.01

AIR SECRETARY/CHIEF EXECUTIVE PERSONNEL MANAGEMENT AGENCY
Air Vice-Marshal I. M. STEWART, CB AFC LLB FRAeS 28.8.98

Staff Officer
Squadron Leader A. J. Wells 20.8.01

OC RAF INNSWORTH
Wing Commander P. J. Hereford, OBE 23.9.01

Director of Personnel Management Agency (Officers and Airmen Aircrew) (RAF)
Air Commodore P. J. HILLING, MA 12.2.01

Director of Personnel Management Agency (Ground Trades & Support) (RAF)
Air Commodore J. A. COLLIER, CBE BSc. 10.12.01

Director of Personnel Management Agency (Policy)
Air Commodore D. A. WALKER, OBE MVO BSc FRAeS MCIPD 3.12.01

DIRECTOR-GENERAL MEDICAL SERVICES (RAF)
Air Vice-Marshal W. J. PIKE, QHP MSc MB BS MRCGP MRCS MFOM DRCOG DAvMed LRCP 4.2.02

Staff Officer
Squadron Leader W. M. Fleetwood 1.6.99

Director Medical Personnel, Policy and Plans
Air Commodore M. RANGER, MB BS DAvMed AFOM MRAeS 12.6.02

Director Health Services
Air Commodore E. J. THORNTON, QHP MB ChB FCMI MFOM DAvMed 13.2.02

Director of Nursing Services (RAF)
Group Captain R. A. Reid, OBE ARRC QHNS RM DipHE 26.3.01

DIRECTOR LEGAL SERVICES (RAF)
Air Vice-Marshal J. WEEDEN, LLB 19.6.97

Deputy Director Legal Services (RAF)
Air Commodore R. A. CHARLES, LLB 12.6.97

CHAPLAIN-IN-CHIEF
The Venerable (Air Vice-Marshal) R. D. HESKETH, QHC BA 17.9.01

Staff Chaplain
Reverend (Squadron Leader) P. A. Owens, ... 4.8.00

COMMAND SECRETARY
Mr R. J. ROOKS . . . .

Group Captains
D. B. Armstrong, BDS MGDSRCS(Eng) DGDP(UK) LDSRCS 4.3.96
N. T. Bale, MLitt BSc MCMI 3.9.01
P. A. Barrett, OBE BSc FRAeS 1.11.99
W. H. Boothby, BA. 4.10.99
H. G. Britten-Austin, MSc BSc CEng FIEE. 25.4.00
F. M. Church, MBE BSc 12.11.01
W. J. Coker, OBE MB ChB BA BSc LLB FRCP DAvMed 27.3.00
Rev E. Core, MTh 11.9.01
J. M. Cruickshank 28.8.01
R. Dharmeratnam, MB BS FRCR DCH 15.4.02
L. H. Elphinstone, MSc MB ChB MRCGP MFPHM 9.4.01
D. R. E. Evans 28.8.01
W. G. Evans, OBE 17.4.01
P. P. V. Gaskin, OBE 22.1.01
N. K. Gillingham, OBE BEd 16.10.00
D. I. Harrison, BSc. 20.10.00
I. Harvey, BSc 22.2.00
P. Heaton 20.8.01
P. J. Hibberd, BA 4.12.00
P. G. H. Hodcroft, BSc MBCS 24.7.01
R. J. Hounslow, FRAeS FCMI 11.12.00
D. A. Ingham, OBE BSc 24.8.98
R. R. Innes, OBE MCMI CDipAF. 4.9.00
L. J. Irvine, MA DipLaw 27.9.00
D. J. Jones, RAFR 1.3.98
R. J. Lackey-Grant, BSc 25.9.00
A. R. Maxwell 3.9.01
G. E. McElroy, MDA BSc CEng MRAeS 6.12.99
A. J. B. McGrigor 27.1.00
N. M. McGuire, BMedSci BM BS 30.4.01
Rev P. W. Mills, QHC BD CPS 29.5.01
P. Nash, OBE BSc 17.9.01
B. W. Newby, CBE AFC 28.1.02
A. J. Pollock, ADC 1.11.99
J. G. Ross, MSc FCMI CDipAF 21.3.02
E. G. Samuel, BSc CEng MIMechE. 31.1.00
A. Sawyer, OBE 9.4.01
M. A. Williams 25.6.01

P. Williams, BSc	1.3.02
T. Winstanley, MA MSc	8.4.02

Wing Commanders

J. Aitken, Bsc MB ChB DAvMed AFOM	2.4.01
J. R. Andrews, MA	2.3.02
D. Ash, LLB	15.4.02
N. J. Barnes, BSc	21.5.01
A. Bartlett	23.7.01
P. N. Bate	9.10.00
I. K. Bell, FInstLM	15.5.00
J. B. Bennett	21.1.00
D. A. Bentley	7.6.01
A. J. Berridge, MA.	28.8.01
L. R. E. Bessant, MHCIMA	10.9.01
S. F. Bolam, MHCIMA.	12.4.99
C. M. Bray	2.7.01
P. L. Bray, BEd	20.8.01
M. Brierley, BA MILT	26.7.99
D. L. Bruce, MBE MSc MB BS FIMCRCS(Ed) MRCGP DAvMed AFOM MRAeS AKC.	28.2.00
C. S. Burns	16.4.01
P. A. Burns, BA.	18.2.02
C. B. Campbell, BSc ACIS	15.10.01
P. A. Campbell, BSc	28.6.01
R. A. J. Castle, MDA BA	18.6.01
L. Chew, RRC	19.3.01
J. J. Clark	4.5.99
P. J. Connell, BA	4.1.00
A. Cowan, MRIPH MCMI DipMgmt.	12.6.00
P. A. Cunningham, BSc	1.3.02
M. S. Dziuba	10.12.01
S. Edgar, MHCIMA.	17.1.00
H. T. Elliott, MA	2.1.01
B. R. Evans, BEng CEng MIMechE.	31.3.01
M. A. Evans, BA	24.6.02
T. P. Farmer, MSc.	5.6.99
J. G. Fidgett, MIISec	29.11.99
T. W. J. Field	8.1.01
K. H. Forshaw, MSc BSc MCIT MILT	2.4.01
S. M. Fox, AFC MA BCom	4.9.00
R. J. Girling.	21.1.02
P. M. Godfrey, BSc.	2.5.00
S. J. Harsley, MA MBA MRAeS.	13.8.01
C. H. Hickman, BSc CEng MRAeS	3.12.01
M. R. Hill.	21.8.00
J. W. Hodgson.	14.8.00
G. D. Horscroft, MA MSc BSc	16.4.01
D. L. Hoyle, MSc MHSM	18.9.00
P. A. Jones, BSc	10.3.00
G. A. Kinvig.	13.5.02
G. Lee, MSc MDA BSc	3.9.01
N. P. D. Lee, BSc MRAeS.	3.9.01
R. B. Lindley, MCMI	24.8.98
P. J. Lloyd	16.10.00
E. D. Mackie.	24.6.02
D. N. F. Marshall, MB ChB MRCGP DRCOG DAvMed	13.9.99
D. A. McCafferty	8.4.02
A. B. McCombe	14.8.00
M. P. McGuigan, BA	6.5.02
A. W. Medford, BSc	5.5.98
D. B. Mellor, MA DMS CertEd	25.3.02

M. J. Milburn, BEd	2.7.01
W. H. Milroy, MA PhD BTh MCIPD MBIFM	13.9.99
P. W. Mountain, MSc BSc CEng MRAeS CertEd.	31.7.00
A. K. Mozumder, MB BS MRCGP MRCS (Eng) LRCP DRCOG DTM&H DAvMed	1.6.00
S. Newton	17.7.00
A. G. O'Neill, MSc CEng MIEE	16.9.96
M. P. O'Sullivan BA	14.5.01
A. C. Offer, OBE	1.12.01
D. I. Ogg, BSc	29.8.00
D. E. Ross, MB ChB	14.2.00
S. P. Russell.	28.1.02
P. J. Sagar, MBE	8.5.00
D. StJ. Salisbury	1.3.00
B. P. Simmonds, OBE BSc CPhys MInstP.	27.4.98
A. Spearpoint, MCMI	5.2.01
J. Stacey.	26.1.98
A. J. Stewart, MRAeS MCMI	3.9.01
C. M. Taylor, FBIFM MCMI DipMgmt	1.6.99
P. A. Taylor, BSc MBCS	26.11.01
J. M. Thomas, MSc BA	1.10.01
P. A. Townsend.	28.8.01
G. Tunnicliffe, MA BA.	20.8.01
D. J. Turner.	12.5.01
J. M. Walsh, B.Tech	26.3.01
B. J. Waterfield, FCIPD	15.1.01
M. R. J. Westcott	6.8.01
A. C. Wilcock, MSc MB ChB MRCGP MFOM DRCOG DAvMed	9.4.01
P. A. Wilson.	12.11.01
A. J. Wolton	17.1.00
S. C. Wood, MCMI.	10.5.99

Retired Officers
Air Commodore R. D. Arnott, CBE FCMI MCIPD
Air Commodore M. K. Widdowson
Group Captain S. J. Barclay, OBE MCIPD
Group Captain G. G. Cullington, CBE AFC BSc
Group Captain P. M. Hall, BA
Group Captain P. W. Hilton
Group Captain M. A. Molloy
Group Captain A. F. Short, OBE MCIPD
Wing Commander K. W. Baldock, OBE
Wing Commander W. Beedie, FInstAM MCMI
Wing Commander K. A. Burford
Wing Commander J. Davies
Wing Commander I. Ellison, MCMI
Wing Commander J. I. Gilson
Wing Commander H. F. Gray-Wallis
Wing Commander D. J. Magee

Open Grade Structure 6
M. Court
J. R. Hollands
P. Wilson

Open Grade Structure 7
A. T. Cordory
A. Cowpe
N. Eadon-Clarke
D. Ellingham
A. J. Hawkins
Ms K. J. Haysman
P. Hopper

C. Perriman
Ms H. Tayler
E. Wallace
M. A. Weetch

NO 1 GROUP

GROUP HEADQUARTERS

Postal Address—RAF HIGH WYCOMBE, BUCKS, HP14 4UE
Telephone No.—01494 461461

AIR OFFICER COMMANDING
Air Vice-Marshal G. L. TORPY, CBE DSO BSc(Eng) 12.3.01
Personal Staff Officer
Wing Commander W. A. Cruickshank 6.11.00
Aide-de-Camp
Flight Lieutenant V. L. Hughes, BSc 25.2.02

AIR COMMODORE OFFENSIVE OPERATIONS
Air Commodore C. M. NICKOLS, MA 21.1.02

AIR COMMODORE DEFENSIVE OPERATIONS
Air Commodore P. W. D. RUDDOCK, CBE 23.10.00

AIR COMMODORE EUROFIGHTER
Air Commodore C. N. HARPER, CBE MA FCMI 19.11.01

BUSINESS AND FINANCE DIRECTOR
Mr J. Rolfe 14.8.00

Group Captain
G. J. Bagwell 22.8.01
*Colonel J. Goodsir, CBE 25.8.97

GROUP ACCOUNTANT
Mr J. H. Evans 9.3.98

Wing Commanders
S. J. Blake, MBE 1.10.01
P. J. Courtnage 20.3.00
J. J. Hitchcock 1.4.02
G. Moulds, MBE 29.4.02
R. O. Rabagliati, ACIS MInstAM 16.10.00
G. R. Scott 1.10.00
D. R. Skinner 9.8.99
K. K. Thomson, MA 1.4.00
G. E. Thwaites 18.9.00
G. G. S. Van Den Berg, MSc 3.9.01
R. C. Whitworth 21.8.00
*Lieutenant Colonel D. J. Hobden 6.7.99

Squadron Leaders
D. R. Andrew 1.3.01
R. M. Aspinall, MA 6.7.98
I. W. Atherton, BSc 12.6.00
D. J. Austen 19.7.99
M. I. Barmby 16.7.01
G. S. Brooks, MSc BA FRGS ACMA 7.12.98
A. J. Coope, BEng 13.11.00
A. W. D. Craig, BSc 10.12.01
M. L. Cunningham 20.8.01
W. J. Cunningham, BSc 30.5.01
M. R. Cutmore 12.12.01
M. J. Gorringe, BA 12.6.00

* Permanent Army Appointment

M. S. Humphreys, BSc	7.2.00
A. J. Jeffs, BSc	14.12.99
D. A. C. Legg, MBE	23.7.01
P. Lovely	5.2.01
C. N. B. Morgan, MBE	19.2.01
W. V. Palmer	7.8.00
R. P. G. Patounas	4.6.02
C. C. Pope, BSc	4.1.01
R. V. Sanderson, BSc	27.5.02
S. L. Smiley	11.3.02
A. G. Tait, BA	23.4.01
M. R. Tinworth	1.3.00
D. A. Waring, AFC	7.10.96
P. Wilkins	12.3.01

NO 2 GROUP

GROUP HEADQUARTERS

Postal Address—RAF HIGH WYCOMBE, BUCKINGHAMSHIRE HP14 4UE
Telephone No.—01494 461461

AIR OFFICER COMMANDING
Air Vice-Marshal N. D. A. MADDOX, CBE 2.8.02

Personal Staff Officer
Squadron Leader G. C. Cook. 5.8.02

Aide-de-Camp
Flight Lieutenant L. S. Pilgrim-Morris, BA. 4.6.01

AIR COMMODORE AIR TRANSPORT/AIR-TO-AIR REFUELLING AND COMMAND, CONTROL, COMMUNICATIONS AND INTELLIGENCE
Air Commodore P. R. OLLIS, CBE BSc 5.9.01

AO REGT & STO
Air Commodore N. A. BAIRSTO, MBE MDA MSc BSc CEng FIMechE FRAeS FCMI 18.4.01

Group Captains
S. Abbott, MPhil BA 1.12.00
M. L. Ashwell, MBE BSc 3.9.01
R. M. Bailey, MSc 8.1.01
N. E. L. Beresford, LVO 17.1.00
B. Smith, OBE BA 12.3.01

Wing Commanders
T. V. Bown 11.9.00
S. W. Bradnam, BSc 13.8.01
P. Burt, MA 20.4.01
J. A. Clegg 12.2.01
D. S. Davenall, BSc 5.5.95
C. R. D. Dickens. 20.11.00
G. Doyle, BSc 19.11.01
C. M. Eames. 5.9.00
R. W. Gray 1.7.02
Lieutenant Colonel R. N. Howard 4.10.01
A. J. King 23.1.01
D. K. Lord, MBE 10.6.02
M. Luton 16.8.99
G. J. Roberts 27.4.01
A. D. Trevett. 15.4.98
D. A. K. Williams 13.8.01
D. V. Williams BA PCGE MCIPD 29.4.02

Squadron Leaders
G. Allcock, BA 31.7.00
J. P. Archer 26.2.01
Major S. A. Archer 10.1.00
R. C. Ashurst 1.4.02
P. G. Atkinson 17.6.02
R. C. Bailey 10.7.00
G. L. Baxter 1.1.97
A. J. Beasant 23.4.01
I. R. Blake 1.4.01
C. J. Breedon 22.1.01
K. P. Brookes 28.8.00
D. P. Brooks 17.1.00
R. P. Bruce, BEng 5.6.00
C. Catterall 13.5.02

G. B. Challenor, BA	6.11.00
G. J. Clayton	17.6.02
B. J. Clover	16.7.01
P. R. S. Collier, BA	14.1.02
J. D. Cumming	24.5.01
R. E. Daft	18.6.02
Lieutenant Commander I. G. Denholm	12.5.02
J. B. Fearon, BSc	30.7.01
A. F. N. St J. Fitzmaurice	31.7.00
S. Gardner, MA MPhil BA	17.4.01
S. J. Gibson	1.4.01
A. J. C. Glazebrook, BA	5.11.00
D. L. Gray, BA	17.6.02
I. D. Green	8.3.00
M. J. Grigg	25.9.00
B. W. Hargrave, BSc	23.7.01
N. Hewson	18.6.01
D. E. K. Hutchinson	19.11.99
W. J. Kendall	12.4.00
H. Marsh, MBE BEd	1.4.01
S. B. McBain	8.8.95
S. J. McManus	1.7.89
S. M. Miller	23.4.01
N. J. Neal, MSc MSc BSc	9.1.02
R. L. Owens, BSc	3.4.00
M. R. K. Palmer, BSc	1.1.00
G. A. Philip	17.6.02
S. P. Plumb, BA	3.4.00
A. R. Povey	1.4.02
N. C. H. Prince	18.6.01
J. Pugh, BEng	15.10.01
W. J. Rooney	3.7.00
P. Scott	27.11.00
P. A. Scott, BA PGCE	14.8.00
R. P. Seymour	1.4.02
J. C. D. Simpson	28.11.00
T. E. Uren, BSc	2.4.02
K. M. D. Vaughan	16.10.00
P. Walsh, MSc BA MCIT MILT	25.8.00
J. M. R. Waring	22.1.01
D. M. Watkins	23.7.01
N. W. Winsor, BEng	14.11.00

USAF Exchange Officers
Major K. Van Ravenswaay
Major K. Edenborough

NO 3 GROUP

GROUP HEADQUARTERS
Postal Address—RAF HIGH WYCOMBE, BUCKINGHAMSHIRE HP14 4UE
Telephone No.—01494 461461

MARITIME ELEMENT
Postal Address—JHQ NORTHWOOD, MIDDLESEX, HA6 3HP
Telephone No.—01923 837205

AIR OFFICER COMMANDING
Rear Admiral I. S. LIDBETTER 24.7.01

Personal Staff Officer
Commander J. C. Rigby, BA MILDM 24.7.00

Aide-de-Camp
Flight Lieutenant N. M. Wood 23.10.00

JOINT FORCE HARRIER
AIR COMMODORE HARRIER
Air Commodore D. WALKER, CBE AFC MA BSc 1.8.01

Captain (RN)
R. C. Hawkins, BSc. 9.3.01

Wing Commander
A. H. Galloway 7.5.01

Commanders
D. H. Mackay 16.12.98
J. P. Milward, MBE. 4.9.01
M. Reid 30.4.01
J. C. Rigby 20.1.02
P. M. G. Schwarz 11.7.00

Squadron Leaders
R. D. Atkinson 18.6.01
I. W. Duguid. 14.8.00
H. J. A. Fane de Salis, BA. 9.5.02
D. A. N. Johnson, BEng 30.10.00
D. W. A. Miller 7.5.01
P. M. de G. Ratcliff, BSc, MCIPD 26.4.00

Lieutenant Commanders
D. D. Acland. 2.8.01
P. C. L. Durham 6.8.01
T. C. Eastaugh 13.9.99
E. Kelbie, BA 1.8.00
J. P. L. Phesse, IEng AMRAeS 1.4.00
M. A. Salmon 30.5.00

HEADQUARTERS ROYAL AIR FORCE
PROVOST AND SECURITY SERVICES

Postal Address—RAF HENLOW, BEDFORDSHIRE SG16 6DN
Telephone No.—01462-851515

HEADQUARTERS

COMMANDING OFFICER
Group Captain M. P. Brzezicki, MPhil MIL 26.9.00

Wing Commanders
S. J. Court, MBE 1.10.01
D. Fairbrother 14.5.01
J. W. Whitmell 5.6.00

Squadron Leaders
J. W. Erskine 14.2.00
E. Lawson, BSc 2.6.99
A. K. Nicholas 9.5.01
D. T. Overend 20.6.01
J. M. Riseley-Prichard, BSc 4.5.98
M. S. Sexton, BA 6.5.02
G. K. Stewart 9.8.00
T. J. Wood, LLB 22.10.02

DEFENCE AVIATION SAFETY CENTRE

Postal Address: PO BOX 333, RAF BENTLEY PRIORY, STANMORE, MIDDLESEX, HA7 3YN
Telephone No.—0208 838 + Ext (VPN 95271)

Director
Air Commodore R. L. DIXON, BSc

Deputy Director
Colonel A. M. Gibson, Late AAC

Policy Branch
Commander R. Leaning
Major R. Hibbert, AAC
Squadron Leader S. D. Hayler, BSc
Squadron Leader S. J. Read
Captain G. Best, AAC
Flight Lieutenant I. R. Heath, BA

Fixed Wing Branch
Wing Commander J. D. Arkell, OBE MA
Squadron Leader R. W. Bond
Squadron Leader R. W. C. Garner

Rotary Wing Branch
Lieutenant Colonel P. G. Adams, AFC AAC
Lieutenant Commander M. Greenland
Squadron Leader T. J. H. Heald

Operations Support Branch
Commander P. J. Dawson
Squadron Leader G. S. Henderson, BEd

Occurrences Branch
Wing Commander B. R. Neal, FCMI

Engineering Policy Branch
Commander I. J. Peck, BSc CEng MRAeS MDA
Major N. Graham, REME
Squadron Leader A. T. MacDonald

Aviation Safety Review Branch
Wing Commander M. G. Salter, MBE MBA BA MRAeS
Squadron Leader E. J. Burrows
Squadron Leader D. Marshall, MBE
Squadron Leader N. M. Sainsbury, IEng AMRAeS

ROYAL AIR FORCE CENTRE OF AVIATION MEDICINE

Postal Address: ROYAL AIR FORCE HENLOW, BEDFORDSHIRE SG16 6DN
Telephone No.—01462 851515 + Ext

OFFICER COMMANDING
Group Captain A. J. Batchelor, CBE BSc MB BS FRCP FRAeS DRCOG DAvMed
(Whittingham Professor of Aviation Medicine (RAF)) 1.9.98

OFFICER COMMANDING AVIATION PATHOLOGY WING
Air Commodore S. A. CULLEN, QHS MB ChB FRCPath FRAeS DCP 31.5.00

Wing Commanders
A. M. Anderson, MB ChB MRCGP 18.9.00
D. Dexter, MA BSc MB ChB MRCGP DRCOG DAvMed 28.11.01
D. P. Gradwell, PhD BSc MB ChB FRAeS DAvMed 16.11.98
A. V. A. Hurley, BA BM DOccMed 4.8.98
D. I. T. Jenkins, MSc BSc MB BS MRCGP MFOM DRCOG DAvMed MRAeS 24.6.00
C. R. W. O'Connell, MB BCh BAO LLMRCP(Irel) LLMRCS(Irel) 1.4.00

Principal Medical Officer (Research)
Dr A. J. F. MacMillan, BSc MB ChB MFOM

AIR WARFARE CENTRE (AWC)
DEFENCE ELECTRONIC WELFARE CENTRE (DEWC)

Postal Address: Thomson Building, RAF Waddington, Lincolnshire, LN5,9WA
Telephone No.—01522 72 + Ext

COMMANDANT AWC/Director DEWC
Air Commodore S. W. PEACH, CBE MPhil BA FRAeS MRIN 28.7.00
Secretariat
Wing Commander J. Lawlor, BA 12.3.01
Squadron Leader R. A. Heath, BA 2.10.00
Flight Lieutenant E. M. M. Doyle, BEM 18.6.01

OPERATIONAL ANALYSIS

Senior Scientific Adviser
Mr A. C. Cowdale, MSc BSc

Scientific Adviser (Development)
Dr R. C. Wheeler, MA DPhil

Scientific Adviser (Operations)
Mr P Stoddart, MA BSc CEng MRAeS

Scientific Adviser (HW) HQ STC
Mr G. J. Onslow, BSc CEng MBCS MRAeS

Scientific Adviser (Mar & Ops) Northwood
Mr J. C. Whitmore, BTech

OPERATIONS DIVISION

Group Captain
R. H. Middleton. 22.12.00

Wing Commanders
J. H. Davies 13.5.02
R. W. Davies, BSc 22.1.01
R. Goodall 25.4.00
D. R. Herriot 25.8.00
P. R. Hunter, OBE 14.1.02
J. P. Hutchings 25.9.00
R. W. Jones 3.4.00
D. W. Knowles 1.4.01
M. A. Wakeman 9.7.01

Royal Navy
Commander A. M. O'Sullivan

Army
Lieutenant Colonel R. J. J. Park, BA MDA RA

USAF Adviser
Lieutenant Colonel J. R. Jeffries

Retired Officer
Wing Commander R. J. C. Green, MRIN MCMI

AIR WARFARE TRAINING
Cranwell

Wing Commanders
I. T. Ashcroft 18.2.02
A. R. Bown 4.5.99
J. R. Brooks 19.11.01
A. P. Stephens 20.5.96

USAF Exchange Officer
Major C. Overman

RAAF Exchange Officer
Squadron Leader G. Downes

DEVELOPMENT DIVISION

Group Captain
N. M. Huckins, MBE BSc BSc 12.4.02

Wing Commanders
A. D. Lister-Tomlinson 19.2.01
J. P. Loader, MBE 3.7.00
D. J. Gledhill 22.1.01

OPERATIONAL EVALUATION UNITS

Air C2 OEU	Wing Commander G. Hewett, BEd	1.2.02
EF OEU	Wing Commander D. K. M. Chan	1.4.02
F3 OEU	Wing Commander R. W. Birtwistle	5.2.01
SA OEU	Wing Commander A. G. Dakin, BSc.	1.9.00
Nimrod OEU	Wing Commander D. A. Angus	23.2.01
JATEU	Lieutenant Colonel A. Teare	28.8.01
RWOETU	Wing Commander K. D. Connor	12.5.00
Hercules OEU	Squadron Leader D. J. Rae, BSc.	19.6.00
AGW OEU	Squadron Leader G. P. Cowling, BSc	14.12.98
GBAD OEU	Flight Lieutenant T. J. Bradley, BA	18.9.00

OPERATIONS SUPPORT DIVISION

Group Captain
D. J. Walker 26.3.01

Wing Commanders
P. C. Jones, MBA 4.9.00
D. A. Holland 15.4.02

Royal Navy
Commander A. J. Healy
Lieutenant Commander J. Heneghan

Army
Major D. Doughty

CAF Liaison
Major D. Masters

591 Signals Unit
Squadron Leader H. Roberts, MSc BSc CPhys MInstP 24.7.00

JOINT SERVICES COMMAND AND STAFF COLLEGE, SHRIVENHAM

Postal Address—JSCSC Faringdon Road, Watchfield, Swindon, Wiltshire SN6 8TS
Telephone No.—01793-788000

COMMANDANT
Rear Admiral R. LIPPIETT, MBE RN. 28.1.02

Aide-de-Camp
Flight Lieutenant K. Warwick, MA MSc 29.5.01

Assistant Commandant (Air)
Air Commodore A. P. N. LAMBERT, MPhil 3.9.01

Advanced Air Command and Staff Course (ACSC)

A Division
Wing Commander A. S. Linstead, MA BSc 29.7.01
Wing Commander K. Duell 20.8.01
Wing Commander K. L. O'Dea, MA MRAeS MCMI 6.8.01

B Division
Wing Commander D. Best, OBE BSc ALCM 3.7.01
Wing Commander M. F. Neal, OBE IEng FIIE 23.10.00
Wing Commander S. J. Howard, MA MBA MRAeS 8.8.01
Wing Commandeer P. J. Jones 25.11.01

C Division
Wing Commander S. C. Cooke, BA. 4.6.01
Wing Commander A. G. Mitchell, BA 2.5.01

D Division
Group Captain A. J. Dey, BSc 12.3.01
Group Captain C. J. Finn, MPhil. 9.6.02
Wing Commander B. Cooper, OBE 28.8.00
Wing Commander S. K. Dobb, MA 25.2.02
Wing Commander A. R. M. Mills, BA 8.10.01

RAF JUNIOR DIVISION (RAFJD)
Group Captain H. M. Randall 6.9.99
Wing Commander C. L. Jones, MCMI 3.12.01
Wing Commander C. W. McDermott 23.7.01

RAF JD—Intermediate Command and Staff Course (ICSC)
Wing Commander P. Shepherd 4.9.99
Squadron Leader J. E. S. Bewsher, MSc 18.3.02
Squadron Leader B. J. McLean, MCMI. 20.11.00
Squadron Leader J. A. Parry, MA BSc 3.5.00
Squadron Leader I. R. Price, MCMI 3.4.00
Squadron Leader K. R. H. Girdwood, BSc. 10.8.01
Squadron Leader C. Little, BEd 19.11.01

RAFJD—Junior Officers Command Course (JOCC)
Wing Commander I. B. Walker, MDA BA 14.1.02
Squadron Leader H. R. Boyes, BEM 17.10.00
Squadron Leader C. C. Carver 8.11.99
Squadron Leader A. J. Killick 7.5.01
Squaderon Leader A. D. Miller, BSc 5.8.00
Squadron Leader R. A. Jarvis 8.4.02
Squadron Leader O. D. Roberts, BEd 29.1.01
Squadron Leader D. J. Griffiths 8.4.02

Royal Navy Junior Division (RNJD)
Squadron Leader D. J. Leward, BSc 4.9.00

RAF—Individual Staff Studies School (ISS)

Wing Commander C. L. Jones, MCMI .	3.12.01
Squadron Leader D. R. Brooks, BSc	8.5.00
Squadron Leader M. L. Jackson, BSc .	23.4.01
Squadron Leader M. L. Large	17.5.99
Squadron Leader J. Lillis .	7.8.00
Squadron Leader C. J. Mandley, BA RGN .	27.11.00
Squadron Leader L. G. Mulholland-Fenton, ACMA .	28.2.00
Squadron Leader A. D. Perkins .	1.1.97
Squadron Leader A. F. Philip, MSc BSc(Eng) .	29.9.97
Squadron Leader M. V. D. Sparrow.	22.8.99
Squadron Leader S. E. Wadsworth, BA	5.5.98

Retired Officers

Wing Commander T. Bradley, MBE BA MRAes
Wing Commander A. G. Corbitt
Wing Commander R. McLaughlin
Wing Commander T. J. Nias, IEng MIIE
Squadron Leader B. T. Clarkin
Squadron Leader A. M. J. Davy, BA
Squadron Leader D. A. Petty, MA MA CertEd

J1/J4 Personnel
Administration/Accounts/Logistics/Infrastructure/Facilities and Warfare

Squadron Leader K. Selway .	25.3.02

J3 Operations and Co-ordination (J3 Co-ord)

Squadron Leader N. A. Hartley .	29.5.01
Flight Lieutenant H. Miller, MSc.	24.9.01

ROYAL AIR FORCE COLLEGE CRANWELL

(Royal Air Force Personnel and Training Command)
Postal Address—ROYAL AIR FORCE COLLEGE, CRANWELL, SLEAFORD, LINCOLNSHIRE NG34 8HB
Telephone No.—01400-261201

Commandant-in-Chief—HM THE QUEEN

Air Commodore-in-Chief Air Training Corps
Marshal of the Royal Air Force H. R. H. The PRINCE PHILIP, DUKE OF EDINBURGH KG KT OM GBE AC QSO

AIR OFFICER COMMANDING AND COMMANDANT OF RAF COLLEGE
Air Vice-Marshal A. J. SMITH, OBE BSc CEng FRAeS MIMechE 27.6.02

Personal Staff Officer
Squadron Leader M. R. Jewsbury, MSc BSc MCIPD 23.8.01

Chief of Staff
Group Captain C. S. Davidson, MA MLitt 6.12.99

College Secretary
Group Captain P. J. Rodgers, MBE (Retd)

DIRECTOR OF RECRUITING AND DEPUTY COMMANDANT OF RAF COLLEGE
Air Commodore D. R. WILLIAMS, OBE FCMI 1.7.02

Staff Officer
Flight Lieutenant C. S. Park, BSc 31.5.02

COMMANDANT AIR CADETS AND AIR TRAINING CORPS
Air Commodore J. P. CHITTY, OBE MA BSc(Eng) CEng FRGS FRAeS ACGI 3.5.02

Aide-de-Camp
Flying Officer K. P. Bryan 20.11.00

OFFICER COMMANDING ROYAL AIR FORCE COLLEGE CRANWELL
Group Captain R. B. Cunningham, MBE MA 24.5.02

DIRECTOR OF ELEMENTARY FLYING TRAINING
Group Captain R. Marston, AFC 6.3.00

DIRECTOR OF DEPARTMENT OF SPECIALIST GROUND TRAINING
Group Captain G. A. Paterson, BSc CEng FIEE FRAeS FCMI 17.8.01

DEPUTY DIRECTORS RECRUITMENT, SELECTION AND INITIAL OFFICER TRAINING
Group Captain G. A. Bowerman, OBE 29.9.00
Group Captain R. J. A. Powell 11.3.02
Group Captain G. Ware 4.3.01
Group Captain J. K. Wheeler, OBE BA FBIFM MCMI 19.10.01

CHIEF OF STAFF AIR CADETS
Group Captain W. M. N. Cross, OBE RAFR

AIR CADETS REGIONAL HEADQUARTERS

Scotland and Northern Ireland (Edinburgh)
Group Captain A. B. Wight-Boycott, OBE RAFR

Wales and West (RAF Cosford)
Group Captain P. S. Kiggell, OBE RAFR

Central and East (RAF Henlow)
Group Captain J. A. F. Ford, FCMI RAFR

London and South East (RAF Northolt)
Group Captain L. Hakin, OBE RAFR

North (RAF Linton-on-Ouse)
Group Captain W. G. Gambold, RAFR

COLLEGES

South West (RAF Locking)
Group Captain M. T. Remlinger, RAFR

Wing Commanders

A. K. Beanland, BA.	21.4.02
J. D. L. England, MBE LLB MCIPD	10.12.01
D. K. Griffiths, MSc MRAeS MCIPS.	12.8.02
A. P. Hawes, BSc	30.5.99
W. Hush, BSc	3.7.00
P. D. Tindall, BSc	5.11.01
T. P. McWilliams	9.10.00

Retired Officers
Wing Commander G. S. Clayton-Jones, MRAeS RAFR
Wing Commander M. Eveleigh, OBE MCMI RAFR
Wing Commander W. W. Wright, BA, BA DipEd RAFR
Wing Commander M. A. Thorley, MRAeS RAFR

ROYAL AIR FORCE CENTRAL FLYING SCHOOL
CRANWELL

(Royal Air Force Personnel and Training Command)

Postal Address—HQ CFS, RAF COLLEGE CRANWELL, SLEAFORD, LINCOLNSHIRE NG34 8HB
Telephone No.—01400 261201

COMMANDANT
Group Captain J. S. Fynes 14.1.02

Personal Assistant
Sergeant H. M. Garrett 14.6.99

Staff Officer HQ CFS
Squadron Leader C. L. Taylor-Powell 4.6.01

Staff Officer (Policy)
Squadron Leader A. S. Bainbridge 7.5.02

Wing Commanders
W. J. Ramsey 11.2.01
S. Chiddention, MBE 19.8.01

Squadron Leaders
R. J. S. G. Clark, MBE MA 15.10.01
D. M. Gray 8.5.01
J. D. Leighton 13.3.00
C. D. Jepson 12.6.01
L. C. Johnson, MVO 13.8.01
R. D. Moir 21.1.02

FIXED WING TUTORIAL SQUADRONS

TUTOR SQUADRON
RAF CRANWELL
Squadron Leader J. G. Temple 12.3.01

TUCANO SQUADRON
RAF LINTON-ON-OUSE
Squadron Leader M. F. Brown 1.7.00

19(F) SQUADRON
RAF VALLEY
Squadron Leader R. W. Bedford, BSc 22.1.01

208 SQUADRON
RAF VALLEY
Squadron Leader R. L. Maskall 13.8.01

ROTARY WING TUTORIAL SQUADRON

GAZELLE SQUADRON
RAF SHAWBURY
Squadron Leader J. E. Taylor 10.8.01

Editor AP3456 RAF CRANWELL
Mr G. Heath

ROYAL COLLEGE OF DEFENCE STUDIES

Postal Address—Seaford House, 37 Belgrave Square, London SW1X 8NS
Telephone No.—020-7915-4800

COMMANDANT
Lieutenant General Sir CHRISTOPHER WALLACE, KBE. 3.1.01

SENIOR DIRECTING STAFF
Major General K. H. CIMA, MA MBA CEng MIMechE 23.4.02
Major General D. A. S. PENNEFATHER, CB OBE RM 23.4.02
Mr. N. W. BROWNE, CMG
Air Vice-Marshal P. W. ROSER, MBE FRAeS 17.12.99

DIRECTING STAFF
Mr M. P. Sweeting
Wing Commander A. S. C. Culbert, BSc 13.3.00
Commander P. Lankester, RN 19.3.01
Lieutenant Colonel A. P. Lake 3.7.01
Mr W. Wilson

SECRETARY
Commander A. C. Gordon-Lennox 25.6.01

JOINT WARFARE STAFF

at Maritime Warfare Centre (Southwick)
HMS DRYAD, Nr Fareham, HAMPSHIRE PO17 6EJ
Telephone No.—02392 284726

Wing Commanders
W. A. D. Carter, BA. 4.1.99
P. W. Gregory, MBE BA MIL 12.12.01

AIR OFFICER SCOTLAND

ROYAL AIR FORCE LEUCHARS
St ANDREWS, FIFE KY16 0JX
Telephone No.—01334 839471

AIR OFFICER
Air Commodore M. J. ROUTLEDGE, ADC BSc MRAeS 5.10.01

Aide-de-Camp and Staff Officer to AOS
Flight Lieutenant M. J. Clulo. 1.7.02

HEADQUARTERS, BRITISH FORCES GIBRALTAR

Postal Address: HEADQUARTERS BRITISH FORCES, THE TOWER, GIBRALTAR BFPO 52

COMMANDER
Commodore R. J. CLAPP, RN 11.12.98

MA to Commander
Squadron Leader, N. B. Stoner 1.7.01

Station Commander RAF Gibraltar
Wing Commander D. J. Trembaczowski-Ryder, BSc 18.8.00

HEADQUARTERS, BRITISH FORCES CYPRUS

Postal Address: HEADQUARTERS, BRITISH FORCES CYPRUS
BRITISH FORCES POST OFFICE 53

COMMANDER
Air Vice-Marshal T. W. RIMMER, CB OBE MA FRAeS 4.9.00

Aide-de-Camp
Flight Lieutenant S. J. L. Lawrence 3.1.02

MA to Commander
Major B. L. Baldwin 21.1.02

CHIEF OF STAFF
Brigadier D. E. RADCLIFFE, OBE 1.6.00

DEPUTY CHIEF OF STAFF
Group Captain The Honourable D. P. Murray, OBE FCMI MBIFM 5.12.00

Wing Commanders
S. Dureau, LLB 7.11.00
R. C. Hornsby, MDA BH MCIT MILT MCMI 27.5.02
R. M. P. Parr, MDA BA 30.10.00
M. J. Wrigley, MSc BSc 3.4.00

MISCELLANEOUS ESTABLISHMENTS
A. V. Kelly . . . . Command Secretary
Mr R. Need . . . . SO1 Media Ops

Group Captain (Retd)
B. J. Comina . . . . SO1 J4 Project Sponsor

HEADQUARTERS INTEGRATED AIR DEFENCE SYSTEM

(ROYAL AIR FORCE ELEMENT)
Postal Address: HEADQUARTERS, INTEGRATED AIR DEFENCE SYSTEM, AIR BASE BUTTERWORTH,
c/o GPO PENANG, MALAYSIA

Senior Officer Air Defence
Wing Commander M. J. Mercer 24.9.01

UNITED KINGDOM MILITARY REPRESENTATIVE TO NATO AND EUROPEAN UNION

(BRITISH ELEMENT—ROYAL AIR FORCE)

Postal Address—BRITISH FORCES POST OFFICE 49

Telephone No.—Brussels 707 72 11

UNITED KINGDOM MILITARY REPRESENTATIVE
Lieutenant General K. O'DONOGHUE 4.5.01

Executive Assistant
Commander K. J. Broadley, RN 13.9.02

Aide-de-Camp
Captain J. T. F. Dakin, RGBW 6.5.02

DEPUTY UK MILITARY REPRESENTATIVE AND CHIEF OF STAFF
Commodore J. TIGHE, OBE RN 15.6.01

DEPUTY UK MILITARY REPRESENTATIVE EUROPEAN UNION
Air Commodore J. H. S. THOMAS, BA MIL 19.4.02

Group Captains
C. K. Adams. 27.7.02
A. I. B. Beedie 7.2.00
P. M. Miles, BSc 19.11.01
A. J. Ovens, OBE BSc 2.11.99
P. D. J. Turner, BSc FCMI FCIPD 1.4.02

Wing Commanders
G. I. August, BA 18.2.01
P. Edwards 20.8.01
A. I. Farmer, MBE BA 1.10.00
M. A. Fulford, MSc MBA BSc CEng MIEE 6.3.00
M. V. Godfrey, AFC 7.1.02
S. J. Hands, MDA BSc CEng MRAeS 1.2.01
F. N. Hutchinson, MCMI 1.8.00
M. J. Loveridge. 13.3.00
P. J. Pharaoh, MSc BSc 8.7.01
A. Proudlove, MBA 10.1.01
J. P. Squelch, BSc 23.3.01
S. J. Taylor, MBE MSc CEng MIEE MCMI 9.7.01
D. J. Tester, MA. 1.4.02
D. M. Casey (Retd)

SUPREME HEADQUARTERS ALLIED POWERS EUROPE

Postal Address: BRITISH FORCES POST OFFICE 26
Telegraphic Address: UKNMR SHAPE
Telephone Exchange: SHAPE MILITARY
Telephone No.—00-32-65-447111

CHIEF OF STAFF
Admiral Sir IAN GARNETT, KCB 11.9.01

Principal Staff Officer
Group Captain C. A. Bairsto 20.8.01

ASSISTANT CHIEF OF STAFF POLICY & REQUIREMENTS DIVISION
Air Vice-Marshal R. A. WRIGHT, AFC FRAeS 2.5.00

EXECUTIVE ASSISTANT TO THE COFS FOR COMMAND STRUCTURE IMPLEMENTATION
Air Vice-Marshal A. G. B. VALLANCE, OBE MPhil FRAeS 23.10.00

CHIEF OF SPECIAL WEAPONS BRANCH
Commodore M. B. AVERY 21.1.02

DEPUTY COMMANDER, NATO AIRBORNE EARLY WARNING FORCE COMMAND
Air Commodore R. J. HORWOOD, CBE FRAeS 4.9.00

UNITED KINGDOM NATIONAL MILITARY REPRESENTATIVE
Brigadier W. O. COOK. 3.5.02

DUKNMR(AIR)
Group Captain I. F. Bruton, BA 18.3.02

Group Captains
P. C. Badcock, MBE 14.7.99
R. M. Jenner 28.9.98

Wing Commanders
R. F. Blunden BA MRAeS MBCS MCMI 3.2.96
R. J. Cassady 1.4.94
R. J. Cowell 6.8.01
R. Crane 22.11.99
K. M. Douglas 29.5.00
N. D. Everall. 1.11.99
C. J. S. Hewat, MBE 6.9.99
C. Jobling 8.5.00
F. B. Jones, IEng MIIE 4.12.00
S. M. Lacey 3.7.01
D. C. Morgan 24.9.01
S. Pearson, BA 30.7.01
M. Rimmer 1.12.99
F. J. P. Smith, BEd 31.7.00

NATO School (SHAPE) OBERAMMERGAU
Wing Commander P. N. Day 1.8.02

NATO Programming Centre GLONS
Wing Commander D. C. Sharma 12.9.99

REACTION FORCE AIR STAFF (RFAS), KALKAR
Von-Seydlitz Kaserne, Kalkar, Germany
(ROYAL AIR FORCE ELEMENT)

Postal Address: c/o Box 2004, British Forces Post Office 105
Telephone: 0049-2824-90-2202/IVSN 234/239/2202
Facsimile Number: 0049-2824-90-2274/IVSN 234/239 2274
DIrect Dial: 0049-0024-90-xxxx/IVSN 234/239 xxxx
E-Mail: RFAS_NATO@-online.de

CHIEF OF STAFF
Air Commodore P. HODGSON 22.4.02

Group Captain
N. V. Vaughan-Smith, BSc CEng MIEE MRAeS 13.11.00

Wing Commander
A. J. Arnold 27.8.01
D. L. Ayers, OBE 27.11.00
A. J. M. Hayward, BSc MRAeS 3.9.01
J. A. Ingham 10.8.01
J. L. Porter 27.4.00
P. H. Steiner, MILT 18.10.98

HEADQUARTERS ALLIED COMMAND EUROPE
RAPID REACTION CORPS (ARRC)

Postal Address: BRITISH FORCES POST OFFICE 40
Telephone Exchange: RHEINDAHLEN MILITARY (94872) plus extension
Telephone No. 00-49-2161-565 plus extension
Direct Dial: 00-49-2161-565-5356
E-Mail: arrc.g3.air@bfg.net.de

SENIOR RAF OFFICER
Wing Commander K. R. Cowieson 23.4.01

Wing Commander
P. H. C. Jochimsem 17.12.00

Squadron Leaders
J. L. Comfort 12.6.00
R. P. W. Hall 11.6.01
C. P. M. Hudson, RAFR 6.4.01
A. C. Page 19.8.02

REGIONAL HEADQUARTERS
ALLIED FORCES NORTH EUROPE

HENDRICK KAMP, BRUNSSUM, NETHERLANDS
(BRITISH ELEMENT: ROYAL AIR FORCE)
BRITISH FORCES POST OFFICE 28
Telephone Exchange: RHQ AFNORTH
(045 261111)

COMMANDER IN CHIEF
General Sir JACK DEVERELL, KCB OBE 23.3.01

Principal Staff Officer
Group Captain M. A. Leakey, BSc RAF 11.12.00

Aide-de-Camp
Captain D. A. M. Burton, BA 30.9.01

Group Captain
B. E. Rogers, MBE 17.6.02

Wing Commanders
T. T. J. Baker 2.4.02
A. E. Leggett, MDA BA FInstAM. 17.7.00
C. D. O'Connell 11.6.01
E. Peacock, BA 1.1.01
M. S. Pearce, BSc CEng MIEE 20.6.98
I. S. Pollitt, MBE MA MDA 16.8.99
R. W. Roberts 16.8.99
M. Rodgers 12.2.01
V. E. Rose 26.3.01
W. L. Vose 25.1.00

JOINT HEADQUARTERS NORTH

Postal Address—JHQ North, BFPO 50
National Correspondence addressed to—UKSE, JHQ North, BFPO 50
Telephone No.—Norway 0047 51572689
Fax No.—Norway 0047 51576635

SENIOR RAF OFFICER
Wing Commander K. Lane, MBA DipMgmt 20.4.02

Wing Commanders
W. J. Turner, MA BSc(Eng) MRAeS MRIN MCGI MCMI 10.3.97
C. E. Wade, BSc 3.4.00
G. D. Yapp 2.10.00

Squadron Leaders
P. W. Haworth 31.5.99
T. C. Padmore 26.2.01

OFFICER COMMANDING UNITED KINGDOM SUPPORT UNIT
Squadron Leader M. A. Cowdrey, BA 31.1.00

JOINT HEADQUARTERS NORTH EAST

(ROYAL AIR FORCE ELEMENT)
Postal Address—HQ BALTAP, NAVAL PARTY 1004, BFPO 486
Telephone No.—Denmark (0045) 86615111 BALTAP CENTRE (MIL)

Communications and Information Systems Division
Group Captain S. D. Ottridge, BSc CEng MIEE MBCS . . ACOS CIS 22.11.99

Operations and Exercises Division
Wing Commander C. F. W. Felger . . . . Staff Officer OCA/AI 1.6.00

HEADQUARTERS COMMANDER
AIR EAST ATLANTIC
AND COMMANDER MARITIME AIR ALLIED NAVAL FORCES NORTH

Postal Address: —
NORTHWOOD HEADQUARTERS NORTHWOOD MIDDLESEX HA6 3HP
Telephone No.—01923 843511

COMMANDER AIR EAST ATLANTIC AND COMMANDER MARITIME AIR ALLIED NAVAL FORCES NORTH
*Rear Admiral S. LIDBETTER 24.7.01

ACOS (AIR)
Air Commodore C. P. IGOE 21.8.00

Group Captain
*C. J. Birks, MA BSc 28.1.02

---

* (Staff serving in national appointments, in HQ No 3 Gp RAF, with additional NATO duties on the staff of the HQs)

HEADQUARTERS
ALLIED AIR FORCES NORTH
AIRNORTH

RAMSTEIN AIR BASE GERMANY

(ROYAL AIR FORCE ELEMENT)

Postal Address: British Forces Post Office 109
Telephone Exchange: Ramstein DSN (606 258 0111-Operator)
Telephone No: 06371–40 (00-Operator)
IVSN 258 0111
U.K. Support Unit Civil No. 06371–476161

CHIEF OF STAFF
Air Marshal Sir RODERICK GOODALL, KBE CB AFC* FRAeS 1.9.99

EXECUTIVE OFFICER TO COMAIRNORTH
Group Captain T. S. Milburn, MA BSc 28.5.01

SENIOR RAF STAFF OFFICER
Group Captain T. P. McDonald, OBE 26.4.02

Group Captain
R. J. Torbet 14.5.01

Wing Commanders
A. J. W. Boyd 9.12.00
C. R. Burchett 26.6.02
B. W. Cox, MBE. 18.1.99
J. S. Davies 11.9.00
R. C. Duance 13.8.01
H. G. Geddes 8.10.97
P. N. Gilbert, BSc CEng MRAeS 13.12.99
W. R. Hartree 3.8.98
G. J. P. Moore, BSc DipEurHum DipAppSS 8.11.99
R. G. Parker, BA 16.5.99
N. C. Smith 25.6.01
P. C. West 7.5.01
A. G. Willenbruch, MA (Eur Ing) CEng MIMechE MRAeS MCMI 27.5.02
C. N. W. Wood, MA 3.1.00

HEADQUARTERS
ALLIED AIR FORCES NORTH
TACTICAL LEADERSHIP PROGRAMME
AIRNORTH/TLP

BASE J. OFFENBERG, B-5620 FLORENNES, BELGIUM

(ROYAL AIR FORCE ELEMENT)

Postal Address: c/o United Kingdom Support Unit SHAPE
British Forces Post Office 26
Telephone No.—0032 71 681506
IVSN 252 1110

SENIOR RAF OFFICER
Wing Commander
D. J. Diamond, BA MRAeS 20.10.01

Squadron Leaders
D. R. Armstrong 9.4.01
J. C. Ash, BEng 22.4.02
S. D. Hayler, BSc 2.9.02
D. P. Morris, BSc 3.5.00
R. J. Turner 10.9.01

ALLIED FORCES SOUTHERN EUROPE

Postal Address—RHQ ALLIED FORCES SOUTHERN EUROPE, BFPO 8
National Correspondence addressed to—UKNSU, HQ AFSOUTH, BFPO 8
Telephone No.—NAPLES 0039-081-7212046
Fax No.—NAPLES 0039-081-5700053

Wing Commanders

I. Barrowcliffe	18.9.00
G. R. Davey	6.9.99
D. L. Laws, MBE MSc BA DESEM MCIT, MILT MIL	13.7.00
M. S. Rafferty, BSc	14.9.00
G. M. Smith	14.8.00
G. M. Stapleton	2.5.00

HEADQUARTERS
JOINT COMMAND SOUTHEAST
SIRINYER, IZMIR, TURKEY

All correspondence concerning national administration to be addressed to
OC UK Support Unit, NATO/TURKEY, BFPO 599

Postal Address—JCSE PK 527, IZMIR, 35148 TURKEY
Telegraphic Address—UKSUPU TURKEY
Telephone No.—IZMIR 90 232 4875862
IVSN 423-8011 Ext. 2092
Fax No.—IZMIR 90 232 4875862

Wing Commander

P. A. Rushmere, MCMI	25.3.00

COMMANDER MARITIME AIR FORCES
SOUTHERN EUROPE

Postal Address—MARAIRSOUTH, BFPO 8
National Correspondence addressed to—UKNSU, HQ AFSOUTH, BFPO 8
Telegraphic Address—COMARAIRSOUTH
Telephone No.—NAPLES 0039-081-568-3673

Wing Commander

D. J. Ford, BA	4.4.00

ALLIED AIR FORCES SOUTHERN EUROPE

Postal Address—RHQ ALLIED FORCES, BFPO 8
National Correspondence addressed to—UKNSU, HQ AFSOUTH, BFPO 8
Telephone No.—NAPLES 0039-081-7212046
Fax No.—NAPLES 0039-081-5709053

Group Captain
J. R. D. Morley, MBE 1.3.00

Wing Commanders
A. B. Batchelor 2.10.00
D. A. Bush, BSc. 10.3.00
P. Chambers. 14.12.00
T. Payne, BSc 16.10.00
S. C. G. Turner, BSc(Econ) MCMI 21.5.01
P. York, OBE 19.3.00

HEADQUARTERS, SUPREME ALLIED COMMANDER ATLANTIC

Postal Address—HQ SACLANT, NORFOLK, NAVAL PARTY 1964, BFPO 493
Telegraphic Address—SACLANT, NORFOLK, VIRGINIA, USA
Telephone No.—757-445-3258

Group Captain
S. F. Warren, MDA 28.6.02

Wing Commanders
P. M. Blee 20.3.00
S. P. Harpum, MSc BSc MILT 30.9.02
M. R. Hooker, MCMI 29.10.99

Squadron Leaders
M. R. Davies, BSc 13.8.01
C. R. Smith, BA 5.8.02

HEADQUARTERS COMMANDER-IN-CHIEF EAST ATLANTIC AND HEADQUARTERS COMMANDER ALLIED NAVAL FORCES NORTH

Postal Address—NORTHWOOD HEADQUARTERS NORTHWOOD, MIDDLESEX HA6 3HP
Telephone No.—01923 826161

Wing Commanders

A. J. Butler	22.4.02
G. A. Preston	21.5.01

Squadron Leaders

A. Brown	26.7.97
J. B. Kenning, BSc	8.4.02
C. J. N. Waller, IEng FIIE AMRAeS RAFR	16.5.02

HEADQUARTERS COMMANDER-IN-CHIEF SOUTH ATLANTIC AREA

(ROYAL AIR FORCE ELEMENT)
Postal Address—HQ CINCSOUTHLANT, BFPO 6
Telephone No.—00351 440 4321
IVSN 529 4321

Squadron Leaders

M. G. Coggon	16.7.01
J. R. A. Grime	4.7.00
N. J. Lloyd, BSc	18.9.00

HEADQUARTERS THIRD AIR FORCE USAF

at RAF Mildenhall, Bury St Edmunds, Suffolk IP28 8NF
Telephone No.—Newmarket (01638) 543000

Senior Royal Air Force Liaison Officer
Wing Commander R. V. Carter, BSc 5.11.01

Royal Air Force Liaison Officer (Armament)
Squadron Leader R. M. Apps, RAFR 20.5.96

EUROPEAN AIR GROUP
(ROYAL AIR FORCE ELEMENT)
Postal Address: RAF High Wycombe, Buckinghamshire HP14 4UE
Telephone No.—01494 497922
Direct Dial—01494 497922
Fax—01494 497952

ASSISTANT CHIEF OF STAFF
Group Captain J. W. White, CBE FRAeS FCMI 4.12.00

Wing Commander
J. S. B. Schollar, MDA MinstAM MCMI 30.5.00

Squadron Leaders
P. S. Gerrard, BSc 8.11.01
N. E. A. Topley, MILT 3.9.01

COMBINED AIR OPERATIONS CENTRE 2

Postal Address: Kalkar, PO Box 2004, BFPO 105
Telephone Number: 0049 2824 902096/26

DIRECTOR OF OPERATIONS
Group Captain S. D. Black 2.7.01

Wing Commanders
A. Kay 23.9.99
J. Pitts 29.10.01

Squadron Leaders
R. L. Hawkins, MBE 8.4.00
C. Taylor, BSc CEng MIEE 17.9.01

COMBINED AIR OPERATIONS CENTRE 3

Postal Address—CAOC 3, BFPO 55
National Correspondence addressed to—UK SNR, CAOC 3, BFPO 55
Telephone No—Norway 0047 75536862
Fax No—Norway 0047 75536125

DEPUTY COMMANDER COMBINED AIR OPERATIONS CENTRE 3
Air Commodore I. A. MILNE, MA MA 20.8.01

OPERATIONS PLANS CHIEF
Group Captain W. K. D. Morrow, OBE 17.7.00

Wing Commanders
J. Leckey. 4.9.00

Squadron Leaders
M. E. Richards 22.5.00
J. Ross 3.4.00

COMBINED AIR OPERATIONS CENTRE 9

Postal Address: ROYAL AIR FORCE HIGH WYCOMBE, BUCKS HP14 4UE
Telephone Number: 01494 495250

COMMANDER COMBINED AIR OPERATIONS CENTRE 9
Air Marshal B. K. BURRIDGE, CBE MBA BSc FCMI 1.2.02

DIRECTOR SUPPORT
Wing Commander P. Bayer 3.3.00

CHIEF CURRENT OPS
Group Captain R. F. R. Carr, MBE 2.5.00

Wing Commanders
J. E. Parker 1.12.00
T. A. Wilkinson, MBE BSc 10.7.00

Squadron Leaders
R. C. Arber 29.5.01
S. E. Collins 15.1.01
R. W. Cook 30.4.01
C. D. Moore 31.8.00
J. Ross 24.6.02
S. M. Stowers, LLB 1.1.03
J. D. Tait, BSc 29.8.00

AIR FORCE DEPARTMENT COMMITTEES AND COMMITTEES ON WHICH THE AIR FORCE DEPARTMENT IS REPRESENTED

AIR CADET COUNCIL

President
Minister of State for the Armed Forces

Vice-President
Air Member for Personnel

Vice-Patron
Air Chief Marshal Sir Michael Graydon, GCB CBE FRAeS

Air League Member
Rt Hon Baroness Emily Blatch

Members
AOC Air Cadets & Commandant RAF Cranwell

Commandant of the Air Training Corps (HQ Air Cadets)

M. J. Marshall Esq, CBE DL MA FRAeS (Central & East Region)

Wing Commander J. P. E. Guiver, RAFVR(T) (Retd) (London and South East Region)

Group Captain A. Ferguson, RAF (Retd) (South West Region)

Wing Commander G. Knight, RAFVR(T) (Retd) (North Region)

Wing Commander D. D. Hemming, MBE BEd RAFVR(T) (Retd) (Wales & West Region)

Mr W. C. Walker, OBE (Scotland and Northern Ireland Region)

Wing Commander E. Cadden, RAFVR(T) (Retd) (Northern Ireland)

Reverend T. W. Tait, BD

Secretary
Head of AMP (Sec)

(In Attendance)
A Representative Regional Commandant
DRFC Representative
D of R&S Representatives
Secretary to the Air Cadet Council Steering Group
Co-opted Members (as required)

ADVISORY PANEL ON THE CHAPLAINCY SERVICES

(Arranged in alphabetical order of the Churches represented)

Representing the Church of England
The Rt Rev D. J. Connor MA Bishop to the Forces

Representing the Jewish Church
Rev M. Weisman, OBE MA OCF

Representing the Methodist Church
Rev J. B. Sherrington, BD BA CertEd MPhil

Representing the Church of Scotland
Mr H. A. Kerrigan, QC

Representing the Presbyterian Church of Ireland
Rev S. Van Os

Representing the Roman Catholic Church
The Rt Rev T. M. Burns, SM BA BD MCMI RC Bishop of the Forces

Representing the United Navy, Army and Air Force Board (Baptist and United Reformed Churches)
Rev J. A. Murray—Secretary

Members of the Panel meet under the Chairmanship of the Air Member for Personnel to advise on matters concerning Royal Air Force Chaplaincy. The Chaplain-in-Chief (RAF), and the two Principal Chaplains attend as required.

COMMONWEALTH WAR GRAVES COMMISSION

2 Marlow Road, Maidenhead, Berkshire SL6 7DX
Telephone No.—01628-634221 Fax No.—01628 771208
For Casualty and Cemetery Enquiries, Tel No: 01628 507200
E-Mail: General Enquiries: general.enq@cwgc.org
E-Mail: Casualty and Cemetery Enquiries: casualty.enq@cwgc.org
Website: www.cwgc.org

President
    H.R.H. THE DUKE OF KENT, KG GCMG GCVO ADC

Members
    The Secretary of State for Defence in the United Kingdom (Chairman)
    General Sir John Wilsey, GCB CBE DL (Vice-Chairman)
    The High Commissioner for Australia
    The High Commissioner for Canada
    The High Commissioner for the Republic of South Africa
    The High Commissioner for New Zealand
    The High Commissioner for the Republic of India
    Baroness Golding
    Mr John Wilkinson, MP
    Sir John Gray, KBE CMG
    Mr Paul Orchard-Lisle, CBE TD DL
    Air Chief Marshal Sir Michael Stear, KCB CBE DL MA FRAeS
    Dame Susan Tinson DBE
    Sir John Keegan, OBE
    Admiral Sir Peter Abbott, GCB KCB

Director-General (Secretary to the Commission)
    R. E. Kellaway

Deputy Director-General (Assistant Secretary to the Commission)
    R. J. Dalley, CBE

Legal Adviser and Solicitor
    G. C. Reddie

Director of Information and Secretariat
    D. R. Parker

Director of Administration
    R. D. Wilson, ACMA

Director of Works
    A. Coombe

Director of Horticulture
    D. C. Parker, Dip Hort (Kew) M.I.(Hort)

Director of Personnel
    D. G. Stacey

Personal Secretary to Director-General
    Mrs H. J. Scott

UNITED KINGDOM AREA

Area Director
    D. Symons

Area Administration Officer
    A. K. Ghosh, MBE

Area Works Officer
    R. J. Bird

Area Horticultural Officer
    C. Griffiths-Hardman

RESERVE FORCES' AND CADETS' ASSOCIATION

As at 1/1/02
NOTE—In some cases in these lists the rank shown against an officer's name is honorary COUNCIL OF RESERVE FORCES' AND CADETS' ASSOCIATION
Duke of York's Headquarters, Chelsea, SW3 4SG
Telephone No.—020-7730-6122 or 020-7414-5587
DFTS: 94631 5587
FAX: 020-7414-5589 DFTS FAX: 94631 5589
E-mail: rfca.council@btinternet.com

President: The Rt Hon The Lord Freeman
Chairman: Colonel M. J. E. Taylor, CBE TD DL
Vice Chairmen:
   Colonel E. C. York, TD DL
   Brigadier M. E. Browne, CBE TD DL
   Commodore G. N. Wood, JP RD
   Colonel Sir David Trippier, RD JP DL
   Air Vice-Marshal A. F. C. Hunter, CBE AFC DL RAF(Retd)
Secretary: Air Vice-Marshal A. J. Stables, CBE RAF (Retd)
Deputy Secretary: Colonel D. H. R. Stephenson, CBE (Retd)

Note—Each Reserve Forces' and Cadets' Association is represented on this Council by its President, Vice-Presidents, Chairman, Vice-Chairmen and Secretary.

EAST ANGLIA ASSOCIATION

President

S. C. Whitbread, Esq JP (HM Lord-Lieutenant)

Vice-Presidents

J. G. P. Crowden, Esq JP
Lord Braybrooke, JP
S. A. Bowes Lyon, Esq JP
The Right Honourable The Lord Belstead, PC JP
Sir Timothy Colman, KG JP DCL

Chairman

Colonel N. H. Kelsey, OBE TD

Vice-Chairmen

Commander T. C. Haile, RD RNR** (Retd)
Colonel A. D. Chissel, TD
Air Commodore J. A. F. Ford, RAF (Retd)

County Chairmen

Colonel A. F. Fairless, TD JP
Colonel P. G. R. Horrell, TD DL
Colonel C. A. F. Thomas, TS** DL
Lieutenant Colonel J. D. Sainsbury, OBE TD
Brigadier R. J. Heywood, OBE
Colonel J. G. Aldous, OBE

Air Force Members

Ex-Officio

The Officer Commanding 3 (RAuxAF) Sqn Tactical Provost Wing
The Officer Commanding, 2620 (County of Norfolk) Squadron Royal Auxiliary Air Force
The Officer Commanding, 2623 (East Anglia) Squadron Royal Auxiliary Air Force Regiment
The Officer Commanding 7630 (VR) Intelligence Squadron Royal Auxiliary Air Force
The Officer Commanding, Cambridge University Air Squadron

Selected

The Station Commander RAF Honington
The Station Commander RAF Marham
The Regional Commandant, HQ Air Cadets Central and East, ATC
Group Captain W. S. Brereton-Martin, CBE RAF (Retd)

Secretary

Colonel J. S. Houchin, OBE, "Springfield Tyrells" 250, Springfield Road, Chelmsford CM2 6BU Tel No: Civil 01245 354262 Fax: 01245 492398
DDI: 01245 244804
Tel MIL: Chelmsford 94651 xxxx Fax: 94651 x4723
E-Mail: offman@reserve-forces-anglia.org
Internet: www.reserve-forces-anglia.org
Deputy Secretary, Lieutenant Colonel J. A. Allan, TD

83

RESERVE FORCES' AND CADETS' ASSOCIATION

EAST MIDLANDS ASSOCIATION

President

Sir Andrew Buchanan, Bt (HM Lord-Lieutenant, Nottinghamshire)

Vice-Presidents

T. G. M. Brooks, Esq, JP (HM Lord-Lieutenant, Leicestershire)

Mrs B. K. Cracroft-Eley (HM Lord-Lieutenant, Lincolnshire)

J. K. Bather, Esq (HM Lord-Lieutenant, Derbyshire)

Air Chief Marshal Sir Thomas Kennedy, GCB AFC* RAF(Retd) (HM Lord-Lieutenant, Rutland)

Lady Juliet Townsend, LVO (HM Lord-Lieutenant, Northamptonshire)

Chairman

Brigadier M. E. Browne, CBE TD DL

Vice-Chairmen

Colonel G. B. Roper, TD

Air Commodore A. J. Griffin, AFC RAF (Retd)

Colonel G. W. C. Newmarch

Colonel R. Merryweather, TD DL

Major G. G. Simpson, TD DL

Colonel I. R. Keers, OBE DL

Commander P. R. Moore, RD* RNR

Air Force Members

Ex-Officio

The Officer Commanding, East Midlands University Air Squadron

The Officer Commanding, 2503 (County of Lincoln) Sqn RAuxAF Regt

OC 504 Squadron RAuxAF Regiment

OC 7006 (VR) Squadron RAuxAF

OC 7010 (VR) Squadron RAuxAF

Selected Air Force Members

Air Commodore A. J. Griffin, AFC RAF (Retd) Vice-Chairman (Air)

The Officer Commanding, RAF Coningsby

The Officer Commanding, RAF Cottesmore

The Officer Commanding, RAF Cranwell

The Officer Commanding, RAF Digby

The Officer Commanding, RAF Waddington

The Regional Commandant, Central and Eastern Region ATC

Vacant, Lincolnshire

Group Captain C. R. Cooper, OBE RAF (Retd) Northamptonshire

Wing Commander P. Giles OBE, Derbyshire

Wing Commander J. McCarthy, RAF Regional Liaison Officer

Secretary/Chief Executive

Brigadier W. J. Hurrell, CBE, 6, Clinton Terrace, Derby Road, Nottingham NG7 1LZ

Tel No: 0115 9476508 Fax: 0115 9473406 Mil: Chilwell (745) 2670 E-Mail: post@eastmidtavra.demon.co.uk

Deputy Chief Executive, Colonel T. J. Ludlam, OBE

GREATER LONDON ASSOCIATION

President

The Lord Imbert, QPM JP (HM Lord-Lieutenant of Greater London)

Vice-Presidents

Field Marshal Sir John Chapple, GCB CBE DL

Colonel Sir Greville Spratt, GBE TD JP DL

Chairman

Brigadier A. P. Verey, QVRM TD

Vice-Chairmen

Commander J. McK. Ludgate RD* DL RNR

Colonel J. C. Power, QVRM TD

Colonel G. E. Godbold, OBE TD DL

Colonel M. E. Hatt-Cook, OBE RD*

Air Vice-Marshal D. R. Hawkins-Leth, CB MBE DL RAF (Retd)

Colonel I. W. B. McRobbie, OBE TD DL

Air Force Members

Ex-Officio

The Officer Commanding, University of London Air Squadron

The Officer Commanding, No 600 (City of London) Squadron, RAuxAF

The Officer Commanding, RAF Northolt

The Officer Commanding, RAF Uxbridge

Selected

Flight Lieutenant V. M. T. Graham-Green AE RAuxAF

Flight Lieutenant S. G. Guy, AE

Group Captain L. Hakin, OBE RAFR

Air Vice-Marshal D. R. Hawkins-Leth, CB MBE DL RAF (Retd)

Wing Commander E. F. Partridge, OBE AE RAuxAF

Secretary

Colonel P. C. Cook, DL Duke of York's Headquarters, Fulham House, 87 Fulham High Street, London SW6 3JS

Tel No: 020 7730 8131 Fax No: 020 7414 5560

Deputy Secretary/City Secretary: Lieutenant Colonel R. B. Paddison, MBE DL

Assistant Secretary (Finance): Squadron Leader C. Allison, RAF (Retd)

DFTS Tel No: 94631 + ext.

DFTS Fax No: 94631 5560

E-mail: secretary@reserve.forces.london.org.uk

HIGHLAND ASSOCIATION

President

Air Vice-Marshal G. A. Chesworth, CB OBE DFC RAF (Retd) (HM Lord-Lieutenant)

Vice-Presidents

Lord Gray of Contin MP

Major G. T. Dunnett, TD DL

Mr E. A. Brodie of Lethen

84

Captain R. W. K. Stirling of Fairburn, TD JP
Major General David Houston, CBE
Mr A. Matheson, OBE JP FRPharmS
George Marwick
John H. Scott
Angus D. M. Farquharson, OBE
The Lord Provost and HM Lieutenant of the City of
Aberdeen
Mr J. A. S. Mcpherson, CBE JP
John D. B. Smart
Mrs Georgiana Osbourne
The Lord Provost and HM Lieutenant of the City of Dundee
Mrs Margaret Dean
Sir David Montgomery, Bt JP
Kenneth MacKinnon, LLB NP WS
Mrs A. B. Cruickshank
Brigadier D. D. G. Hardie, TD JP
Lieutenant Colonel J. Stirling, CBE TD

Chairman

Colonel G. S. Johnston, OBE TD DL

Vice-Chairmen

Group Captain J. P. Dacre RAFR
Commander M. D. Simpson, RD* RNR
Squadron Leader B. M. Donald
Major A. C. Oag, TD
Brigadier A. G. Dorward, TD
Colonel R. L. Steele
Colonel C. W. Pagan, MBE TD

Air Force Members

Ex-Officio: The Officer Commanding, Aberdeen University
Air Squadron
The Officer Commanding, RAF Leuchars

Selected

The Officers Commanding, RAF Leuchars, RAF Kinloss,
RAF Buchan, RAF Lossiemouth
2622(H) Squadron RAuxAF Regiment
Group Captain Reserves RAF Innsworth

Secretary

Brigadier C. S. Grant, OBE, Seathwood, 365 Perth Road,
Dundee DD2 1LX. Tel No: 01382 668283 Fax No: 01382
566442
DFTS Tel: 94747 4371
E-mail: info@hrfca.co.uk

Deputy Secretary

Wing Commander J. M. Henderson RAF (Retd)

Assistant Secretary

Squadron Leader E. P. Weatherhead, RAF (Retd)

NORTH WEST OF ENGLAND AND ISLE OF MAN ASSOCIATION

President

Colonel W. A. Bromley-Davenport, JP (HM Lord-Lieutenant
of Cheshire)

Vice-Presidents

Colonel J. B. Timmins, OBE TD JP (HM Lord-Lieutenant of
Greater Manchester)
His Excellency Air Marshal I. D. Macfadyen, CB OBE
(Lieutenant Governor Isle of Man)
Colonel A. W. Waterworth, JP (HM Lord-Lieutenant of
Merseyside)
Colonel J. A. Cropper (HM Lord-Lieutenant of Cumbria)
Colonel The Right Honourable The Lord Shuttleworth, JP
(HM Lord-Lieutenant of Lancashire)

Chairman

Colonel Sir David Trippier, RD JP DL

Vice-Chairmen

Commodore R. H. Walker RD** DL RNR
Lieutenant Colonel C. T. Hillock, RD*
Major D. Gee, TD
Colonel J. A. Harkon, MBE TD
Colonel S. H. Spackman, TD DL
Group Captain M. H. Bruce

Air Force Members

Ex-Officio: The Officer Commanding, Manchester &
Salford University Air Squadron
The Officer Commanding, Liverpool University Air
Squadron

Selected

Air Commodore J. Broughton, DL RAF (Retd)
Group Captain M. J. Bruce, RAF (Retd)
Wing Commander D. Forbes RAFVR(T) (Retd)
Group Captain W. G. Gambold, RAFR
Group Captain P. S. Kiggell, OBE RAFR
Squadron Leader R. Massey
G. Moore, Esq
Squadron Leader G. J. T. Moore, RAFR

Chief Executive

Colonel G. J. O. Wells-Cole, OBE, Alexandra Court, 28
Alexandra Drive, Liverpool L17 8YE
Tel No: 0151-727 4552 Fax No: 0151 727 8133
DFTS Tel No: 94552 810
DFTS Fax No: 94552 8133
E-mail: nwrfca@compuserve.com

Deputy Chief Executive

Lieutenant Colonel I. J. Sawers

LOWLANDS ASSOCIATION

President

Lieutenant General Sir Norman Arthur, KCB (HM Lord-
Lieutenant of the Stewartry of Kirkudbright)

Vice-Presidents

Major R. Y. Henderson, TD (HM Lord-Lieutenant of Ayrshire
and Arran)

Major A. R. Trotter (HM Lord-Lieutenant of Berwickshire)
Captain R. C. Cunningham-Jardine (HM Lord-Lieutenant of Dumfries)
Mr W. G. Morrison, CBE (HM Lord-Lieutenant of East Lothian)
Mr G. K. Cox MBE JP (HM Lord-Lieutenant of Lanarkshire)
Captain G. W. Burnet, LVO (HM Lord-Lieutenant of Midlothian)
Mr C. J. Parker, OBE (HM Lord-Lieutenant of Renfrewshire)
Dr J. Paterson-Brown, CBE MBChB (HM Lord-Lieutenant of Roxburgh, Ettrick and Lauderdale)
Captain J. D. B. Younger (HM Lord-Lieutenant of Tweeddale)
Mrs I. Brydie (HM Lord-Lieutenant of West Lothian)
Major E. S. Orr Ewing (HM Lord-Lieutenant of Wigtown)
The Right Honourable the Lord Provost of The City of Edinburgh
The Right Honourable the Lord Provost of the City of Glasgow

Chairman

Colonel D. A. Scott, OBE TD

Vice-Chairmen

Captain C. J. P. Hall, RD RNR
Colonel D. J. Cameron, TD
Colonel N. J. F. Dalrymple Hamilton, OBE TD DL
Lieutenant Colonel I. Ballantyne
Major W. S. Turner, MC
Colonel J. W. Mackay, TD
Colonel P. K. Neil, DL
Group Captain R. G. Kemp, QVRM AE ADC RAuxAF
Group Captain J. D. Needham, RAF (Retd)

Air Force Members

Ex-Officio

The Officer Commanding, Glasgow and Strathclyde University Air Squadron
The Officer Commanding, East Lowlands University Air Squadron
The Officer Commanding, No 603 (City of Edinburgh) Squadron
Warrant Officer D. C. McQueen, MBE RAuxAF

Selected

Air Commodore The Right Honourable The Lord Selkirk of Douglas, QC MSP
Air Commodore B. N. J. Speed, OBE RAF (Retd)
The Regional Commandant, Scottish and Northern Ireland Region, ATC
Group Captain D. A. Needham, RAF (Retd)
Group Captain R. G. Kemp, QVRM AE ADC RAuxAF
The Officer Commanding, Royal Air Force Prestwick
Squadron Leader J. B. Blanche, QVRM AE RAuxAF
Squadron Leader S. B. Greenhalgh, RAuxAF

Secretary

Colonel R. S. B. Watson, OBE, Lowland House, 60 Avenuepark Street, Glasgow G20 8LW
Tel No: 0141-945 4951 Fax No: 0141 945 4869
DFTS 94561 2009
E-mail: info@lowland.rfca.org.uk
Deputy Secretary Major M. R. Knox

NORTHERN IRELAND ASSOCIATION

President

Major W. J. Hall (HM Lord Lieutenant)

Vice-Presidents

Colonel The Lord O'Neill, TD
Lady Carswell, OBE
The Right Honourable The Earl of Erne
Colonel J. T. Eaton, CBE TD
Mr D. Desmond, CBE
The Right Honourable The Earl of Caledon
His Grace the Duke of Abercorn

Chairman

Colonel S. M. Elder, TD JP DL

Vice-Chairmen

Lieutenant Colonel C. T. Hogg, MBE UD JP DL
Colonel A. H. Reid, OBE TD JP DL
Major W. B. S. Buchanan, MBE TD
Lieutenant Colonel R. W. C. T. Barbour, MBE TD
Lord Maginnis of Drumglass
Colonel J. M. Steele, CB OBE TD DL
Major S. Irwin, TD
Viscountess Brookeborough
Captain N. J. E. Reynolds, RD RNR
Group Captain B. G. Freeman, OBE RAF (Retd) (AIR)

Air Force Member

Ex-Officio

Flight Lieutenant J. McAtamney RAFVR(T)

Selected

Group Captain M. A. Sharp, OBE ADC RAF
Wing Commander E. Cadden
Squadron Leader A. McClure RAFVR
Wing Commander W. G. F. Blair, MBE RAFVR

Secretary

Brigadier I. N. Osborne, OBE, 25, Windsor Park, Belfast BT9 6FR
Tel No: 01232 665024 Fax No: 01232 662809
Email: Secretary@rfcani.co.uk

Deputy Secretary

Major R. C. W. Chisholm

NORTH OF ENGLAND ASSOCIATION

President

Sir Paul Nicholson (HM Lord-Lieutenant)

Vice-Presidents

Sir John Riddell, Bt CVO (HM Lord-Lieutenant)
The Lord Crathorne, JP (HM Lord-Lieutenant)
N. Sherlock, Esq (HM Lord Lieutenant)

Chairman

Colonel A. A. E. Glenton, MBE TD DL

RESERVE FORCES' AND CADETS' ASSOCIATION

Vice-Chairmen

Captain A. I. B. Moffat, RD DL RNR
Colonel W. P. Catesby, DL
Colonel J. G. W. Feggetter, TD QHS DL
Colonel D. W. Herring, TD QHS
Colonel A. W. Illingworth, TD JP
Air Vice-Marshal A. F. C. Hunter, CBE AFC DL RAF (Retd)

Air Force Members

Ex-Officio

The Officer Commanding, Northumbria Universities Air Squadron
The Officer Commanding, RAF Boulmer

Selected

Wing Commander G. R. Duff, RAFVR(T)
Squadron Leader M. Q. Gilson, RAF (Retd)
Air Vice-Marshal A. F. C. Hunter, CBE AFC DL RAF (Retd)
Air Vice-Marshal D. A. Hurrell, CB AFC RAF (Retd)
Wing Commander E. H. Lowe, OBE RAFVR(T)

Secretary

Brigadier N. G. R. Hepworth, OBE 53, Old Elvet, Durham DH1 3JJ
Tel No: 0191-384 7202 Fax No: 0191 384 0918
DFTS Tel: 94721 3158
E-mail: ne.reserveforces@virgin.net
Deputy Secretary: Lieutenant Colonel D. R. Summers

SOUTH EAST ASSOCIATION

President

P. L. Wroughton, Esq JP (HM Lord-Lieutenant for Berkshire)

Vice-Presidents

Sir Nigel Mobbs, JP (HM Lord-Lieutenant for Buckinghamshire)
Mrs F. M. Fagan, JP (HM Lord-Lieutenant for Hampshire)
C. J. Bland Esq, JP (HM Lord-Lieutenant for Isle of Wight)
A. Willett Esq, CMG (HM Lord-Lieutenant for Kent)
H. Brunner Esq, JP (HM Lord-Lieutenant for Oxfordshire)
Mrs S. J. F. Goad, JP (HM Lord-Lieutenant for Surrey)
Mrs P. K. Stewart-Roberts, OBE (HM Lord-Lieutenant for East Sussex)
H. R. Wyatt Esq, (HM Lord-Lieutenant for West Sussex)

Chairman

Colonel J. R. G. Putnam, CBE TD DL

Deputy Chairman

Lieutenant Colonel C. H. Ainsley, TD

Vice-Chairmen

Sir Nicholas Bonsor, BT
Lieutenant Colonel R. C. B. Dixon, TD DL
Colonel R. P. Bateman, TD
Brigadier J. N. B. Mogg, DL
Colonel P. A. D. Storie-Pugh, MBE TD ADC
Colonel D. E. Stevens, OBE TD DL

Commander D. J. Belfield, RD*
Group Captain R. Dixon, OBE
Colonel C. D. A. Blessington, OBE JP
Lieutenant Colonel G. H. Wright, TD DL

Air Force Members

Ex Officio

Squadron Leader R. B. Williams, RAuxAF, 501 (City of Gloucester) Squadron, RAuxAF
Squadron Leader R. D. Grimshaw, BSc, RAF, 606 (Chiltern) Sqn, RAuxAF
Wing Commander M. L. Symonds, AE RAuxAF, 4624 (County of Oxford) Squadron, RAuxAF
Wing Commander S. Dargan, RAF, 7644 Sqn, RAuxAF
Squadron Leader C. C. Taylor RAF, Southampton University Air Squadron
Squadron Leader P. G. Hallett RAF, Oxford University Air Squadron
Squadron Leader M. Green, 612 VGS

Selected

Group Captain R. Dixon, OBE (*Vice Chairman (Air)*)
Group Captain P. G. Pinney, CVO
Air Commodore D. C. Andrews, MBE
Wing Commander B. Dibb
Group Captain F. F. Amroliwala OBE, MBA, MA, RAF, RAF Halton
Wing Commander D. Burkinshaw RAF, RAF High Wycombe
Group Captain A. D. Pulford RAF, RAF Odiham
Group Captain N. R. Jagger, RAF, RAF Brize Norton
Group Captain M. G. Lloyd RAF, RAF Benson
The Regional Commandant, London and South-East Region, ATC

Secretary

Brigadier J. S. W. Powell, OBE, Seely House, Shoe Lane, Aldershot, Hants GU11 2HJ
Tel: (Gen Office) 01252 357604
Fax: 01252 357620
Email: hq@serfca,co.uk
Deputy Secretary (West) – Colonel A. C. Miéville OBE
Deputy Secretary (East) – Lieutenant Colonel C. J. Parslow

WALES ASSOCIATION

President

Captain N. Lloyd Edwards, GCStJ RD* LLB JP RNR (HM Lord-Lieutenant for South Glamorgan)

Vice-Presidents

Professor E. Sunderland, OBE JP CStJ (HM Lord-Lieutenant for Gwynedd)
T. G. Jones, Esq, CBE (HM Lord-Lieutenant for Clwyd)
Sir David Mansel Lewis, KCVO KStJ BA JP (HM Lord-Lieutenant for Dyfed)
M. A. McLaggan Esq KStJ MA JP (HM Lord-Lieutenant for Mid Glamorgan)
Commodore R. C. Hastie, CBE CStJ RD* JP RNR (HM Lord-Lieutenant for West Glamorgan)

RESERVE FORCES' AND CADETS' ASSOCIATION

The Honourable Mrs Legge Bourke, LVO (HM Lord-Lieutenant for Powys)

S. Boyle, Esq (HM Lord-Lieutenant for Gwent)

Chairman

Colonel P. Eyton-Jones, TD DL

Vice Chairman Naval

Commander J. M. D. Curteis, SBStJ RD* FCA DL RNR

Vice-Chairmen Military

Colonel G. E. J. Blythe, BSc
Lieutenant Colonel D. G. Clarke, TD
Colonel D W Forrest, TD**

Vice-Chairman Air

Air Commodore A. J. Park, CBE RAF (Retd)

Air Force Members

Ex-Officio

Group Captain L. Garside-Beattie, OBE RAF
Air Commodore M. J. Good, ADC RAF
Group Captain P. S. Kiggell, OBE RAFR
Squadron Leader M. G. Stanway

Selected

Wing Commander D. A. Davies, RAF (Retd)
Squadron Leader D. Warneford, MBE RAF (Retd)
Air Commodore A. J. Park, CBE RAF (Retd)

Secretary

Brigadier W. A. Mackereth, DL RFCA for WALES, Centre Block, Maindy Barracks, Cardiff, CF14 3YE
Deputy Secretary: Major P. J. Mullings, MBE, RFCA for Wales, (as secretary)
Tel No: 02920 220251 Fax No: 02920 224828
DFTS: Tel No: 94355 x8205 Fax: 94355 x8313
E-mail: info@rfca-wales. org.uk

THE WESSEX ASSOCIATION

President

Lieutenant-General Sir Maurice Johnston, KCB OBE (HM Lord Lieutenant for Wiltshire)

Vice-Presidents

J. N. Tidmarsh, Esq MBE JP (HM Lord-Lieutenant for City & County of Bristol)
Lady Mary Holborow, JP (HM Lord Lieutenant for Cornwall)
E. Dancer, Esq CBE JP (HM Lord Lieutenant for Devon)
Captain M. Fulford-Dobson, CVO KStJ RN (HM Lord Lieutenant for Dorset)
H. W. G. Elwes Esq., JP (HM Lord Lieutenant for Gloucestershire)
Lady Gass, JP MA (HM Lord Lieutenant for Somerset)

Chairman

Commodore I. R. Pemberton RD**DL RNR

Vice-Chairmen

Colonel J. C. Blackwood, OBE TD DL (Bristol)
Wing Commander M. J. Metherell, RAF (Retd) (Cornwall)
Colonel J. F. B. Hills, TD (Devon)
Colonel J. F. Penley, OBE TD (Gloucestershire)
Brigadier R. C. Wolverson, OBE (Somerset)
Major M. J. A. Bond, JP (Dorset)
Lieutenant Colonel J. R. Arkell, TD DL (Wiltshire)
Commodore G. N. Wood, RD JP RNR (Naval)
Colonel R. A. Hooper, L/RM (Marine)
Group Captain R. J. Colver, OBE RAuxAF (AIR)

Air Force Members

Ex-Officio

The Officer Commanding, Bristol University Air Squadron
The Officer Commanding, No 2625 (County of Cornwall) RAuxAF Regiment Squadron
The Officer Commanding, 4626 (County of Wiltshire) Aeromedical Evacuation Squadron RAuxAF

Selected

Station Commander, RAF St Mawgan
Station Commander, RAF Innsworth
Station Commander, RAF Lyneham

Chief Executive/Secretary

Brigadier B. C. Jackman, OBE MC, Mount House, Mount Street, Taunton, Somerset TA1 3QE
Tel No: 01823 254571
Fax No: 01823 259935
E-mail: hq@reserve-forces-wessex.org.uk

Deputy Chief Executive/Secretary

Colonel C. J. Constable

Assistant Secretary

Major C. E. Marsh, TD

WEST MIDLAND ASSOCIATION

President

Major J. A. Hawley, TD JP MA (HM Lord-Lieutenant for the County of Stafford)

Vice-Presidents

Colonel Sir Thomas Dunne, KCVO KStJ JP (HM Lord-Lieutenant for the County of Herefordshire)
Mr M. A. Brinton (HM Lord-Lieutenant for the County of Worcestershire)
Colonel R. R. Taylor, OBE KStJ JP (HM Lord-Lieutenant for the West Midlands Metropolitan County)
Colonel A. E. H. Heber-Percy, JP (HM Lord-Lieutenant for the County of Shropshire)
Mr M. Dunne, JP (HM Lord-Lieutenant for the County of Warwick)

Chairman

Colonel T. D. C. Lloyd, TD

RESERVE FORCES' AND CADETS' ASSOCIATION

Vice-Chairmen

Commander J. S. Walker, RD RNR (Vice-Chairman (NAVY))
Air Vice-Marshal M. D. Smart, RAF (Retd) (Vice-Chairman (AIR))
Colonel T. M. Evans, TD DL
Colonel R. L. Cariss, MBE TD
Colonel S. J. Cartwright, TD
Colonel C. E. Comport, OBE TD

Air Force Members

Ex-Officio

The Officer Commanding, University of Birmingham Air Squadron
The Officer Commanding, The Training and Standardisation Squadron

Selected

Air Vice-Marshal M. D. Smart, RAF (Retd)
Wing Commander J. E. Bates, OBE DL
Group Captain P. S. Kiggell, OBE RAFR
Group Captain R. J. Allen, ADC RAF

Secretary

Brigadier J. M. Patrick, MBE, Tennal Grange, Tennal Road, Harborne, Birmingham, B32 2HX
Tel No: 0121-427 5221
Fax No: 0121-427-8380

Deputy Secretary: Major M. Young
DFTS Tel: 9442184 Fax: 9422184
E-mail: depsec@wmrfca.org.uk

YORKSHIRE AND HUMBER ASSOCIATION

President

The Earl of Scarbrough (HM Lord-Lieutenant)

Vice-Presidents

John Lyles, CBE JP (HM Lord-Lieutenant)
Richard Marriott, TD (HM Lord-Lieutenant)
The Lord Crathorne, JP (HM Lord-Lieutenant)

Chairman

Colonel E. C. York, TD DL

Vice-Chairmen

Commodore P. R. Sutermeister, RN
Brigadier G. B. Smalley, OBE TD
Colonel C. J. Tattersall, TD DL
Air Commodore W. G. Gambold RAFR

Air Force Members

Ex-Officio

The Officer Commanding, RAF Leeming
The Officer Commanding, RAF Linton-on-Ouse
The Officer Commanding, Yorkshire Universities Air Squadron
The Officer Commanding, 609 (West Riding) Squadron RAuxAF

Selected

Air Commodore S. N. Bostock RAF (Retd)
Air Commodore W. G. Gambold RAF (Retd)
Group Captain J. Middleton, RAF (Retd)
Squadron Leader K. W. T. Noyes, MBE RAF (Retd)
Squadron Leader G. J. T. Moore, RAFR
Professor A. C. Marvin

Secretary

Brigadier N. F. Wood, 20, St. George's Place, York, YO24 1DS
Tel No: 01904 623081 and 639008
Fax No: 01904 622245

Deputy Secretary: Lieutenant Colonel M. R. U. McCartney
DFTS Tel No: 04777 2568
E-mail: admin@rfcayork.demon.co.uk

THE NAVY, ARMY AND AIR FORCE INSTITUTES

Registered Office: London Road, Amesbury, Wiltshire, SP4 7EN Tel 0198 062 7000
(A company limited by guarantee)

PATRON—HM THE QUEEN

COUNCIL

Service Member Appointed by the Admiralty Board of the Defence Council
Vice-Admiral P. Spencer, KCB ADC
Commodore P. Wilkinson

Service Members Appointed by the Army Board of the Defence Council
Lieutenant General Sir Timothy Granville-Chapman, KCB CBE
Brigadier N. J. Cottam, OBE

Service Members Appointed by the Air Force Board of the Defence Council
Air Marshal Sir Christopher Coville, KCB BA FCIPD FRAeS RAF
Air Commodore M. J. Good, ADC MIDPM MCMI RAF

Other Members Appointed jointly by the Admiralty, Army and Air Force Boards of the Defence Council
Air Chief Marshal Sir Malcolm Pledger, KCB OBE AFC BSc FRAeS RAF (President)
B. Miller

BOARD OF MANAGEMENT

Director Nominated Jointly by the Admiralty, Army and Air Force Boards of the Defence Council
A. Hales (Chairman)

Directors Nominated by the Board of Management

A. J. Cole
V. J. Steel
C. Reilly (Chief Executive)
T. Morgan

GRADATION LISTS BY BRANCHES

of Officers Serving on the Active List

Marshal of the Royal Air Force

H.R.H. The Prince Philip, Duke of Edinburgh, KG KT OM GBE AC QSO psc(n)　　.　(GD)　15 Jan 53

FORMER CHIEFS OF THE AIR STAFF

Marshals of the Royal Air Force

Grandy, Sir John GCB GCVO KBE DSO idc psc(m) cfs* Born 8/2/13　　.　.　.　.　(GD)　1 Apr 71
Beetham, Sir Michael GCB CBE DFC AFC idc psc Born 17/5/23　.　.　.　.　.　.　(GD)　15 Oct 82
Williamson, Sir Keith GCB AFC rcds psc cfs* Born 25/2/28　.　.　.　.　.　.　(GD)　15 Oct 85
Craig of Radley, The Lord GCB OBE MA DSc FRAeS rcds psc cfs Born 17/9/29　.　(GD)　14 Nov 88

Air Chief Marshals

Graydon, Sir Michael GCB CBE FRAeS rcds ndc psc cfs Born 24/10/38　　.　.　.　(GD)　31 May 91
Johns, Sir Richard GCB CBE LVO FRAeS rcds psc cfs Born 28/7/39　　.　.　.　.　(GD)　30 June 94

AIR RANK LIST

Air Chief Marshals

H.R.H. Princess Alice, Duchess of Gloucester GCB CI GCVO GBE　　.　.　.　.　.　.　23 Feb 90
Squire, Sir Peter GCB DFC AFC ADC DSc FRAeS psc(n) cfs Born 7/10/45　.　.　.　(GD)　29 Mar 99
Bagnall, Sir Anthony KCB OBE FRAeS rcds psc qwi Born 8/6/45　　.　.　.　.　.　(GD)　6 Apr 00
Day, Sir John KCB OBE ADC BSc rcds psc cfs Born 15/7/47　.　.　.　.　.　.　(GD)　5 Apr 01

Air Marshals

Coville, Sir Christopher KCB BA FCIPD FRAeS rcds psc qwi Born 2/6/45　.　.　.　(GD)　6 Aug 98
Pledger, Sir Malcolm KCB OBE AFC BSc FRAeS rcds psc cfs Born 24/7/48　.　.　.　(GD)　30 Apr 99
Goodall, Sir Roderick KBE CB AFC* FRAeS rcds psc qwi Born 19/1/47　.　.　.　(GD)　1 Sept 99
Spink, Clifford Rodney CB CBE FCMI FRAeS rcds ndc qwi(AD) Born 17/5/46　.　.　(GD)　19 June 00
Stirrup, Sir Jock KCB AFC FRAeS FCMI rcds hcsc jsdc cfs qwi Born 4/12/49　.　.　(GD)　6 Nov 00
French, Joseph Charles CBE FRAeS rcds psc Born 15/7/49　.　.　.　.　.　.　(GD)　13 Nov 00
Burridge, Brian Kevin CBE MBA BSc FCMI hcsc df psc(n) cfs Born 26/9/49　.　.　(GD)　4 Feb 02

Air Vice-Marshals

Thompson, John Hugh CB rcds hcsc psc(m) qwi Born 18/9/47	(GD)	1 July 96
Stewart, Ian Michael CB AFC LLB FRAeS psc Born 27/7/45	(GD)	1 Jan 97
Wright, Robert Alfred AFC FRAeS psc qwi Born 10/6/47	(GD)	1 July 97
Filbey, Keith David CBE FRAeS rcds psc Born 16/12/47	(GD)	1 Jan 98
Sturley, Philip Oliver CB MBE BSc FRAeS jsdc Born 9/7/50	(GD)	1 Jan 98
Niven, David Miller CB CBE BSc rcds psc Born 18/9/46	(GD)	1 July 98
H.R.H. The Prince of Wales KG KT GCB AK QSO ADC	(GD)	14 Nov 98
Gardiner, Martyn John OBE BSc FRAeS psc asq Born 13/6/46	(GD)	1 Jan 99
Rimmer, Thomas William CB OBE MA FRAeS rcds osc(Fr) cfs Born 16/12/48 . .	(GD)	1 Jan 99
Couzens, David Cyril MA MBA CEng FIMechE FRAeS DLUT rcds psc ae Born 15/10/49	(ENG)	1 Jan 99
Burton, Andrew John OBE BSc FCIS FCIPD odc(US) psc Born 11/11/50 . .	(ADMIN)	1 Jan 99
Liddell, Peter CB BSc CEng FIEE FRAeS rcds aws psc amec Born 9/10/48 . .	(ENG)	1 July 99
Scott, Peter John MSc BSc CEng FIMechE FRAeS rcds psc Born 4/4/49 . .	(ENG)	1 July 99
Corbitt, Ian Stafford MSc CDipAF hcsc psc Born 30/7/47	(GD)	1 Jan 00
Roser, Phillip Wycliffe MBE FRAeS rcds psc qwi Born 11/7/48	(GD)	1 Jan 00
Sudborough, Nigel John CB OBE FCIPD rcds hcsc psc Born 23/3/48	(GD)	1 July 00
Vallance, Andrew George Buchanan OBE MPhil FRAeS psc Born 7/4/48 . . .	(GD)	1 July 00
Mackay, Hector Gavin CB OBE AFC BSc FRAeS rcds psc(n) cfs Born 3/10/47 . .	(GD)	1 Jan 01
Torpy, Glenn Lester CBE DSO BSc(Eng) rcds hcsc psc qwi Born 27/7/53 . . .	(GD)	1 Jan 01
Thornton, Barry Michael MSc BSc CEng FIMechE FRAeS FCMI rcds psc Born 19/11/52	(ENG)	1 Jan 01
Walker, Peter Brett CBE BA jsdc qwi Born 29/9/49	(GD)	1 July 01
Hobart, David Anthony MPhil MCMI rcds jsdc psc semc Born 24/12/51 . .	(ENG)	1 July 01
Day, Nigel James CBE BSc(Eng) ACGI rcds hcsc psc qwi Born 13/2/49	(GD)	1 Jan 02
Willis, Gerald Edward BSc FRAeS rcds psc semc Born 25/10/49	(ENG)	1 Jan 02
McNicoll, Iain Walter CBE BSc FRAeS psc qwi Born 3/5/53	(GD)	1 July 02
Miller, Graham Anthony jsdc cfs qwi Born 31/10/51	(GD)	1 July 02
Robinson, Paul Anthony OBE FRAeS psc cfs Born 8/8/49	(GD)	1 July 02
Jones, Grahame CBE BSc CEng MIEE psc Born 6/7/50	(ENG)	1 July 02
Smith, Alan Jeffrey OBE BSc CEng FRAeS MIMechE psc Born 13/6/53 . . .	(ENG)	1 July 02

Air Commodores

Feenan, Michael Leonard CBE MA FCMI psc i* Born 18/9/47	(GD)	1 July 96
Kennedy, John Drummond BA psc cfs Born 23/8/46	(GD)	1 Jan 97
Simpson, Geoffrey Dennis CBE AFC FRAeS rcds psc(n) Born 10/4/48	(GD)	1 July 97
Dixon, Raymond Lawrence BSc psc qwi Born 7/5/48	(GD)	1 Jan 98
Waldron, Alan Peter CBE AFC jsdc cfs Born 8/9/47	(GD)	1 Jan 98
Lang, Alistair Cochrane MBE BA CEng FIMechE FRAeS rcds semc psc Born 19/10/47	(ENG)	1 Jan 98
Good, Michael John ADC MIDPM MCMI jsdc qwi(AD) Born 11/1/49 . .	(OPS SPT)	1 July 98
Horwood, Raymond James CBE FRAeS ocds(Can) psc snc Born 28/9/49 . . .	(GD)	1 Jan 99
Maddox, Nigel David Alan CBE hcsc psc(n) Born 1/4/54	(GD)	1 Jan 99
Chandler, John Edgar CBE CEng FRAes qs Born 26/10/47	(ENG)	1 Jan 99
Blencowe, Christopher John MA BA rcds osc(FR) i Born 27/3/50	(SUP)	1 Jan 99
Collier, James Andrew CBE BSc psc Born 6/7/51	(ADMIN)	1 Jan 99
McLoughlin, John Allan MBE MA rcds psc Born 28/8/50	(ADMIN)	1 Jan 99
Luker, Paul Douglas OBE AFC rcds hcsc awcc psc Born 8/7/51	(GD)	1 July 99
Sweetman, Andrew David OBE BA rcds hcsc psc qwi Born 10/7/53	(GD)	1 July 99
Williams, David Richard OBE FCMI aws psc Born 12/5/49	(GD)	1 July 99
Rennison, David Ralph Gray MSc BSc psc semc Born 28/6/51	(ENG)	1 July 99
Whalley, Peter psc Born 22/5/51	(SUP)	1 July 99
Pocock, David John BA jsdc df Born 1/6/53	(ADMIN)	1 July 99
Walker, David Allan OBE MVO BSc FRAeS MCIPD qs Born 14/7/56	(ADMIN)	1 July 99
Dalton, Stephen Gary George BSc FRAeS MCMI hcsc psc qwi Born 23/4/54 . .	(GD)	1 Jan 00
Jarron, John Cole aws psc(n) Born 18/1/48	(GD)	1 Jan 00
Metcalfe, Wilson MCMI psc Born 1/9/48	(GD)	1 Jan 00
White, Andrew David BTech jsdc qwi Born 2/1/52	(GD)	1 Jan 00
Fuller, Malcolm John psc Born 22/10/50	(OPS SPT)	1 Jan 00
Moore, Richard Charles MBE BSc psc Born 5/8/50	(OPS SPT)	1 Jan 00
Dye, Peter John OBE BSc(Eng) CEng MRAeS ACGI rcds hcsc psc Born 17/8/53	(ENG)	1 Jan 00
Ness, Charles Wright BEng CEng FRAeS jsdc semc Born 6/11/57	(ENG)	1 Jan 00
Chisnall, Steven MPhil BA CertEd psc Born 12/6/54	(ADMIN)	1 Jan 00
Thomas, Paul Royston MBE BSc psc Born 16/3/55	(ADMIN)	1 Jan 00
Heath, Michael Christopher CBE FRAeS rcds psc psc(n) qwi snc Born 21/12/50 .	(GD)	1 July 00
Loader, Clive Robert OBE hcsc psc qwi Born 24/9/53	(GD)	1 July 00
Wood, Nigel Richard OBE MRAeS psc tp Born 21/7/49	(GD)	1 July 00
Schofield, Stephen Bryan MSc BSc CEng MRAeS jsdc qs Born 26/5/48 . .	(ENG)	1 July 00
Sobey, Bruce Leonard BA CEng MIEE MCMI psc Born 9/12/48	(ENG)	1 July 00
Hilling, Peter James MA rcds odc(US) qs Born 1/11/53	(ADMIN)	1 July 00
Cliffe, John Alfred OBE FRAeS rcds psc(n) qwi Born 14/6/53	(GD)	1 Jan 01
Hudson, Alan Thomas OBE BSc hcsc psc qwi Born 27/4/51	(GD)	1 Jan 01
Lacey, Richard Howard MA BA rcds psc Born 11/12/53	(GD)	1 Jan 01
Lambert, Andrew Peter Noel MPhil awcc psc qwi Born 12/10/48	(GD)	1 Jan 01
Moran, Christopher Hugh OBE MVO MA BSc hcsc psc(j) qwi Born 28/4/56 . .	(GD)	1 Jan 01
Peach, Stuart William CBE MPhil BA FRAeS MRIN hcsc psc qwi Born 22/2/56 .	(GD)	1 Jan 01
Witts, Jeremy John DSO FRAeS psc Born 18/6/50	(GD)	1 Jan 01
Case, David Nathaniel MSc BSc CEng FRAeS psc Born 19/8/52	(ENG)	1 Jan 01
Kane, James Ian BSc CEng MIEE MCMI psc Born 30/10/53	(ENG)	1 Jan 01
Rawson, Paul David BA IEng FRAeS rcds psc semc Born 13/3/53	(ENG)	1 Jan 01
Williams, Dilwyn Nigel OBE BSc CEng FRAeS jsdc semc qs Born 1/10/54 . .	(ENG)	1 Jan 01
Cook, Ronald CBE BTech awcc psc Born 19/2/53	(GD)	1 July 01
Igoe, Christopher Paul hcsc rcds cfs Born 15/10/52	(GD)	1 July 01
Ruddock, Peter William David CBE psc qwi Born 5/2/54	(GD)	1 July 01
Bairsto, Nigel Alexander MBE MDA MSc BSc CEng FIMechE FRAeS FCMI hcsc rcds psc Born 27/8/53	(ENG)	1 July 01
Leeson, Kevin James BSc CEng FIEE rcds psc semc Born 11/6/56	(ENG)	1 July 01
Wynn, Bruce Martin OBE BSc psc Born 4/7/52	(ENG)	1 July 01
Hedges, Desmond Paul psc ssc Born 2/3/48	(SUP)	1 July 01
Morris, Nicholas Steven MSc BA MIL MILT osc(Fr) ssc i* Born 22/2/55 . . .	(SUP)	1 July 01
Wood, Stephen MHCIMA psc Born 29/6/52	(ADMIN)	1 July 01
Hodgson, Raymond Bruce MBA BA psc Born 2/7/49	(GD)	1 Jan 02

Air Commodores

Ollis, Peter Rennie CBE BSc rcds psc cfs Born 10/2/55	(GD)	1 Jan 02
Walker, David CBE AFC MA BSc hcsc psc qwi Born 30/10/56	(GD)	1 Jan 02
Spinks, Andrew Charles FRAeS FCIT FILT rcds jsdc ssc qs Born 16/9/52 . .	(SUP)	1 Jan 02
Morgan, Clive Richard jsdc scc Born 7/2/51	(ADMIN)	1 Jan 02
Tonks, John David BSc psc adp Born 2/2/49	(ADMIN)	1 Jan 02
Coker, Peter Anthony OBE FCMI FRAeS jsdc cfs qwi(AD) qs Born 1/4/56 . . .	(GD)	1 July 02
Harper, Christopher Nigel CBE MA FCMI hcsc psc qwi Born 25/3/57	(GD)	1 July 02
Milne, Ian Alexander MA MA hcsc qwi qwi(T) psc(j) Born 18/9/51	(GD)	1 July 02
Nickols, Christopher Mark MA hcsc psc qwi Born 23/7/56	(GD)	1 July 02
Ponsonby, John Maurice Maynard OBE hcsc psc cfs Born 8/8/55	(GD)	1 July 02
Routledge, Martin John ADC BSc MRAes psc Born 22/11/54	(GD)	1 July 02
Warnes, Andrew Everett MA BSc CEng MIEE rcds jsdc semc Born 11/4/53 .	(ENG)	1 July 02
Howson, Timothy George MSc BA jsdc im ssc qs Born 13/7/52 . . .	(SUP)	1 July 02
Anderson, David Hugh MA rcds psc Born 24/6/55	(ADMIN)	1 July 02
Jerstice, Brian James CBE BA FCIPD psc Born 29/2/52	(ADMIN)	1 July 02
Thomas, John Henry Stanley BA MIL jsdc qs i* Born 13/2/54	(ADMIN)	1 July 02

GENERAL DUTIES BRANCH

Group Captains

1989

Brindle, Geoffrey psc Born 22/6/44 . . . . (P) 1 Jan

1991

Carr, Roger Frederick Richard MBE hcsc psc snc Born 18/5/47 . . . . . . (N) 1 Jan
Gleave, Malcolm OBE psc Born 5/7/47 . . . . (P) 1 July
Morris, Christopher John OBE FRIN rcds psc(m) asq snc i* Born 9/7/48 . . . (N) 1 July

1993

Morley, John Robert Douglas MBE hcsc nadc psc Born 28/3/47 . . . . . (P) 1 Jan
Ray, David Alan hcsc psc qwi Born 23/1/47 . . . . (P) 1 Jan
Wildman, Peter Gordon BA FRAeS nadc aws psc cfs Born 10/2/47 . . . . . (P) 1 Jan
Ball, James Allan AFC oaws(UK) asq jsdc Born 14/5/48 . . . . (P) 1 July
Beney, Trevor John FCMI psc qwi Born 20/1/48 . . . . (P) 1 July
Joseph, Robert William CBE BSc hcsc psc(n) asq Born 6/10/49 . . . . . . (N) 1 July
Rusling, Nicholas Charles BA oaws psc qwi Born 13/12/47 . . . . (P) 1 July

1994

Jones, David Martin psc(m) Born 28/6/48 . . . . (P) 1 Jan
Milne-Smith, David Henry oaws(US) psc qwi Born 6/2/47 . . . . (P) 1 Jan
Mitchell, Michael jsdc Born 3/8/47 . . . . (P) 1 Jan
Williams, Timothy John AFC psc cfs Born 29/1/48 . . . . (P) 1 Jan
Travers Smith, Ian DSO psc qwi Born 14/11/46 . . . . (P) 1 July

1995

Beedie, Alastair Ian Bartlett psc snc Born 9/8/49 . . . . (N) 1 Jan
Le Bas, Christopher Brian BSc MCMI odc(US) Born 28/12/48 . . . . . . (P) 1 Jan

1996

Barrett, Peter Alan OBE BSc FRAeS psc asq Born 5/7/47 . . . . (P) 1 Jan
Burrough, Robert Francis BA BSc jsdc Born 12/8/48 . . . . (P) 1 Jan
Hounslow, Robert John FRAeS FCMI psc Born 19/11/50 . . . . (N) 1 Jan
Lockwood, Alan John AFC rcds psc Born 31/10/51 . . . . (P) 1 Jan
Moss, David Malcolm psc(n) Born 24/6/47 . . . . (P) 1 Jan
Turner, Frank Lester hcsc psc qwi Born 21/10/50 . . . . (P) 1 Jan
Brewer, Timothy Paul OBE BSc psc asq Born 22/6/53 . . . . (N) 1 July
Sawyer, Alan OBE osc(GE) qwi i Born 6/11/48 . . . . (N) 1 July

Group Captains

1997

Black, Stuart Douglas psc(n) qwi Born 4/1/55	(N)	1 Jan
Butler, Stuart Denham cfs Born 15/1/56	(P)	1 Jan
Hodgson, Peter psc qwi Born 30/7/52	(P)	1 Jan
Spiller, Nicholas Bertram psc Born 15/8/46	(P)	1 Jan
White, John William CBE FRAeS FCMI jsdc qwi qs Born 21/2/48	(P)	1 Jan
Bullen, Jeffrey Donald OBE psc Born 12/5/48	(P)	1 July
Corney, Hugh Richard OBE BA nadc awcc psc Born 1/2/51	(N)	1 July
Dee, Anthony George Oakley odc(US) psc cfs Born 2/1/49	(P)	1 July
Goodman, Philip Charles MBE ADC BSc hcsc jsdc qwi qs Born 23/4/54	(N)	1 July
Newby, Brian Walter CBE AFC qwi Born 11/9/54	(P)	1 July
Threapleton, Norman Edward BSc jsdc psc qwi Born 4/11/51	(N)	1 July
Utley, Roger OBE BA jsdc cfs qs i Born 18/9/50	(P)	1 July

1998

Capewell, Ian BSc psc qwi Born 27/9/52	(P)	1 Jan
Drew, David John aws psc cfs Born 31/7/47	(P)	1 Jan
Edge, Glenn Howard OBE BSc jsdc cfs Born 23/11/51	(P)	1 Jan
Middleton, Richard Hugh psc Born 1/10/51	(N)	1 Jan
Morrow, William Kyle David OBE psc Born 6/10/49	(N)	1 Jan
Parkinson, Stephen Leo psc Born 18/7/51	(N)	1 Jan
Scoffham, Peter Douglas AFC psc Born 19/8/48	(P)	1 Jan
Stringer, Martin Derek jsdc awcc cfs(n)* snc qs Born 21/9/52	(N)	1 Jan
Walton, Andrew George jsdc qwi Born 16/12/54	(P)	1 Jan
White, David Harold jsdc qab cfs qs Born 21/2/48	(P)	1 Jan
Barter, Michael Carl CBE hcsc psc(m) cfs Born 18/8/54	(P)	1 July
Dezonie, Andre Ferdinand Paul OBE hcsc psc(m) cfs Born 10/2/56	(P)	1 July

1999

Allen, Richard John jsdc cfs qs Born 20/6/49	(P)	1 Jan
Barnes, Michael Anthony Joseph BSc psc asq Born 22/9/53	(N)	1 Jan
Bowerman, Graham Alan OBE psc qab qwi Born 20/10/49	(P)	1 Jan
Collins, Bryan Raymond oaws(US) psc qwi Born 17/7/52	(P)	1 Jan
Crowley, James William qab qs Born 7/6/48	(N)	1 Jan
Dugmore, Ian Leonard BSc hcsc psc Born 23/10/53	(P)	1 Jan
Halsall, Martin William psc Born 10/2/54	(N)	1 Jan
Huckins, Nigel Morrell MBE BSc BSc psc Born 3/2/51	(P)	1 Jan
Lamonte, Jonathan MA BSc CMath FIMA FRIN MRAeS MCMI CDipAF hcsc psc asq Born 30/12/59	(N)	1 Jan
Leakey, Mark Arundell BSc rcds qwi psc Born 28/3/56	(P)	1 Jan
Pixton, George William DFC AFC nadc awcc psc qwi Born 14/6/51	(P)	1 Jan
Vincent, Alan James MA hcsc jsdc psc(j) qwi Born 20/2/53	(N)	1 Jan
Bryant, Simon MA BA psc Born 20/6/56	(N)	1 July
Cunningham, Robert Bourke MBE MA psc Born 27/6/57	(N)	1 July
Daffarn, Gavin Charles BSc FCMI jsdc asq qab snc Born 14/4/49	(N)	1 July
Jones, James Richard CBE rcds jsdc psc(j) Born 17/11/52	(N)	1 July
Lloyd, Michael Guy psc cfs Born 7/12/59	(P)	1 July
Rycroft, Peter William OBE ADC psc cfs(n)* snc Born 16/9/53	(N)	1 July

Group Captains

2000

Cobelli, Ricardo Dominic OBE BSc psc qwi(T) Born 15/3/56	(P)	1 Jan
Cornfield, Kenneth Leslie OBE MA psc cfs Born 27/11/55	(P)	1 Jan
Dixon, Graham Patrick BSc psc Born 17/3/55	(P)	1 Jan
Gray, Peter William MPhil BSc LLB hcsc jsdc qs Born 13/6/53	(N)	1 Jan
Harrison, David Ian BSc hcsc psc qwi Born 23/1/56	(P)	1 Jan
Harwood, Michael John MBE MA hcsc psc cfs qwi Born 29/10/58	(P)	1 Jan
McAlpine, Robert Ian DFC MA BSc MRAeS hcsc psc qwi Born 17/9/56	(P)	1 Jan
Pulford, Andrew Douglas hcsc psc Born 22/3/58	(P)	1 Jan
Skinner, Stephen Neil BSc psc cfs Born 9/11/54	(P)	1 Jan
Stinton, Julian MA BA hcsc psc qab qwi Born 5/7/57	(P)	1 Jan
Almond, Timothy MBE MA BA FRIN MCMI psc asq qwi Born 28/12/53	(N)	1 July
Anderson, Timothy Michael DSO MA MRAeS psc Born 2/2/57	(P)	1 July
Ayres, Stephen Peter BSc osc(Fr) cfs i Born 1/3/55	(P)	1 July
Beresford, Nigel Edward Lord LVO oaws(US) psc qab cfs Born 10/10/48	(P)	1 July
Dennison, Keith BSc FRAeS jsdc tp qwi qs Born 10/6/57	(P)	1 July
Duffill, Steven MA MCMI psc cfs Born 19/4/51	(P)	1 July
Garwood, Richard Frank DFC ADC MA psc(m) qwi Born 10/1/59	(P)	1 July
Hillier, Stephen John DFC MA BA psc cfs Born 22/4/62	(P)	1 July
Leaming, Michael William BSc psc Born 29/8/52	(P)	1 July
Moloney, John Patrick MA BA psc Born 22/5/56	(P)	1 July
Porter, Garry Reginald Roy BSc psc qab Born 9/5/55	(N)	1 July
Swan, Mark LLB psc qwi(T) Born 10/8/57	(P)	1 July
Vacha, Iain David jsdc odc(US) Born 14/11/48	(N)	1 July
Whittingham, David Laurence BSc psc cfs Born 31/5/56	(P)	1 July

2001

Bates, Brian Lawrence ADC BA hcsc psc qwi Born 15/6/57	(N)	1 Jan
Coulls, Christopher John hcsc psc(j) qwi(T) Born 23/6/57	(N)	1 Jan
Dey, Andrew James BSc psc Born 31/7/57	(N)	1 Jan
Dixon, Carl William OBE psc Born 15/1/60	(P)	1 Jan
Randle, Nicholas Carl BSc MRAeS MRIN psc asq snc Born 31/12/56	(N)	1 Jan
Bagwell, Gregory Jack psc(j) qwi Born 6/10/61	(P)	1 July
Bailey, Robert Michael MSc qs Born 31/7/52	(N)	1 July
Bairsto, Clive Arthur psc(j) qab qwi(AD) Born 25/12/59	(N)	1 July
Colley, Michael Paul OBE psc qab qwi Born 27/8/59	(N)	1 July
Falla, Simon Owen DSO jsdc cfs qs Born 25/12/55	(P)	1 July
Fradgley, Jeremy Nicholas OBE AFC BSc FRAeS psc qwi(T) Born 16/12/58	(N)	1 July
Fynes, Jonathan Peter Spencer psc cfs Born 30/4/54	(P)	1 July
Garside-Beattie, Leslie OBE cfs jsdc qs Born 10/8/55	(P)	1 July
Jagger, Neil Robert BSc psc(j) cfs(n) snc Born 29/8/53	(N)	1 July
Lock, Raymond BSc psc(j) cfs* Born 2/11/58	(P)	1 July
Marston, Robert AFC jsdc cfs qs Born 20/11/47	(P)	1 July
McGeown, Mark Samuel MA psc Born 7/3/55	(P)	1 July
Milburn, Trevor Stefan MA BSc psc(m) Born 10/2/62	(P)	1 July
Tizard, Robert Walter psc(m) cfs Born 22/9/57	(P)	1 July
Torbet, Russell John MA MRAeS qwi psc Born 13/5/59	(P)	1 July

2002

Birks, Christopher John MA BSc psc Born 3/6/58	(P)	1 Jan
Fidler, David Charles psc cfs Born 9/3/52	(P)	1 Jan

Group Captains

2002—contd

Green, Mark Colin BSc psc cfs Born 10/5/59	(P)	1 Jan
Hilditch, Stanley Laurence BSc FRAeS jsdc tp qwi qs Born 2/9/54	(P)	1 Jan
Kirkpatrick, Andrew Shane BSc jsdc cfs qs Born 4/2/56	(P)	1 Jan
Meyrick, Nicholas David psc Born 8/9/53	(N)	1 Jan
Parkes, Keith John MBE BA BSc psc cfs Born 6/7/49	(P)	1 Jan
Sharp, Martin Ashley OBE ADC MRAeS psc n Born 16/5/60	(N)	1 Jan
Warren, Simon Francis MDA psc(j) cfs Born 27/11/54	(P)	1 Jan
Young, Andrew Anderson MA MRAeS psc(n) tp qwi i Born 5/11/53	(P)	1 Jan
Adams, Christopher Kenneth psc Born 18/5/49	(N)	1 July
Barrett, Andrew John jsdc fc qs Born 31/5/53	(P)	1 July
Dunsford, Roger James BSc qab qss Born 28/1/49	(P)	1 July
Elliott, Robert Ian OBE BSc psc asq Born 1/11/59	(N)	1 July
Evans, Wyn Griffith OBE jsdc tp qab Born 5/1/53	(P)	1 July
Finn, Christopher John MPhil jsdc awcc psc(j) qab qwi Born 21/11/53	(N)	1 July
Golledge, Andrew DSO BSc qs Born 17/4/58	(P)	1 July
Greaves, Keith Robert Colin OBE BSc qs Born 20/3/48	(P)	1 July
McDonald, Thomas Paul OBE rcds jsdc cfs qs Born 16/4/49	(P)	1 July
Powell, Ronald James Albert psc cfs Born 4/4/55	(P)	1 July
Smith, Barry OBE BA jsdc asq qs Born 1/9/52	(N)	1 July
Smyth, William Stephen BA awcc psc qwi Born 27/1/54	(N)	1 July
Williams, Peter BSc jsdc snc qs Born 27/1/54	(N)	1 July

Wing Commanders

1985

Felger, C. F. W. psc
osc(Ku) (N) 1 July

1986

Douglas, K. M. awcc
psc (P) 1 Jan
Guest, D. M. aws
psc(m) (P) 1 Jan
Mahaffey, B. S. BA psc
qab qwi (P) 1 July
Whitney, J. R. A. AFC
MRAeS psc tp (P) 1 July

1987

Hudson, N. C. L. MA
jsdc psc(j) cfs (P) 1 Jan

1988

Cassady, R. J. jsdc nadc
snc (N) 1 Jan

1989

Common, M. F. F. MBE
osc(GE) cfs i (P) 1 Jan
Miskelly, I. R. jsdc (N) 1 Jan
Neal, B. R. FCMI jsdc
psc (P) 1 Jan
Tench, N. R. MBE
qs (P) 1 Jan
Yeldham, N. S. psc(m)
qtm (N) 1 Jan
Forsythe, R. A. OBE psc
cfs (P) 1 July
Godfrey, M. V. AFC psc
qwi (P) 1 July

1990

Bonney-James, R. M.
psc cfs (P) 1 Jan
Eames, C. M. psc
cfs(n)* snc (N) 1 Jan
Fox, N. G. BA awcc
psc(m) cfs (P) 1 Jan

Keenan, D. J. OBE psc
qwi (P) 1 Jan
Pitts, J. aws psc cfs (P) 1 Jan
Blee, P. M. nadc psc(n)
cfs (P) 1 July
Cullum, P. J. G. E. McG.
MCMI psc cfs (P) 1 July
Ellaway, M. J. jsdc asq
snc qs (N) 1 July
Flowerdew, B. N.
psc(n) (AEO) 1 July
Foster, R. psc qab
cfs (P) 1 July
Haines, P. J. J. BSc rcds
psc asq snc (N) 1 July
Richardson, A. K. nadc
psc(m) (P) 1 July
Roberts, P. BSc psc (P) 1 July

1991

Barber, G. OBE asq snc
qs (N) 1 Jan
Burns, C. S. psc (N) 1 Jan
Chambers, R. I. jsdc
osc(Ku) cfs(n)
snc (N) 1 Jan
Dickens, C. R. D. psc
cfs(n) snc (N) 1 Jan
Goodsell, G. V. psc
snc (N) 1 Jan
Hawes, C. M. H. BA psc
asq snc adp (N) 1 Jan
King, R. W. jsdc qwi
snc (N) 1 Jan
Musgrave, D. awcc psc
snc (N) 1 Jan
Pierce, J. W. MRAeS
osc(Fr) tp qwi (P) 1 Jan
Radley, R. P. jsdc tp
cfs* (P) 1 Jan
Arkell, J. D. OBE MA
jsdc qab qwi qs (P) 1 July
Babraff, J. K. L. cfs
qs (P) 1 July
Bishopp, J. B. psc
cfs (P) 1 July
Elliott, H. T. MA psc(n)
cfs (P) 1 July
Harper, T. A. jsdc
oaws(US) qwi qs (P) 1 July
Lawrence, C. J. MRAeS
MRIN awcc psc (N) 1 July
Richey, F. A. BA psc asq
cfs(n) snc (N) 1 July
Stephens, A. P. qab
cfs(n)* snc qs (N) 1 July

York, P. OBE psc cfs(n)
snc (N) 1 July

1992

Angus, D. A. jsdc
qs (P) 1 Jan
Blunden, R. F. BA
MRAeS MBCS MCMI
psc asq snc (N) 1 Jan
Boyd, A. J. W.
psc(m) (N) 1 Jan
Horwood, G. M. psc
asq cfs (P) 1 Jan
Macartney, S. M. J. BSc
awcc psc (P) 1 Jan
Richardson, M. G. OBE
awcc psc (N) 1 Jan
Leadbetter, P. M. MVO
MCMI jsdc snc
qs (N) 1 July

1993

Chacksfield, C. C. MBE
qs (P) 1 Jan
Furniss, N. J. MBE psc
ac (P) 1 Jan
Main, A. P. T. OBE
MRAeS MCIPD
MCMI (N) 9 Mar
Cooke, J. A. OBE
psc (ALM) 1 July
Edmonds, C. C. BSc
psc (N) 1 July
Harbottle, F. jsdc
psc(j) (P) 1 July
Hartree, W. R. cfs
psc (P) 1 July
Huddleston, F. A. psc
cfs (P) 1 July
Hush, W. BSc psc
cfs(n) (N) 1 July
Keating, P. K. MA BSc
MRAeS psc(m) (P) 1 July
Price, H. W.
DPhysEd (P) 1 July
Rodgers, M. snc cfs(n)
qs (N) 1 July
Rosentall, P. H. psc
cfs (P) 1 July

1994

Bond, C. L. oaws(US)
psc(j) cfs(n)* snc (N) 1 Jan
Bown, A. R. jsdc qs (N) 1 Jan

99

Wing Commanders

1994—contd

Burgess, K. J. psc   (P)   1 Jan
Gunner, S. BSc(Eng)
qs   (P)   1 Jan
Herriot, D. R. qab qwi
qwi(T) psc   (N)   1 Jan
Knowles, D. W.
psc   (AEO)   1 Jan
Pitt, C. R. BSc jsdc
psc(n)   (N)   1 Jan
Pollitt, M. M. BSc rcds
psc cfs   (P)   1 Jan
Randall, N. B. jsdc qwi
qs   (N)   1 Jan
Simmonds, B. P. OBE
BSc CPhys MInstP
psc cfs   (P)   1 Jan
Bone, A. M. AFC jsdc
asq qs   (P)   1 July
Dixon, P. R. MBA
BSc(Eng) MRAeS
rcds psc cfs   (P)   1 July
Ferries, A. I. BSc jsdc
nadc psc asq cfs(n)
snc   (N)   1 July
Hurst, W. J. psc
osc(Ku)   (P)   1 July
Rackham, C. M. cfs
qss   (P)   1 July
Skinner, D. R. psc(j)
snc   (N)   1 July
Crane, R.   (N)   10 Nov

1995

Clifford, J. M. MSc BSc
jsdc asq cfs(n) cfs
qs   (N)   1 Jan
Davies, J. S. psc
snc   (N)   1 Jan
Dear, A. J. psc snc   (N)   1 Jan
Ford, D. J. BA
psc(n)   (AEO)   1 Jan
Rimmer, J. A. J. BSc
psc   (P)   1 Jan
Squelch, J. P. BSc jsdc
qab qs   (P)   1 Jan
Walne, K. BSc asq
qs   (N)   1 Jan
Whitehouse, M. B. BSc
qs   (N)   1 Jan
Wilson, D. A. MA BSc
psc   (P)   1 Jan
Brown, E. S. psc
snc   (N)   1 July

Malcolm, C. D. psc(j)
asq cfs(n) snc   (N)   1 July
Marrison, C. G. psc
qwi(T)   (N)   1 July
Wright, R. D. BSc MRIN
MRAeS psc   (N)   1 July

1996

Bartram, J. A. MSc
FCMI MREC snc   (N)   1 Jan
Cameron, I. A. jsdc   (N)   1 Jan
Cleland-Smith, D. J.
jsdc qs   (N)   1 Jan
Coote, J. E. MBE psc
asq snc   (N)   1 Jan
Davenall, D. S. BSc jsdc
qs   (N)   1 Jan
Goodbourn, J. A. BSc
psc(j)   (P)   1 Jan
Hill, J. A. MSc BSc
MRAeS psc snc   (N)   1 Jan
Kelly, P. M. psc qwi   (N)   1 Jan
Maxwell, K. H. MA BSc
oaws(US) psc(n)
asq   (N)   1 Jan
Stapleton, G. M. psc
qwi   (N)   1 Jan
Thomson, K. K. MA psc
qwi   (N)   1 Jan
Carter, W. A. D. BA psc
qwi qwi(T)   (N)   1 July
Cummings, S. jsdc
qs   (P)   1 July
Johnston, R. T. MA qwi
qs   (P)   1 July
Jupp, J. A. BA psc(n)
qwi(AD)   (P)   1 July
O'Meeghan, P. M.
psc   (P)   1 July
Orwell, S. J. psc cfs   (P)   1 July
Pearson, S. BA jsdc
qs   (N)   1 July
Randerson, R. N. MA
BSc psc qwi   (N)   1 July
Watson, N. J. psc qwi
i*   (P)   1 July

1997

Bond, G. R. psc   (N)   1 Jan
Brook, P. J. OBE BA BSc
CEng MBCS MRAeS
MCMI psc asq snc
adp   (N)   1 Jan
Culbert, A. S. C. BSc
jsdc   (P)   1 Jan

Cunningham, P. A. BSc
cfs psc(m)   (P)   1 Jan
Davis, N. J. BSc MRAeS
MRIN psc asq   (N)   1 Jan
Hull, C. P. A. BSc psc
asq   (N)   1 Jan
Jenkins, R. D. psc tp
cfs   (P)   1 Jan
Killen, M. F. BSc psc(j)
qab cfs   (P)   1 Jan
Lawlor, J. BA psc qab
qwi(T) qwi   (N)   1 Jan
Morris, I. OBE jsdc
cfs   (P)   1 Jan
Morrison, I. C. psc
qwi   (N)   1 Jan
Paton, D. R. OBE BA
osc(Fr)   (N)   1 Jan
Roche, M. J. jsdc cfs
qs   (N)   1 Jan
Soul, G. D. psc(n)(AEO)   1 Jan
Stewart, A. J. MRAeS
MCMI psc cfs   (P)   1 Jan
Sudlow, A. J. MBE BSc
psc qwi   (P)   1 Jan
Turner, L. BSc jsdc
qs   (N)   1 Jan
Walker, I. B. MDA BA
jsdc osc(KU) cfs   (P)   1 Jan
Barmby, A. S. BSc psc
cfs   (P)   1 July
Booth, G. H. psc
qwi(AD)   (N)   1 July
Cross, T. MA MBA BA
jsdc psc(j)   (N)   1 July
Dobson, W. G. S. BSc
psc   (P)   1 July
Forward, S. D. BSc jsdc
qab qss   (P)   1 July
Gunby, A. D. psc   (N)   1 July
Kerr, A. W. BA AIL qs
i*   (N)   1 July
Oborn, P. N. psc   (P)   1 July
Simpson, D. A. BSc psc
tp   (P)   1 July
Stewart, I. R. W. BSc
jsdc cfs qs   (P)   1 July
Welham, A. R. D.
psc   (P)   1 July
Whitaker, P. J. W. BA
osc(Fr) i*   (P)   1 July
Williams, W. D. BA psc
cfs   (P)   1 July
Wright, G. A. OBE BSc
psc(m)   (P)   1 July

Wing Commanders

1998

Ashcroft, I. T. asq		
cfs(n)* qs	(N)	1 Jan
Atherton, P. A. psc	(P)	1 Jan
Barber, S. B. J. MA		
psc(n)	(N)	1 Jan
Bell, I. K. FInstLM psc		
cfs	(P)	1 Jan
Burley, D. qab cfs(n)		
snc qs	(N)	1 Jan
Bye, D. M. I. osc(US)		
qwi	(P)	1 Jan
Dobb, S. K. OBE MA		
psc qwi(T)	(P)	1 Jan
Draper, I. M. BA psc		
cfs	(P)	1 Jan
Footer, S. G. MBE jsdc		
psc(j)	(P)	1 Jan
Fox, S. M. AFC MA		
BCom psc cfs		
qwi	(P)	1 Jan
Fryer, A. D. psc	(N)	1 Jan
Goodall, R. jsdc qs	(N)	1 Jan
Harborne, P. N. jsdc		
cfs(g)	(P)	1 Jan
Hawes, A. P. BSc cfs		
qs	(P)	1 Jan
Hill, M. R. jsdc	(N)	1 Jan
Horrocks, J. MA		
psc(n)	(P)	1 Jan
Howard, S. J. MA MBA		
MRAeS psc qab	(P)	1 Jan
Huggett, A. D. psc		
qwi	(N)	1 Jan
Jenkins, M. J. M. BSc		
jsdc cfs qs	(P)	1 Jan
Kennedy, J. M. BSc		
qs	(N)	1 Jan
Kirkin, T. R. MRIN cfs(n)		
snc qs	(N)	1 Jan
Lloyd, P. O. MBE MBA		
psc(j) cfs*	(P)	1 Jan
MacInnes, G. W. BSc		
jsdc qs	(P)	1 Jan
McCann, K. B. psc(m)		
qab qwi	(P)	1 Jan
McWilliams, T. P. psc		
qab snc	(N)	1 Jan
Mercer, M. J. jsdc		
qwi(AD) qs	(P)	1 Jan
Moulds, G. MBE jsdc		
qss	(N)	1 Jan
Newton, S. psc	(N)	1 Jan
Osborn, P. C. psc		
qwi	(N)	1 Jan
Plumb, J. V. qwi qs	(N)	1 Jan

Poole, R. M. MA psc		
qwi(T) qtm	(N)	1 Jan
Prowse, D. L. OBE BA		
jsdc qab qs	(P)	1 Jan
Robertson, D. G. psc		
qwi(T)	(N)	1 Jan
Scholtens, J. H. BA jsdc		
qs	(N)	1 Jan
Seward, N. I. M. psc		
cfs	(P)	1 Jan
Stevenson, A. D. OBE		
psc qab qwi	(P)	1 Jan
Sutton, P. R. MA		
MRAes psc cfs	(P)	1 Jan
Teakle, I. D. OBE jsdc		
qab qwi(T) qs	(N)	1 Jan
Thwaites, G. E. psc	(N)	1 Jan
Trembaczowski-Ryder,		
D. J. BSc psc	(N)	1 Jan
Barton, P. R. BSc psc(j)		
cfs	(P)	1 July
Birtwistle, R. W. psc		
qwi(AD)	(N)	1 July
Duell, K. psc(j)	(AEO)	1 July
McAuley, A. W. J.		
psc(j)	(P)	1 July
Morris, P. A. psc	(N)	1 July
Nash, H. W. MBE MA		
psc(j) qab	(P)	1 July
North, B. M. MBE MA		
pcs(m)	(P)	1 July
Purkiss, C. C. MBE BSc		
psc(Spa) i*	(N)	1 July
Revell, K. A. BA osc(Fr)		
qab i*	(N)	1 July
Robertson, G. W. BSc		
psc	(N)	1 July
Russell, S. P. jsdc		
qs	(N)	1 July
Shields, I. E. psc(j)		
cfs(n)*	(N)	1 July
Stubbs, D. J. qs	(P)	1 July
Suddards, A. J. Q. MA		
BA psc(j) qab		
qwi	(P)	1 July
Taylor, J. MCMI psc	(P)	1 July
Tull, G. A. J. adp qs	(N)	1 July
Turner, W. J. MA		
BSc(Eng) MRAeS		
MRIN MCGI MCMI		
asq psc	(N)	1 July
Wade, C. E. BSc asq		
qs	(N)	1 July
Warner, J. E. AIB psc(j)		
cfs	(P)	1 July
West, P. C. qs	(N)	1 July

1999

Bell, S. M. BSc(Eng)		
psc cfs qwi	(P)	1 Jan
Benn, C. R. oaws(US)		
qs	(P)	1 Jan
Bentham, A. qss	(N)	1 Jan
Bruce, G. J. BSc psc(j)		
asq	(P)	1 Jan
Chapman, J. G. MA		
MSc BA BSc psc qab		
cfs	(P)	1 Jan
Connell, N. M. BSc psc		
cfs	(P)	1 Jan
Connor, K. D. qs	(P)	1 Jan
Dakin, A. G. BSc qwi		
qs	(P)	1 Jan
Diamond, D. J. BA		
MRAeS osc(Fr)		
cfs	(P)	1 Jan
Havelock, K. psc(j)	(P)	1 Jan
Judson, R. W. jsdc		
qs	(P)	1 Jan
Klein, J. B. qwi qs	(N)	1 Jan
Lyall, P. DMS psc(j)	(P)	1 Jan
Maas, J. D. osc(US)	(P)	1 Jan
Meadows, N. MA BSc		
MRAeS psc(j) cfs	(P)	1 Jan
O'Connell, C. D. jsdc		
cfs(n) snc	(N)	1 Jan
Reeves, C. MA BSc		
psc(j)	(ENG)	1 Jan
Todd, R. E. BSc(Econ)		
qs	(N)	1 Jan
Van Den Berg, G. G. S.		
MSc psc qab	(P)	1 Jan
Atha, S. D. BSc cfs		
psc(j)	(P)	1 July
Cockram, S. H. odc(US)		
qab qwi(T) qtm		
qs	(P)	1 July
Davey, G. J. BSc		
psc(j)	(P)	1 July
Docker, P. A. BA MCGI		
psc(j) asq	(P)	1 July
Edwards, P. W. MBE		
BSc psc asq i*	(P)	1 July
Green, S. J. jsdc qs	(N)	1 July
Guz, N. BSc psc(j)		
cfs	(P)	1 July
Hallett, L. T. BSc psc(j)		
qwi(AD)	(P)	1 July
Hobson, R. A.		
MDefStud BSc		
psc	(P)	1 July
Hopkins, M. W. G. MBE		
MA MSc psc cfs	(P)	1 July
Kessell, J. B. psc(j)	(N)	1 July
McDermott, C. W. psc(j)		
qab	(N)	1 July

Wing Commanders

1999—contd

McNamara, S. P.
qs   (AEO) 1 July
Meade, S. C. OBE
qs   (P) 1 July
Reynolds, S. K. P. DFC
psc(j) cfs (P) 1 July
Turner, S. C. G.
BSc(Econ) MCMI jsdc
cfs qs (P) 1 July
Wharmby, N. E. OBE
MA BSc psc(j)
qwi (P) 1 July
Whittingham, R. T. MA
BSc psc(j) asq (AEO) 1 July
Wilder, R. A. BSc
jsdc (N) 1 July
Willis, P. A. osc(Fr)
qwi(AD) (P) 1 July

2000

Allan, P. BA psc(j)
cfs* (P) 1 Jan
Bayer, P. qs (N) 1 Jan
Birch, R. S. OBE psc(j)
qwi(AD) (P) 1 Jan
Brecht, M. A. B. BA
psc(j) (P) 1 Jan
Budd, P. H. qs (N) 1 Jan
Carter, R. V. BSc jsdc cfs
qs (P) 1 Jan
Chan, D. K. M.
psc(j) (P) 1 Jan
Davey, G. R. qs (ENG) 1 Jan
Dawson, N. S.
BSc(Eng) ACGI
psc(j) (P) 1 Jan
Deas, A. S. BSc
psc(j) (N) 1 Jan
Fenlon, M. C. BSc(Eng)
CEng MRAeS psc(j)
asq (N) 1 Jan
Flint, A. P. MSc BA
psc(j) (N) 1 Jan
Garden, S. N. MA BSc
psc(j) (P) 1 Jan
Goodison, A. J. MA
BSc MCMI psc(j)
cfs(n) (N) 1 Jan
Greene, R. A. D. psc(j)
cfs (P) 1 Jan
Hill, T. J. BA qs i (N) 1 Jan
Hyslop, R. M. psc(j) (N) 1 Jan

Jeffery, M. A. OBE BSc
ARCS psc(j)
cfs(n) (N) 1 Jan
McSherry, A. L. BSc asq
qs (N) 1 Jan
Richardson, J. G. BSc
psc cfs (P) 1 Jan
Roberts, M. L. MBE
psc(j) (P) 1 Jan
Round, P. A. MA BSc
MRAeS psc(j) cfs (P) 1 Jan
Scott, G. R. psc (N) 1 Jan
Seares, M. J. MBE MA
psc(j) qwi (P) 1 Jan
Smith, N. A. qab
qs (AEO) 1 Jan
Stringer, E. J. MBE
BEng psc qwi (P) 1 Jan
Tucker, A. psc(j) qwi(T)
qtm (N) 1 Jan
Wood, I. N. BA psc(j)
qwi (P) 1 Jan
Atkinson, R. J. psc(j)
qwi(AD) (P) 1 July
Ayres, N. P. BSc asq
qs (N) 1 July
Baker, M. F. psc(j)
cfs(n) (N) 1 July
Baldwin, K. J.
psc(j) (N) 1 July
Bowen, A. P. qab
qwi(AD) qs (N) 1 July
Bremer, G. T. MA MDA
BSc CEng MRAeS
MCMI psc(j)
qwi(AD) (N) 1 July
Cairncross, A. K. cfs
qs (P) 1 July
Cottell, P. snc qs (N) 1 July
Courtnage, P. J. qwi
qs (P) 1 July
D'Arcy, Q. N. P. qab
qs (N) 1 July
Davies, R. W. BSc asq
qs (N) 1 July
Dixon, P. G. psc(j) (P) 1 July
Evans, S. C. psc(Aus)
cfs qwi(T) (P) 1 July
Gregory, P. W. MBE BA
MIL osc(Ge) i* (P) 1 July
Johnston, D. H. MA
BSc psc(j) qab (N) 1 July
Jones, P. J. psc(j)
qwi (N) 1 July
Jones, T. W. qab
cfs (P) 1 July
Kerr-Sheppard, D. A.
psc(j) cfs (P) 1 July
Lander, R. J. snc qs (N) 1 July

Linstead, A. S. MA BSc
psc(j) qwi(T) (N) 1 July
Loveridge, M. J.
psc(n) (N) 1 July
Mardon, J. BSc cfs qwi
qs (P) 1 July
Monkman, A. BA psc(j)
qwi (P) 1 July
Morgan, D. C. nadc
qs (N) 1 July
Ramsey, W. J. qab cfs
qs (P) 1 July
Sharpe, N. D. BA
psc(j) (N) 1 July
Shaw, D. M. psc(j)
qwi(AD) (N) 1 July
Stockill, G. qwi qs (P) 1 July
Tetlow, M. J. MA
psc(j) (N) 1 July
Townsend, S. P. MA
psc(j) cfs (P) 1 July
Turner, A. M. MSc BA
MRAeS psc qab
qhti (P) 1 July
Watson, K. J. BSc
psc(j) (P) 1 July
Webb, J. M. L. BSc
qs (P) 1 July

2001

Ball, J. C. qwi qs (N) 1 Jan
Basnett, C. psc(j)
qwi(T) (N) 1 Jan
Birch, P. N. MBE qwi
qs (P) 1 Jan
Brown, D. W. qs (AEO) 1 Jan
Byard, J. J. psc(j) (N) 1 Jan
Chapman, P. J. snc
qs (N) 1 Jan
Cunningham, C. S.
psc(j) cfs (P) 1 Jan
Dobson, M. qab snc
qs (N) 1 Jan
Duance, R. C. psc(j)
fc (P) 1 Jan
Edwards, G. D. MA
MRAeS psc(j) qab
cfs(n) (N) 1 Jan
Farmer, A. I. MBE BA
psc(j) (N) 1 Jan
Geddes, H. G. qs (N) 1 Jan
Gledhill, D. J. qs (N) 1 Jan
Goodenough, N. J. MA
BSc MRAeS psc(j)
asq (N) 1 Jan
Groves, A. K. cfs qs (P) 1 Jan
Hitchcook, J. J.
qwi(AD) psc (P) 1 Jan

Wing Commanders

2001—contd

Hutchings, J. P. qab		
qs	(N)	1 Jan
Johnston, J. C. M. BSc		
psc(j)	(P)	1 Jan
Kendall, J. F. cfs(n) snc		
psc	(N)	1 Jan
Laird, N. W. G. BA		
psc(j)	(P)	1 Jan
Longstaff, M. C.		
psc(j)	(P)	1 Jan
Neville, M. C. BSc		
psc(j)	(N)	1 Jan
Newton, H. E. BSc jsdc		
snc	(N)	1 Jan
Oldham, M. G. BSc		
psc(j)	(N)	1 Jan
Porter, J. L. snc qs	(N)	1 Jan
Powell, R. J. C. psc(j)		
qwi	(N)	1 Jan
Rafferty, M. S. BSc asq		
cfs(n) qss	(N)	1 Jan
Robertson, R. A. D. BSc		
qs	(P)	1 Jan
Ruddock-West, S. C.		
BSc asq qs	(N)	1 Jan
Smith, K. A. BSc		
psc(j)	(N)	1 Jan
Smyth, S. G. MBE		
qab	(P)	1 Jan
Storey, P. A. BSc psc(j)		
qwi(AD)	(N)	1 Jan
Thompson, R. T. N.		
MSc BSc psc(n) qab		
qwi	(N)	1 Jan
Viney, G. M. BSc asq		
qs	(N)	1 Jan
Wakeman, M. A.		
qwi(AD) qs	(N)	1 Jan
Ward, R. J. R. MSc BSc		
asq snc qs	(N)	1 Jan
Watson, D. C. MA psc(j)		
qwi(T)	(P)	1 Jan
White, W. A. qab		
qs	(P)	1 Jan
Whitworth, R. C. cfs(n)		
qs	(N)	1 Jan
Wilkinson, T. A. MBE		
BSc qab qs	(N)	1 Jan
Yapp, G. D. qs	(N)	1 Jan
Ager, J. N. MA		
psc(j)	(N)	1 July
Alexander, W. J. cfs(n)		
snc qs	(N)	1 July
Best, D. OBE BSc ALCM		
psc(j) tp	(P)	1 July

Blount, C. S. MA BSc		
FRIN MRAeS psc(j)		
asq cfs(n)*	(N)	1 July
Borland, G. A. psc(j)		
tp	(P)	1 July
Byford, A. J. MA MA		
psc(j)	(P)	1 July
Calvert, D. P. MBE BSc		
cfs qs	(P)	1 July
Cameron, I. MBE BSc		
psc(j) cfs*	(P)	1 July
Chalmers, I. D. MA		
psc(j) cfs	(P)	1 July
Cowieson, K. R. jsdc		
qab qs	(N)	1 July
Craig, I. J. MBE qs	(N)	1 July
Gibson, W. R. BSc		
psc(j) qwi(T)	(P)	1 July
Hedley, B. H. MBE		
psc(j) qwi	(P)	1 July
Jacobs, P. C. qab cfs(n)		
qs	(N)	1 July
Jochimsen, P. H. C. qab		
cfs qs	(P)	1 July
Kemsley, M. H. M. MBE		
BSc qs	(N)	1 July
Knight, M. asq qs	(P)	1 July
Laver, M. D. M. BA		
psc(j) cfs	(P)	1 July
Norton, C. J. R. DFC		
BSc psc(j) qwi	(P)	1 July
Offer, A. C. OBE cfs qwi		
qss1	(P)	1 July
Pearce, L. E. F. qab		
qs	(N)	1 July
Preston, D. L. qs	(N)	1 July
Reid, J. P. Q.		
psc(j)	(ENG)	1 July
Slater, R. C. psc(j)	(N)	1 July
Toner, A. psc(j)	(N)	1 July
Truss, K. P. cfs qs	(P)	1 July
Veitch, C. A. cfs qs	(P)	1 July
Walsh, J. M. BTech qab		
qs	(P)	1 July

2002

Allchorne, R. M. qwi		
qs	(P)	1 Jan
Bentley, D. A. qwi		
qs	(P)	1 Jan
Broadbent, J. R. MSc		
BEng psc(j) asq	(N)	1 Jan
Brooks, J. R. qab		
qs	(N)	1 Jan
Burr, J. DFC BSc cfs		
qs	(P)	1 Jan
Cass, D. N. psc	(P)	1 Jan

Chiddention, S. MBE		
cfs qs	(P)	1 Jan
Clifford, N. LLB psc(j)		
cfs	(P)	1 Jan
Cockbill, S. C. BSc qab		
qss	(N)	1 Jan
Comer, P. K. psc(j)		
cfs	(P)	1 Jan
Cookson, N. T. qs	(N)	1 Jan
Coxen, J. BSc cfs		
qs	(P)	1 Jan
Davies, J. H. qs	(N)	1 Jan
Gillan, J. qs	(AEO)	1 Jan
Guest, T. A. qs	(N)	1 Jan
Hallwood, J. Q. BSc cfs		
qs	(P)	1 Jan
Hayward, A. J. M. BSc		
MRAeS asq snc		
qs	(N)	1 Jan
Hughes, W. R.		
psc(j)	(AEO)	1 Jan
Jarmain, S. P. cfs		
qss	(P)	1 Jan
Lister-Tomlinson, A. D.		
qab qwi qs	(N)	1 Jan
Mitchell, C. T. psc(j)	(N)	1 Jan
Naismith, A. psc(j)		
cfs	(P)	1 Jan
Newby, T. asq cfs(n)		
snc qs	(N)	1 Jan
Noel, R. psc(j)	(N)	1 Jan
Prescott, J. C. psc(j)		
qwi(AD)	(N)	1 Jan
Purser, C. R. qs	(N)	1 Jan
Roberts, G. J. qs (ENG)		1 Jan
Rose, V. E. snc qs	(N)	1 Jan
Scott, C. M. AFC MPhil		
BA psc(j)	(P)	1 Jan
Seaward, G. L. psc(n)		
qwi	(N)	1 Jan
Wescott, M. R. J. qab		
qwi qs	(N)	1 Jan
Willey, N. W. cfs qs	(P)	1 Jan
Wilson, S. J. BA cfs(n)		
qs	(N)	1 Jan
Adlam, R. H. qwi qs	(P)	1 July
Barnfield, S. K. BSc		
qwi(T) qs	(N)	1 July
Beach, P. J. MBE BSc		
qab qwi(AD) qs	(N)	1 July
Blake, S. J. MBE		
psc(j) cfs	(P)	1 July
Conway, J. B. qs	(N)	1 July
Cruickshank, W. A. qwi		
qs	(P)	1 July
Dixon, J. M. AFC BSc		
qs	(P)	1 July
Frost, A. S. BSc		
psc(j)	(N)	1 July
Hill, C. R. qwi qs	(P)	1 July

Wing Commanders

2002—contd

James, W. A. W. MBE psc(j) qab cfs	(P)	1 July
Lee, D. J. F. BSc psc(j) cfs	(P)	1 July
Lee, N. P. D. BSc MRAeS qs	(P)	1 July
Mackay, A. J. M. cfs qs	(P)	1 July
Mitchell, A. G. BA psc(j) qab	(N)	1 July
Richards, S. I. BSc psc(j) qwi(AD)	(N)	1 July
Rochelle, S. P. DFC qs	(N)	1 July
Simpson, M. J. qwi(AD) qs	(P)	1 July
Willis, A. S. psc(j)	(P)	1 July

Squadron Leaders

1977

Webley, D. L. BTech cfs qss*	(P)	1 July

1978

Rouse, E. G. C. cfs qs	(P)	1 Jan

1979

Pegrum, R. G. qs	(N)	1 July

1980

Bruce, P. R. cfs	(P)	1 Jan
Miles, P. G. MBE BSc qs	(P)	1 Jan
Sitch, T. MBE snc	(N)	1 Jan
McCloud, R. C. qs	(P)	18 June
Blenkinsop, J. W.	(N)	1 July
Clemett, A. L. BSc snc qs	(N)	1 July
Walker, R. S. BA snc qs	(N)	1 July
Coryton, G. R. A.	(P)	2 Oct

1981

Cole, B. F. MBE qss	(N)	1 Jan
Hall, R. J. MRIN snc qs	(N)	1 Jan
Sullivan, L. qs	(N)	1 Jan
Waring, D. A. AFC qs	(P)	1 Jan

1982

Constable, E. C. MCMI cfs cfs(pn) qs	(P)	1 Jan
Hampton, I. J. snc	(N)	1 Jan
Laing, G. H. B. MA qss	(P)	1 Jan
Oldham, D. V. cfs qss	(P)	1 Jan
Pickering, R. J. BSc cfs qs	(P)	1 Jan
Busby, J. M. BSc cfs qs	(P)	1 July

King, R. F. MVO cfs (P) 1 July

1983

Baker, J. E. AFC cfs* qs	(P)	1 Jan
Cocking, R. K. BSc snc qs	(N)	1 Jan
Moody, R. M. cfs qss	(P)	1 Jan
Wright, J. T. qs	(N)	1 Jan
Buckland, M. R. G. BSc psc cfs	(P)	1 July
Coleman, P. MCMI cfs qss	(P)	1 July
Cranswick, C. E. BSc cfs qs	(P)	1 July
McNeill-Matthews, J. H. F. qwi qs	(N)	1 July
Melville-Jackson, A. qs	(P)	1 July
Mulligan, G. H. MBE MBA MCMI qs	(N)	1 July
Phillips, R. A.	(P)	1 July
Shields, R. M. MVO qss	(N)	1 July

1984

Collins, R. qs	(ENG)	1 Jan
Desai, A. K. MCMI snc qs	(N)	1 Jan
Goodman, D. F. psc(m) cfs	(P)	1 Jan
Ross, R. asq cfs(n) snc qs	(N)	1 Jan
Sharman, P. B. qss	(P)	1 Jan
Fallis, R. J. H. AFC cfs	(P)	1 July
Rounds, T. W. B. psc snc	(N)	1 July
Thomas, D. J. cfs qss	(P)	30 Aug
Clements, A. N. BSc(Eng) ACG cfs* cfs(t)*	(P)	10 Oct
Bennett, N. K.	(P)	15 Oct

1985

Horton, D. qs	(P)	1 Jan
Norris, D. J. snc qs	(N)	1 Jan
Reay, P. BSc asq snc qss	(N)	1 Jan

Squadron Leaders

1985—contd

Peeke, G. BSc MCIPD
snc qs   (N)   1 July

1986

Burrows, J. A. cfs(n)
snc qss   (N)   1 Jan
Gardiner, J. F. cfs
qs   (P)   1 Jan
Herbertson, P. S. qab
cfs(n) snc qs   (N)   1 Jan
Penny, A. T. snc qs (N)   1 Jan
Sinclair, C. M. BA
cfs   (P)   1 Jan
Bryan, M. J. BSc(Eng)
MRAeS MInstD
MCMI qab cfs qs (P)   1 July
Clark, A. McG. MRAeS
MCMI asq psc
snc   (N)   1 July
Clark, B. M. qss   (N)   1 July
Doig, C. G. qs   (N)   1 July
Hallett, P. Q. MA BSc
FRGS psc qab   (P)   1 July
Heath, C. cfs(n) snc
qs   (N)   1 July
Hudson, R. A. BA
CertEd asq cfs(n) snc
qss   (N)   6 Sept

1987

Beard, P. R. cfs(n) snc
qs   (N)   1 Jan
Burgoyne, H. C.
AFC   (P)   1 Jan
Cunningham, J. D.
MBE   (N)   1 Jan
Davies, P. A.
asq qs   (AEO)   1 Jan
Ford, R. B.   (N)   1 Jan
Hunt, M. J. cfs*   (P)   1 Jan
Irving, R. BSc cfs*
qs   (P)   1 Jan
King, R. L. qss   (N)   1 Jan
Rowley, C. M. MBE cfs
qss   (P)   1 Jan
Smith, P. S. BA asq
qs   (N)   1 Jan
Collis, J. J. cfs qss (P)   2 Apr
Aitken, R. T. cfs(n)
qs   (N)   15 Jun

Burges, R. R. cfs(n) snc
qs   (N)   1 July
Carver, C. C. psc asq
cfs(n) snc   (N)   1 July
Clephane, W. B. J.
MCMI qs   (N)   1 July
Coleman, I. M. cfs(n)
snc qss   (N)   1 July
Deane, J. H. asq qs (N)   1 July
Jones, D. K. qs   (N)   1 July
Landsburgh, A.
qs   (AEO)   1 July
Lunnon-Wood, A. K.
qwi(AD)   (P)   1 July
Reynolds, M. BSc cfs(n)
qs   (N)   1 July
Robinson, S.   (P)   1 July
Smith, S. P. cfs(n)* snc
qs   (N)   1 July
Thompson, R. W.
qss   (AEO)   1 July
Wilkinson, J. BSc cfs
qwi qss   (P)   1 July

1988

Aspinall, R. M. MA qab
qs   (P)   1 Jan
Bolton, M. W. MCMI
snc qss   (N)   1 Jan
Clapham, C. M. qs (N)   1 Jan
Frost, D. W. cfs qs (P)   1 Jan
Lund, R. M. MRAeS asq
qs   (P)   1 Jan
Macartney, J. K. cfs
qss   (P)   1 Jan
Medland, W. J. qss (N)   1 Jan
Milnes, R. A. BSc cfs(n)
qs   (N)   1 Jan
Parker, A. L. qs   (N)   1 Jan
Rees, M. S. qs   (P)   1 Jan
Sparrow, M. V. D. cfs
qss i*   (P)   1 Jan
Alexander, E. C. cfs
qs   (P)   1 July
Ankerson, R. BTech asq
qs   (N)   1 July
Boxall, A. C. W. cfs
qss   (P)   1 July
Dart, J. N. FIIP qab
qss   (N)   1 July
Fallon, R. D. MBE
qss   (N)   1 July
Jukes, M. H. BSc cfs
qss   (P)   1 July
Robinson, J. E. BA
cfs   (P)   1 July

Williams, S. G. snc
qss   (N)   1 July

1989

Boyle, A. BSc cfs(n) snc
qs   (N)   1 Jan
Byatt, N. E. qab qs (N)   1 Jan
Cooper, S. J. qs   (N)   1 Jan
Daughney, R. cfs(n) snc
qss   (N)   1 Jan
Druitt, R. K. BSc qs (P)   1 Jan
Francis, A. G.   (N)   1 Jan
Griffin, J. T.   (N)   1 Jan
Hodgson, I. snc   (N)   1 Jan
King, R. A. cfs qss (P)   1 Jan
MacIntosh, D. R. BA
qss   (P)   1 Jan
O'Gorman, P. D. snc fc
qss   (N)   1 Jan
Pugh-Davies, M. D. BA
BTech qs   (N)   1 Jan
Pynegar, P. G. AFC BSc
qss   (P)   1 Jan
Richardson, G. F. BSc
asq qab qs   (N)   1 Jan
Steer, D. H. snc qs (N)   1 Jan
Sully, A. K. qab cfs(n)*
snc qs   (N)   1 Jan
Thomson, D. H. MDA
BSc asq qs   (P)   1 Jan
Smyth, A. J. N. W.
BEcon   (P)   10 June
Batson, P. K. MBE
cfs*   (P)   1 July
Bradley, D. J. BSc qwi
qs   (P)   1 July
Graves, R. D. cfs qs (P)   1 July
Haslam, S. J. qs   (N)   1 July
Haworth, P. W. qs (N)   1 July
Muse, R. C. BSc cfs
qss   (P)   1 July
Roe, R. A. qs   (N)   1 July
Smith, K. W. snc qs (N)   1 July
Trace, B. E. MBE qs (N)   1 July
Howden, A. J.   (P)   1 Oct
Emmerson, K. M.   (P)   17 Dec

1990

Anderson, R. BSc
cfs(n)   (N)   1 Jan
Atherton, I. W. BSc qab
qss   (N)   1 Jan
Barrett, I. BSc qs   (N)   1 Jan
Boyd, C. J. MBE BSc
qwi   (P)   1 Jan
Collier, J. F.   (N)   1 Jan

Squadron Leaders

1990—contd

Crichton, C. H. qs	(N)	1 Jan
Davies, C. D. qs	(N)	1 Jan
Froude, C. L. BSc MCMI		
cfs qs	(P)	1 Jan
Gilday, E. J. W. BSc		
qs	(P)	1 Jan
Hall, R. P. W.	(N)	1 Jan
Knight, C. A. snc qs	(N)	1 Jan
Lillis, J. snc qss	(N)	1 Jan
Moody, J. K. BSc cfs(c)		
qss	(AEO)	1 Jan
Philip, A. F. MSc		
BSc(Eng) tp qs	(P)	1 Jan
Pierce, H. R. BA qs	(P)	1 Jan
Scarffe, M. G. qwi		
qs	(N)	1 Jan
Wilkin, R. cfs qs	(P)	1 Jan
Leckenby, P. J. MBE		
qs	(N)	15 Jan
Barrett, P. J. cfs qss	(P)	1 July
Bridger, S. P. psc		
qwi(T)	(P)	1 July
Cole, R. A. cfs qss	(P)	1 July
Gale, G. snc	(N)	1 July
Harrison, W. P. BSc		
cfs*	(P)	1 July
Leaviss, R. E. cfs		
qss	(P)	1 July
MacLennan, K. M.	(P)	1 July
McBain, S. B. snc	(N)	1 July
Mochan, J. P. qwi(T)		
snc qss	(N)	1 July
Neal, A. C.	(P)	1 July
Rosie, P. I. cfs qss	(P)	1 July
Vince, S. D. qss	(P)	1 July

1991

Barrett, G. J. BSc asq		
qs	(N)	1 Jan
Brakewell, C. S. snc	(N)	1 Jan
Brayn Smith, I. A. M.		
cfs qss	(P)	1 Jan
Byron, K. B. qss	(N)	1 Jan
Cairns, J. L. qss	(N)	1 Jan
Corry, A. qs	(AEO)	1 Jan
Cowling, G. P. BSc asq		
qss	(P)	1 Jan
Dancey, A. N. BA asq		
qs	(N)	1 Jan
Ewer, M. H. cfs qss	(P)	1 Jan
Gagen, S. P. qs	(AEO)	1 Jan
Gosling, A. T. BSc asq		
qs	(N)	1 Jan

Gunning, K. E. BSc cfs		
qs	(P)	1 Jan
Hedley, A. T. BA cfs qwi		
qss	(P)	1 Jan
McLeod, J. E. qs	(P)	1 Jan
Menage, C. P. qs	(N)	1 Jan
Morgan, D. T. BSc		
psc(j) cfs	(P)	1 Jan
Smithson, J. D. BSc cfs		
qss	(P)	1 Jan
Snowball, A. J. BSc asq		
snc qs	(N)	1 Jan
Stangroom, M. F.		
qs	(P)	1 Jan
Taylor, C. C.		
qwi(AD)	(P)	1 Jan
Shaw, D.	(N)	13 May
Bond, R. W. cfs qss	(P)	1 July
Cairns, J. BSc asq		
qs	(N)	1 July
Crump, D. G. BSc asq		
adp qs	(P)	1 July
Dooley, C. F. MBE BSc		
asq qss	(N)	1 July
Fauchon, T. T. qs	(P)	1 July
Marr, J. qss	(N)	1 July
Pick, K. E. qs	(AEO)	1 July
Robinson, B. G. M.		
DFC	(P)	1 July

1992

Brunning, I. BSc qs	(N)	1 Jan
Chatterton, R. J.		
qs	(AEO)	1 Jan
Lawless, A. A. BA		
qs	(P)	1 Jan
Lawrie, I. G. BEng		
qss	(N)	1 Jan
Ledward, D. J. qss	(N)	1 Jan
Mason, R. K. MBE BSc		
cfs(n) snc qs	(N)	1 Jan
Newton, R. J. BSc		
cfs(n)	(N)	1 Jan
Pennell, L. J. BSc cfs		
qs	(P)	1 Jan
Perrem T. J. AFC		
qss	(N)	1 Jan
Reeves, K. J. qwi(AD)		
qss	(N)	1 Jan
Reid, S. G. BSc cfs		
qs	(P)	1 Jan
Richards, M. E.		
qss	(AEO)	1 Jan
Roberts, D. G.	(P)	1 Jan
Sanders, J. T. qss	(N)	1 Jan
Wealleans, E. A.		
qwi	(P)	1 Jan
Bostock, S. P. qs	(N)	1 July

Christen, J. R. R. MEng		
BSc cfs qs	(P)	1 July
Hewitt, K. cfs	(P)	1 July
Milne, G. D. qs	(AEO)	1 July
Setterfield, M. J. qab		
cfs(n) snc qs	(N)	1 July
Steel, B. B. BSc asq adp		
qs	(N)	1 July
Wooldridge, J. B. BSc		
qab qs	(P)	1 July
Jones, C. A.	(N)	13 Sept

1993

Cairns, T. P. M. MBE		
cfs	(P)	1 Jan
Cunningham, M. asq		
qwi	(AEO)	1 Jan
Errington, M. E.		
qss	(AEO)	1 Jan
Morgan, C. N. B. MBE		
asq qs	(N)	1 Jan
Moss, G. P. qss	(AEO)	1 Jan
Piper, D. cfs cfs(g)		
qs	(P)	1 Jan
Smith, J. P. snc qss	(N)	1 Jan
Thomas, S. R. cfs qwi		
qss	(P)	1 Jan
Townend, R. J. S. cfs		
qss	(P)	1 Jan
Farley, R. F. qss	(P)	1 July
Fortune, T. F.	(AEO)	1 July
Russell, W. H. BSc		
qs	(N)	1 July
Smith, A. J. qs	(N)	1 July
Temple, M. L. L.	(P)	1 July
Thomas, C. C. BSc asq		
adp qs	(N)	1 July
Watson, N. M.	(P)	1 July

1994

Brain, I. B. asq	(N)	1 Jan
Davis, S.	(AEO)	1 Jan
Fisher, A. BSc qs	(N)	1 Jan
Girling, R. J. cfs qs	(P)	1 Jan
Griffin, G. cfs qss	(P)	1 Jan
Macey, G. qab qs(AEO)		1 Jan
Middleton, E.		
qwi(T)	(N)	1 Jan
Miller, A. D. BSc cfs(c)		
qs	(N)	1 Jan
Philpott, C. N. BSc cfs		
qs	(P)	1 Jan
Rae, D. J. BSc cfs		
qs	(P)	1 Jan
Richardson, A. D.	(P)	1 Jan
Ross, J. W. qs	(N)	1 Jan

Squadron Leaders

1994—contd

Simmons, I. J. cfs		
qs	(P)	1 Jan
Spirit, H. E. BSc		
cfs*	(P)	1 Jan
Stewart, R. J. snc		
qss	(N)	1 Jan
Thorne, G. T. qss	(N)	1 Jan
Tomlinson, A. J.		
qs	(ENG)	1 Jan
Triccas, A. P. qs	(N)	1 Jan
Trout, A. J. qss	(P)	1 Jan
Turner, R. J. cfs(n) snc		
qss	(N)	1 Jan
Carey, R. J. L. BSc qwi		
qwi(T) qs	(P)	1 July
Dryburgh, B. A.		
qs	(AEO)	1 July
Hillman, G. A. qs	(N)	1 July
Hochkins, S. D. qwi		
qss	(P)	1 July
Jenkins, J. K. psc(j)	(P)	1 July
Kingdon, A. A.	(ALM)	1 July
Lence, M. S. asq qs	(N)	1 July
Levick, P. asq qss	(N)	1 July
Lord, D. P. BSc cfs		
qs	(P)	1 July
Maskall, R. L. cfs qs	(P)	1 July
McKay, I. J. BEM	(ENG)	1 July
Neill, F. R. J. cfs qs	(P)	1 July
Nielsen, R. E. BA qwi		
qs	(P)	1 July
Niven, J. G. qwi qs	(N)	1 July
Reeves, J. W.	(AEO)	1 July
Revell, P. R.	(ENG)	1 July
Ross, D. McD. tp	(P)	1 July
Scorer, D. G. BSocSc		
cfs(n) qs	(N)	1 July
Spires, B.	(ALM)	1 July
Thompson, C. W. cfs		
qss	(P)	1 July

1995

Collier, P. R. S. BA snc		
qs	(N)	1 Jan
Ede, H. snc qss	(N)	1 Jan
Harcourt, S. J. R. cfs		
qs	(P)	1 Jan
Hawley, M. D. BSc		
qs	(N)	1 Jan
Hunt, G. I. qss	(N)	1 Jan
Marshall, L. asq qs	(N)	1 Jan
Meadows, N. P.	(P)	1 Jan
Middleton, D. J. qs	(P)	1 Jan

Morgan, G. M. BSc asq		
qs	(N)	1 Jan
Sayers, S. R. MA asq		
qs	(N)	1 Jan
Solomon, A. G.		
qs	(AEO)	1 Jan
Sommerville, R. A. cfs		
qs	(P)	1 Jan
Southcott, G. P. asq		
qs	(AEO)	1 Jan
Stainforth, M. A. BSc		
asq cfs(n) snc		
qss	(N)	1 Jan
Torrance, I. A. cfs		
qs	(P)	1 Jan
Vallance, M. H.		
qs	(ENG)	1 Jan
Wheeler, T. J. cfs		
qs	(P)	1 Jan
Bland, P. C.	(AEO)	1 July
Chambers, P. J. asq		
qss1	(N)	1 July
Gegg, J. D. J. cfs(n) snc		
ac	(N)	1 July
Houlton, J. A. D. cfs		
cfs(pn) qss	(P)	1 July
Martin, P. BA cfs*	(P)	1 July
Pierson, R. M. cfs		
cfs(pn) qss	(P)	1 July
Shaw, A. J. BEng cfs		
qss	(P)	1 July
Waudby, S. L. cfs		
qs	(P)	1 July
Williams, D. I. qs	(P)	1 July
Groombridge, M. J.		
BSc PGCE cfs		
qss	(P)	5 July

1996

Brown, G. B. cfs	(P)	1 Jan
Floyd, J. R. MA cfs*		
qss	(P)	1 Jan
Green, A. D. OBE BA		
psc(AUS) qs	(P)	1 Jan
Grout, M. J. cfs(n)	(N)	1 Jan
Hewson, P. W. BA qs		
cfs(n)	(N)	1 Jan
Knowles, D. J. BA cfs		
cfs(g) qss	(P)	1 Jan
Marshall, S. BA qwi		
qs	(P)	1 Jan
Martin, P. cfs qs	(P)	1 Jan
McMahon, R. M. qs	(N)	1 Jan
Riches, P. M. snc	(P)	1 Jan
Rose, R. C. cfs	(P)	1 Jan
Smyth, P. J. psc(j)		
cfs(n)	(N)	1 Jan
Sutcliffe, D. M. cfs	(P)	1 Jan

Trask, L. J. MBE BSc cfs		
qs	(P)	1 Jan
Muskett, A. J. MBE qab		
qwi qs	(P)	20 Apr
Atkins, R. F. BSc asq		
qs	(N)	1 July
Bennett, A. A. BSc		
qs	(P)	1 July
Benson, N. J. qs	(N)	1 July
Bohill, W. P. BSc		
qwi(T) qs	(P)	1 July
Bowen, D. K. B. qs	(P)	1 July
Doyle, G. BSc cfs		
qs	(P)	1 July
Falvey, M. K. qab cfs		
qs	(P)	1 July
Gray, A. P. psc(j) cfs	(P)	1 July
Head, R. BSc cfs		
qss	(P)	1 July
Hunt, B. D. qwi qss	(P)	1 July
Legg, D. A. C. MBE qab		
qs	(P)	1 July
Little, A. H. cfs qss	(P)	1 July
Luck, C. J. MBE cfs		
qs	(P)	1 July
Oddy, R. T. snc	(N)	1 July
Stanway, M. F. qss	(P)	1 July
Thrale, T. qs	(N)	1 July
Jones, A. psc(j) qab	(P)	30 Sept
Bryant, I.	(P)	7 Dec

1997

Andrews, M. R. asq		
qss	(AEO)	1 Jan
Baker, A. K. AIB cfs qhti		
qs	(P)	1 Jan
Baxter, G. L. qs	(N)	1 Jan
Blockley, M. A. qab		
qs	(AEO)	1 Jan
Boyle, B. qs	(N)	1 Jan
Brailsford, S. MVO		
qs	(N)	1 Jan
Brazier, C. E. J. psc(j)		
qwi(T)	(N)	1 Jan
Brooks, J. H.		
cfs(c)	(AEO)	1 Jan
Cooper, D. G. cfs qwi		
qss	(P)	1 Jan
Davies, H. B. cfs(n) snc		
qss	(N)	1 Jan
Deas, E. J. cfs(n)	(N)	1 Jan
Gillies, S. C. qs	(P)	1 Jan
Gray, K. R. BA qss	(N)	1 Jan
Harland, M. C. asq		
cfs(n)* qs	(N)	1 Jan
Head, J. S. BSc qs	(N)	1 Jan
Heames, C. V. J. cfs	(P)	1 Jan

107

Squadron Leaders

1997—contd

Huffington, M. C. BSc		
qs	(N)	1 Jan
Hughes, K. L. W.		
qs	(AEO)	1 Jan
Hunter, C. T. qab qs	(P)	1 Jan
Lawson, J. BSc qs	(N)	1 Jan
Lloyd, S. J. BA asq		
qss	(N)	1 Jan
Lord, D. K. MBE		
qs	(AEO)	1 Jan
McMillen, P. T.		
qss	(AEO)	1 Jan
Notman, S. R. qs	(N)	1 Jan
Smart, M. A. qs	(N)	1 Jan
Stewart, D. J. CertEd		
qs	(ALM)	1 Jan
Thomson, A. J.	(AEO)	1 Jan
Toft, M. C. qs	(N)	1 Jan
Traynor, E. J. qss	(AEO)	1 Jan
Turnbull, D. T. BSc qab		
cfs qs	(P)	1 Jan
Walters, A. J. C. BSc		
qs	(P)	1 Jan
Wells, G. R. qs	(N)	1 Jan
Wills, C. J. qwi(AD)		
qss	(N)	1 Jan
Young, R. J. qss (ENG)		1 Jan
Pitcher, S. J. qs	(P)	1 Mar
Arden, J. P. qs	(N)	1 July
Barley, M. P. BA qwi(T)		
qs	(N)	1 July
Baxter, I. P. qs	(N)	1 July
Beardmore, M. J.		
cfs	(P)	1 July
Below, T. D. Q. BSc		
psc(j) tp	(P)	1 July
Best, P. K. cfs qss	(P)	1 July
Blair, R. C. qwi qs	(P)	1 July
Brown, M. O. psc(j) qab		
cfs	(P)	1 July
Calder, J. M. BSc qab		
qs	(N)	1 July
Clark, G. qss	(N)	1 July
Cochrane, A. W.		
qwi(AD) qs	(N)	1 July
Cole, M. J. qs	(ALM)	1 July
Crosby, D. M. M.	(P)	1 July
Dalley, G. P. BA qs	(P)	1 July
Dyson, R. K. cfs qs	(P)	1 July
Evans, P. MA BA qwi(T)		
qs	(P)	1 July
Goatham, J. M. qs	(P)	1 July
Hancock, J. P. MRIN		
qs	(N)	1 July

Hardy-Gillings, B.		
qss	(N)	1 July
Hawkins, R. L. MBE	(N)	1 July
Hill, A. P. qwi qs	(P)	1 July
Hindmarsh, S. qab		
qs	(N)	1 July
Huckstep, C. R. DFC MA		
FRGS tp qs	(P)	1 July
Huggett, J. P.	(N)	1 July
Lawrence, R. H. cfs		
qss	(P)	1 July
Lenihan, P. J. D. BSc		
qwi(T) qs	(N)	1 July
MacCormac, R. M. J.		
qwi qs	(P)	1 July
MacKenzie, K. J.	(P)	1 July
Parker, M. R. qss	(N)	1 July
Ramsden, C. P. BSc		
qss	(P)	1 July
Read, S. J. qs	(N)	1 July
Rust, T. J. cfs qss	(P)	1 July
Sampson, M. E. qwi		
qs	(P)	1 July
Simpson, T. D. cfs		
qss	(P)	1 July
Snowden, M. cfs	(P)	1 July
Swindlehurst, W. (AEO)		1 July
Waterfall, G. M. qwi		
qs	(P)	1 July
Wilson, W. J. qs	(P)	1 July

1998

Adams, R. M. asq		
qs	(N)	1 Jan
Andrew, D. R. qs	(N)	1 Jan
Armstrong, D. R. qwi		
qss	(P)	1 Jan
Bailey, R. C. cfs qs	(P)	1 Jan
Balaam, A. W. L. BSc		
qs	(P)	1 Jan
Barker, R.	(N)	1 Jan
Barr, N. J. MBE qs	(N)	1 Jan
Beardmore, S. M.		
qwi(T) qtm qs	(N)	1 Jan
Bennington, T. BSc cfs		
qs	(P)	1 Jan
Brown, M. F. cfs qs	(P)	1 Jan
Bruce, R. P. BEng		
qss	(P)	1 Jan
Bullement, T. J. BSc		
qs	(P)	1 Jan
Burch, S. C. B. cfs		
qs	(P)	1 Jan
Calderwood, L. D. cfs		
qss	(P)	1 Jan
Cannard, M. W. qs	(N)	1 Jan
Chaskin, S. R. qs	(N)	1 Jan

Clark, R. J. S. G. MBE		
BA cfs qs	(P)	1 Jan
Cobb, M. R. BSc		
qwi(AD) qss	(P)	1 Jan
Cooper, D. J. E. BEng		
qs	(N)	1 Jan
Craib, J. W. qab		
qs	(AEO)	1 Jan
Cryer, N. G. MBE		
qs	(N)	1 Jan
Da'Silva, C. D. qs	(N)	1 Jan
Elliott, E. A. C. MA		
qs	(P)	1 Jan
Fisher, L. qab qwi		
qs	(N)	1 Jan
Foote, D. A. cfs qss	(P)	1 Jan
Foote, S. J. BSc cfs		
qs	(P)	1 Jan
Forbes, R. W.	(AEO)	1 Jan
Ford, C. J.	(P)	1 Jan
Gent, A. J. qwi qss	(P)	1 Jan
Gray, J. J. cfs qss1	(P)	1 Jan
Griffiths, H. M. BSc		
qs	(N)	1 Jan
Grime, J. R. A. qs	(P)	1 Jan
Harrison, P. K. qwi		
qss	(P)	1 Jan
Hayler, S. D. BSc cfs*		
qs	(P)	1 Jan
Hinchcliffe, R. A. MBA		
BSc qss	(N)	1 Jan
Jackson, B. G. BSc		
qs	(P)	1 Jan
James, R. S. MBE		
qs	(N)	1 Jan
Jones, C. cfs(n)*	(N)	1 Jan
Jones, C. qab cfs(n)*		
qs	(N)	1 Jan
Lovell, A. B. cfs qs	(P)	1 Jan
Lovell, R. H. BA	(N)	1 Jan
Lumb, D. M. V. qwi(T)		
MacFarlane, I. J. M.		
CGC DFC qs	(P)	1 Jan
Marson, A. C. snc		
qss	(N)	1 Jan
Padmore, T. C. qs	(N)	1 Jan
Pinner, A. C. BSc qwi		
qs	(P)	1 Jan
Richardson, I. BSc		
qs	(N)	1 Jan
Ross, R. A. BSc qs	(P)	1 Jan
Saunders, M. A. qab		
qwi(T) qs	(P)	1 Jan
Smith, A. G. qab qs	(N)	1 Jan
Steel, A. qss	(AEO)	1 Jan
Taylor, P. J. BSc qs	(N)	1 Jan
Thomas, D. G. BSc		
qs	(N)	1 Jan

Squadron Leaders

1998—contd

Thomas, G. E. MBE
FRIN cfs(n)   (N)   1 Jan
Torrance, A. I. MacA.
qs   (N)   1 Jan
Trapp, D. G. qab qs   (N)   1 Jan
Vagg, M. J. qhti qs   (P)   1 Jan
Waddington, D. J.
qwi(T) qs   (P)   1 Jan
Walters-Morgan, R.
qwi(AD) qs   (N)   1 Jan
Ward, P. M. BSc cfs
qss   (P)   1 Jan
Webber, W. H. J. BSc
qs   (P)   1 Jan
White, D. K. BSc qs   (P)   1 Jan
Wilson, J. M. BSc
qs   (P)   1 Jan
Pilling, J. A. BSc qwi
qss   (P)   25 May
Barrett, T. A. qwi qs (P)   1 July
Bartlett, P. J. BEng
qs   (P)   1 July
Boulden, A.   (P)   1 July
Boyle, S. J. BSc qab
qs   (N)   1 July
Brass, A. J. BEng cfs
qss   (P)   1 July
Bruce, G. BSc asq
qss   (N)   1 July
Buckingham, S. C. BA
qss   (P)   1 July
Carter, D. E. MBE
cfs   (P)   1 July
Coope, A. J. BEng cfs
qs   (P)   1 July
Costello, J. M. BSc
qss   (P)   1 July
Counter, G. C. qs   (N)   1 July
Cowie, A. J. BA asq
qs   (N)   1 July
Craig, A. W. D. BSc
qs   (P)   1 July
Cross, B. J. qss   (P)   1 July
Dolding, A. E. cfs
qss   (P)   1 July
Dunn, L. G. BSc qs   (P)   1 July
Evans, J. D. cfs(c)   (N)   1 July
Ferrier, J. A. qss   (N)   1 July
Foster, P. cfs(n) qs (N)   1 July
Francis, I. R. BSc
qss   (N)   1 July
Gair, G. C. qs   (P)   1 July
Gallie, D. W. qss   (P)   1 July
Girdwood, K. R. H. BSc
cfs qs   (P)   1 July

Hargreaves, I. J. qwi
qs   (P)   1 July
Harrison, J. J. qs   (P)   1 July
Hay, N. J. qwi(T) qs (N)   1 July
Hine, A. C. MA psc(j)
qwi(T)   (P)   1 July
Hoole, P. qs   (AEO) 1 July
Hornby, R. cfs(n) qs (N)   1 July
Jeffrey, A. K. qwi(T)
qs   (N)   1 July
Kellett, A. J. C. BSc cfs
qss   (P)   1 July
Kennett, P. D. qwi(T)
qs   (N)   1 July
Leach, S. C. BSc cfs
qs   (P)   1 July
Lewis, K. A. BEng qwi
qs   (P)   1 July
Maunder, C. N. J. BEng
qab qwi(T) qs   (P)   1 July
McCarthy, K. R. BSc cfs
qss   (P)   1 July
McFarlane, A. J. cfs(n)
qs   (N)   1 July
Moran, E. M. BSc
qss   (N)   1 July
Neighbour, J. D. E.   (P)   1 July
Peace, C. M. qs   (N)   1 July
Postlethwaite, D. BEd
cfs(n) qs   (N)   1 July
Pottle, H. W. AFC*   (P)   1 July
Raffles, I.   (N)   1 July
Savage, S.   (N)   1 July
Shell, S. J. psc(j)   (P)   1 July
Sullivan, J. M. qwi
qs   (P)   1 July
Wilcock, N. J. BSc
cfs   (P)   1 July
Wistow, M. R. cfs(n)*
qss   (N)   1 July

1999

Annas, D. R. cfs(n)
qs   (N)   1 Jan
Barnett, J. R. qss   (P)   1 Jan
Barrett, L. F. qs   (N)   1 Jan
Bennett, L. J. BSc
qwi(T) qs   (P)   1 Jan
Bishop, N. A. qs   (N)   1 Jan
Bonner, P. B. BSc
MRAeS asq qss   (N)   1 Jan
Bostock, P. J. BA qs (N)   1 Jan
Brennan, B. qss   (N)   1 Jan
Brennan, S. D. F. BA
qab qs   (P)   1 Jan
Butler, T. S. qs   (P)   1 Jan
Collins, N. D. cfs
qss   (P)   1 Jan

Couston, T. qwi qss   (P)   1 Jan
Cracroft, P. N. BEng
qwi(AD) qs   (P)   1 Jan
Cunningham, W. J. BSc
cfs qs   (P)   1 Jan
Daft, R. E. qs   (P)   1 Jan
Duguid, I. W. qwi
qs   (P)   1 Jan
Dunne, J. P. asq qs   (N)   1 Jan
Easthope, N. C. V.
cfs   (P)   1 Jan
Evans, I. A. qss   (N)   1 Jan
Firth, D. S. J. BSc cfs
qss   (P)   1 Jan
Forrester, C. W. J.
BSc(Eng) qwi(AD)
qs   (N)   1 Jan
Gow, D. G. BSc cfs
qss   (P)   1 Jan
Gray, D. M. cfs qss   (P)   1 Jan
Harris, T. N. qwi(T)
qs   (N)   1 Jan
Hayward, S. A. qss   (P)   1 Jan
Hazell, D. J. qs   (P)   1 Jan
Hewitt, J. P. qs   (N)   1 Jan
Heycock, S. A. BSc
qs   (N)   1 Jan
Hockenhull, W. J.
qwi(AD) qs   (P)   1 Jan
Holmes, D. qs   (AEO) 1 Jan
Hughes, A. BSc cfs   (P)   1 Jan
Hunt, E. S. J. qs   (P)   1 Jan
Huskisson, E. S. BSc
cfs* qs   (P)   1 Jan
Kelly, G. S. BSc cfs
qs   (P)   1 Jan
Kemp, B. V. BEng tp
qss   (P)   1 Jan
Kendall, P. A. BSc
qs   (N)   1 Jan
Laing, I. cfs qs   (P)   1 Jan
Lalley, M. T. cfs qss (P)   1 Jan
Littley, B. qs   (ALM) 1 Jan
Lovely, P. qs   (N)   1 Jan
Luck, R. K. cfs qhti
qs   (P)   1 Jan
Maginnis, R. J. qs   (N)   1 Jan
Manwaring, M. T.
qs   (N)   1 Jan
McEvoy, S. BA qs   (P)   1 Jan
Muir, I. BSc cfs(n) snc
qss   (N)   1 Jan
Nicholson, F. J. BSc
qs   (P)   1 Jan
Nicholson, P. D. BSc
qs   (N)   1 Jan
O'Connor, G. M. qab
cfs(n) qs   (N)   1 Jan

109

Squadron Leaders

1999—contd

Payling, C. A. PhD BSc
LLB CPhys CEng
MInstP asq qs   (N)   1 Jan
Richardson, M. P.   (N)   1 Jan
Ridley, M. J. tp qss   (P)   1 Jan
Sanderson, R. V. BSc
qss   (N)   1 Jan
Sheldon, M. cfs qss   (P)   1 Jan
Smith, D. W. qss   (P)   1 Jan
Staunton, G. J. BSc asq
qss   (N)   1 Jan
Verner, A. D. cfs(n) snc
qss   (N)   1 Jan
Wain, S. qs   (N)   1 Jan
Wallace, P. J. BSc
qwi(T) qs   (N)   1 Jan
Warmington, N. B. BSc
cfs qss   (P)   1 Jan
Webster, P. E. qab
qs   (N)   1 Jan
Wensley, C. C. cfs(n)
snc   (N)   1 Jan
Whitmore, M. J. BA
qs   (N)   1 Jan
Wilkins, P. cfs(t) qs   (N)   1 Jan
Witcombe, T. J. AFC cfs
qs   (P)   1 Jan
Aston, M. R. asq
qss   (AEO)   1 July
Ball, S. W. BSc cfs
qs   (P)   1 July
Bowles, S. J. MBE
qss   (N)   1 July
Brown, G. G.   (N)   1 July
Bundock, P.   (ALM)   1 July
Charlton, G. R. cfs
qss   (P)   1 July
Collier, S. J. qss   (P)   1 July
Colquhoun, W. M. BA
tp cfs   (P)   1 July
D'Aubyn, J. A. BSc cfs
qss   (P)   1 July
Dickson, A. G. qs   (N)   1 July
Dowdeswell, J. L. BSc
cfs qs   (P)   1 July
Ferguson, I. D. cfs
qss   (P)   1 July
Firth, S. T. BSc qss   (N)   1 July
Fowell, J. P. BSc
qss   (P)   1 July
Galletly, D. R. W. BSc
cfs qs   (P)   1 July
Gerrard, P. S. BSc cfs
qs   (P)   1 July

Haynes, J. M. BA qab
cfs qs   (P)   1 July
Houghton, D. A. cfs(n)
qs   (N)   1 July
Huskie, A. J. MBE   (P)   1 July
Hutchinson, P. T. asq
qab qss   (N)   1 July
Kosogorin, P. tp cfs*
qss   (P)   1 July
Linter, J. E. MA qwi(T)
qs   (N)   1 July
Lyons, T. P. BEng tp qwi
qs   (P)   1 July
Maddison, R. C. cfs
qs   (P)   1 July
March, K. C. W. cfs
qss   (P)   1 July
McAuley, D. qss   (P)   1 July
Millbank, J. MacD.
qs   (AEO)   1 July
Newnham, N. cfs qwi
qs   (P)   1 July
Parsons, J. J. qs   (N)   1 July
Roberts, G. L. qwi
qs   (P)   1 July
Robinson, P. BSc
qwi(T) qss   (P)   1 July
Ross-Thomson, A. J. tp
qss   (P)   1 July
Rowley, A. E. asq
qss   (N)   1 July
Scopes, N. R. MA cfs
qs   (P)   1 July
Somers-Cocks, R. V. BA
cfs(n) qs   (N)   1 July
Spence, F. qs   (N)   1 July
Squires, P. J. M. BEng
qwi qs   (P)   1 July
Stamp, D. A. qs   (P)   1 July
Temple, J. G. cfs qs   (P)   1 July
Tickle, S. R. qwi qss   (P)   1 July
Ward, P. L. qs   (N)   1 July
Watson, J. R. qs (ALM)   1 July
Wharmby, P. W. BSc
qwi qs   (P)   1 July
Whatmore, A. G.   (N)   1 July
Wigham, R. C. BSc cfs
qss   (P)   1 July
Williams, S. T. BA qhti
qs   (P)   1 July
Wood, M. A. cfs ac
snc(n)   (N)   1 July
Wright, M. J. BSc
qs   (N)   1 July

2000

Brammer, C. M. BSc
qss   (N)   1 Jan

Buckley, J. P. qss (AEO)   1 Jan
Burley, G. cfs(n)
snc   (N)   1 Jan
Carr, S. R. cfs qs   (P)   1 Jan
Cherry, D. F. asq
snc   (N)   1 Jan
Clarke, D. J. BA asq
qss   (N)   1 Jan
Clover, B. J. qss   (P)   1 Jan
Colligan, G. R. BEng
qwi qss   (P)   1 Jan
Culpin, R. W. qwi(AD)
qss   (P)   1 Jan
Cunningham, P. M. BSc
cfs qss   (P)   1 Jan
Davies, G. C. qss   (N)   1 Jan
Day, M. N. qs   (P)   1 Jan
Devenish, S. A. BEng
qs   (N)   1 Jan
Dowling, S. N.
BSc(Econ) qwi
qs   (P)   1 Jan
Dunsmore, S. M. BSc
cfs(n) qs   (N)   1 Jan
Dyche, M. W. MA qss
i   (N)   1 Jan
Gillespie, A. K. BSc qab
qwi(AD) qs   (N)   1 Jan
Gladston, J. G. MBE
BEng qs   (P)   1 Jan
Holden, A. R. BSc asq
qss   (N)   1 Jan
Hooper, R. T. cfs qs   (P)   1 Jan
Howell, R. J. qwi(T)
qs   (N)   1 Jan
Innes, A. J. qwi(AD)
qs   (P)   1 Jan
Jacobs, D. M. H. BSc
cfs qs   (P)   1 Jan
Jeffries, M. J. qs   (N)   1 Jan
Knight, R. A. asq qs   (N)   1 Jan
Lawson, D. A. BSc
qwi(AD) qs   (N)   1 Jan
Mansfield, J. J. qs   (N)   1 Jan
Matthews, R. qwi
qs   (P)   1 Jan
Mayhew, G. M. D. qwi
qs   (P)   1 Jan
McLaren, T. M.
qs   (AEO)   1 Jan
Meikleham, F. G.
cfs   (P)   1 Jan
Muir, R. asq qss (ENG)   1 Jan
Parry, G. W. H. BSc
qs   (P)   1 Jan
Pell, G. W. Y. cfs qs   (P)   1 Jan
Perrett, S. D. cfs
qss1   (P)   1 Jan
Preece, W. R. asq
qs   (N)   1 Jan

Squadron Leaders

2000—contd

Presland, R. D. BEng		
qwi(T) qss1	(P)	1 Jan
Price, R. S. BSc cfs		
qss	(P)	1 Jan
Pritchard, E. J. qab		
qss	(AEO)	1 Jan
Rees, R. G. qss2	(P)	1 Jan
Richardson, P. T. BSc		
qss	(P)	1 Jan
Rooney, A. J. BSc		
qss	(P)	1 Jan
Sanders, R. G. qs	(N)	1 Jan
Shakespeare, P. B.		
BEng qwi(T) qss	(P)	1 Jan
Shepherd, D. J. (AEO)		1 Jan
Skinner, A. W. M. BSc		
asq qs	(N)	1 Jan
Smith, A. M. cfs(t)		
qs	(N)	1 Jan
Snashall, S. M. BEng		
qhti qss	(P)	1 Jan
Sutton, R. C. cfs(n)		
qss	(N)	1 Jan
Thomas, M. L. BSc cfs		
qss	(P)	1 Jan
Tinworth, M. R. qab		
qs	(N)	1 Jan
Tucker, M. P. BSc asq		
qs	(N)	1 Jan
Turner, J. qwi(T) qs	(N)	1 Jan
Vallely, I. F. qs	(P)	1 Jan
Vickers, S. qs	(N)	1 Jan
Walsh, I. J. BSc asq		
qs	(N)	1 Jan
Ward, J. D. R. BSc qwi		
qss	(P)	1 Jan
Warren, M. D. A.		
qss	(N)	1 Jan
Wells, R. P. D. BSc		
cfs(n) qs	(N)	1 Jan
Wigston, M. MA qwi(T)		
qs	(P)	1 Jan
Wren, J. D. cfs qs	(P)	1 Jan
Yates, T. J. qs	(AEO)	1 Jan
Attridge, J. J. qwi(AD)		
qss	(ALM)	1 July
Barnes, P. J. M.	(ALM)	1 July
Barr, A. BSc qhti qs	(P)	1 July
Bendall, D. H.	(P)	1 July
Cook, G. C. qs	(P)	1 July
Dudman, D. A. qs	(P)	1 July
Edwards, G. D. BSc cfs		
qs	(P)	1 July
Evans, H. F. J. MBE PhD		
BA qss	(P)	1 July

Gorringe, M. J. BA		
qs	(N)	1 July
Goulding, N. B.	(P)	1 July
Hargrave, B. W. BSc		
qss	(N)	1 July
Howard, S. M. BSc cfs		
qss	(P)	1 July
Humphreys, M. S. BSc		
qwi(T) qs	(N)	1 July
Humphries, R. W. tp		
qs	(P)	1 July
Hunt, D. J. fc qss	(N)	1 July
Hunter, J. H. BSc cfs		
qs	(P)	1 July
Jobling, C. L. qss	(N)	1 July
Johnstone, R. W. S.		
BSc qab qs	(P)	1 July
Kevan, R. M. BA cfs(n)		
qs	(N)	1 July
Knight, R. M. qss	(P)	1 July
Lushington, S. F. cfs		
qcc	(P)	1 July
Mace, C. J. MCMI		
qs	(P)	1 July
Makepeace, A. D. E.		
BSc tp cfs qs	(P)	1 July
Martin, A. T. BSc		
qwi(AD) qs	(P)	1 July
Meston, J. M. qss	(N)	1 July
Milne, J. D. DFC qwi		
qss	(P)	1 July
Morris, P. A. cfs qss	(P)	1 July
Morrison, A. F. BSc		
cfs	(P)	1 July
Myers, A. M. qwi(T)		
qss2	(P)	1 July
Nelson, N. J.	(ENG)	1 July
O'Brien, S. T. MA MSc		
LLB qs	(N)	1 July
O'Connor, A. C. cfs		
qss	(P)	1 July
Paines, J. D. B. MSc BA		
tp qss	(P)	1 July
Parker, G. D. A. BSc		
qcc	(P)	1 July
Pattle, R. E. G. BA		
qss2	(P)	1 July
Pearce, M. D. qss	(P)	1 July
Platt, D. asq qss	(N)	1 July
Plumb, S. P. BA qs	(N)	1 July
Pout, C. L. qab cfs(n)		
qs	(N)	1 July
Preston-Whyte, R. A.		
BA qss	(P)	1 July
Reeves, S. E. BEng		
qwi(T) qss	(P)	1 July
Richards, R. P.		
qss	(AEO)	1 July
Robinson, M. N.		
BA	(N)	1 July

Rose, M. B. qs	(N)	1 July
Rovery, S. W. BA cfs		
qss	(P)	1 July
Rundle, N. C. cfs(c) qhti		
qss	(ALM)	1 July
Sall, I. qs	(ENG)	1 July
Sanders, P. S. BSc asq		
qs	(N)	1 July
Seal, C. T. BPharm cfs		
qss	(P)	1 July
Senior, D. A. qs	(N)	1 July
Sharman, P. R. BSc qwi		
qss1	(P)	1 July
Sheppeck, G. J. qs	(P)	1 July
Shinner, A. M. BSc cfs		
qs	(P)	1 July
Slingsby, S. B. BEng cfs		
qs	(P)	1 July
Smith, A. P. qss	(P)	1 July
Smith, H. F. MA cfs		
qwi(T) qs	(P)	1 July
Smith, I. W. qs	(N)	1 July
Smith, N. E. MA		
qcc	(P)	1 July
Smith, P. A. qs	(N)	1 July
Stringer, J. J. BA qwi		
qss2	(P)	1 July
Strode, T. M. qhti		
qs	(P)	1 July
Taylor, L. S. BEng qwi		
qcc	(P)	1 July
Thomas, A. S.	(N)	1 July
Timbrell, C. P.		
qss2	(AEO)	1 July
Tunnard, J. J. BSc asq		
qss	(N)	1 July
Watson, C. S. H. asq		
snc	(N)	1 July
Winwright, G. A. cfs(t)		
qs	(N)	1 July
Wood, D. R. W. BA		
qwi(T) qs	(P)	1 July

2001

Atkinson, P. G.	(P)	1 Jan
Ball, J. D. qwi(AD)		
qss	(N)	1 Jan
Bolton, P. M. qss	(N)	1 Jan
Bracken, M. J. qs	(N)	1 Jan
Brand, C. W. BSc		
qss	(N)	1 Jan
Brindley, R. A. cfs(n)		
qss	(N)	1 Jan
Brookes, K. P. qs	(N)	1 Jan
Burnell, P. N. BTech		
qcc	(N)	1 Jan
Carter, T. P. qs	(AEO)	1 Jan

111

Squadron Leaders

2001—contd

Cheseldene-Culley, R.
  A. qss (N) 1 Jan
Clancy, J. M. E. qss (P) 1 Jan
Clarke, J. W. qs (N) 1 Jan
Clarke, S. R. BSc qs (N) 1 Jan
Cochrane, J. G. qwi(T)
  qss (N) 1 Jan
Cormack, H. R. C. BA
  qhti qs (N) 1 Jan
Cowie, M. J. qs (ALM) 1 Jan
Crook, R. J. M. BTech
  qss (N) 1 Jan
Davis, G. J. qwi(T)
  qss (N) 1 Jan
Dingwall, I. R. qss (P) 1 Jan
Donnelly, I. D. qss (N) 1 Jan
Edmunds, K. W. (AEO) 1 Jan
Elliott, S. W. (ENG) 1 Jan
Gregory, S. P. qs (P) 1 Jan
Griffin, S. J. asq
  qss (AEO) 1 Jan
Gunn, M. J. BSc asq
  qs (N) 1 Jan
Harrington, N. qss (N) 1 Jan
Hough, C. R. qss (P) 1 Jan
House, G. K. qss (P) 1 Jan
Hulley, S. F. qs (N) 1 Jan
Johnson, D. A. N. BEng
  qwi qcc (P) 1 Jan
Kennish, B. E. qab
  qss (N) 1 Jan
Kettles, A. W. BSc cfs
  qss (P) 1 Jan
Lawson, R. J. tp
  qss (P) 1 Jan
Lay, C. J. qss (P) 1 Jan
Marston, I. C. BSc cfs
  qs (P) 1 Jan
Mason, R. D. qs (P) 1 Jan
McBryde, D. W.
  qwi(AD) qss (P) 1 Jan
McNulty, M. D. MSc
  MCGI MRIN asq
  qss (N) 1 Jan
Mepham, R. P.
  qs (AEO) 1 Jan
Molsom, S. J. qss (P) 1 Jan
Nelson, A. W.
  qss (AEO) 1 Jan
O'Hora, G. A.
  qss (AEO) 1 Jan
Palmer, A. D. BSc
  qss1 (P) 1 Jan
Parker, T. J. tp cfs (P) 1 Jan
Platt, C. qwi(T) qs (N) 1 Jan

Potter, A. J. AFC
  qss (P) 1 Jan
Potter, D. J. A. BA
  qs (N) 1 Jan
Prior, S. C. qs (P) 1 Jan
Provost, J. D. cfs
  qss1 (P) 1 Jan
Puncher, A. W. (N) 1 Jan
Purves, N. L. BSc
  qss (P) 1 Jan
Rea, J. C. qs (N) 1 Jan
Rechten, I. O. H.
  cfs* (P) 1 Jan
Robinson, I. D. qwi(T)
  qss (P) 1 Jan
Russell, B. L. BTech cfs
  qss (P) 1 Jan
Sawyer, G. P. BEng cfs
  qss (P) 1 Jan
Scott, D. W. qs (N) 1 Jan
Smith, G. N. qwi(T)
  qs (N) 1 Jan
Smith, T. G. asq
  qss (N) 1 Jan
Smyth, P. J. snc (N) 1 Jan
Stevens, C. P. qwi
  qss (P) 1 Jan
Stopforth, P. J. asq
  qss1 (N) 1 Jan
Strevens, N. C. (P) 1 Jan
Stubbs, D. M. BA
  qs (AEO) 1 Jan
Tait, J. cfs cfs(t) qss (P) 1 Jan
Thirtle, C. B. BSc
  qss (P) 1 Jan
Thomas, A. J. (AEO) 1 Jan
Thorne, D. E. qss (AEO) 1 Jan
Toriati, D. J. qs (P) 1 Jan
Vaughan, K. M. D. qab
  qs (N) 1 Jan
Ward, A. M. qss (P) 1 Jan
Waring, J. M. R.
  qss (N) 1 Jan
Wells, T. J. G. BSc cfs
  qss (P) 1 Jan
Williamson, P. M. BSc
  qss (P) 1 Jan
Wilson, M. J. qs (P) 1 Jan
Winsor, N. W. BEng
  qs (N) 1 Jan
Withington, D. J.
  qwi(AD) qss (P) 1 Jan
Adcock, M. R. qss (P) 1 July
Astbury, A. J. MBE fc
  qss (N) 1 July
Avent, S. D. qss (N) 1 July
Barrow, R. P. qwi(AD)
  qs (N) 1 July
Bremer, G. J. BSc asq
  qss (N) 1 July

Burton, A. BSc qwi(T)
  qss2 (N) 1 July
Carder, C. D. cfs
  qss1 (P) 1 July
Catterall, R. P. qcc (P) 1 July
Chadwick, S. J. cfs
  qcc (P) 1 July
Chappell, M. W. J.
  qwi(AD) qs (P) 1 July
Cooke, C. V. BSc qwi
  qcc (P) 1 July
Craghill, C. M. qwi(T)
  qss (N) 1 July
Crosby, G. R. qs (AEO) 1 July
Cullen, A. J. E. qwi
  qs (P) 1 July
Davies, N. A. BSc
  qs (P) 1 July
Edwards, G. A. BEng
  cfs qs (P) 1 July
Evans, A. D. E. BEng cfs
  qss (P) 1 July
Fellowes, D. A. qwi
  qss (P) 1 July
Fielding, S. BSc tp (P) 1 July
Fitzgerald, J. F. BEng
  cfs (P) 1 July
Flynn, R. J. BSc cfs
  qss (P) 1 July
Frampton, J. K. MBE
  BA qss (N) 1 July
Garland, M. M. E. V.
  qwi qcc (P) 1 July
Grant, S. G. BSc qwi
  qcc (P) 1 July
Green, A. J. cfs qss (P) 1 July
Grigg, M. J. cfs qs (P) 1 July
Grindley, G. A. BSc qab
  qss (P) 1 July
Haines, D. F. qab qwi
  qs (P) 1 July
Hale, M. D. BSc cfs
  qss (P) 1 July
Hamilton, C. I. qss (N) 1 July
Hartford, C. R. BSc
  qss (N) 1 July
Holland, J. A. BSc
  qs (N) 1 July
Howells, J. MBE (AEO) 1 July
Hynd, A. N. BSc
  qss (P) 1 July
Jepson, C. D. qwi
  qs (P) 1 July
Jones, J. M. G. BSc
  qss (P) 1 July
Kelly, B. R. BEng cfs
  qss (P) 1 July
Kidson, M. qss (N) 1 July
Macdonald, J. B. BTech
  tp qwi qss (P) 1 July

Squadron Leaders

2001—contd

Manning, D. P. qss (P) 1 July
Marshall, D. J. qss (N) 1 July
McGregor, I. cfs qs (P) 1 July
McNamara, P. A. M. cfs
   qss (P) 1 July
Morris, D. P. BSc
   qss (N) 1 July
O'Kennedy, P. L. qhti
   qcc (N) 1 July
Parry, A. J. qs (N) 1 July
Russell, N. G. asq
   qss (N) 1 July
Smyth, H. qwi qcc (P) 1 July
Stocker, S. C. BSc cfs
   qss (P) 1 July
Tait, A. G. BA qss (N) 1 July
Taylor, P. J. N. qss1 (N) 1 July
Walton, I. W. R. BEng
   qwi(T) (P) 1 July
Ward, S. M. R. qss (N) 1 July
Watson, I. BSc qss (P) 1 July
Webber, R. B. cfs
   qss (P) 1 July
Whinton, A. J. cfs
   qss (P) 1 July
Wigglesworth, D. J. cfs
   qwi qss (P) 1 July
Williams, H. cfs qcc (P) 1 July

2002

Alexander, D. J. BEng
   cfs qs (P) 1 Jan
Arnold, A. D. BSc
   qss (N) 1 Jan
Avery, D. K. BEng
   qss (P) 1 Jan
Barker, R. A. BSc tp cfs
   qss (P) 1 Jan
Bartle, D. J. cfs qss (N) 1 Jan
Bastable, A. D. qss (P) 1 Jan
Bentley, S. A. BSc qhti
   qss2 (P) 1 Jan
Boag, D. A. BSc qs (N) 1 Jan
Boughton, S. J. qs (N) 1 Jan
Bowland, J. D. R. BSc
   qss (N) 1 Jan
Boyes, M. S. qwi(AD)
   qs (P) 1 Jan
Brown, P. J. BSc
   qcc (N) 1 Jan
Bull, A. J. MB ChB
   qcc (P) 1 Jan
Cable, M. qss1 (P) 1 Jan

Calmus, D. (AEO) 1 Jan
Carver, M. H. G.
   qss (P) 1 Jan
Clark, J. W. qss (P) 1 Jan
Cooke, D. J. qss (AEO) 1 Jan
Cowell, J. J. asq qs (N) 1 Jan
Cox, S. N. qss (ENG) 1 Jan
Cranstoun, C. D. J.
   qss (P) 1 Jan
Dean, T. R. L. BSc
   qss (P) 1 Jan
Edwards, J. K. cfs
   qss (P) 1 Jan
Edwards, S. S. cfs
   qcc (P) 1 Jan
Emtage, J. A. BSc
   qab (P) 1 Jan
Esau, R. G. BSc cfs
   qss (P) 1 Jan
Fairs, M. R. R. BSc
   qwi(AD) qss (P) 1 Jan
Ferrol, W. A. cfs (P) 1 Jan
Fraser, E. C. BSc
   qwi(T) qss (N) 1 Jan
Gale, I. D. qwi(T)
   qss2 (P) 1 Jan
Grapes, S. A. R. BSc
   qss (N) 1 Jan
Hales, D. W. BEng cfs
   qss (P) 1 Jan
Hall, A. R. BSc asq
   qss (N) 1 Jan
Hammond, S. M. BSc
   qwi(T) qss1 (P) 1 Jan
High, P. A. qab qss (N) 1 Jan
Howard, A. BEng (P) 1 Jan
Hulme, S. J. qwi(T)
   qss (P) 1 Jan
Ingle, N. J. W cfs
   qcc (P) 1 Jan
Innes, J. E. qss (ENG) 1 Jan
Jones, K. R. qwi(T)
   qcc (N) 1 Jan
Mason, J. P. qss (N) 1 Jan
McCormick, R. A. BSc
   asq qss (N) 1 Jan
Miller, A. B. BSc
   qss (P) 1 Jan
Mills, A. M. (AEO) 1 Jan
Morgan, S. C. qwi(T)
   qcc (P) 1 Jan
Morris, G. D. qss (N) 1 Jan
Neilson, B. J. T. cfs(n)
   qss (N) 1 Jan
Newton, D. J. (N) 1 Jan
O'Brien, T. J. qcc (P) 1 Jan
Plain, C. N. cfs qss2 (P) 1 Jan
Rainier, M. D. DFC qwi
   qs (P) 1 Jan
Rawnsley, S. qcc (P) 1 Jan

Rea, S. A. BSc qss (P) 1 Jan
Rumens, K. R. cfs
   qcc (P) 1 Jan
Seymour, A. J. BSc
   qwi(AD) qcc (P) 1 Jan
Shields, J. H. qwi(AD)
   qss (N) 1 Jan
Stringer, N. J. MSc
   BEng MCGI MRAeS
   asq qs (N) 1 Jan
Thorpe, P. A. qss (N) 1 Jan
Walker, R. W. BA qwi
   qcc (P) 1 Jan
Ward, J. K. qcc (P) 1 Jan
Wilkie, D. W. qss (N) 1 Jan
Abrahams, M. D. qhti
   qss2 (ALM) 1 July
Allen, D. J. qcc (AEO) 1 July
Appleby, D. J. R. cfs(n)
   qss (N) 1 July
Appleton, J. L. cfs(n)
   qcc (N) 1 July
Ashurst, R. C. qcc (N) 1 July
Barker, M. H. R. cfs qhti
   qss (P) 1 July
Barmby, M. I. qwi(AD)
   qss1 (N) 1 July
Bausor, N. T. cfs (P) 1 July
Beck, J. R. BA qss (P) 1 July
Beddoes, S. L. BSc
   qss (N) 1 July
Bedford, R. W. BSc
   qwi(H) qss (P) 1 July
Binns, P. B. qwi qcc (P) 1 July
Boulter, D. J. (AEO) 1 July
Bradshaw, D. G. BSc
   qwi qcc (P) 1 July
Breese, D. L. qs (P) 1 July
Brennan, R. N. BSc
   qss (P) 1 July
Brewer, S. J. qss (N) 1 July
Brown, C. T. BEng cfs
   qss (P) 1 July
Brown, S. E. cfs qcc (P) 1 July
Burrough, G. D.
   qcc (AEO) 1 July
Coleman, G. P.
   qss1 (N) 1 July
Colman, N. J. qhti
   qss (N) 1 July
Cunningham, M. L. qab
   qss1 (P) 1 July
Cutmore, M. R. qwi
   qss1 (P) 1 July
D'Lima, D. J. BEd cfs
   qs (P) 1 July
Dyer, I. C. BSc qss2 (N) 1 July
Fairhurst, M. BEng
   qss2 (N) 1 July

Squadron Leaders

2002—contd

Fewtrell, R. A. cfs cfs(t)
qwi qss1   (P) 1 July
Finnimore, D. T. cfs (P) 1 July
Flynn, S. A. BA qss (P) 1 July
Gleave, C. cfs cfs(t) qwi
qss   (P) 1 July
Green, J. H. qwi
qcc   (P) 1 July
Hackett, P. L. MBE
qcc   (P) 1 July
Haskins, J. M. A. qwi
qcc   (P) 1 July
Hawker, J. R. cfs
qss1   (P) 1 July
Hinton, B. K. MA cfs(n)
snc qss   (N) 1 July
Holmes, G. M.
qss   (AEO) 1 July
Iavagnilo, R. G. qss (P) 1 July
Kelly, P. J. BSc cfs (P) 1 July
Lawrence, M. E.
qss   (N) 1 July
Lawson, J. D. qwi(T)
qss   (P) 1 July
Leonard, A. R. qcc (P) 1 July
Lewis, R. D. BSc cfs(t)
qss   (N) 1 July
McGregor, C. J. BSc
qwi(T) qcc   (P) 1 July
McInroy, S. D. BSc
qss2   (N) 1 July
Mcara, D. cfs(n)
qss   (N) 1 July
Moir, R. D. cfs(n)
qcc   (N) 1 July
Morton, I. R.   (ENG) 1 July
Moseley, N. G. cfs(n)
snc qss   (N) 1 July
Mulholland, J. P. BSc
qwi(T) qcc   (N) 1 July
Nash, M. S. qss   (P) 1 July
Oliphant, G. G. BSc
qss   (P) 1 July
Patounas, R. P. G. cfs
qs   (P) 1 July
Pope, C. C. BSc qss (N) 1 July
Pugh, J. BEng qs (N) 1 July
Puzey, M. E. qwi(AD)
qss2   (P) 1 July
Reuter, J. S. qwi(AD)
qcc   (N) 1 July
Savage, S. W. qcc (N) 1 July
Smiles, J. A. BSc ghti
qss   (P) 1 July

Smiley, S. L. qwi(AD)
qcc   (P) 1 July
Smith, J. A. BEng
qwi(AD) qss1   (N) 1 July
Stellmacher, D. BEng
qss   (P) 1 July
Taylor, K. D. BEng cfs
qcc   (P) 1 July
Toms, J. E. qcc (ALM) 1 July
Warren, J. D. tp qss (P) 1 July
Webber, D. J. BEng qhti
qcc   (P) 1 July
Woods, M. J. qss2 (N) 1 July

Flight Lieutenants

1969

Williamson, J.   (N) 28 Aug
Burnett, D. J.
qss*   (AEO) 22 Nov

1970

Bishop, D. E.   (P) 4 Nov

1971

Canning, J. A. snc (N) 2 Aug

1972

Miller, G. R. cfs(n) snc
qss   (N) 8 Mar
Hawkins, P. J.   (N) 23 Mar
Hammond, S. P. cfs fc
qss   (P) 28 Apr
Funnell-Bailey, C. C.
cfs   (P) 4 May
Barr, A.   (P) 30 Sept
Davies, R. J. cfs (P) 28 Oct

1973

Skene, A. J. cfs (P) 7 Jan
Milburn, R. L. BSc (P) 15 Apr
Goff, D. K. qss (N) 10 July
Smyth, P. M. BSc
cfs   (P) 3 Oct
Skelton, A. M.   (P) 20 Oct
Wheeler, O. J. cfs(n)
snc   (N) 7 Dec
Rees, G. D. BSc qss (P) 15 Dec
Cooper, D. BSc snc
qss   (N) 30 Dec

1974

Gulliver, J. cfs(n) snc
qss   (N) 12 Jan
Slack, A. D.   (N) 12 Jan
Priest, J. S. D. snc (N) 16 Feb
Stilwell, N. J.   (P) 16 Feb
Crick, S. E. cfs(n) snc
qss   (N) 10 Mar
Todd, P. A.   (N) 20 Mar

Flight Lieutenants

1974—contd

Pitchforth, N. A. BSc cfs		
qss	(P)	15 Apr
Horler, D. C. cfs(n)	(N)	16 Apr
Hickin, D. J. T. BSc		
qss	(P)	14 May
Craig, R. E.	(P)	29 Dec

1975

Hobkirk, B. D.	(P)	8 Feb
Hamilton, S. P. cfs	(P)	25 Feb
Barnes, D. A.	(N)	15 Mar

1976

Harris, D. J. cfs	(P)	17 Jan
Smith, A. J. qss i	(P)	15 Mar
Jackson, P. B. BA		
qss	(N)	6 July
Chatterton, M. J.		
BSc	(P)	15 Oct

1977

Ayliffe, A. C. MBE BA		
asq cfs(n) snc		
qss	(N)	19 Jan
Blackie, G. C. AFC cfs		
qss	(P)	22 Jan
McNichol, P. qss	(N)	19 Feb
Palmer, P. E.	(P)	11 May
Walters, P. S. qss	(N)	12 June
Hawker, J. BSc cfs(pn)		
qss	(P)	3 July
Wilson, G. C. qss	(P)	13 July
Needham, E. G. cfs(n)		
qss	(N)	10 Aug
Hendy, J. W. MCIPD		
cfs(n) snc qss	(N)	6 Oct
Watkins, B. J. BSc cfs		
qss	(P)	15 Oct
Abbot, A. C. cfs		
qss1	(P)	4 Nov
Partridge, S. M. qss	(P)	1 Dec

1978

Saunders, I. R. cfs		
qss	(P)	27 Jan
Hildred, K. BSc cfs	(P)	7 Feb

Dewhurst, A. R.		
BSc	(N)	2 Apr
Benke, R. N. BSc cfs		
qss	(P)	11 Apr
Hext, A. BA qss	(N)	15 Apr
Atkins, S. R. BSc asq		
qss	(P)	6 June
Best, J. L. snc	(N)	18 July
Robertson, I. W. BSc		
qhti	(P)	15 Oct
Wrigley, C. M.		
BSc(Eng) ACGI asq		
qss	(N)	6 Dec
Smith, G. cfs qss1	(P)	7 Dec

1979

Dyer, P. J. BSc	(P)	15 Apr
Collins, N. D.	(P)	24 July
Gregory, S. StJ.	(N)	24 July
Harrod, V. W. BA asq		
qss	(N)	6 Aug
Emery, S. J.	(N)	16 Nov
Taylor, G. L. cfs	(P)	18 Nov
Frostick, A. T. BA		
qss	(N)	30 Nov

1980

Thorpe, A. A. BSc		
MMar qss	(N)	2 Mar
Counter, M. J. BSc cfs		
qss	(P)	15 Apr
Jones, P. C. BA cfs	(P)	15 Apr
Kilgour, J. A. BSc cfs		
qss	(P)	15 Apr
Bull, D. I BSc qss	(P)	2 June
Taylor, D. A. cfs(n)	(N)	21 June
Bradshaw, P. cfs		
qss	(P)	30 July
Hodgson, S. A.	(P)	31 July
Hornby, L. cfs	(P)	23 Aug
Knowles, R. T. qss	(P)	27 Aug
Pollock, N. D. BSc		
qss	(P)	15 Oct
Coombs, D. C. BSc		
qss	(N)	12 Nov

1981

Howell, D. W. BSc asq		
qss	(N)	8 Jan
Bellis, D. E.	(ALM)	11 Jan
Robinson, N. S.		
BA	(AEO)	22 Feb
Powell, M. BEng cfs		
qss	(P)	28 Mar

Poolman, J. C. BSc asq		
qss	(P)	15 Apr
Chisholm, R. G. BSc		
asq qss	(N)	12 May
Davies, J. qss	(AEO)	17 May
Jillett, M. S.	(P)	20 May
Chamberlain, S. J.		
cfs(n)	(N)	1 Oct
Fryer, C. G.	(N)	7 Oct
Castle, M. J. D. BSc cfs		
qss	(P)	15 Oct
Astle, P. W. cfs qss	(P)	1 Nov
Russell, S. F.	(P)	13 Nov
Spratt, A. B. BSc		
asq	(N)	17 Nov
Williams, S. C. qss	(N)	13 Dec

1982

Coxon, K. A. cfs		
qss	(P)	5 Feb
McKernan, P. R. BSc		
asq qss	(N)	5 Feb
Petherick, S. T. cfs		
qss	(P)	5 Feb
Johnson, P. A. BSc		
qss	(P)	9 Feb
Raymond, M. I.		
BSc	(P)	15 Apr
Dobson, P. S. BSc cfs		
qss	(P)	17 Apr
Hannam, G. A. BSc		
qss	(N)	17 May
Davis, H. D.	(N)	9 June
Challis, P. W. cfs(n)		
qss	(N)	9 July
Batin, M. V. BSc		
qss	(N)	18 July
Paul, H. A. BSc asq		
qss	(N)	15 Oct
Brook, K. H. cfs(n)		
qss	(N)	17 Oct
Binsted, P. D. qss	(P)	21 Oct
Dean, C. P.	(N)	2 Dec
Harrison, J. D.	(P)	23 Dec

1983

Taylor, G. qss	(N)	14 Jan
McCredie, K. I. BSc	(P)	15 Apr
Weightman, G. R. cfs		
qss	(P)	7 May
Brown, C. V. BSc		
cfs*	(P)	6 June
Crouchman, M. W. AFC		
cfs	(P)	5 July
Holmes, J. A. M.		
cfs(n)	(N)	5 July

Flight Lieutenants

1983—contd

Thirkell, P. A.	(N)	2 Aug
Whitworth, P. D. BSc		
cfs qss	(P)	15 Oct
Wilson, C. qwi(T)	(N)	11 Nov

1984

Burgon, B. E. A.		
qss	(N)	20 Jan
Jenkins, C. D. BSc		
cfs(n)	(N)	7 Feb
Phillips, B. K. qss	(N)	20 Mar
Allen, D. W. BSc(Eng)		
asq qss	(N)	15 Apr
Biddle, D. R. BSc(Eng)		
asq cfs(n) qss	(N)	15 Apr
Jones, M. C. BSc	(P)	15 Apr
Kenrick, W. R. BSc cfs		
qss	(P)	15 Apr
Williams, J. M. BA		
qss	(P)	15 Apr
Vickers, M. E.		
qss	(ENG)	26 Apr
Gear, A. C. J.	(P)	29 Apr
Simmons, A. J. qss	(N)	2 May
Macintyre, R. A. BSc		
qwi(AD)	(P)	26 June
James, K. G. BSc		
qss	(N)	27 June
Watts, R. A. BSc cfs		
qss	(P)	27 June
McCrea, J. D. cfs	(P)	11 July
Starr, C. J. qss	(P)	20 July
Moxon, N. P. cfs		
qss	(P)	22 Aug
Anderson, D. C. E. A.		
BSc	(N)	15 Oct
Harris, K. BA qss	(N)	15 Oct
Henderson, H. BSc		
qss	(P)	15 Oct
Higginbottom, R. P.		
cfs(n) qss	(N)	17 Nov
Moore, K. E. BSc asq		
qss	(N)	17 Nov
Weir, A. W. qss	(N)	17 Nov

1985

Jackson, R.	(P)	1 Jan
Fletcher, R. M. BSc	(P)	16 Jan
Carter, R. W. asq cfs(n)		
qss	(N)	13 Mar

Cunningham, J. cfs(n)		
qss	(N)	6 Apr
Gordon, A. G. BA		
qss	(P)	15 Apr
Simpson, R. A. C. BSc		
cfs qss	(P)	15 Apr
Wood, M. A. BTech		
cfs	(P)	15 Apr
Thompson, S. G.		
A.	(P)	1 May
Mellor, S. G. BSc asq		
cfs(n) qss	(N)	11 June
Moule, J. R. qss	(P)	13 June
Johnson, D. A.	(N)	15 June
Taylor, M. A. qss	(P)	19 July
Read, W. R. qss	(P)	31 July
Robinson, C. P. qss	(N)	31 July
Thornhill, A. qss	(P)	31 July
Roberts, C. T.	(AEO)	8 Sept
Humphreys, P. J.	(P)	26 Sept
Gibby, R. M. BSc cfs(n)		
qss	(N)	27 Oct
Greer, A. S. qss	(N)	22 Nov
Hesketh, J. I.	(N)	22 Nov
Paige, C. R. qhti		
qss	(N)	22 Nov
Palastanga, P. R. cfs(n)		
qss	(N)	22 Nov
Stewart, D. E. BSc		
cfs	(P)	19 Dec

1986

Harrison, D. M. qss	(N)	3 Jan
Hawkins, P.	(N)	3 Jan
Stockton, I. D. BSc		
qss	(N)	5 Feb
Stevens, V. A. cfs(n)		
qss	(N)	14 Feb
Williams, W. cfs(n)		
qss	(N)	14 Feb
Wilson, A. D. BSc asq		
qss	(N)	2 Mar
Smith, N. P. BSc		
qss	(P)	11 Mar
Moss, D. E. qss	(N)	16 Mar
Powell, P. R. qss	(P)	12 Apr
Rees, N. C. R. BSc cfs		
qss	(P)	15 Apr
Witts, C. B. BSc cfs	(P)	30 Apr
Dearden, J. A. qss	(P)	5 May
Baber, C. W. BSc cfs(n)		
qss	(N)	25 May
Randells, T. M. qss	(N)	5 Aug
Seely, P. A. A. BA		
qss	(P)	5 Aug
Simm, G. E. asq	(N)	5 Aug
Paton, A. D. asq		
qss	(N)	29 Aug

Fullerton, R. G. BSc		
cfs(n) qss	(N)	18 Sept
Campbell, I. M.	(P)	19 Sept
Evans, J. C. BSc cfs	(P)	15 Oct
Paul, A. G. BSc cfs		
qss	(P)	15 Oct
Hudson, A. M.	(P)	19 Oct
White, W. B. MSc BSc		
MCGI asq cfs(n)		
qss	(N)	29 Oct
Spencer, J. qss	(AEO)	22 Nov
Smalldon, R. J.	(P)	8 Dec
Clark, R. D. qss	(N)	11 Dec
Harvey, D. J. qwi	(P)	11 Dec
Wright, E. G. qss	(N)	11 Dec
Wynn, J. K. qss	(N)	13 Dec

1987

Kemp, P. G. BSc cfs	(P)	15 Jan
Williams, G. W. BSc		
qss	(P)	15 Jan
Farrington, P. R.		
qss	(AEO)	17 Jan
Millar, H. A. W. G.		
qss	(AEO)	17 Jan
Nash, J. B. BSc cfs		
qss	(P)	22 Jan
Davis, R. A.	(N)	24 Jan
Settery, G. BSc qss	(N)	18 Feb
Sheppard, G. J. AFC		
cfs	(P)	25 Feb
Brown, D. W. T. BSc cfs		
qss	(P)	2 Mar
Jones, G. V. BSc cfs(n)		
qss	(N)	2 Mar
Sansford, S. M. BCom		
qss	(N)	2 Mar
Pearson, S. M. asq		
qss	(N)	4 Mar
Snowdon, R. E.	(P)	4 Mar
Palgrave, C. W. J.		
qss	(N)	15 Apr
Cauchi, M. J. V. qss	(P)	21 Apr
Witts, P. D. BSc	(N)	25 May
Evans, A. M. asq	(N)	26 May
Hayes, S. P. cfs(n)		
qss	(N)	26 May
Lloyd, D. cfs	(P)	4 July
Millbank, P. cfs(c)		
qss	(ALM)	4 July
Halpin, D. R. BEd		
qss	(N)	5 July
Hands, R. L. BSc asq		
qss	(N)	20 July
Marshall, J. BA qss	(N)	20 July
Cornes, B. R. cfs		
qss	(P)	25 Aug

Flight Lieutenants

1987—contd

Wilkins, S. J. cfs
qss (P) 1 Sept
Bulteel, C. J. B. BSc (P) 3 Sept
Harris, D. J. BSc asq
cfs(n) (N) 3 Sept
Hilton, C. E. J. BA (N) 3 Sept
Wilson, W. D. M.
BSc (P) 14 Sept
Hill, G. J. (P) 24 Sept
Mortimer, A. P. (AEO) 26 Sept
Couper, P. BSc qss (N) 30 Sept
Sheath, N. T. qss (P) 8 Oct
Straw, E. T. BA cfs
qss (P) 11 Nov
Dearie, I. A. S. asq
qss (N) 20 Nov
Saunders, I. W. (P) 20 Nov

1988

Evans, J. M. cfs
qss1 (P) 1 Jan
Letton, J. S. (P) 1 Jan
Spooner, D. M. J. BSc
asq qss (N) 7 Jan
Vallance, S. F. (P) 12 Jan
Ambury, S. B. BSc
asq (N) 15 Jan
Coulton, L. W. J. BA cfs
qss (P) 15 Jan
Martin, D. J. BSc cfs
qss (P) 15 Jan
Williams, G. J. BSc
cfs (P) 15 Jan
Johnston, N. A. BSc
qwi(T) qss (N) 3 Feb
Smyth, K. BEd asq
qss (N) 3 Feb
Wolfendale, P. cfs (P) 13 Feb
Beaumont, R. G. BSc
asq cfs(n) qss (N) 18 Feb
Holmes, R. J. BSc asq
qss (P) 18 Feb
Collyer, P. BA (P) 5 Mar
Toyne, R. C. BA qss (P) 5 Mar
Balshaw, M. J. F. BSc
cfs qss (P) 14 Mar
Wattam, D. M. BSc cfs
qss1 (P) 14 Mar
Macdonald, P. J. S. D.
cfs(n) qss (N) 23 Mar
Scoines, D. A. qss (N) 25 Mar
Berry, M. R. BSc asq
qss (N) 29 Mar

Carr, G. BSc qss (N) 29 Mar
Mallinson, C. P. BSc
qss (P) 29 Mar
Perrins, R. H. MSc BSc
MCGI MRIN asq
qss (N) 29 Mar
Shaw, I. M. BSc (N) 26 Apr
Docker, C. E. BSc
asq (N) 5 June
Andrew, N. R. BSc (N) 7 June
Aston, S. N. BEng
qss (P) 7 June
Wood, S. G. qss (N) 8 June
Goodrum, R. M. cfs
cfs(pn) qss (P) 16 June
Evans, M. D. MBE
qwi(AD) (N) 21 July
Thomas, R. K. (AEO) 31 July
Roxburgh, D. K.
BSc (P) 1 Aug
Glover, A. S. BSc cfs(n)
qss (N) 4 Aug
Wilson, C. B. BSc asq
qss (N) 16 Aug
Mellor, D. J. (AEO) 30 Aug
Howieson, W. B. MBA
BSc MRAeS cfs(n)
qss (N) 15 Sept
Laws, D. J. BEng tp (P) 15 Sept
Hendry, T. qss (N) 24 Sept
Jenkins, G. P. cfs (P) 24 Sept
Smith, P. D. BA cfs
qss (P) 30 Sept
Stobie, D. N. cfs qwi
qss (P) 6 Nov
Trainor, P. R. D. cfs
qss (P) 6 Nov
Williams, N. P. cfs
qss (P) 6 Nov
Doherty, G. P. BSc (N) 11 Nov
Liston, G. A. (AEO) 4 Dec
Ouston, C. M.
qss (AEO) 15 Dec

1989

Bennett, M. W. qss (N) 15 Jan
Dawe, A. G. BA cfs
qss (P) 15 Jan
Gales, A. J. BA (P) 15 Jan
Howard-Smith, P. M.
BSc qss (N) 15 Jan
Mitchell, D. J. G. BSc
qcc (P) 15 Jan
Harcombe, O. M.
asq (N) 29 Jan
Mackenzie, N. H. (N) 29 Jan
Duffin, J. R. (P) 1 Feb

Cadman, T. L. BSc
qss (P) 3 Feb
Hoaen, A. J. BA cfs (P) 3 Feb
Durke, P. qwi(T) (N) 8 Mar
Hathaway, N. T. qss (N) 8 Mar
Newman, P. G. (P) 8 Mar
Carson, B. J. qss (N) 12 Mar
Forbes, A. MacP.
asq (N) 14 Mar
Phipps, A. L. BSc cfs
qss (P) 14 Mar
Smith, A. M. BSc
qss (P) 14 Mar
Taylor, R. N. BSc cfs
cfs(pn) (P) 14 Mar
Ware, D. J. asq qss (N) 14 Mar
Bearblock, P. D. BSc
qss (P) 11 Apr
Sheard, M. J. B. BSc cfs
qss1 (P) 11 Apr
Smith, M. G. (P) 20 Apr
Walker, G. P. qss (P) 20 Apr
Harris, M. R. BSc
qss (N) 26 Apr
Hippman, R. S. (AEO) 4 June
Curry, R. L. S.
BSc(Eng) qss (P) 7 June
Heaney, S. R. BA
cfs (P) 7 June
Ready, M. S. BA cfs
cfs(pn) (P) 7 June
Williams, D. R. BSc
qss (N) 7 June
Edwards, K. A. J. asq
qwi(T) (N) 8 June
Hodgson, C. P. qss (P) 8 June
Smith, I. S. cfs (P) 8 June
Tett, P. E. cfs (P) 8 June
Wright, W. S. qss (N) 12 July
Henderson, N. McL.
cfs(c) (ALM) 17 July
Wardrop, T. BSc asq
qss (N) 1 Aug
Davidson, A. G. G. cfs
qss (P) 2 Aug
Thomas, J. P. (P) 2 Aug
Brotherton, J. BEng
qss1 (N) 14 Aug
Nichols, W. H. BSc (N) 6 Sept
Dalton, A. G. (P) 15 Sept
Heathcote, G. BSc asq
qss (P) 15 Sept
Hopkinson, P. E. BA
qss (P) 15 Sept
Tennant-Bell, N. R. (P) 15 Sept
Thyng, I. F. qss (N) 15 Sept
Marshall, I. F. (N) 8 Oct
Taylor, J. E. cfs qss (P) 12 Oct
Jannaty, Y. BSc (N) 26 Oct
Mangan, M. T. BSc (N) 26 Oct

Flight Lieutenants

1989—contd

Miller, P. C. R. BSc tp cfs		
qss	(P)	26 Oct
Parkinson, A. F.	(P)	26 Oct
Gray, A. S. qss	(N)	11 Nov
Hambleton, A. E.		
cfs	(P)	8 Dec
Smith, P. A. cfs	(P)	8 Dec
Buxton, S. G. cfs	(P)	18 Dec

1990

Phillis, I. R.	(P)	3 Jan
Beeston, M. D. MA	(P)	15 Jan
Davy, J. BEng cfs		
qss1	(P)	15 Jan
Edwards, R. C. BA cfs		
qss	(P)	15 Jan
Gell, A. P. BSc cfs	(P)	15 Jan
Goldstraw, D. A. BSc		
asq qss	(N)	15 Jan
Harris, J. I. MEng cfs		
qss	(P)	15 Jan
Helm, D. A. BEng		
qss	(P)	15 Jan
Hopson, P. BSc	(P)	15 Jan
Hugall, D. R. BA		
qss	(P)	15 Jan
Hughes, P. J. BA		
qss	(P)	15 Jan
Mobbs, P. W. BEng cfs		
qss	(P)	15 Jan
Robertshaw, N. J. BA		
cfs qss2	(P)	15 Jan
Russell, I. J. L. BSc cfs		
qwi qcc	(P)	15 Jan
Slatford, T. K.		
BTech	(P)	15 Jan
Telfer, J. C. BSc	(P)	15 Jan
Wright, J. BSc	(N)	15 Jan
Cook, I. V. BSc qss	(P)	19 Jan
Harbron, S. E.	(P)	19 Jan
Mullen, A. cfs	(P)	19 Jan
Whitwood, S. L. cfs		
qss	(P)	19 Jan
Kelly, A. M. qss	(N)	12 Feb
Birnie, F. BEng qss	(N)	14 Feb
Dornan, I. S. BA cfs		
qcc	(P)	14 Feb
Griffiths, K. I.	(AEO)	25 Feb
Ead, I. S. qss	(N)	28 Feb
Frost, P. A. BSc cfs	(P)	28 Feb
Goodman, P. St. J.		
qss1	(P)	28 Feb
Smith, A. J.	(P)	28 Feb
Stirton, I. N. cfs	(P)	28 Feb
Wood, J. R.	(P)	28 Feb
Yorston, R. A. BEng		
qss	(N)	28 Feb
Boulton, M. S. BA		
qss	(N)	11 Apr
Coote, S. M. BSc		
qss	(P)	11 Apr
Eccles, C. J. BSc cfs	(P)	11 Apr
McCarthy, S. F. BSc cfs		
qss	(P)	11 Apr
Myhill, J. S. qss	(N)	11 Apr
Tucker, D. L. BSc MIL		
qss	(N)	11 Apr
Vicary, P. N. L. BSc		
qwi(AD) qss1	(P)	11 Apr
Williams, C. D.	(P)	15 Apr
Collins, M. D. qss	(N)	2 May
Jones, C. D.	(N)	5 May
Taylor, N. qss	(AEO)	5 May
Peacey, S. BSc cfs		
qss	(P)	6 May
Smith, D. A. BSc		
qss	(N)	6 May
Hughes, D. K. cfs		
qss	(P)	7 May
Fancett, P. A.	(P)	22 May
Sell, A. cfs	(P)	22 May
Heald, T. J. H. cfs		
qss	(P)	23 May
Nash, J. E.	(AEO)	16 June
Mudgway, A. P. cfs	(P)	29 June
Sumner, A. P. qss1	(P)	9 July
Morris, P. G.	(P)	17 July
Stafford, M. I. qss	(N)	17 July
Stradling, C. J. qss	(N)	17 July
Gilbert, N. P. qcc	(P)	24 July
Adkinson, S.	(N)	28 July
Charles, R. L.	(AEO)	28 July
Wesley, N. P. cfs qwi		
qss	(P)	28 July
Baxter, M. E. BSc		
qss1	(P)	14 Aug
Austin, R. P.	(P)	28 Aug
Bell, S.	(P)	28 Aug
Crennell, N. J. qwi(T)		
qss1	(P)	28 Aug
Faulkner, S. C.	(P)	28 Aug
Hiscox, B. J. asq		
qss	(N)	28 Aug
Lings, G. B. qss	(P)	28 Aug
Willson, S.	(P)	28 Aug
Elliott, S. J. BSc		
qss	(N)	27 Sept
Matthews, M. W. BSc		
qss1	(N)	27 Sept
Ross, A. BSc	(P)	2 Oct
Davey, P. M.	(P)	11 Oct
Dazeley, J. M.	(P)	11 Oct
Garner, R. W. C.		
qss	(N)	11 Oct
Jackson, J. A. cfs	(P)	11 Oct
Salisbury, D. A. qs	(P)	11 Oct
Williams, P. J. qss	(N)	11 Oct
Gallagher, J. J.		
qss1	(N)	13 Oct
Foggo, C. H. qss	(ENG)	2 Nov
Williams, N. P. BSc		
cfs(pn)	(P)	8 Nov
Fairbrother, P. J.	(P)	23 Nov
Griffiths, S. M. tp		
cfs	(P)	23 Nov
Hare, G. W. J. qss	(P)	23 Nov
Wood, M. L. qss	(N)	23 Nov
Howells, I. M. qss	(N)	10 Dec
Dunne, P. J. qss	(ALM)	15 Dec
Fascione, T. M. BSc		
qss	(N)	19 Dec
Evans, D. A. W.		
qss2	(N)	24 Dec

1991

Cawthorne, P. qwi(T)		
qss	(P)	4 Jan
Chadwick, G. C. cfs	(P)	4 Jan
Cockerill, D. cfs qss	(P)	4 Jan
Jones, K. R. qss1	(N)	4 Jan
Laing, G. W. cfs		
qss1	(P)	4 Jan
Powell, P. J. qss	(P)	4 Jan
Robson, M. cfs qss	(P)	4 Jan
Rowley, T. G. S.	(P)	4 Jan
Westwood, P. G.		
BSc	(P)	4 Jan
Ballance, D. J. BSc tp		
cfs qcc	(P)	15 Jan
Carby, H. R. BSc cfs		
qss	(P)	15 Jan
Hossle, T. BA qss	(P)	15 Jan
Johnson, S. A. BSc		
qcc	(P)	15 Jan
Lewis, M. T. MB ChB		
DAvMed tp qcc	(P)	15 Jan
Moore, N. MSc BSc asq		
qss	(N)	15 Jan
Pike, H. J. BEng		
qwi	(P)	15 Jan
Potter, D. J. BA cfs		
qss	(P)	15 Jan
Roxburgh, S. I. BEng		
qcc	(P)	15 Jan
Ryder, A. S. BA qcc	(P)	15 Jan
Sickling, A. M. BSc	(P)	15 Jan
Thornton, M. J.		
BSc	(P)	15 Jan
Walton, R. I. BSc		
cfs	(P)	15 Jan

Flight Lieutenants

1991—contd

Easton, M. S.	(P)	17 Jan
Cookson, S.	(ALM)	29 Jan
Day, C. J. qss	(N)	7 Feb
Chattaway, M. S.		
BEng	(P)	14 Feb
Kirby, S. BSc qss	(N)	14 Feb
Cooper, A. E. R.	(N)	15 Feb
Hadley, S. C. qwi(T)		
qss	(N)	15 Feb
Kay, S. T. E.	(N)	15 Feb
Parke, R. J.	(N)	15 Feb
Strookman, R. D. cfs		
qss	(P)	15 Feb
Warwick, P. J. cfs		
qcc	(P)	15 Feb
Stephens, M. F. asq		
qss	(AEO)	16 Feb
Booth, J. H. J. BEng		
asq qss	(N)	20 Feb
Bradshaw, M. C. BSc		
qss1	(P)	20 Feb
Deboys, R. G. BSc		
qss	(N)	20 Feb
Thombs, D. U. BEd		
qss	(P)	20 Feb
Smith, J. A.	(P)	1 Mar
Janaway, C. D. qss	(P)	22 Mar
Beal, M. A. BSc	(P)	25 Mar
Dyson, J. BSc qss	(N)	25 Mar
Stewart, G. BA	(P)	25 Mar
Allsop, D. A.	(P)	26 Mar
Brown, V. C. qss	(P)	26 Mar
Fenton, S. D. qss1	(P)	26 Mar
Jarvis, A. R. qss	(N)	26 Mar
Harris, P. J. qhti		
qss	(ALM)	30 Mar
Liivet, P. qss	(AEO)	30 Mar
Gourlay, D. C. MacG.		
BEng asq qs	(N)	1 Apr
Letch, M. J. BEng		
qcc	(N)	1 Apr
Johnston, N. D. S.		
MA	(P)	6 May
Squires, A. J. BSc cfs		
qss	(P)	6 May
Tucker, J. D. BSc		
qss	(N)	6 May
Weedon, G. C. BSc cfs		
qss	(P)	6 May
Geeson, C. T. cfs	(P)	7 May
Higgs, S. K. qss	(P)	7 May
Lowry, M. R. J. cfs	(P)	7 May
Dennis, M.	(P)	11 May
Duffy, C. P. qss1	(AEO)	11 May

Morton, N. D. BEng		
qss	(N)	12 May
Simmonds, M. A. BEng		
cfs qss2	(P)	12 May
Woodley, P. qss	(P)	26 May
Brown, G. J.		
MIOSH	(AEO)	22 June
Piercey, B. A. BA		
qss1	(N)	8 July
Sweatman, J. BSc qhti		
qss	(P)	8 July
Nixon, A. qss	(N)	11 July
Robinson, A. W.		
qss	(N)	13 Aug
Wilson, R. A.	(P)	13 Aug
Morris, D. J. R. qcc	(N)	15 Aug
Cant, A. J. BSc	(P)	18 Aug
Kinrade, I. G. BSc cfs		
qss1	(P)	18 Aug
Parkinson, F. C. J. BA		
cfs qss	(P)	18 Aug
Ashworth, D. C.		
MDefStud BSc	(N)	19 Aug
Hargreaves, A. K.		
qss	(N)	22 Aug
Mason, S. J. qcc	(N)	8 Sept
Tennant, J. A. cfs	(P)	27 Sept
Hulmes, T. A.	(ENG)	28 Sept
Bird, A. P. BSc qwi		
qcc	(P)	1 Oct
Faulds, M. D. MA		
qss1	(P)	1 Oct
Cavey, P. A. BA cfs		
qss1	(P)	2 Oct
Skinner, J. qss	(N)	12 Oct
James, B. F.	(P)	3 Nov
Fawcett, S. I. cfs(n)		
qss1	(N)	8 Nov
Jonas, W. M. tp		
qwi	(P)	8 Nov
Mitchell, F. G. asq		
qss	(N)	8 Nov
Othen, M. J. qss	(P)	8 Nov
Williams, R. O. cfs	(P)	8 Nov
Taylor, E. S. BA		
qss1	(N)	13 Nov
Atkinson, R. qss	(N)	19 Dec
Carlton, P. cfs	(P)	19 Dec
McGlone, A. T. qss	(N)	19 Dec
McLean, K.	(N)	19 Dec
Mewes, A. S. cfs	(P)	19 Dec
Parker, J. G. qwi		
qss	(P)	19 Dec
Poppleton, C. A.	(P)	19 Dec
Ward, N. P. D. cfs		
qss1	(P)	19 Dec
Palmer, A. qss	(P)	21 Dec
Oughton, N. M. BEd		
qss	(P)	24 Dec

Jenkins, J. H. BSc		
qwi(T) qcc	(N)	25 Dec

1992

Hughes, J. P. BSc		
qcc	(P)	8 Jan
Barrow, C. BA cfs		
qs	(P)	15 Jan
Clayphan, R. J. BSc		
tp	(P)	15 Jan
Dawson, A. E. L. BEng		
qss	(P)	15 Jan
Dean, S. J. BSc cfs		
qss	(P)	15 Jan
Farmer, N. J. BEng		
qss	(P)	15 Jan
Felgate, N. J. BEng qwi		
qcc	(P)	15 Jan
Grant, R. D. BEng cfs		
qcc	(P)	15 Jan
Harland, G. C. BSc		
qcc	(P)	15 Jan
Hooper, R. S. BSc		
qss	(N)	15 Jan
Hopkins, P. W. BSc	(P)	15 Jan
Hopkinson, A. M. BEng		
cfs	(P)	15 Jan
Kenworthy, D. I. BSc cfs		
qss	(P)	15 Jan
Kerley, A. A. BEng		
qss	(P)	15 Jan
Malcolm, J. M. W.		
BA	(P)	15 Jan
Powell, G. S. BEng		
qss	(P)	15 Jan
Watkins, P. A. BA		
qss2	(P)	15 Jan
Whyatt, O. B. BSc		
qss	(P)	15 Jan
King, M. J.	(P)	19 Jan
Johnson, S. asq cfs(n)		
qss	(N)	28 Jan
Bullick, G. B. cfs	(P)	31 Jan
Charlton, D. H. qss	(N)	31 Jan
Cullen, A. J.	(P)	31 Jan
Kingscott, R. A. asq		
qss	(N)	31 Jan
Squires, D. J.	(N)	31 Jan
Thomas, P. qss	(N)	31 Jan
Stinchcombe, C. G.		
qcc	(P)	4 Feb
Munro, W. P. qss	(N)	13 Feb
Wheeler, M. A.	(P)	17 Feb
Bailey, H. R. BSc		
qss	(P)	19 Feb
Brooker, J. G. BEng	(P)	19 Feb
McQuade, S. BSc		
cfs	(P)	19 Feb

119

Flight Lieutenants

1992—contd

Thomas, C. R. BEng			
cfs	(P)	19 Feb	
Tyson, P. J. BEng			
qs	(P)	19 Feb	
Reade, S. E. LLB			
qss1	(P)	20 Feb	
Robertson, A. MacD.			
qss	(P)	6 Mar	
Allan, M. S. qss1	(N)	8 Mar	
Burgess, T. J. DFC	(P)	11 Mar	
Davidson, G. S. qss	(P)	11 Mar	
Delaney, P. G.	(P)	11 Mar	
Green, M. J. qwi	(P)	11 Mar	
Littlejohns, G. E. tp	(P)	11 Mar	
Mutty, D. J.	(P)	11 Mar	
Roberts, G. P. qcc	(P)	11 Mar	
Rogan, J. G.	(ALM)	29 Mar	
Coolbear, R. A. BEng			
qwi qcc	(P)	30 Mar	
Cullen, S. M. BEd qhti			
qcc	(P)	30 Mar	
Edwards, O. E. BSc			
qss	(P)	30 Mar	
Freeman, S. E. G. BEng			
cfs	(P)	30 Mar	
Quick, A. N. BA			
qss1	(P)	30 Mar	
Wood, E. J. BSc			
qss1	(N)	30 Mar	
Hamill, S. J. BA qcc	(P)	1 Apr	
Oliver, S. C. BSc			
qcc	(N)	1 Apr	
Trueman, R. E. BEng tp			
qs	(P)	1 Apr	
Watts, P. A. F. BSc cfs			
qss	(P)	1 Apr	
McDermott, A. W.	(P)	8 Apr	
Cartwright, L. J.	(N)	23 Apr	
Correia, J. C.	(N)	23 Apr	
Eves, P. M. qss	(N)	23 Apr	
Glover, A. D. qss	(N)	23 Apr	
Jackson, R. G.	(N)	23 Apr	
Mattinson, R. G.			
qss	(P)	23 Apr	
Newton, N. D. qss	(P)	23 Apr	
Voigt, P. G. O.	(P)	23 Apr	
Reed, A. W. qss	(N)	29 Apr	
Lewis, I. J. qss	(AEO)	10 May	
McWilliams, I. R.			
BEng	(P)	11 May	
Wirdnam, G. T.			
BTech	(P)	11 May	
Baber, M. A. BSc			
qss1	(P)	12 May	

Cosens, I. J. BEng			
qss	(P)	12 May	
Hill, J. W. A. BEng			
cfs	(P)	12 May	
Manson, J. H. BEng cfs			
qss	(P)	12 May	
McLaughlin, S. J.			
qss	(N)	4 June	
Millington, J. C. asq			
qss	(N)	4 June	
Wilson, D. qwi(T)	(N)	4 June	
Hatzel, S. A. qss	(N)	20 June	
Ferris, S. J. qss	(AEO)	21 June	
Green, N. M. BA qs	(P)	6 July	
Brockett, J. W. A. BSc			
cfs qss	(P)	7 July	
Hannigan, S. D. BA			
qss	(P)	7 July	
Matson, R. C. qss1	(P)	7 July	
Morgan, P. R. BEng			
qss	(P)	7 July	
Chapman, S. R. qwi(T)			
qss	(N)	17 July	
Barrett, R. W. qwi(T)			
qss	(N)	29 July	
Beckett, P. C. qss	(N)	29 July	
Conner, A. G. qss	(P)	29 July	
Crowe, J. A. cfs qss	(P)	29 July	
Curtis, D. M. cfs			
qss	(P)	29 July	
Fazal, P. A.	(P)	29 July	
Gray, F. T. cfs qcc	(P)	29 July	
Oliver, M. J. cfs qss	(P)	29 July	
Rumsey, N. K. qss	(P)	29 July	
Rutherford, T. W.			
qss	(P)	29 July	
Jury, N. M. A.	(P)	31 July	
Dack, G. T. cfs	(P)	7 Aug	
Munns, P. N. BEng	(P)	17 Aug	
Shepherd, P. G. DFC			
BEng qcc	(P)	17 Aug	
Sykes, P. C. BSc qhti			
qss2	(P)	17 Aug	
Frost, D. K. BSc cfs			
qss	(P)	18 Aug	
Housley, R. S. A.			
BSc	(P)	18 Aug	
Pugh, A. D. BEng	(P)	18 Aug	
Bullen, M. P.	(P)	21 Aug	
Bradshaw, A. asq			
qss	(N)	12 Sept	
Fowler, M. L.	(P)	12 Sept	
Maggs, C. D. qss	(P)	12 Sept	
Merritt, P. J. tp qss	(P)	12 Sept	
Hardwick, M. qss (AEO)		26 Sept	
Smyth, D. M. qhti			
qs	(N)	26 Sept	
Ball, G. R. BEng			
asq	(N)	30 Sept	

Blake, R. D. BEng			
qcc	(P)	30 Sept	
Dale, A. L. BEng			
qcc	(P)	30 Sept	
Soul, M. D. MEng	(N)	30 Sept	
Baddeley, J. J. G.			
BSc	(P)	1 Oct	
Hadlow, C. D. BSc qwi			
qcc	(P)	1 Oct	
Wootton, W. J. BSc			
qwi(T) qcc	(P)	1 Oct	
Jury, J. G.	(P)	4 Oct	
Robertson, R. N. BA cfs			
qss	(P)	6 Oct	
Boyd, S. asq qss	(N)	23 Oct	
Burley, C. J. qcc	(N)	23 Oct	
Cottle, N. qss	(P)	23 Oct	
Davies, M. W. qss	(P)	23 Oct	
Hopcroft, I. D. qss	(P)	23 Oct	
McCallum, D. P.	(N)	23 Oct	
Monk, T. I. qss	(N)	23 Oct	
Panter, C. S.	(P)	23 Oct	
Curtis, A. C.	(P)	8 Nov	
Lauder, A. M. BSc	(P)	9 Nov	
Hodgkison, J. BSc	(N)	13 Nov	
Strang, J. R. BSc			
qss	(N)	13 Nov	
McGarrigle, S. B.	(P)	16 Nov	
Morrin, A. J. cfs	(P)	19 Nov	
Hamilton, D. J. qss	(P)	30 Nov	
Aspinall, M. E. qwi(T)			
qss1	(N)	4 Dec	
Beresford, A. qss1	(N)	4 Dec	
Davies, S. qss1	(P)	4 Dec	
Gray, A. cfs qss1	(P)	4 Dec	
Main, K. B. cfs qss	(P)	4 Dec	
Parker, A. M. B.	(N)	4 Dec	
Rodden, M. O. asq			
qss	(P)	4 Dec	
Abson, I. T.	(N)	12 Dec	
Ring, M. J. cfs(n)			
qss	(N)	20 Dec	
Truesdale, J.	(AEO)	20 Dec	
Cooper, N. R. BSc			
qss	(N)	24 Dec	
Donaghue, C. E. BSc			
qss	(N)	24 Dec	
Williams, M. P. BSc			
qss	(P)	24 Dec	

1993

Sumner, R. A. qss	(N)	1 Jan	
Strickland, C. E.	(P)	14 Jan	
Bayman, P. MBA MA			
BA	(P)	15 Jan	
Blythe, A. N. BEng			
qwi(T)	(P)	15 Jan	

Flight Lieutenants

1993—contd

Bradshaw, J. P. BSc
qwi(AD) qss (P) 15 Jan
Courtis, N. C. BSc
qss (P) 15 Jan
Day, M. J. BSc cfs (P) 15 Jan
Edwards, P. J. BA
cfs(pn) (P) 15 Jan
Foley, A. P. BEng
qss (N) 15 Jan
Gabriel, T. A. BSc (P) 15 Jan
Harrison, R. A. BSc cfs
qss (P) 15 Jan
Homer, R. StJ. BEng
qwi qcc (P) 15 Jan
Hoskison, R. J. BA cfs
qcc (P) 15 Jan
James, B. BEng qwi(T)
qss2 (P) 15 Jan
Kinnersley, S. J. BEng
cfs (P) 15 Jan
Lawrence, M. D.
BSc (P) 15 Jan
Maguire, A. J. BEng cfs
qcc (P) 15 Jan
McDermott, A. E. R.
BEng (P) 15 Jan
Nash, M. BSc qcc (P) 15 Jan
Seymour, R. P. qs (P) 15 Jan
Tomlinson, C. J. BSc
qss (P) 15 Jan
Waller, T. M. BSc
qss1 (P) 15 Jan
Weller, T. R. BSc cfs (P) 15 Jan
Williams, A. J. BSc
qss (N) 15 Jan
Archer, B. M. cfs qwi
qcc (P) 17 Jan
Duckworth, I. N. cfs
qss (P) 17 Jan
Nicholas, M. A.
qwi(AD) qs (P) 21 Jan
Pomeroy, A. I. cfs (P) 2 Feb
Rich, C. A. cfs(c)
qss (ALM) 14 Feb
Andrew, R. J. qss (N) 18 Feb
Burrows, D. H. BSc qwi
qcc (P) 18 Feb
Doyle, M. G. BA
qss2 (P) 18 Feb
Meneely, D. W. BA
qcc (P) 18 Feb
Bacon, A. D. BSc
qss2 (P) 19 Feb
Bromley, P. R. BSc
qss1 (P) 19 Feb

Cooney, S. qhti
qss2 (N) 19 Feb
Formoso, S. G. BSc qwi
qcc (P) 19 Feb
Humphrey, P. A. BSc
qcc (P) 19 Feb
Knight A. M. BEng
qcc (P) 19 Feb
Lilleyman, S. A. BSc
qcc (N) 19 Feb
Moreton, J. BEng
qwi(T) qss (P) 19 Feb
Reed, S. M. BSc
qcc (P) 19 Feb
Webster, P. J. BEng
qcc (P) 19 Feb
Butler, J. D. cfs
qss1 (P) 27 Feb
Houghton, A. M. cfs(n)
qss (N) 27 Feb
Traill, D. I. G. (P) 27 Feb
Williams, L. P. qss (N) 27 Feb
Heal, M. D. (ENG) 28 Mar
McKeith, T. N. (P) 28 Mar
Millward, A. A. (AEO) 28 Mar
Beard, D. BA (P) 29 Mar
Edwards, N. J. qcc (P) 29 Mar
McDermott, K. W. R.
BSc qcc (N) 29 Mar
Monahan, J. F. MA BA
qss (P) 29 Mar
Clancy, N. G. BSc cfs
qss (P) 30 Mar
Dale, B. E. LLB qss (P) 30 Mar
Fryar, D. N. BEng
qss1 (P) 30 Mar
McIlfatrick, G. R.
BEng (P) 30 Mar
Millns, P. A. BSc cfs
qss (P) 30 Mar
Parkin, K. BSc (P) 30 Mar
Poole, B. V. J. BEng
CEng MRAeS
qss (P) 30 Mar
Sharman, S. E. BA
qcc (N) 30 Mar
Smith, A. P. T. BA tp
qcc (P) 30 Mar
Storr, D. J. BSc
qss1 (N) 30 Mar
Woodward, J. E. BSc
qcc (P) 30 Mar
Bennison, M. A. asq
qss (N) 8 Apr
Crawley, N. R. qss (N) 8 Apr
Dix, R. P. qss (N) 8 Apr
Dodd, P. A. qss (P) 8 Apr
Entwisle, M. J. qs (P) 8 Apr
Hunter, G. M. qss (N) 8 Apr
Townshend, A. C. (P) 8 Apr

Cole, P. W. (N) 30 Apr
Forster, S. D. qss (P) 5 May
Barnsley, S. W.
qss1 (N) 9 May
Cripps, G. A. qss (ENG) 9 May
Gimenez, J. C. qcc (N) 9 May
Ash, J. C. BEng
qwi(AD) qcc (N) 11 May
Benham, P. W. BSc (P) 11 May
Bhasin, D. BEng
MRAeS qwi qss1 (P) 11 May
Cook, M. N. MA BA
qcc (P) 11 May
Flynn, A. G. G. BEng tp
qss (P) 11 May
Harden, R. J. BSc
qss1 (P) 11 May
James, S. F. MSc BEng
qcc (P) 11 May
Jones, J. P. BSc qcc (N) 11 May
Jurd, M. L. BSc qhti
qcc (N) 11 May
Kidd, P. BEng (P) 11 May
Kinsler, K. A. BSc
qcc (P) 11 May
Melvin, A. J. BA
qss1 (P) 11 May
Slow, D. J. BSc (P) 11 May
Sterritt, J. M. BEng
cfs (P) 11 May
Tarry, M. J. BEng (P) 11 May
Andrews, N. F.
qss1 (P) 18 May
Clegg, A. asq qss (N) 19 May
Cooke, R. BSc qss (N) 19 May
Daly, C. A. qhti
qss1 (P) 19 May
Coates, C. R. (P) 20 June
Noble, A. J. qss (AEO) 20 June
Searle, B. A. T. (AEO) 20 June
Clarke, S. J. G. (P) 27 June
Goodwyn, A. N. cfs
qss2 (P) 1 July
Pardoel, P. M. BSc (N) 3 July
Beck, K. J. BA qss (P) 6 July
Davies, N. F. BEng asq
qss (N) 6 July
Gardiner, H. M. BA
qcc (P) 6 July
Buckland, H. M. cfs
qss (P) 14 July
Dodds, A. M. qwi
qcc (P) 14 July
Gilling, P. R. T. qss (P) 14 July
Thompson, I. M.
qss (N) 14 July
Dodwell, G. D. (AEO) 29 July
Valentine, A. (ENG) 29 July
Wildey, S. K. T. tp qwi
qss (P) 5 Aug

Flight Lieutenants

1993—contd

Barlow, P. R. qss	(N)	16 Aug
Farmer, N. A.	(P)	16 Aug
Elliot, M. T. BEng		
qwi(AD)	(P)	17 Aug
Warren, D. J. BSc		
qss1	(N)	17 Aug
Williams, M. BEng asq		
qss1	(N)	17 Aug
Armeanu, A. R.	(P)	25 Aug
Grafton, J. E. asq		
qss	(N)	25 Aug
Leighton, J. D. cfs(g)*		
qss	(P)	25 Aug
Waugh, P. qss	(P)	25 Aug
Stevens, S. D. BSc	(P)	3 Sept
Jones, P. I.	(P)	5 Sept
Hodson, R. B. H.		
qcc	(P)	13 Sept
Drinkwater, G. M.		
qss1	(P)	26 Sept
Martin, R. C. MPhil		
BEng	(P)	29 Sept
Frecknall, I. T. BA	(N)	30 Sept
Evans, A. D.	(N)	5 Oct
Lismore, M. R. qcc	(N)	8 Oct
Auckland, G. W. cfs		
qcc	(P)	5 Nov
Cairns, S. J. N.	(P)	5 Nov
Everett, M. D. cfs		
qcc	(P)	5 Nov
Organ, R. W. qss1	(P)	5 Nov
Pearce, R. H. qss	(N)	5 Nov
Smith, R. I. qwi(T)		
qss1	(N)	5 Nov
Berry, K. P.	(P)	7 Nov
Radford, M. BEng		
qcc	(P)	12 Nov
Sinclair, D. BSc	(P)	12 Nov
Tiddy, J. N. BSc qcc	(P)	12 Nov
Wall, D. A. BSc qcc	(N)	12 Nov
Mitchell, N. R. qss	(P)	1 Dec
Honey, R. J.	(N)	14 Dec
Collins, S. qss	(P)	16 Dec
Leckey, M. J. cfs	(P)	16 Dec
McDonald, M. qss2	(P)	16 Dec
Mitchell, B. G. qcc	(N)	16 Dec
Norris, R. S. cfs qss	(P)	16 Dec
O'Rourke, J. P. qcc	(P)	16 Dec
Purkis, E. R. qcc	(N)	16 Dec
Seymour-Dale, S. A. tp		
qss	(P)	16 Dec
Brooks, M. W. BSc		
qcc	(P)	23 Dec
Lamping, S. J.		
BEng	(P)	23 Dec

Warren, C. J. BSc	(P)	23 Dec

1994

Tagg, A. M. cfs qss	(P)	10 Jan
Baxter, A. MSc BEng		
cfs qcc	(P)	15 Jan
Belton, A. C. MA		
qss2	(P)	15 Jan
Burge, A. S. BSc		
qss1	(N)	15 Jan
Burke, T. J. P. MA BSc		
qcc	(P)	15 Jan
Cann, A. D. BA qwi		
qcc	(P)	15 Jan
Chevli, R. J. MA BSc		
qwi(T) qss1	(P)	15 Jan
Chitty, F. M. BSc	(P)	15 Jan
Conner, A. C. BSc	(N)	15 Jan
Denyer, K. A. BEng		
qcc	(N)	15 Jan
Fletcher, P. A. BEng qwi		
qcc	(P)	15 Jan
Lawrenson, D. J. MSc		
BA	(P)	15 Jan
Linsley, A. BSc		
qss1	(P)	15 Jan
May, J. M. BSc		
qss1	(N)	15 Jan
Molyneux, E. T. U. BA		
qcc	(P)	15 Jan
Rendall, M. R. BEng		
qwi(AD) qcc	(N)	15 Jan
Ritchie, A. J. BSc		
qss	(P)	15 Jan
Sanderson, D. P. BSc		
qss1	(N)	15 Jan
Smith, P. A. BSc		
qwi(AD)	(P)	15 Jan
Zarecky, C. P. J. MA		
BSc(Econ)	(P)	15 Jan
Blair, S. A.	(P)	17 Jan
Oldfield, S. C. R.		
qcc	(N)	20 Jan
Tuck, M. A.	(N)	20 Jan
Chadderton, D. M.		
qss	(N)	28 Jan
Hamilton, A. E. R.	(P)	28 Jan
Holleworth, L. A.	(N)	28 Jan
Marwood, R. qss	(N)	28 Jan
Moss, D. R. K.	(P)	28 Jan
Powers, D. R. qwi		
qss1	(P)	28 Jan
Wright, R. J.	(N)	28 Jan
Roll, K. S.	(P)	31 Jan
Slatter, F. G.	(P)	31 Jan
Daly, C. M.	(P)	9 Feb
Bloomer, G. A. M.		
asq	(AEO)	13 Feb

Ramsay, D. G. qcc	(AEO)	13 Feb
Armstrong, I. R. B. BSc		
qss	(P)	16 Feb
Gaskell, A. S. BEng		
qcc	(P)	16 Feb
Sealey, L. J. BSc		
qss1	(P)	16 Feb
Freeman, T. J. BSc		
qcc	(P)	18 Feb
Hindley, N. J. BEng qwi		
qcc	(P)	18 Feb
Knight, T. J. BA qss	(P)	18 Feb
McCombie, P. B.		
BSc	(P)	18 Feb
Richards, D. BEng		
qcc	(N)	18 Feb
Claringbould, S. E.		
qss1	(P)	22 Mar
Kennedy, G. G. cfs		
qss1	(P)	22 Mar
Roberts, D. G. qss1	(P)	22 Mar
Rolfe, S. R. cfs qss	(P)	22 Mar
Rutter, K. J. qss	(P)	22 Mar
Thompson, D. P. cfs		
qcc	(P)	22 Mar
Watts, R. D. qss	(N)	22 Mar
Bond, M. qss1	(AEO)	26 Mar
Burlingham, P. A.	(P)	26 Mar
Ackland, P. M. BSc		
qss	(P)	29 Mar
Baulkwill, M. R. BEng		
qwi qss1	(P)	29 Mar
Copple, J. A. BEng		
qss1	(P)	29 Mar
Davis, I. S. BA qcc	(P)	29 Mar
Evans, J. E. MSc BEng		
qcc	(P)	29 Mar
Forster, N. J. BSc	(P)	29 Mar
Hall, D. P. BEng	(P)	29 Mar
McNeil, J. D. BSc	(P)	29 Mar
Summers, C. M. BSc		
qss	(P)	29 Mar
Williams, J. V. BSc	(P)	29 Mar
Cochrane, D. S.		
BSc	(P)	11 Apr
Millar, P. F. BSc	(P)	11 Apr
Morris, J. B. BCom	(P)	11 Apr
Rhind, M. G. BEng	(P)	11 Apr
Shepherd, D. J. qcc	(P)	12 Apr
Cooper, C. C.	(P)	19 Apr
Carrodus, A. J. cfs		
qcc	(P)	2 May
Foster-Bazin, S. M.		
qss	(P)	2 May
Smylie, P. qss	(N)	2 May
Hutchinson D. E. K.		
qss	(ALM)	7 May
Kneen, C. T. E.	(AEO)	7 May
Farman, D. J. BSc	(P)	10 May

Flight Lieutenants

1994—contd

Harris, R. J. BEng		
qcc	(P)	10 May
Heaney, N. C. BSc		
qss	(P)	10 May
Ponting, T. M. BSc	(P)	10 May
Reid, A. I. A. BA		
qss1	(N)	10 May
Robertson, N. G. BEng		
qss1	(P)	10 May
Squires, C. C. M. MA		
BEng qwi qcc	(P)	10 May
Sodeau, M. D.	(P)	16 May
King, E. N. F. BSc		
qss1	(N)	6 June
Lewry, J. R. qss	(P)	15 June
Perrin, N. A.	(P)	15 June
Blackburn, C. A. (ENG)		16 June
Bingham, J. H.	(N)	18 June
Mackenzie-Brown, P. E.		
BSc	(P)	29 June
Woodward, M. J.		
BEng	(P)	5 July
Kilkenny, G. M.		
qcc	(AEO)	30 July
McColl, A. qcc	(N)	9 Aug
Wareham, M. J.	(N)	12 Aug
Brown, L. F. BA qcc	(P)	14 Aug
Cogley, N. M. B. BSc		
qcc	(P)	14 Aug
MacNaughton, K. BA		
qcc	(P)	14 Aug
Perilleux, G. B. J. BA		
qcc	(P)	14 Aug
Miller, P. D. qcc	(P)	16 Aug
Witcombe, P. R.		
qcc	(P)	16 Aug
Pilliner, A. N. MA		
qcc	(P)	29 Sept
Cepelak, G. P. qss	(N)	30 Sept
Colman, J. M. qss	(P)	30 Sept
Denton, R. A. qwi(AD)		
qss	(P)	30 Sept
MacMillan, I. D.	(P)	30 Sept
Taylor, L. A. qhti		
qcc	(N)	30 Sept
Tully, D. H. qss	(P)	30 Sept
Maclachlan, C. C.	(P)	31 Oct
Murphy, T. J. L. qcc	(P)	1 Nov
Diggle, I. J. BEng		
qss2	(P)	10 Nov
Quinn, M. P. BEng		
qcc	(P)	10 Nov
Barnes, J. A. F. cfs		
qss1	(P)	11 Nov
Lilley, A. qcc	(P)	11 Nov

MacDonald, F. J.		
qcc	(N)	11 Nov
Nichols, R. J. qcc	(P)	11 Nov
Leeder, J. D. qss	(N)	15 Nov
Hake, D. qcc	(N)	30 Nov
Gregory, A. J. qss2	(P)	21 Dec
Baines, M. W. qcc	(P)	22 Dec
Dewes, R. J. M. qss	(P)	22 Dec
Gubb, P. J. qss	(P)	22 Dec
James, D. J. qss	(P)	22 Dec
Pappini, N. J. cfs		
qcc	(P)	22 Dec

1995

Davenhill, J. C. M.		
BEng qcc	(P)	5 Jan
Abra, S. M. BEng		
qcc	(N)	15 Jan
Brosch, I. M. MA BSc		
qcc	(P)	15 Jan
Clarke, D. I. T. BSc	(P)	15 Jan
Crawford, J. B. BEng		
qss1	(N)	15 Jan
Datson, R. I. BSc	(P)	15 Jan
Elworthy, R. J. BA	(P)	15 Jan
Froome, P. D. BEng		
qcc	(P)	15 Jan
Gambold, K. A. BSc		
qss	(P)	15 Jan
Gatenby, N. J. BSc		
qss	(P)	15 Jan
Glaves, G. R. BA	(P)	15 Jan
Grogan, I. BSc	(P)	15 Jan
Hamilton, T. G. W. BA		
qcc	(P)	15 Jan
Helliwell, J. BSc		
qwi(AD) qcc	(P)	15 Jan
Jones, G. A. BEng		
qss	(P)	15 Jan
Laugharne, P. A. BEng		
qss1	(P)	15 Jan
Ling, R. J. D. BSc		
qcc	(P)	15 Jan
Mackereth, J. E. BSc		
qss	(N)	15 Jan
Marsh, K. BEng cfs		
qcc	(P)	15 Jan
Meikle, J. C. BSc	(P)	15 Jan
Milward, R. J.		
BEng	(P)	15 Jan
Nelson, J. W. BEng	(P)	15 Jan
Sargent, B. BEng		
qhti	(P)	15 Jan
Sawbridge, T. C. BSc		
qss1	(P)	15 Jan
Smith, S. H. BSc		
qss1	(P)	15 Jan

Yates, R. J. BEng qwi(T)		
qss	(N)	15 Jan
Bartrip, J. R. L. qcc	(P)	27 Jan
Coombs, D. J. qss	(P)	27 Jan
Hamilton, S. F. qss	(N)	27 Jan
Oakes, S. L. qwi(T)		
qss1	(P)	27 Jan
Sheffield, J. A. qhti	(P)	27 Jan
Discombe, M. cfs		
qss2	(P)	29 Jan
Lindsay, J. W. qhti		
qss	(N)	30 Jan
Hamilton, T. A. (ALM)		11 Feb
Peebles, A. B. qss2	(P)	11 Feb
Roscoe, M. W.	(P)	11 Feb
Watson, D. C. (ALM)		11 Feb
Lafferty, J. P. BSc	(P)	15 Feb
Brown, R. G. BEng		
qss1	(P)	16 Feb
Cartlidge, R. BSc qhti		
qcc	(N)	16 Feb
Eyles, T. BEng	(P)	16 Feb
Gibbs, D. A. BSc qhti		
qss2	(N)	16 Feb
Heald, J. E. BEng		
qwi	(P)	16 Feb
Hughes, S. G. BEng qwi		
qss	(P)	16 Feb
Martin, S. A. BEng		
qss	(P)	16 Feb
McKenzie, R. L.		
BSc	(P)	16 Feb
Michael, R. J. BEng		
qcc	(P)	16 Feb
Moyes, D. R. BEng	(P)	16 Feb
Myers, H. J. MA BSc		
qss1	(P)	16 Feb
Parsons, R. BSc	(P)	16 Feb
Williams, S. P. BEng		
qwi qss	(P)	16 Feb
Roberts, A. G. qwi(T)		
qcc	(N)	18 Feb
Castle, B. C.	(P)	25 Feb
Aveling, G. qcc	(P)	28 Mar
Bensly, R. W. qcc	(N)	28 Mar
Bethell, S. F. qss1	(P)	28 Mar
Frick, R. E. cfs	(P)	28 Mar
Harbottle, E. G. M. cfs		
qcc	(P)	28 Mar
Lewis, M. qcc	(N)	28 Mar
McKeon, A. J. cfs		
qcc	(P)	28 Mar
Rosser, A. G. cfs		
qcc	(P)	28 Mar
Richardson, A. G.		
qss1	(P)	2 Apr
Dawson, A. J. BA		
qss	(P)	10 Apr
McCrory, P. M. BA	(N)	10 Apr

123

Flight Lieutenants

1995—contd

Adamson, J. P. M. BSc		
qs	(P)	11 Apr
Banks, S. M. BEng		
qss1	(P)	11 Apr
Best, D. A. BSc	(N)	11 Apr
Gault, G. W. K. BA	(P)	11 Apr
Gibb, R. J. BSc	(P)	11 Apr
Holland, M. R. BEng		
qcc	(P)	11 Apr
Kennard P. K. BA qhti		
qcc	(P)	11 Apr
Kenyon, D. J. BEng	(P)	11 Apr
Lloyd-Evans, G. BEng		
qhti qcc	(N)	11 Apr
Millward, P. T. BEng		
qss	(P)	11 Apr
Moore, S. I. BSc	(P)	11 Apr
Morley, N. R. BSc	(P)	11 Apr
Murphy, W. R. BEng		
qcc	(P)	11 Apr
Rushmere, L. D. G.		
BSc	(P)	11 Apr
Singleton, P. R. BSc	(P)	11 Apr
Stradling, A. P. BSc		
qss2	(P)	11 Apr
Crocker, P. T. qss	(P)	9 May
Jevons, A. P.	(N)	9 May
Sharp, M. J. qcc	(P)	9 May
Skene, R. K.	(P)	9 May
Wright, D. qss1	(P)	9 May
Renshaw, M.		
qss1	(ENG)	3 June
Scott, A. J.	(ENG)	3 June
Dixon, R. S. BSc		
qcc	(N)	6 June
Flewers, J. A. BSc	(P)	6 June
Hendy, I. D. BSc		
qwi(T) qcc	(N)	6 June
Mack, A. P. BSc qcc	(N)	6 June
Robinson, J. R.		
BEng	(P)	6 June
Startup, D. J. BSc		
qcc	(P)	6 June
Barratt, C. D. cfs(n)		
qss	(N)	21 June
House, G. E. W. MBA		
qcc	(P)	21 June
Lock, G. R.	(N)	21 June
Luggar, A. J. cfs		
qss	(P)	21 June
Middleton, D. N. cfs		
qss	(P)	21 June
Tickle, A. qcc	(N)	21 June
Crane, R.	(AEO)	28 July

Robertson, R. L.		
qss2	(ENG)	28 July
Thomas, D. qwi		
qcc	(P)	3 Aug
Marston, S. K. qcc	(P)	12 Aug
Bowes, J. P. BEng		
qss	(P)	13 Aug
Moss, P. S. BEng	(P)	13 Aug
Wisely, A. C. E. BSc		
qss	(P)	13 Aug
Bell, S. J. BSc qcc	(N)	14 Aug
Taylor, P. R. BEng	(P)	14 Aug
Upward, J. BEng		
qss1	(P)	14 Aug
Geary, N. J. qss	(P)	15 Aug
Moriarty, E. P. cfs		
qss2	(P)	15 Aug
Parker, R. S. qss	(P)	15 Aug
Tyzack, J. A. DipMgmt		
qss	(P)	15 Aug
Adey, S. K. qwi		
qss1	(P)	29 Sept
Burrows, E. J. qcc	(P)	29 Sept
Cox, P. C. qcc	(N)	29 Sept
Cripps, S. T. qss2	(P)	29 Sept
Daniels, S. M. qcc	(P)	29 Sept
Donnelly, J. A. F.		
qhti	(P)	29 Sept
Evans, W. L. qss1	(P)	29 Sept
Flynn, M. A. cfs qcc	(P)	29 Sept
Green, E. B. H. qhti	(P)	29 Sept
Lippiatt, S. D. cfs	(P)	29 Sept
Massey, P. C. cfs		
qss	(P)	29 Sept
Maund, J. C. qcc	(P)	29 Sept
Mills, D. W. qss	(P)	29 Sept
Reece, J. MEng qss	(P)	10 Oct
Hobkirk, J. D.	(P)	9 Nov
Alcock, M. L. qcc	(P)	10 Nov
Applegarth, C. G.		
cfs	(P)	10 Nov
Batey, R. qhti	(P)	10 Nov
Bosworth, P. C. cfs	(P)	10 Nov
Clayton, G. J. qcc	(N)	10 Nov
Dann, G. J. cfs qss2	(P)	10 Nov
Dobie, A. F. qcc	(P)	10 Nov
Eaton, D. J. qs	(N)	10 Nov
Franklin, A. R. cfs		
qss1	(P)	10 Nov
Hepburn, P. R. qs	(P)	10 Nov
Howett, D. qwi(T)		
qss	(P)	10 Nov
Kay, D. J. qcc	(P)	10 Nov
Owen, D. E. qss1	(P)	10 Nov
Waller, R. D. qss	(P)	10 Nov
McCann, B.	(P)	9 Dec
Booth, D. L. qhti	(P)	21 Dec
Farrell, D. S. qs	(N)	21 Dec
Marshall, P. B. qcc	(P)	21 Dec
McAdam, W. J.	(P)	21 Dec

Payne, J. C. qwi(T)		
qcc	(N)	21 Dec

1996

Sutherland, S. A.		
M.	(N)	11 Jan
Arthurton, D. S. BEng		
qwi(T) qss	(P)	15 Jan
Evans, J. C. BEng		
qwi(AD) qss1	(N)	15 Jan
Fraser, N. A. BEng qwi		
qss	(P)	15 Jan
Hampson, M. BA		
qss	(P)	15 Jan
Houston, R. S. BSc	(P)	15 Jan
MacMillan, A. A.	(P)	15 Jan
Marsden, D. F. BA		
qcc	(P)	15 Jan
Mason, D. P. BA	(P)	15 Jan
Paterson, S. A. BSc		
qss2	(P)	15 Jan
Pollard, N. G. BSc		
qcc	(P)	15 Jan
Poulter, J. L. BEng		
qcc	(N)	15 Jan
Priestnall, A. R. BEng		
qcc	(P)	15 Jan
Ratcliffe, B. E. BSc		
qcc	(P)	15 Jan
Reeks, S. I. BSc	(P)	15 Jan
Rigby, J. D. qhti	(P)	15 Jan
Saunders, R. J.		
BEng	(P)	15 Jan
Sington, D. K. BS cfs		
qss	(P)	15 Jan
Slattery, M. L. BEng		
qs	(P)	15 Jan
Stanley, J. M. BEng		
qss	(P)	15 Jan
Stilwell, J. M. BEng		
qss	(P)	15 Jan
Thomas, E. M. BEng cfs		
qss1	(P)	15 Jan
West, C. R. BSc	(P)	15 Jan
Berris, D. C. D. qss	(P)	2 Feb
Hayes, M. A. qwi		
qss1	(P)	2 Feb
Holder, I. D. qs	(P)	2 Feb
Jewiss, S. E. qss	(P)	2 Feb
McKay, J. G.	(P)	2 Feb
Sparks, C. D. cfs(pn)		
qcc	(P)	2 Feb
Stead, D. K. qss1	(N)	2 Feb
Stevenson, C.	(P)	2 Feb
Toomey, L. D. cfs	(P)	2 Feb
Jones, S. R. cfs	(P)	4 Feb
Livingstone, D. A.		
BEng	(P)	14 Feb

Flight Lieutenants

1996—contd

Fisher, S. A. BEng	(P)	15 Feb
Guest, J. A. BEng	(P)	15 Feb
Harding, P. C. B. BA		
qcc	(P)	15 Feb
Henderson-Begg, R. I.		
BEng qss	(N)	15 Feb
Higgins, M. J. BEng		
cfs	(P)	15 Feb
Means, S. W. BSc	(P)	15 Feb
Mounsey, P. N. BSc		
qwi	(P)	15 Feb
Netherwood, A. G.		
BSc(Econ) qcc	(P)	15 Feb
Pollard, S. M.	(N)	15 Feb
Beddall, J. T. qss1	(P)	26 Mar
Hasted, M. R. qcc	(P)	26 Mar
Holland, A. K. qwi		
qcc	(P)	26 Mar
Howe, J. B.	(P)	26 Mar
Jess, R.	(N)	26 Mar
Marshall, R. D. qcc	(P)	26 Mar
Shirley, S. B. qwi(H)		
qcc	(P)	26 Mar
Doncaster, M. R. cfs		
qcc	(P)	1 Apr
Oxford, M. G. qss	(N)	2 Apr
Keen, S.	(ALM)	7 Apr
Lilly, P. D. MBE	(AEO)	7 Apr
Donald, C. S. BEng	(P)	9 Apr
Hopkins, G. A.		
BEng	(P)	9 Apr
Morton, N. C. B.		
BEng	(P)	9 Apr
Pocock, M. F. BEng	(P)	9 Apr
Stewart, M. J. MA	(P)	9 Apr
Twidell, A. J. BEng	(P)	9 Apr
Averty, C. J. BA qcc	(P)	10 Apr
Baker, M. T. BSc	(P)	10 Apr
Brandon, B. BEng	(P)	10 Apr
Bridge, E. K. L. BEng		
qss1	(N)	10 Apr
Brown, P. J. BA qss	(P)	10 Apr
Cook, N. P. BSc qcc	(N)	10 Apr
Counter, J. S. BSc		
qcc	(N)	10 Apr
Frewin, K. R. BSc	(P)	10 Apr
Holt, C. A. MSc BSc	(P)	10 Apr
Johns, D. E. H. BA		
qss1	(P)	10 Apr
Oetzmann, D. M.		
BEng	(P)	10 Apr
Stevens, J. A. BSc		
qcc	(P)	10 Apr
Towell, A. M. BEng		
qss	(P)	10 Apr

Trasler, K. F. MLitt BA		
qcc	(P)	10 Apr
Turner, J. J. BA	(P)	10 Apr
Spain, D.	(AEO)	7 May
Bloom, A. H. qss2	(P)	8 May
Brown, K. P. cfs qss	(P)	8 May
Buchanan, I. M. qcc	(P)	8 May
Creese, L. B.	(P)	8 May
Griggs, J. P. qwi(T)	(P)	8 May
Owen, T. E. qwi(T)		
qcc	(N)	8 May
Rawlins, D. G. qcc	(P)	8 May
Shenton, A. G.		
qss	(ALM)	9 May
McLean, T. J. BEng	(P)	2 June
Jessett, S. P. qwi		
qcc	(P)	5 June
Crowther, J.	(P)	10 June
Cockram, M. S. BEng		
qcc	(P)	18 June
Fitch, S. A. cfs qss	(P)	20 June
Forbes, D. R. qwi(T)		
qss1	(P)	20 June
Kirby, D. J. qwi(T)		
qcc	(P)	20 June
Moran, K. R.	(P)	20 June
Thompson, J. R.		
qss1	(N)	20 June
Anderson, S. W.	(P)	7 July
Scott, A. J.	(P)	18 July
Burgess, A. J. qss1	(P)	28 July
Chadwick, L. A.	(ALM)	28 July
Courtaux, N. P.		
qss	(ENG)	28 July
Gresham, A. P.		
qss2	(AEO)	28 July
Harris, L. A. qcc	(ALM)	28 July
Lawrence, I. M.	(ALM)	28 July
Paynton, P. J.	(AEO)	28 July
Steele, P. C.	(ENG)	28 July
Simmons, J.	(AEO)	30 July
Dunn, J. F. BEng	(P)	12 Aug
Berry, R. I. BSc		
qss1	(P)	13 Aug
Ervine, B. J. qss1	(P)	14 Aug
Fraser, C. L. cfs	(P)	14 Aug
Hirst, J. M.	(P)	14 Aug
Penrice, I. W.	(P)	9 Sept
Bousfield, R. J. qcc	(P)	28 Sept
Connor, R. A. qss2	(N)	28 Sept
Cree, S. J. S. qcc	(P)	28 Sept
Davies, R. A. qwi(T)		
qcc	(P)	28 Sept
Moore, G. P. qcc	(P)	28 Sept
Ormiston, J. A. qss	(P)	28 Sept
Palmer, M. S.	(P)	28 Sept
Smith, R. C. W.	(P)	28 Sept
Whitehill, J.	(P)	28 Sept
Gusterson, L. qhti		
qss2	(P)	29 Sept

Holman, M. J.		
cfs(c)	(ALM)	6 Oct
Barker, N. S. BA	(P)	9 Oct
Hollywood, M. J.		
BSc	(N)	9 Oct
Jones, J. L. H. BA	(P)	9 Oct
Mayo, L. M. MA	(N)	9 Oct
Rae, C. MEng	(P)	9 Oct
Eden, J. K. BSc	(P)	10 Oct
Joel, R. W. H.		
BSocSc	(P)	10 Oct
McGurk, D. G. BEng		
qss1	(N)	10 Oct
Walden, D. R. BEng	(N)	10 Oct
Pearce, M. A. qss1	(P)	27 Oct
Austin, S. J. BEng		
qss	(P)	9 Nov
Bazalgette, G. R.		
qcc	(N)	9 Nov
Dickens, A. qcc	(P)	9 Nov
Driscoll, N. J. S.		
qss	(P)	9 Nov
Edwards, H. qwi(T)		
qcc	(P)	9 Nov
Farrant, R. P. qss	(N)	9 Nov
Fraser, R. M. qwi(T)		
qcc	(P)	9 Nov
Godfrey, P. A. qwi		
qss1	(P)	9 Nov
Jardine, E. S. R.	(P)	9 Nov
Sharpe, P. R. cfs		
qcc	(P)	9 Nov
Smith, R. R. asq		
qcc	(P)	9 Nov
Stewart, N. R.	(P)	9 Nov
Wood, A. M. qcc	(N)	9 Nov
Heamon, P. J.	(N)	11 Dec
Brewis, S. T. qs	(P)	20 Dec
Jamieson, D. S. cfs	(P)	20 Dec
Lapham, P. A. A.	(N)	20 Dec
Mason, D. C. qwi		
qcc	(P)	20 Dec
Millar, H. M. qs	(N)	20 Dec
O'Brien, P. A.	(P)	20 Dec
Olsen, M. P. L.	(N)	20 Dec
Parker, D. A.	(P)	20 Dec
Richards, J. B. qcc	(P)	20 Dec
Simpson, S. P. MA	(P)	20 Dec
Turk, A. D. qwi(T)		
qcc	(N)	20 Dec

1997

Long, R. C. J. R.		
qcc	(N)	6 Jan
Bagnall, G. BSc	(P)	15 Jan
Bowlzer, D. J. M.	(P)	15 Jan
Cochrane, P. G. BA		
qcc	(P)	15 Jan

Flight Lieutenants

1997—contd

Cole, S. R. MA qcc	(N)	15 Jan
Crutchlow, P. S. BSc		
qss	(P)	15 Jan
Dewar, J. E. BEng		
qss	(P)	15 Jan
Johnson, A. M. BEng		
ACGI qcc	(P)	15 Jan
Lund, A. J. K. BSc	(P)	15 Jan
Marshall, A. P. MA qwi		
qss	(P)	15 Jan
McNaught, R. S. BEng		
qss	(P)	15 Jan
Percival, I. qss	(P)	15 Jan
Philpot, T. J. qss	(P)	15 Jan
Priest, J. DFC qss	(P)	15 Jan
Sanders, D. T.		
BEng	(P)	15 Jan
Simpson, K. BSc	(P)	15 Jan
Snaith, C. D. BA		
qss	(P)	15 Jan
Stewart, D. I. qcc	(P)	15 Jan
Tandy, M. J. qcc	(P)	15 Jan
Tompkins, S. M.	(P)	15 Jan
Trimble, S. BA	(P)	15 Jan
Whitney, M. A.	(P)	15 Jan
Breeze, J. P.	(P)	29 Jan
Collings, S. J. qss1	(P)	29 Jan
Cox, S. J.	(P)	29 Jan
Dunn, R. B. qss1	(N)	29 Jan
Freeman, S. cfs	(P)	29 Jan
Nolan, B.	(P)	29 Jan
Read, A. J.	(P)	29 Jan
Simmons, D. J. qwi		
qss1	(P)	29 Jan
Smith, M. B. qwi(T)		
qcc	(P)	29 Jan
Wells, R. A. C. qcc	(N)	29 Jan
Hemlin, K. W.		
BEng	(AEO)	6 Feb
Hopkins, K. R.	(AEO)	9 Feb
Peebles, L. A.		
qcc	(ALM)	9 Feb
Dark, E. A. BA	(P)	13 Feb
Dunning, J. R. BA	(P)	13 Feb
Hunter, L. J. BEng	(P)	13 Feb
Loughran, S. MA	(P)	13 Feb
McArthur, C. P. D.		
BSc	(P)	13 Feb
Seymour, C. W. E.		
BA	(P)	13 Feb
Sutherland, M. J.		
BCom	(P)	13 Feb
Thomson, J. A. C.		
BSc	(N)	13 Feb

Beldon, J. R. BSc		
qss2	(N)	14 Feb
Bond, H. R. MSc		
BSc	(P)	14 Feb
Burnet, A. E. BA		
qcc	(N)	14 Feb
Davison, P. BSc	(P)	14 Feb
Dow, A. V. BEng	(P)	14 Feb
Giles, N. S. BEng	(P)	14 Feb
Hedley Lewis, H. C.		
LLB	(P)	14 Feb
Hillier, S. W. BEng	(P)	14 Feb
Keenlyside, P. G. BSc		
cfs	(P)	14 Feb
Ludman, A. I. BEng	(P)	14 Feb
Ruscoe, T. J. BEng		
qss	(P)	14 Feb
Sagar, G. M. BSc	(P)	14 Feb
Wightman, D. J. BEng		
qss1	(N)	14 Feb
Challen, A. P. qcc	(P)	26 Mar
Dennis, R. J. qwi(T)		
qcc	(P)	26 Mar
Hargreaves, V. J.	(P)	26 Mar
Ollis, J. P.	(P)	26 Mar
Paine, R. N. qwi(T)	(P)	26 Mar
Pook, S. A. qwi(AD)	(P)	26 Mar
Preece, A. D.	(P)	26 Mar
Smith, M. G.	(P)	26 Mar
Tudge, E. V. qss	(P)	26 Mar
Williams, D. qss2	(P)	26 Mar
Hazell, C. S. qss	(N)	1 Apr
Crockett, M. L.	(P)	6 Apr
Jopling, B. W.		
QGM	(ALM)	6 Apr
Jones, T. T. BSc qcc	(P)	8 Apr
Lenahan, C. A. BA	(N)	8 Apr
Maslin, A. C. BSc	(P)	8 Apr
Middleton, C. S.		
BSc	(N)	8 Apr
Sheldon, J. B. BSc	(P)	8 Apr
Battersby, N. BEng	(P)	9 Apr
Berry, N. S. BSc	(P)	9 Apr
Blackwell, S. E. BEng		
qcc	(P)	9 Apr
Bunn, T. BSc	(P)	9 Apr
Carvosso, P. F. BSocSc		
qss	(P)	9 Apr
Cloke, S. J. BEng	(P)	9 Apr
Davis, I. A. BSc	(P)	9 Apr
Everitt, J. M. BEng	(P)	9 Apr
Goodfellow, P. R.		
BA	(N)	9 Apr
Hanlon, A. D. BA		
cfs	(P)	9 Apr
Hough, J. T. W. BSc		
qss	(P)	9 Apr
Kellett, R. J. BEng	(P)	9 Apr
Lindsell, S. BSc	(P)	9 Apr

Marshall, S. A. LLB		
qwi(AD)	(N)	9 Apr
Murphy-Latham, P. R.		
BSc qcc	(P)	9 Apr
South, M. R. BSc	(P)	9 Apr
Wells, A. E. BSc	(P)	9 Apr
Wyatt, P. J. BSc	(P)	9 Apr
Allison, R. P. G. cfs		
qss1	(P)	24 Apr
Carr, T. D. qwi(T)		
qcc	(N)	7 May
Checkley-Mills, A. D.	(P)	7 May
Main, S. J. AFC cfs		
qss	(P)	7 May
May, B. J. S. qss1	(P)	7 May
Whipp, R. I. qcc	(N)	7 May
Wood, D. G. D. qcc	(P)	7 May
Wright, A. J. qss2	(N)	26 May
Page, G. qwi(T) qcc	(N)	3 June
Caley, J. J.	(P)	6 June
Crawford, J. qwi(T)	(P)	8 June
Braid, B. R. cfs qwi(H)		
qcc	(P)	19 June
Cartner, J. G. S.		
qss1	(P)	19 June
Drew, N. R.		
qwi(AD)	(N)	19 June
Horrigan, A. J.	(P)	19 June
Mills, R. M.	(P)	19 June
Molineaux, M. K.		
qwi(T) qss	(P)	19 June
Robins, A. C. R. qss	(P)	19 June
Stuchfield, D. J.	(P)	19 June
Davey, M. F. qss1	(P)	11 July
Graham, A. G.	(ENG)	28 July
Hockley, D. C.		
qcc	(AEO)	28 July
Mackay, A. J.		
qcc	(ENG)	28 July
Bradford, I. J. BEng	(N)	11 Aug
Dunlop, M. T. MA		
qcc	(P)	11 Aug
Gillan, C. J. BA qss	(N)	11 Aug
Kovach, S. J. BA	(P)	11 Aug
Rolfe, J. H. BA	(P)	11 Aug
Curzon, R. T. BA		
qcc	(N)	12 Aug
Graham, M. C.		
BEng	(P)	12 Aug
Page, M. BA	(N)	12 Aug
Spencer-Jones, M. G.		
BEng	(P)	12 Aug
Wilkes, J. BA qcc	(N)	12 Aug
Dean, M. S. cfs	(P)	13 Aug
Hickey, S. M.	(P)	13 Aug
Rayne, S. E. qss1	(P)	13 Aug
Wootten, P. W. qss	(N)	13 Aug
Inman, A. P.	(P)	22 Aug
Evison, W. C.		
BSc	(AEO)	5 Sept

Flight Lieutenants

1997—contd

Cole, P. A. qss2	(P)	26 Sept
Cooper, P. D.	(P)	26 Sept
Henning, I. C. cfs	(P)	26 Sept
Kane, D. P. qwi qcc	(P)	26 Sept
Killeen, D. qwi qcc	(P)	26 Sept
McCullagh, J. qss1	(P)	26 Sept
Richardson, D. T.		
qss	(P)	26 Sept
Rogers, C. P.	(P)	26 Sept
Lennon, M. M.	(P)	5 Oct
Collins, L. BEng	(N)	7 Oct
Dempster, C. S.		
BEng	(P)	7 Oct
Phoenix, N. BA qss	(P)	7 Oct
Ross, S. BSc	(P)	7 Oct
Altoft, P. B. BSc	(P)	9 Oct
Cothill, G. M. J. BSc	(P)	9 Oct
Dales, N. M. C. BA	(P)	9 Oct
English, M. J. BA	(P)	9 Oct
Green, R. A. BEng	(P)	9 Oct
Hart, W. BEng	(P)	9 Oct
Ingall, D. A. BEng	(P)	9 Oct
John, C. T. B. BSc	(P)	9 Oct
Lindley, M. C. BCom	(P)	9 Oct
Long, S. C. BA	(P)	9 Oct
Mikellides, A. BEng	(P)	9 Oct
Pickup, A. G. MSc	(P)	9 Oct
Pollard, D. M. BSc	(P)	9 Oct
Richings, S. P. BSc	(P)	9 Oct
Street, M. J. BA	(P)	9 Oct
Warmerdam, P. J. R.		
BSc	(P)	9 Oct
Brown, M. R.	(P)	7 Nov
Catlow, D. W.	(P)	7 Nov
Curnow, P. R. qss2	(N)	7 Nov
Griffiths, P. L. qss	(P)	7 Nov
Hough, S. H. qss	(N)	7 Nov
Lloyd-Jones, E.	(P)	7 Nov
Lord, A. S. qss1	(P)	7 Nov
Newberry, W. K.	(P)	7 Nov
Nixon, J. P. qwi(T)		
qcc	(P)	7 Nov
Robinson, P. J. qhti		
qss1	(P)	7 Nov
Tucker-Lowe, N. A. qwi		
qss	(P)	7 Nov
Turner, J. H. qwi		
qss	(P)	7 Nov
Rennet, A.	(AEO)	1 Dec
Bland, I. D.	(N)	3 Dec

1998

Lambert, I. R.	(P)	14 Jan
Butler, W. S. BSc	(P)	15 Jan
Farquhar, B. W.		
BEng	(P)	15 Jan
Francis, P. S. BSc cfs		
qss	(P)	15 Jan
Hodges, B. F. L.		
BSc	(P)	15 Jan
Holmes, E. BSc	(P)	15 Jan
Hurley, D. D. BEng cfs		
qss	(P)	15 Jan
Kinsella, A. J. LLB	(P)	15 Jan
Layden, C. J. BA	(P)	15 Jan
MacDougall, K. C.		
BEng	(P)	15 Jan
Shand, R. G. P. BA	(P)	15 Jan
Stanton, N. D. BSc	(P)	15 Jan
Vance, R. M. BSc	(P)	15 Jan
Batt, J. G.	(P)	30 Jan
Grieve, S. N.	(P)	30 Jan
Grimsey, S. R. qhti	(P)	30 Jan
Newcombe, S. L.	(N)	30 Jan
Strasdin, S. R. qwi(T)		
qcc	(N)	30 Jan
Townsend, I. J. qwi(T)		
qcc	(P)	30 Jan
Batu, A. BSc	(P)	11 Feb
Dalby, N. L. BSc	(N)	11 Feb
Edmondson, J. M.		
BEng	(P)	11 Feb
James, G. S. BSc	(N)	11 Feb
James, T. R. T. BA	(P)	11 Feb
Morrison-Smith, D. J.		
BA	(P)	11 Feb
Taylor, J. J. BEng		
qss	(P)	11 Feb
Bell, D. BSc	(N)	13 Feb
Blackburn, M. J. BSc		
qcc	(N)	13 Feb
Boulton, D. C. BA	(N)	13 Feb
Butler, S. J. BEng	(P)	13 Feb
Cronin, S. A. BSc	(P)	13 Feb
Dyer, K. B. BA	(P)	13 Feb
Lucas, P. A. BSc	(P)	13 Feb
Martin, D. BEng	(P)	13 Feb
Meakins, S. J. BA	(P)	13 Feb
Millikin, A. P. BSocSc		
qss	(P)	13 Feb
Stephen, D. M. BEng		
cfs qss	(P)	13 Feb
Turner, L. BEng	(P)	13 Feb
Webb, O. W. BA	(P)	13 Feb
Done, A. J. P. MEng	(N)	15 Mar
Bethell, R. A.	(P)	24 Mar
Gasson, L. F.	(P)	24 Mar
Hailey, A. T. qss	(P)	24 Mar
Kilby, S. B. cfs qcc	(P)	24 Mar
Maxey, N. D. qss2	(P)	24 Mar
Wells, R. qcc	(P)	24 Mar
Cannon, S. R.	(P)	4 Apr
Barley, F. J. R. BEng		
cfs	(P)	6 Apr
Ellacott, D. R. BSc		
cfs	(P)	6 Apr
Haley, M. S. BSc	(N)	6 Apr
Lea, M. R. MEng	(P)	6 Apr
Melville, G. C.		
BEng	(P)	6 Apr
Yeoman, D. BEng	(N)	6 Apr
Borthwick, G. J.		
BEng	(P)	8 Apr
Clague, M. J. BSc	(P)	8 Apr
Daykin, C. R. BSc	(P)	8 Apr
Dibden, R. S. BSc	(P)	8 Apr
Farrell, M. J. BA	(N)	8 Apr
Farrow, J. BEng	(N)	8 Apr
Greenhowe, J. M. BSc		
qwi(T) qss	(P)	8 Apr
Lyle, A. J. BSc qss	(N)	8 Apr
Murnane, J. M. BA	(N)	8 Apr
Scully, K. J. BSc	(N)	8 Apr
Street, N. A. BA	(P)	8 Apr
Talbot, T. S. BSc	(P)	8 Apr
Thomas, D. E.		
BEng	(P)	8 Apr
Waring, M. W. BSc	(P)	8 Apr
Waterson, J. A. BA	(P)	8 Apr
Wylde, P. F. BSc	(P)	8 Apr
Meadows, J. B.		
qwi(T)	(N)	6 May
Partridge, G. J. qss	(N)	6 May
Errico, S. C. BSc	(P)	24 May
Henderson, J. R.		
qcc	(N)	28 May
James, D. MEng		
BA	(P)	1 June
Ritchley, K. M. MEng	(N)	1 June
Stratton, A. K. qcc	(N)	5 June
Farrant, P. J. qhti	(P)	17 June
Mason, C. R.	(P)	15 July
Chapman, A. P. K. BSc		
qcc	(ENG)	25 July
Boardman, R. J.		
BEng	(P)	9 Aug
Cartmell, C. M. BA	(P)	9 Aug
Ixer, J. W. BA	(N)	9 Aug
Baxter, N. J. BEng	(P)	11 Aug
Curtis, W. H. BEng	(P)	11 Aug
Dixon, R. M. BEng		
qcc	(P)	11 Aug
Fairley, C. T. BSc	(P)	11 Aug
Gilbert, S. J. BA	(N)	11 Aug
Jewitt, K. D. BEng	(N)	11 Aug
Jones, P. J. BEng	(N)	11 Aug
Larkam, D. J. D.		
BSc	(N)	11 Aug
Perks, C. BEng	(N)	11 Aug
Richardson, N. G.		
BSc	(P)	11 Aug

Flight Lieutenants

1998—contd

Stretton-Cox, M. L.		
BSc	(P)	11 Aug
Firth, P. M.	(P)	14 Aug
Pumford, S. M. qcc	(P)	24 Sept
Barnett, M. P. C.		
MEng	(P)	6 Oct
Enright, C. B. BSc	(P)	6 Oct
Fisher, A. R. BSc	(N)	6 Oct
Adams, A. L. LLB	(P)	7 Oct
Berry, R. G. BEng	(P)	7 Oct
Biggadike, M. E.		
BSc	(N)	7 Oct
Bowell, S. V. BEng	(P)	7 Oct
Cone, G. E. BSc	(N)	7 Oct
Kilvington, S. P.		
BSc	(N)	7 Oct
Lockyer, S. J. BA	(P)	7 Oct
Rafferty, D. J. BEng	(P)	7 Oct
Scourfield, J. D.		
BSc	(P)	7 Oct
Smyth, M. J. BA	(N)	7 Oct
Ashley, D. A.	(P)	8 Oct
Kay, M. qhti qcc	(P)	8 Oct
Lewis, P. B. qss	(P)	8 Oct
Pymm, M. L.	(P)	8 Oct
Whitehead, G. P.	(P)	9 Oct
Shanahan, P. A.		
BSc	(P)	4 Nov
Allsop, A. J. cfs qss	(P)	3 Dec
Aspinall, M. J. qss1	(P)	3 Dec
Barnes, A. E.		3 Dec
Jarvis, M. R. qwi		
qss	(P)	3 Dec
Killerby, J. A.	(P)	3 Dec
Littlechild, G. J. M.	(N)	3 Dec
Margiotta, C. A.		
qwi	(P)	3 Dec
Pemberton, G. A.		
qss	(P)	3 Dec
Roberts, A. J. qcc	(N)	3 Dec
Roberts, A. N. qss1	(P)	3 Dec
Warren, C. A.	(P)	3 Dec

1999

Melen, C. A.	(P)	14 Jan
Berry, S. A. MEng	(P)	15 Jan
Elliott, R. G. BEng	(P)	15 Jan
Evans, R. O. BA	(P)	15 Jan
Gossling, S. M.		
BEng	(P)	15 Jan
Ireland, N. R. BSc	(P)	15 Jan
Massie, A. MA	(P)	15 Jan
McKay, D. J. BSc	(P)	15 Jan

Nicol, C. S. MA	(P)	15 Jan
Ormshaw, N. J.		
BSc	(P)	15 Jan
Smith, W. G. BEng	(N)	15 Jan
Thomson, M. J.		
MA	(P)	15 Jan
Walls, J. R. E. MA	(P)	15 Jan
Grindlay, J. P. qss1	(P)	28 Jan
Harvey, G. qcc	(N)	28 Jan
Morley, S. qwi qss	(P)	28 Jan
Mullen, C. A. qhti		
qss	(P)	28 Jan
Webb, K. R.	(P)	28 Jan
Westwood, M. D.		
qss	(P)	28 Jan
Hynes, J. M. BMedSci		
BM BS	(P)	10 Feb
Keenan, W. MEng	(P)	10 Feb
McAllister, J. BSc	(P)	10 Feb
Robertson, E. A.		
BVMS	(P)	10 Feb
Smith, M. A. BSc	(N)	10 Feb
Airey, A. M. R. BSc	(N)	11 Feb
Anderson, D. I. BEng		
qss	(P)	11 Feb
Ball, C. D. BSc	(P)	11 Feb
Duff, G. BEng	(P)	11 Feb
Garlick, D. J. B. BSc	(P)	11 Feb
Greenhalgh, S. D.		
BEng	(P)	11 Feb
Hart, G. F. BEng	(P)	11 Feb
Harvey, G. T. BSc	(P)	11 Feb
Laidlar, R. E. BSc	(N)	11 Feb
McKee, C. J. BSc	(P)	11 Feb
Mcphee, R. K. J.		
BEng	(P)	11 Feb
Militis, G. M. BEng	(P)	11 Feb
Ollerton, C. L. E.		
BSc	(P)	11 Feb
Phillips, T. L. BA	(P)	11 Feb
Tomala, R. J.		
BPharm	(P)	11 Feb
West, D. J. BEng	(P)	11 Feb
Whiteman, T. J. BA	(P)	11 Feb
Edwards, G.		
MBE	(AEO)	14 Feb
Ebberson, N. E. qcc	(N)	28 Mar
Croydon, T. G.		
qss	(AEO)	3 Apr
Meleady, M.	(P)	3 Apr
Bridges, D. R.		
MPhys	(P)	5 Apr
Cripps, R. B. MEng	(P)	5 Apr
Keys, A. T. J. BEng	(P)	5 Apr
Mallon, B. J. BEng	(P)	5 Apr
Sheldon, J. A. BD	(P)	5 Apr
Thompson, C. S.		
BEng	(N)	5 Apr
Belford, J. S. BSc	(N)	6 Apr
Bundock, G. E. BA	(N)	6 Apr

Caple, L. C. BSc	(P)	6 Apr
Davies, G. T. BEng	(N)	6 Apr
Farrell, N. G. A. BSc		
qss	(P)	6 Apr
Freeborough, J. A.		
BEng	(P)	6 Apr
Gover, K. M. A.		
BScEcon	(P)	6 Apr
Grindal, D. J. BEng	(P)	6 Apr
Morton, C. J. BSc	(P)	6 Apr
Payne, M. B. BSc	(P)	6 Apr
Smith, J. M. BSc	(P)	6 Apr
Staudinger, S. J.		
BEng	(P)	6 Apr
Thorpe, B. C. B.		
BEng	(P)	6 Apr
Wilson, D. C. LLB qhti		
qss	(P)	6 Apr
Wright, A. J. BSc	(P)	6 Apr
Clarke, P. A.	(P)	7 Apr
Hale, P. N.	(P)	7 Apr
Redfern, C. C. qss	(P)	7 Apr
Wilson, B. qss	(P)	7 Apr
Arch, D. J.	(P)	6 May
Stokes, N. J.	(AEO)	29 May
Clark, D. J. BCom	(N)	1 June
Fleckney, M. A.		
BEng	(P)	1 June
Hague, S. C. BA	(P)	1 June
Hurcomb, R. J. BA	(N)	1 June
Missen, R. A. C.		
BSc	(P)	1 June
Moon, C. J. BEng	(P)	1 June
Plummer, A. L. BA	(N)	1 June
Pote, C. F. BEng	(P)	1 June
Schofield, J. A. A.		
BSc	(P)	1 June
Spencer, R. BSc	(P)	1 June
Tano, A. BEng qcc	(P)	1 June
Vaughan, M. J. BSc	(N)	1 June
Firth, P. T. qcc	(P)	6 July
Doyle, A. B. MSc		
BA	(P)	7 July
Monslow, K.	(AEO)	24 July
Murray, I. R.	(AEO)	24 July
Owen, A. K.	(P)	24 July
Parker, A.	(N)	24 July
Triccas, R. P.	(ENG)	24 July
Wilkinson, S. J.	(ALM)	24 July
Wright, I. qcc	(AEO)	24 July
Watson, J. A.	(P)	2 Aug
Berry, J. E. MA BSc	(N)	9 Aug
Blythe, A. T. BEng	(P)	9 Aug
Boyle, S. J. BA	(P)	9 Aug
Chapple, C. O. BA	(P)	9 Aug
Dickerson, K. N.		
BSc	(P)	9 Aug
Forward, G. S. BA	(N)	9 Aug
Hutchinson, I. C.		
BA	(N)	9 Aug

Flight Lieutenants

1999—contd

Mordecai, P. D. BA	(N)	9 Aug
Murphy, B. D. BA	(P)	9 Aug
Smith, L. R. P. BSc	(P)	9 Aug
Squires, M. J.		
BEng	(P)	9 Aug
Williams, D. M.		
BEng	(N)	9 Aug
Scuffham, S. J. qss	(P)	10 Aug
Baptie, D. C.	(N)	1 Sept
Bateman, S. A. MBE		
qcc	(P)	2 Oct
Flewin, M. R. BEng	(P)	5 Oct
Macbrayne, A. A.		
BVMS	(P)	5 Oct
Marston, L. BEng	(P)	5 Oct
Arlett, D. J. BEng	(P)	6 Oct
Baker, R. D. F. BA	(N)	6 Oct
Crawford, M. J. BA	(N)	6 Oct
Cripps, R. E. BEng	(P)	6 Oct
Dunlop, T. E. BEng	(P)	6 Oct
Galbraith, K. L. BSc	(N)	6 Oct
Kay, A. M. BSc	(P)	6 Oct
McLenaghan, L.		
BEng	(N)	6 Oct
Mitchell, J. G. C.		
BSc	(P)	6 Oct
Peterson, I. M. BSc	(P)	6 Oct
Riches, A. S. BSc	(P)	6 Oct
Young, P. L. BSc	(P)	6 Oct
Holmes, J. D. qss	(P)	10 Oct
Kimberley, S. D.	(P)	27 Nov
Wardrope, A. B.	(P)	27 Nov
Gale, D. R. BSc	(P)	30 Nov
Ross, J. A. BSc	(P)	30 Nov
Bury, N. P. BSc	(N)	1 Dec
Salam, A. BA	(P)	1 Dec
Thomas, D. J. BSc	(N)	1 Dec
Woodward, J.		
BEng	(P)	1 Dec

2000

Keith, A. R.	(P)	11 Jan
Bamford, H. BSc	(P)	15 Jan
Barraclough, H. E.		
BSc	(P)	15 Jan
Batt, S. P. BEng cfs		
qss	(P)	15 Jan
Clayton, J. A. BSc	(P)	15 Jan
Crichton, A. BEng	(P)	15 Jan
Davies, S. G. MEng		
BA	(P)	15 Jan
Fowler, D. J. BSc	(N)	15 Jan
Hillard, R. J. BA cfs	(P)	15 Jan

Hudson, J. D. BA	(P)	15 Jan
Knight, C. W. BSc	(P)	15 Jan
Lewis, I. S. BSc	(P)	15 Jan
Lindsay, T. J. BSc	(P)	15 Jan
Littlejohn, P. A. T.		
BA	(P)	15 Jan
Mannering, R. E.		
BEng	(P)	15 Jan
Owen, J. J. BEng	(P)	15 Jan
Parr, A. J. MEng BA	(P)	15 Jan
Scott, A. J. BSc	(P)	15 Jan
Tipper, J. A. MEng	(P)	15 Jan
Wilkinson, A. J.		
MEng	(P)	15 Jan
Williams, P. J. BSc	(P)	15 Jan
Ball, A. L.	(ALM)	16 Jan
Buxton, R.	(ALM)	16 Jan
Herman, G. M.	(ENG)	16 Jan
Newton, N. J.	(ENG)	16 Jan
Rath, N. T. cfs(c)	(AEO)	16 Jan
Caine, R. A.	(P)	28 Jan
Dahroug, M. qss	(P)	28 Jan
Hoare, M. D.	(P)	28 Jan
Lees, R. M. qss	(P)	28 Jan
Cockroft, J. M.		
BEng	(P)	9 Feb
Cooper, G. E. BSc	(N)	9 Feb
Goggin, B. D. J.		
BEng	(P)	9 Feb
Grafton, M. J.		
BEng	(N)	9 Feb
Hale, E. L. BA	(N)	9 Feb
Hederman, R. W.		
MEng	(P)	9 Feb
Landy, D. C. MEng	(P)	9 Feb
McCulloch, E. A.		
BSc	(P)	9 Feb
Spoor, B. J. BSc	(P)	9 Feb
Thompson, A. R.		
BSc	(P)	9 Feb
Beck, J. A. BEng	(P)	10 Feb
Butler, V. R. P. BSc		
qss	(P)	10 Feb
Campion, S. J.		
BEng	(P)	10 Feb
Clement, T. J. BSc	(P)	10 Feb
Farndon, C. A. BSc	(N)	10 Feb
French, D. C. BEng	(P)	10 Feb
Hollingworth, J. L.		
BSc	(P)	10 Feb
Kent, J. D. BEng	(N)	10 Feb
Logan, C. R. G. BA	(P)	10 Feb
Marr, P. J. B. BEng	(P)	10 Feb
McCann, S. O.		
BEng	(P)	10 Feb
Ouellette, A. D. BEng		
qss	(P)	10 Feb
Rutland, M. F. BEng	(P)	10 Feb
Foster, D. A. qcc	(ENG)	2 Apr
Healing, J. M. BSc	(N)	4 Apr

Howard, J. M.		
BEng	(N)	4 Apr
Kemp, T. MEng	(P)	4 Apr
McCabe, I. MEng	(N)	4 Apr
Roberts, L. A. BA	(P)	4 Apr
Talbot, C. G. BSc	(P)	4 Apr
Whitehead, N. C.		
MEng	(N)	4 Apr
Bressani, M. J. BSc	(N)	5 Apr
Colley, M. BEng	(P)	5 Apr
Deyes, S. BEng	(P)	5 Apr
Diacon, A. K. BSc	(P)	5 Apr
Dixon, J. P. BEng	(P)	5 Apr
Ellson, A. M. BSc	(P)	5 Apr
Graham, N. J. BSc	(P)	5 Apr
Guertin, J. A. BSc	(P)	5 Apr
Hill, T. BSc	(P)	5 Apr
Kenworthy, E. S.		
BSc	(P)	5 Apr
Macniven, D. J.	(N)	5 Apr
Massingham, D. P.		
BSc	(P)	5 Apr
Melville, C. R. BEng	(N)	5 Apr
Norton, P. S. BSc	(P)	5 Apr
Radley, J. P. BA	(P)	5 Apr
Redican, C. J. BSc	(N)	5 Apr
Shaw, M. R. BSc		
qss	(P)	5 Apr
Shorey, T. D. G.		
BA(Econ)	(P)	5 Apr
Wadlow, P. J. BEng	(P)	5 Apr
Walker, S. BSc	(P)	5 Apr
Willers, S. J. BA	(N)	5 Apr
Cavendish, T. qss	(N)	6 Apr
Evans, G. J. qss2	(P)	6 Apr
Griffiths, G. O.	(P)	6 Apr
Keer, M. B. qss	(P)	6 Apr
Lovett, G. S.	(P)	6 Apr
Redman, A. P.	(P)	6 Apr
Covell, S. P. qcc	(ENG)	28 May
Deeney, P. J. M.	(AEO)	28 May
Eccleshall, N.	(AEO)	28 May
Lee, M. P. qcc	(ALM)	28 May
Stowell, J. M.		
qss	(AEO)	28 May
Strutt, S. R.	(AEO)	28 May
Swan, A. J. qcc	(ALM)	28 May
Baker, G. J. MSc	(P)	29 May
Dunnigan, R. M.		
BEng	(N)	29 May
Masters, M. W.		
MEng	(P)	29 May
Mathew, N. BSc	(N)	29 May
Millikin, N. J. BA	(P)	29 May
Nicol, C. MA	(P)	29 May
Owens, G. A. BSc	(N)	29 May
Pearson, D. L. BSc	(P)	29 May
Randall, M. C.		
MPhys	(P)	29 May
Roycroft, J. BEng	(N)	29 May

Flight Lieutenants

2000—contd

Shave, A. R. J. BSc	(P)	29 May
Wilson, C. T. BEng	(P)	29 May
Baker, A. C. M.		
BEng	(P)	30 May
Leather, R. W. BA	(P)	30 May
Morrell, B. M. BEng	(P)	30 May
Purkis, R. J. BEng	(P)	30 May
Reardon, A. J. BSc	(N)	30 May
Stewart, K. D. BA	(P)	30 May
Hullah, B. D. BTech	(P)	18 June
Appleby, P. R.		
qcc	(ALM)	23 July
Crawford, D. S.	(AEO)	23 July
Eden-Hamilton, J. M.		
AFC BSc	(ALM)	23 July
Ford, A. G.	(ALM)	23 July
Pearce, S. G.	(AEO)	23 July
Walsh, S. W.	(AEO)	23 July
Williams, R. M.	(AEO)	23 July
Cassells, I.	(AEO)	25 July
Mottram, D.	(AEO)	25 July
Bailey, S. E. BEng	(N)	7 Aug
Courtnadge, S.		
BEng	(P)	7 Aug
Setterfield, C. J.		
MSc	(P)	7 Aug
Currie, D. D. BSc	(N)	8 Aug
Griffiths, T. M. BSc	(N)	8 Aug
Sharpe, D. J. C.		
BSc	(P)	8 Aug
Swinton, M. L. BSc	(N)	8 Aug
White, C. A. BA	(N)	8 Aug
Prangley, D.	(N)	1 Oct
Badel, N. M. BA	(P)	4 Oct
Goodey, D. J. MSc		
BA	(N)	4 Oct
Allen, J. W. BA	(N)	5 Oct
Buxton, K. M. L.		
BEng	(P)	5 Oct
Dean, D. R. BEng	(P)	5 Oct
Stratford, G. BSc	(P)	5 Oct
Webster, C. BEng	(P)	5 Oct
McKie, J. E. BSc	(N)	9 Oct
Whitworth, J. A.	(P)	12 Oct
Cowan, S. J. BSc	(P)	30 Nov
Davies, D. B. BEng	(P)	30 Nov
Flynn, D. M. BSc	(P)	30 Nov
Hammond, P. N.		
BEng	(P)	30 Nov
Harkin, J. C. BSc	(N)	30 Nov
McLaren, R. S. MA	(P)	30 Nov
Payne, A. G. BEng	(P)	30 Nov
Rushworth, T. J. H.		
BA	(P)	30 Nov

Reilly, B. J. BSc	(P)	4 Dec

2001

Rea, S. P.	(P)	9 Jan
Saunders, P. R. C.		
	(ENG)	14 Jan
Webster, N. J. R.	(ALM)	14 Jan
Beevers, P. D. BSc	(P)	15 Jan
Bews, I. M. MEng	(P)	15 Jan
Chisholm, A. BA	(P)	15 Jan
Clarke, D. J. BSc	(P)	15 Jan
Coe, A. BSc	(P)	15 Jan
Durban, P. M. BEng	(P)	15 Jan
Garbutt, A. M. BSc	(P)	15 Jan
Hanson, P. A. MSc	(P)	15 Jan
Kingdon, N. R.		
MEng	(P)	15 Jan
Lakin, I. K. H. MEng	(P)	15 Jan
Rogers, A. J. BSc	(P)	15 Jan
Shepherd, B. BEng	(P)	15 Jan
Stewart, K. A.		
MEng	(P)	15 Jan
Williams, S. M. BSc	(P)	15 Jan
Brough, C.	(P)	28 Jan
Moore, R. D. G.	(P)	28 Jan
Wylie, D. R.	(P)	28 Jan
Glanville, M. S. BA	(N)	8 Feb
Gray, D. E. BSc	(P)	8 Feb
Harris, D. J. BSc	(P)	8 Feb
McCann, S. P. BSc	(P)	8 Feb
Moon, S. O. MEng	(P)	8 Feb
Raphael, J. R.		
MEng	(N)	8 Feb
Riley, R. MPhys	(P)	8 Feb
Baron, A. P. BEng	(P)	9 Feb
Barrett, M. P. BSc	(P)	9 Feb
Blakemore, D. BSc	(P)	9 Feb
Jones, M. J. L.		
BEng	(P)	9 Feb
Jordan, T. M. BSc	(P)	9 Feb
Kidd, C. R. BEng	(P)	9 Feb
Krol, P. BEng	(P)	9 Feb
Laisney, D. J. BSc	(P)	9 Feb
Oakley, S. P. BEng	(P)	9 Feb
Pengelly, O. J. BA	(P)	9 Feb
Russell, B. C. R.		
BEng	(P)	9 Feb
Sennett, Z. R. BSc	(P)	9 Feb
Stewart, A. M. BSc	(P)	9 Feb
Tuer, R. J. BEng	(P)	9 Feb
Watts, A. P. BEng	(P)	9 Feb
Woodward, A. K.		
BSc	(P)	9 Feb
Wright, M. J. BEng	(P)	9 Feb
Coxall, A. P.	(P)	10 Feb
Daffey, M. A. qcc	(P)	1 Apr
Horsman-Turner,		
P. C.	(P)	1 Apr

Howard, J. R.	(N)	1 Apr
Richardson, P. K.	(P)	1 Apr
Vickery, M. A.	(ALM)	1 Apr
Willson, P. A.	(P)	1 Apr
Bailey, C. G. MEng	(P)	3 Apr
Bailey, R. J. BSc	(P)	3 Apr
Barnett, M. G.		
MEng	(P)	3 Apr
Boddy, C. G. MEng	(P)	3 Apr
Jones, G. H. BSc	(P)	3 Apr
Millinson, J. BA	(N)	3 Apr
Slack, R. D. BEng	(P)	3 Apr
Whalley, S. H.		
BEng	(P)	3 Apr
Aboboto, R. BSc	(P)	4 Apr
Bott, D. F. BSc	(P)	4 Apr
Burdett, G. J. BA	(P)	4 Apr
Catton, D. M. BSc	(P)	4 Apr
Clark, K. N. BA	(P)	4 Apr
Dachtler, S. R. BSc	(P)	4 Apr
Dawson, H. J. BSc	(N)	4 Apr
De candole, N. J.		
BA	(P)	4 Apr
Fowler, J. BA	(N)	4 Apr
Gallagher, M. J. BA	(N)	4 Apr
Hulme, S. B. BSc	(P)	4 Apr
Laidlaw, B. L. BSc	(P)	4 Apr
Lee, P. J. BEng	(P)	4 Apr
Lee, S. A. BA	(N)	4 Apr
McLarnon, P. D.		
BSc	(P)	4 Apr
Mills, S. BA	(N)	4 Apr
Padbury, O. M. BSc	(P)	4 Apr
Platt, R. A. BEng	(P)	4 Apr
Shaw, S. M. BSc	(P)	4 Apr
Winnister, P. A.		
BSc(Econ)	(P)	4 Apr
Elsey, M. J. qwi(T)		
qss	(N)	5 Apr
Epps C. P.	(P)	5 Apr
Everett, A. R.	(P)	5 Apr
Keeling, R. L.	(P)	5 Apr
Wills, B. T.	(P)	5 Apr
Parr, O. R. BSc	(P)	30 Apr
O'Grady, P. cfs	(P)	1 May
Cade, A. J.	(P)	18 May
Fokerd, N. B.	(AEO)	27 May
Thompson, D. V.	(ALM)	27 May
Thresher, T. J.	(ALM)	27 May
Cuthbertson, I.		
BEng	(P)	28 May
Porter, C. W. BEng	(P)	28 May
Redford, C. E. MSci	(N)	28 May
Whitnall, S. B.		
MEng	(P)	28 May
Wilkinson, D. C.		
MEng	(P)	28 May
Gray, C. B. BSc	(P)	29 May
Hunt, G. BEng	(P)	29 May
Lee, G. J. BSc	(P)	29 May

Flight Lieutenants

2001—contd

Mason, B. J. BEng	(P)	29 May
McDowell, A. J.		
BEng	(P)	29 May
Metcalfe, J. R. BSc	(P)	29 May
Nassif, T. P. BEng	(P)	29 May
Sell, A. D. M. BA	(P)	29 May
Thorpe, D. BSc	(P)	29 May
Whitehouse, S. R.		
BEng	(P)	29 May
Keen, B. F.	(P)	9 July
Cross, M.	(AEO)	22 July
Cullimore, S. R.	(AEO)	22 July
Donoghue, S.	(AEO)	22 July
Hives, C. M.	(P)	22 July
Hood, D. A.	(AEO)	22 July
King, D. S.	(N)	22 July
McDonagh, S.	(ALM)	22 July
Williams, M. M.	(P)	22 July
Willcox, G. B.		
MEng	(P)	26 July
Allanach, G. MEng	(N)	6 Aug
Williams, A. S.		
MPhys	(P)	6 Aug
Davey, S. R. BEng	(P)	7 Aug
Elsey, S. J. BSc	(P)	7 Aug
Holboj, M. A. BSc	(P)	7 Aug
Hollowood, M. J.		
BA	(P)	7 Aug
Inman, N. T. BA	(P)	7 Aug
Johnson, A. M.		
BSc	(P)	7 Aug
Lane, N. BSc	(P)	7 Aug
Miller, A. T. BEng	(N)	7 Aug
Nightingale, J. R.		
BA	(N)	7 Aug
Renton, C. R. BEng	(P)	7 Aug
Shergill, J. S. BA	(P)	7 Aug
Simmons, T. C.		
BMus	(P)	7 Aug
Simpson, T. M.		
BEng	(P)	7 Aug
Coffey, S. M.	(P)	8 Aug
Pepper, A. E.	(N)	8 Aug
Richley, P. J.	(N)	8 Aug
Wood, J. P. qss	(P)	8 Aug
Naismith, P. J.		10 Aug
Saunders, W. D. R.	(P)	20 Aug
Town, D. R.	(P)	30 Sept
Bailey, T. E. MEng	(P)	2 Oct
Balmer, A. J. L. BA	(P)	2 Oct
Moore, L. E. BA	(N)	2 Oct
Charter, K. L. BSc	(N)	4 Oct
Cornish, C. J. BSc	(P)	4 Oct
Cox, J. M. BEng	(N)	4 Oct
Ferris, K. E. BEng	(N)	4 Oct

Lownds, D. M. LLB	(N)	4 Oct
Mason, B. P. BSc	(P)	4 Oct
Montenegro, D. A.		
BA	(P)	4 Oct
Thorbjornsen, P.		
BA	(N)	4 Oct
Tucker, S. J. BEng	(P)	4 Oct
Whittaker, B. BA	(P)	4 Oct
Knight, S. J.	(AEO)	25 Nov
Walker, G. W.	(P)	25 Nov
Allan, R. D. BSc	(N)	28 Nov
Brennan, K. M. BSc	(N)	28 Nov
Goodman, M. J.		
MEng	(P)	28 Nov
Milner, S. J. MSc	(P)	28 Nov
Ruffle, P. W. MEng		
BEng	(P)	28 Nov
Furness, J. A. S.		
BSc	(N)	30 Nov
Hooper, M. R. BA	(P)	30 Nov
Jackson, M. G. BSc	(P)	30 Nov
Paget, D. C. BSc	(N)	30 Nov
Smith, R. J. BA	(N)	30 Nov
Taylor, M. R. MSc		
BA	(N)	30 Nov
Vardy, C. J. BA	(P)	30 Nov
Searle, M. P. BSc	(N)	7 Dec

2002

Cleminson, A.	(AEO)	13 Jan
Halliwell, M. R.	(AEO)	13 Jan
Thomas, H. MBE (ALM)		13 Jan
Clayton, J. S.		
MEng	(P)	15 Jan
Collins, A. S. BEng	(P)	15 Jan
Fortune, S. A. BSc	(P)	15 Jan
Heeps, J. D. MSc		
BA	(P)	15 Jan
Lefroy, G. B.	(P)	15 Jan
Mark, B. S. MEng	(P)	15 Jan
McLean, M. F.		
BEng	(P)	15 Jan
Welsh, C. BEng	(P)	15 Jan
Elwell, M.	(N)	25 Jan
Hewer, S. M.	(N)	25 Jan
Lock, M. D.	(P)	25 Jan
Lockwood, S. I.	(N)	25 Jan
Prochera, D. J.	(P)	25 Jan
Pryor, A. M.	(P)	25 Jan
Birtwistle, J. R.		
MMath	(P)	6 Feb
Deighton, D. S.		
MEng	(P)	6 Feb
Duncan, A. M.		
BEng	(P)	6 Feb
Garland, M. J. K.		
MEng	(N)	6 Feb

Williams, R. A. D.		
MEng	(N)	6 Feb
Smith, E. C. BSc	(N)	7 Feb
Barker, M. J. BSc	(P)	8 Feb
Beasant, A. S.		
BEng	(P)	8 Feb
Binfield, P. BEng	(P)	8 Feb
Brook, D. B. BSc	(P)	8 Feb
Brookes, T. BA	(P)	8 Feb
Campbell, J. D. C.		
BSc	(N)	8 Feb
Davies, P. A. BSc	(P)	8 Feb
Edwards, B. R. W.		
BSc	(N)	8 Feb
Griffiths, I. BEng	(P)	8 Feb
Heasman, P. BSc	(P)	8 Feb
Hume, M. BSc	(P)	8 Feb
Jackson, G. A.		
BEng	(P)	8 Feb
Jackson, J. BSc	(P)	8 Feb
Jenkins, M. L.		
BEng	(P)	8 Feb
Mackinnon, S. E.		
BA	(P)	8 Feb
Paton, N. J. BSc	(P)	8 Feb
Peterson, J. A. BSc	(P)	8 Feb
Peterson, M. J. BSc	(P)	8 Feb
Phyo, C. S. BSc	(P)	8 Feb
Porteous, J. M. BSc	(P)	8 Feb
Shaw, D. C. BA	(P)	8 Feb
Stewart, P. R. BEng	(P)	8 Feb
Strudwick, R. J. A.		
BSc	(P)	8 Feb
Sutton, M. J. E. BA	(P)	8 Feb
Tennant, A. J. BSc	(P)	8 Feb
Terrett, K. J. BSc	(P)	8 Feb
Thomas, N. S.		
BEng	(N)	8 Feb
Todd, S. S. BSc	(N)	8 Feb
Bell, S. D.	(ALM)	30 Mar
Baker, M. R. BEng	(P)	1 Apr
Howell, M. M. T.		
BSc	(P)	1 Apr
Macfarland, S. E.		
MA	(P)	1 Apr
Macgillivray, J. F.		
BEng	(P)	1 Apr
Mander, J. R.		
MEng	(P)	1 Apr
McCormack, G.		
BSc	(N)	1 Apr
McCormick, P. G.		
MA	(P)	1 Apr
Morris, B. BSc	(N)	1 Apr
Pearson, T. M.		
MEng	(P)	1 Apr
Rickards, E. E. MA	(P)	1 Apr
Stringer, N. A. MSc	(P)	1 Apr
Brooker, G. W.		
BEng	(P)	3 Apr

Flight Lieutenants

2002—contd

Bull, A. I. BSc	(P)	3 Apr
Cole, G. W.	(P)	3 Apr
Cooper, W. D.	(P)	3 Apr
Curd, A. J. BSc	(P)	3 Apr
Donoghue, I. D.		
BSc	(P)	3 Apr
Fincher, S. J.	(N)	3 Apr
Gannon, J. F. BEng	(P)	3 Apr
Gardiner, P. M.		
BEng	(P)	3 Apr
Hamilton, P. T. LLB	(N)	3 Apr
Hermolle, C. H. A.		
MA	(P)	3 Apr
Mason, J. R.	(P)	3 Apr
McConnell, P. S.		
BA	(P)	3 Apr
Robinson, L. V. BSc	(P)	3 Apr
Steel, J. A. BSc	(P)	3 Apr
Thornton, R. I. N.		
BSc	(P)	3 Apr
Turnbull, V. E. BA	(P)	3 Apr
Walker, P. J. BEng	(P)	3 Apr
Wallace, S. P. BA	(P)	3 Apr
Wild, M. A. BSc	(N)	3 Apr
Wilson, M. I. BSc	(P)	3 Apr
Winchester, R. J.		
LLB	(P)	3 Apr
Madden, L. T.	(N)	9 May
Alderman, D.	(AEO)	25 May
Garven, A.	(ENG)	25 May
Lawson, J. A. BEng	(N)	25 May
Meeker, A. D.	(ALM)	25 May
Sloan, C. E.	(ALM)	25 May
Abbott, P. BSc	(N)	26 May
Beattie, S. J. BEng	(P)	26 May
Emeny-Smith, D.		
MEng	(N)	26 May
Horne, E. J. F.		
MEng	(P)	26 May
Hoyle, C. J. MEng	(P)	26 May
Roberts, J. L. BSc	(P)	26 May
Tough, D. G. MEng	(P)	26 May
Brodie, M. D. BSc	(P)	28 May
Buckle, J. P. BSc	(P)	28 May
Dutton, S. P. BEng	(P)	28 May
Keeping, R. J. BA	(N)	28 May
Quaife, R. P. BEng	(P)	28 May
Swainston, D. F. J.		
BSc	(P)	28 May
Thorne, M. F. BSc	(N)	28 May
Wilson, R. M. BSc	(P)	28 May
Wright, S. K. BSc	(P)	28 May

Flying Officers

1993

Nicholas, G. R.	(AEO)	31 Mar
Diacon, P. R. BEng	(P)	15 July
Harris, R. P. BA qcc	(P)	15 July
Irvine, D. A.	(AEO)	30 Aug

1994

Ward, K. N. BSc	(P)	13 Aug

1995

Fleming, G. R.	(ENG)	25 June
Copsey, S. M.	(AEO)	9 July
Capon, T. M.	(ALM)	25 Aug

1996

O'Donnell, C. A.	(AEO)	20 June
Sommers, D. G.	(ALM)	16 Nov

1997

Boreham, D.	(ALM)	30 June
Willcox, D. M.	(ALM)	30 June
Kelly, C. J.	(P)	10 Sept
Johnson, L. M. BSc	(P)	4 Nov

1998

Astle, P. M.	(N)	23 Mar
Cummins, S. BEng	(N)	2 Apr
Edwards, S. M.	(ALM)	11 June
Thorpe, N. K.	(N)	19 June
Boyce, P. A.	(P)	3 Oct
Lowe, D. R. BSc	(N)	3 Oct
Page, K. L.	(P)	30 Oct
Ryder, J. P. BSc	(P)	28 Nov
Baker, J. D.	(P)	31 Dec

1999

Mudgway, R. T.	(P)	14 Jan
Callis, M. D. BEng	(P)	4 Feb
Mitchell, A. G. E.		
MSc	(P)	4 Feb
Crouchman, N. BSc		
PGCE	(N)	6 Feb

Cunningham, S. J.		
BEng	(P)	6 Feb
Doyle, J. S. BA	(N)	6 Feb
Elliott, N. A.	(P)	6 Feb
Hickinbotham, R.		
BA	(P)	6 Feb
Marchant, L. P. BSc	(P)	6 Feb
Orr, J. N. BSc	(P)	6 Feb
Philp, N. M. BEng	(P)	6 Feb
Richards, T. V. BA	(P)	6 Feb
Robins-Walker, J. A. J.		
BEng	(P)	6 Feb
Robinson, D. A.	(P)	6 Feb
Smolak, A. M.		
BEng	(P)	6 Feb
Stevenson, P. A.		
BSc	(P)	6 Feb
Verney, H. L. BA		
PGCE	(N)	6 Feb
Wright, A. D. BSc	(N)	6 Feb
Holmes, K. B. BA	(P)	1 Apr
Jefferson, A. M.		
MEng	(N)	1 Apr
Smith, C. M.	(P)	1 Apr
Sugden, M. D. BA	(P)	1 Apr
Thompson, B. W.		
MEng	(P)	1 Apr
Beecroft, N. M.		
BSocSc	(P)	2 Apr
Bellman, D. F. J.		
BSc	(P)	2 Apr
Birchall, I. J. BEng	(P)	2 Apr
Brassington, A. P.		
BSc	(P)	2 Apr
Grassby, D. BSc	(P)	2 Apr
Griffiths, A. C.		
BEng	(P)	2 Apr
Hanson, J. J. BSc	(N)	2 Apr
Inglis, R. W. BEng	(P)	2 Apr
Larkman, A. BEng	(P)	2 Apr
McVay, P. M. BSc	(P)	2 Apr
Nichols, H. J. W.		
BEng	(P)	2 Apr
Peterson, M. G. BA	(P)	2 Apr
Robinson, W. J.		
BEng	(P)	2 Apr
Slater, A. BEng	(P)	2 Apr
Slater, O. BSc	(P)	2 Apr
Stiger, S. LLB	(P)	2 Apr
Thompson, A. E.		
BA	(P)	2 Apr
Warren, T. J.	(N)	3 Apr
Wright, C. A. MEng	(P)	27 May
Armstrong, L. BSc	(P)	28 May
Bayless, D. R. M.		
BSc	(P)	28 May
Butler, R. M. BSc	(N)	28 May
Davison, G. J. BSc	(P)	28 May
Dickson, A. J. MSc		
BSc	(P)	28 May

Flying Officers

1999—contd

Green, C. E. BSc	(N)	28 May
Green, J. B. BSc	(N)	28 May
Hewat, D. J. S.		
BEng	(N)	28 May
Jones, R. D. BSc	(P)	28 May
Kluth, M. J. BSc	(P)	28 May
Lowe, R. P. BSc	(P)	28 May
Meighan, J. R. H.		
BA	(P)	28 May
Page, N. M. BSc		
PGCE	(N)	28 May
Pye, T. J. BSc	(P)	28 May
Roberts, D. P. BSc	(P)	28 May
Wrigley, D. S. J.		
BSc	(N)	28 May
Lucas, C. J.	(N)	29 May
Bhangu, J. S.		
MEng	(P)	15 July
D'Aubyn, M. J.		
MChem	(P)	15 July
Gross, J. R. A.		
BEng	(P)	15 July
King, D. J. R. BEng	(P)	15 July
Pollard, S. M. BEng	(P)	15 July
Richardson, J. M.		
MSc	(P)	15 July
Soar, R. W. H.		
MEng	(P)	15 July
White, H. L. BSc	(P)	15 July
Heasman, N. R. BA	(P)	16 July
Stokel, G. G. BSc	(AEO)	22 July
Thurrell, J. T.	(P)	22 July
Ahern, L. C. BA	(P)	6 Aug
Aston, C. J. BEng	(P)	6 Aug
Barclay, M. G. T.		
BEng	(P)	6 Aug
Borrow, L. J. BSc	(N)	6 Aug
Clark, D. S. BSc	(P)	6 Aug
Cutting, M. G.		
BEng	(N)	6 Aug
Eagles, T. R. BSc	(P)	6 Aug
Egging, J. W. J.		
BSc	(P)	6 Aug
Goundry, N. J.		
BEng	(P)	6 Aug
Hearnshaw, M. D.		
BEng	(P)	6 Aug
Hunkin, J. O. BSc	(P)	6 Aug
Jones, R. A. BSc	(N)	6 Aug
Kershaw, A. S. M.		
BA	(N)	6 Aug
King, A. J. BEng	(P)	6 Aug
Lawson, M. A.		
BEng	(P)	6 Aug
Lazenby, M. R.		
BEng	(P)	6 Aug
Lester, A. G. BSc	(N)	6 Aug
Luke, J. W. BSc	(P)	6 Aug
Parkinson, A. BSc	(P)	6 Aug
Plank, B. M. BA	(P)	6 Aug
Simpson, R. P. M.		
BSc	(P)	6 Aug
Smith, A. P. BSc	(P)	6 Aug
Tye, D. M. BEng	(P)	6 Aug
Watts, A. D. R. BSc	(P)	6 Aug
Arnold, D. R. MEng	(P)	12 Aug
Ballantyne, C. J.		
MEng	(N)	12 Aug
Graham, A. M.		
MEng	(P)	12 Aug
Phillips, S. G.		
MEng	(P)	12 Aug
Baker, J. D. BEng	(P)	1 Oct
Ball, T. D. BEng	(P)	1 Oct
Bowles, J. BSc	(N)	1 Oct
Buchler, F. B. K.		
BSc	(P)	1 Oct
Burrows, M. J.		
BEng	(P)	1 Oct
Cunningham, L. A.		
BA	(P)	1 Oct
Davies, R. P. BSc	(P)	1 Oct
Dodds, M. J. BEng	(P)	1 Oct
Durcan, S. J. BSc	(P)	1 Oct
Fawkes, R. W.		
BEng	(P)	1 Oct
Franks, J. G. BEng	(N)	1 Oct
Hartwell, I. D. BSc	(P)	1 Oct
Holland, D. F. O.		
BSc	(N)	1 Oct
Huggins, D. P. BA	(N)	1 Oct
King, S. J. BA	(N)	1 Oct
Liddle, A. J. BEng	(P)	1 Oct
McIntyre, A. J. BSc	(P)	1 Oct
Norman, R. A. BSc	(P)	1 Oct
Pickford, M. BEng	(P)	1 Oct
Rycroft, J. E. BA	(P)	1 Oct
Seanor, P. R. BSc	(N)	1 Oct
Stafford, S. G. BA	(P)	1 Oct
Warboys, W. A.		
BEng	(P)	1 Oct
Williams, E. B. BA	(N)	1 Oct
Williams, G. S. M.		
BSc	(P)	1 Oct
Worrall, N. M. BSc	(N)	1 Oct
Frazer, M. T.	(N)	2 Oct
Jackson, O. J.	(P)	2 Oct
Osborne, J. W.	(P)	2 Oct
Staite, N. P.	(P)	2 Oct
Brassington, S. A.		
BSc	(N)	7 Oct
Card, G. A. BSc	(N)	7 Oct
Drysdale, A. D. M.		
BEng	(P)	7 Oct
Fellowes-Freeman, A. I.		
C. MEng	(P)	7 Oct
Greenwood, C. J.		
MSci	(P)	7 Oct
Hampson, A. R.		
MEng	(P)	7 Oct
Keeble, M. C.		
MEng	(P)	7 Oct
Lawson, S. R. BSc	(N)	7 Oct
Livesey, B. L. BSc	(P)	7 Oct
Meza, L. MEng	(P)	7 Oct
Sawle, T. W. MSc	(P)	7 Oct
Wood, F. J. BSc	(P)	7 Oct
Bell, R. J. BA	(N)	26 Nov
Brant, P. G. BEng	(P)	26 Nov
Charlton, M. J. BSc	(P)	26 Nov
Cooper, N. M. BSc	(P)	26 Nov
Crockford, M. I.		
BSc	(P)	26 Nov
Eastlake, J. P. BSc	(P)	26 Nov
Furness, S. J. BA	(P)	26 Nov
Goodman, D. M.		
BA	(P)	26 Nov
Johnstone, E. W.		
BSc	(P)	26 Nov
Kassapian, J. N. L.		
LLB	(P)	26 Nov
Milmine, J. D. BSc	(P)	26 Nov
O'Neill, K. A. BSc	(P)	26 Nov
Pearson, C. BSc	(N)	26 Nov
Prendergast, G. BA	(N)	26 Nov
Sampson, R. L.		
BEng	(P)	26 Nov
Sandhu, R. S. BSc	(P)	26 Nov
Smiley, P. J. BEng	(P)	26 Nov
Wood, I. P. BA	(N)	26 Nov
Wright, S. P. BA	(P)	26 Nov
Howe, C. J.	(P)	27 Nov
Meakin, K. S.	(P)	27 Nov
Owczarkowski, N.		
E.	(P)	27 Nov
Reader, G. S.	(P)	27 Nov
Thorne, I. D.	(P)	27 Nov

2000

Nuttall, P. R.	(P)	10 Jan
Blackwell, T.		
BSc(Econ)	(P)	4 Feb
Docherty, C. M.		
BSc	(N)	4 Feb
Jarratt, K. J. BSc	(N)	4 Feb
Margetts, S. G. BSc	(P)	4 Feb
Mullineux, C. A.		
BSc	(N)	4 Feb
Powell, C. G. BSc	(P)	4 Feb
Royston-Airey, C. D.		
BA	(N)	4 Feb

Flying Officers

2000—contd

Ruddick, C. E. C.		
BSc	(N)	4 Feb
Brown, A. A. F.	(N)	5 Feb
Edwards, G. T.	(P)	5 Feb
Green, M. W.	(P)	5 Feb
Smith, A. W. cfs	(P)	30 Mar
Basnett, G. M. BSc	(N)	1 Apr
Davis, C. J. A. BSc	(P)	1 Apr
Krzyz, P. LLB	(N)	1 Apr
Le cornu, J. P. M.		
BSc	(P)	1 Apr
Maccoll, S. S. BSc	(P)	1 Apr
Savage, D. W. BSc	(P)	1 Apr
Snelling, I. M. BA	(N)	1 Apr
Swarbrick, S. BSc	(P)	1 Apr
Taylor, T. M. B. BSc	(P)	1 Apr
Finley, S. N.	(AEO)	25 May
Buxton, D. F. MA	(P)	27 May
Downs, C. T. BSc	(P)	27 May
Durham, R. L. BA	(P)	27 May
Knox, J. BEng	(P)	27 May
McGeough, S. A.		
BSc	(P)	27 May
McMiken, W. J. B.		
BSc	(N)	27 May
Mitchelmore, L. A.		
BA	(N)	27 May
Muir, J. C. BA	(P)	27 May
King, R. J.	(N)	28 May
Townsend, J. D.	(P)	28 May
Woolley, M.	(P)	28 May
Heinowski, T.	(P)	20 June
Bullivant, M. C.		
BSc	(P)	15 July
McLaughlin, C. BA	(P)	15 July
Elstow, M. A.	(P)	20 July
Northway, R. M.	(ALM)	20 July
Gough, C. E. J.	(N)	23 July
Holford, D. D.	(N)	23 July
Small, R. K.	(N)	23 July
Stanford, D. C.	(P)	23 July
Cochrane, C. M.		
BSc	(P)	8 Aug
Banning, G. E. LLB	(N)	12 Aug
Benson, T. C. J. BA	(P)	12 Aug
Blaikley, A. P. LLB	(P)	12 Aug
Brown, H. M. BSc	(P)	12 Aug
Eldridge, S. A. BSc	(P)	12 Aug
Fairman, J. A. W.		
BA	(P)	12 Aug
Graham, N. A. H.		
BSc	(P)	12 Aug
Hall, I. D. BSc	(P)	12 Aug
Hill, J. I. BA	(P)	12 Aug

Lambert, N. P. J.		
BA	(P)	12 Aug
Lloyd, M. G. BA	(P)	12 Aug
Lyon, I. S. BSc	(N)	12 Aug
McAdam, S. G.		
BEng	(N)	12 Aug
Morris, E. G. N.		
BEng	(P)	12 Aug
Smith, N. P. BSc	(N)	12 Aug
Sola, B. D. I. BA	(N)	12 Aug
Surtees, P. T. BA	(P)	12 Aug
Weare, C. W. J. BSc	(P)	12 Aug
Woollard, J. D. BSc	(P)	12 Aug
Young, C. P. MA	(P)	12 Aug
Belmont, S. A.	(P)	5 Sept
Walker, J. A.	(AEO)	28 Sept
Beilby, P. C.	(P)	1 Oct
Dutton, B. G.	(P)	1 Oct
Marshall, M. R.	(P)	1 Oct
McMeeking, J. J.	(P)	1 Oct
Steel, H. A.	(P)	1 Oct
Birkett, C. G. BSc	(P)	7 Oct
Bissett, K. J. BSc	(N)	7 Oct
Brown, S. C. BSc	(P)	7 Oct
Game, M. J. BA	(P)	7 Oct
Hourston, J. W.		
BEng	(P)	7 Oct
Jackson, M. B. BSc	(P)	7 Oct
Jewsbury, N. J.		
BSc	(P)	7 Oct
Phillips, C. J. BEng	(P)	7 Oct
Rodger, L. H. BA	(P)	7 Oct
Ryznar, J. E. BSc	(P)	7 Oct
Simpson, K. A. BA	(P)	7 Oct
Smith, P. A. BEng	(P)	7 Oct
Tomlinson, P. BA	(P)	7 Oct
Watson, A. N.		
BEng	(P)	7 Oct
Webster, C. I. BSc	(P)	7 Oct
Williams, G. BSc	(P)	7 Oct
Williams, S. M. BSc	(N)	7 Oct
Matthews, C. J.	(P)	2 Nov
Butterfield, C. J.	(P)	24 Nov
Ling, M. R.	(P)	26 Nov
Ward, P. H. J.	(P)	26 Nov
Morgan, M. J.	(N)	15 Dec

2001

Campbell, K. S.	(N)	23 Jan
Baldry, G. R. T.	(P)	26 Jan
Williams, A. K.	(P)	4 Feb
Rowsell, E. M.	(N)	6 Feb
Ingram, N. D.	(P)	19 Mar
Butcher, J. R.	(P)	1 Apr
Footitt, A.	(P)	1 Apr
McAuley, T. G. A.	(N)	1 Apr
Roberts, P. A.	(P)	1 Apr
Dugdale, O. J.	(P)	3 Apr

Hemsley, S. G.	(N)	22 May
Davies, S. R.	(AEO)	24 May
Bolton, J. A.	(P)	27 May
Evans, R. D.	(P)	27 May
Hammond, D. A.	(P)	27 May
Lyndon-Smith, C.		
D.	(P)	27 May
Moore, M. P. G.	(P)	27 May
Norman, M. W.	(N)	27 May
Whyte, E.	(P)	27 May
Williamson, B. J.	(N)	27 May
McMillan, J. I. S.	(P)	14 June
O'Brien, S. A.	(ALM)	19 July
Bailey, F. L.	(P)	22 July
Dilley, M. D.	(P)	22 July
Holland, M. J.	(P)	22 July
Jones, G. E.	(P)	22 July
Lilly, A. N.	(P)	22 July
Maddock, T. J.	(P)	22 July
McGlone, P. R.	(N)	22 July
Rowe, D. G. A.	(P)	22 July
Simcock, R. H.	(P)	22 July
Smith, J. P.	(P)	22 July
Taylor-Head, J. M.	(P)	22 July
Thurston, J. K.	(P)	22 July
Turner, L. R.	(P)	22 July
Watkinson, S. A.	(N)	22 July
Wright, C. N.	(N)	22 July
McNicholas, I.	(P)	21 Sept
Field, J. A.	(P)	30 Sept
Hawkins, B. C.	(P)	30 Sept
Kane, C. G.	(P)	30 Sept
Newman, D.	(P)	30 Sept
Baldwin, C. J.	(P)	25 Nov
Bloom, C. R.	(P)	25 Nov
Gogerty, G. P.	(P)	25 Nov
Lee, J. M.	(P)	25 Nov
Myhill, V. T.	(N)	25 Nov
Redgwell, R. N.	(P)	25 Nov
Summers, P. A.	(P)	25 Nov
Jurd, M. J.	(P)	30 Dec

2002

Cholmondeley-Smith,		
R. M.	(P)	25 Jan
Badham, S. D.	(P)	3 Feb
Gardner, K. G.	(P)	3 Feb
Gray, P. W.	(P)	3 Feb
Hale, B. J.	(P)	3 Feb
Jones, A. W.	(N)	3 Feb
McCreedy, P. M. S.	(P)	3 Feb
Taylor, M. C.	(P)	3 Feb
Williams, B. T.	(P)	3 Feb
Alexander, S. C.	(P)	30 Mar
Bird, G. E.	(P)	30 Mar
Gomm, P. L.	(P)	30 Mar
Jones, C. W. T.	(P)	30 Mar
Latchman, K. H. T.	(P)	30 Mar

Flying Officers

2002—contd

Macmillan, N. A. J.	(P)	30 Mar
Manisty, R. E.	(P)	30 Mar
Nash, T. P. J.	(N)	30 Mar
Phillips, S. C.	(P)	30 Mar
Riley, S. M.	(P)	30 Mar
Rodriguez, M. J.	(P)	30 Mar
Swierczek, G. P.	(P)	30 Mar
Tease, B. C.	(P)	30 Mar
Wooler, C. J. S.	(N)	30 Mar
Redmond, M.		
BSc	(AEO)	4 Apr
Cummins, D. J.	(P)	25 May
Dempster, B. J.	(N)	25 May
Edwards, G.	(P)	25 May
Fleet, M.	(P)	25 May
Garrigan, J. P.	(P)	25 May
Jenkinson, M. A. I.	(P)	25 May
Kerr, A. D. D.	(P)	25 May
Montgomery, L. A.	(P)	25 May
Shaw, A. J.	(P)	25 May
Still, M. N.	(N)	25 May

Pilot Officers

2001

Knapton, M. E.		
MEng	(N)	27 May
Wharry, M. G.	(P)	15 July
Bohane, D. P. C.	(N)	20 July
Doneth-Hillier, C.		
R.	(P)	20 July
Lamb, S. D.	(P)	20 July
Mackenzie, D. M.	(P)	20 July
Taylor, J. C. L.	(P)	20 July
Todhunter, P. J.	(N)	20 July
Tonks, S. M.	(P)	20 July
Wigglesworth, F. A.	(P)	20 July
Jenkins, A. B. BSc	(P)	12 Aug
Cunningham, C. L.	(P)	28 Sept
Dawkins, L. W. A.	(P)	28 Sept
Hall, S. K. C.	(P)	28 Sept
Howell, T. L.	(P)	28 Sept
Killick, M. J.	(P)	28 Sept
Kups, D.	(P)	28 Sept
Pert, M. E. W.	(P)	28 Sept
Siwicki, J. A.	(N)	28 Sept
Thorne, N. E.	(N)	28 Sept
Weatherhead, E. P.	(P)	28 Sept
Butler, G. L.	(P)	23 Nov
Gatland, K. L.	(N)	23 Nov
Hurford, W. E.	(P)	23 Nov
Roberts, J. A.	(N)	23 Nov
Shipley, A. J.	(P)	23 Nov
Trueman, J. D.	(P)	23 Nov
Wilders, S. J.	(P)	23 Nov
Bjonness, L. C. LLB	(P)	2 Dec
Cable, B. S. L. BEng	(P)	2 Dec
Child, M. J. BSc	(P)	2 Dec
Exley, S. BEng	(P)	2 Dec
Forsyth, M. E. BSc	(P)	2 Dec
Hamilton, J. M.		
BSc	(P)	2 Dec
Henwood, J. BSc	(P)	2 Dec
Jakubowski, J. A. B.		
BSc	(P)	2 Dec
Lakey, R. E. BSc	(P)	2 Dec
Leavey, C. S. BSc	(P)	2 Dec
Sandberg, R. D.		
BEng	(P)	2 Dec
Sergeant, V. BEng	(N)	2 Dec
Smith, I. BSc	(P)	2 Dec
Taylor, R. M. BEng	(P)	2 Dec
Wall, B. S. BSc	(P)	2 Dec
Walton, P. BSc	(P)	2 Dec

2002

Mason, M. A. P.	(P)	1 Feb
Woodman, S. H.	(N)	1 Feb

Bird, P. J. BA	(P)	10 Feb
Broadbent, S. J.		
MPhys	(P)	10 Feb
Coates, C. M. BSc	(P)	10 Feb
Colledge, T. BSc	(N)	10 Feb
Cox, E. K. BSc	(P)	10 Feb
Dore, G. M. BSc	(P)	10 Feb
Flanaghan, M. J.		
BSc	(N)	10 Feb
Flemington, L. D.		
BAv	(P)	10 Feb
Griffiths, D. J.		
MEng	(P)	10 Feb
Heal, M. A. BA	(P)	10 Feb
Hogg, D. A. BEng	(P)	10 Feb
Kelly, P. R. J. MEng	(P)	10 Feb
Martin, N. C. BEng	(N)	10 Feb
Masterton, D. J.		
BSc	(P)	10 Feb
Mather, M. I. BSc	(N)	10 Feb
McGreevy, A. P.		
MEng	(P)	10 Feb
Mulhall, J. J. BSc	(P)	10 Feb
Rowe, J. M. BSc	(P)	10 Feb
Stobs-Stobart, C.		
BEng	(P)	10 Feb
Tait, D. S. BEng	(P)	10 Feb
Titchener, M. O. S.		
BSc	(N)	10 Feb
Tucker, B. P. BSc	(P)	10 Feb
Webster, L. S. BSc	(N)	10 Feb
Hewitt, B. J.	(P)	29 Mar
Joseph, N. M.	(P)	29 Mar
Mountfield, B.	(P)	29 Mar
Babber, S. BSc	(N)	7 Apr
Bradbury, D. I. BSc	(P)	7 Apr
Chatterton, P. T. BA	(N)	7 Apr
Cowen, N. M. BA	(P)	7 Apr
Crowe, R. J. BA	(N)	7 Apr
Dunstan, M. P. BSc	(P)	7 Apr
Fenton, B. D. LLB	(P)	7 Apr
Howard, P. J. BSc	(P)	7 Apr
Javens, N. A. BEng	(N)	7 Apr
Kelly, P. B. BSc	(N)	7 Apr
Lunnon-Wood, B.		
BSc	(N)	7 Apr
Milner, P. S. BSc	(P)	7 Apr
Morris, P. BSc	(P)	7 Apr
Pucill, L. W. BSc	(P)	7 Apr
Rigg, J. W. BEng	(P)	7 Apr
Sandhu, G. BEng	(N)	7 Apr
Springford, M. J. P.		
BSc	(P)	7 Apr
Thompson, M. P.		
BSc	(P)	7 Apr
Watts, G. P. MEng	(N)	7 Apr
Wilson, R. L. BA	(N)	7 Apr
Blackburn, D. A.	(P)	24 May
Fleming, O. P.	(P)	24 May
Fryer, G. I.	(P)	24 May

Pilot Officers

2002—contd

Hasler, C. M.	(P)	24 May
Jenkins, J. A.	(P)	24 May
Lloyd-Davies, G. P.	(P)	24 May
Marsh, S. A.	(P)	24 May
Pockett, J. M.	(P)	24 May
Taylor, A. J.	(P)	24 May

Acting Pilot Officers

1998

Williams, E. L.	(P)	1 Sept

2001

Groves, D.	(N)	24 May
Bennett, J. N.	(P)	19 July
Hathaway, M. R.	(N)	19 July
Hutton, T. A.	(N)	19 July
Margrett, G. J.	(N)	19 July
Morris, R. S.	(P)	19 July
Morton, E. D.	(P)	19 July
Owen, M. J.	(P)	19 July
Robertson, M.	(P)	19 July
Shallcross, J. R.	(P)	19 July
Smith, J. A.	(N)	19 July
Wight-Boycott, M. D.	(P)	19 July
Bendall, T. N.	(P)	4 Oct
Boyd, C. K. T.	(P)	4 Oct
Chambers, M. W.	(P)	4 Oct
Cruickshank, R. A.	(P)	4 Oct
Denman, R. J.	(P)	4 Oct
Gordon, L. P. R.	(P)	4 Oct
Hawkes, A. G.	(P)	4 Oct
Murphy, M. J.	(N)	4 Oct
Twaite, T. C.	(N)	4 Oct
Barnes, T. B.	(P)	29 Nov
Burgon, C. J.	(P)	29 Nov
Compton, M. S.	(P)	29 Nov
Dale, J. W.	(P)	29 Nov
Farndon, E. J.	(P)	29 Nov
Haddock, J. P.	(P)	29 Nov
Hodge, A. L.	(P)	29 Nov
Holgate, T. E.	(P)	29 Nov
Lee, V. L.	(N)	29 Nov
Staples, D. R.	(P)	29 Nov

2002

Harris, K.	(P)	7 Feb
Murray, A. S.	(N)	7 Feb
Turk, M. C.	(P)	7 Feb
West, J. N.	(P)	7 Feb
Chapman, M. J.	(P)	4 Apr
Davison, M. T.	(P)	4 Apr
Stewart, R. A.	(P)	4 Apr
Whitechurch, W. E. P.	(N)	4 Apr

OPERATIONS SUPPORT BRANCH

Group Captains

1990

Fishwick, Robert, John psc G(a) Born 18/6/45 . . . . (REGT)   1 July

1996

Dingle, Barry Thomas psc Born 24/11/48 . . . . (ATC)   1 Jan

1997

Anderton, Stephen Harper MSc BSc FCMI psc Born 29/8/50 . . . . (REGT)   1 Jan
Bettel, Martyn Roswell OBE BSc FCMI MInstAM jsdc qs Born 16/10/49 . . . . . (FC)   1 Jan
Jenner, Richard Mark jsdc qwi qs Born 22/8/53. . . . . (FC)   1 Jan
Lloyd, Stephen James BSc FRAeS FCMI jsdc qs Born 8/5/51 . . . . (INT)   1 Jan
Pellatt, Kevin John FCMI rcds jsdc qs Born 26/1/52 . . . . (FC)   1 Jan
Williams, Nigel jsdc qss Born 3/2/51 . . . . (ATC)   1 Jan

1998

Evans, David Robert Evan jsdc psc Born 19/10/52 . . . . (REGT)   1 Jan
McPhee, Ian Alexander psc Born 17/4/53 . . . . (REGT)   1 Jan
Rogers, Brian Edward MBE psc Born 6/1/49 . . . . (FC)   1 Jan
Drissell, Peter James MA BSc MInstD jsdc qs Born 24/11/55 . . . . (REGT)   1 July

1999

Hallam, Martin Rupert psc Born 18/1/55 . . . . (INT)   1 Jan
Gregory, Norman Alan BA ACII psc Born 31/8/47 . . . . (ATC)   1 July
Pennington, Andrew John MCMI psc Born 3/2/50 . . . . (INT)   1 July
Stacey, Graham Edward MBE BSc psc(m) G(a) Born 1/9/59 . . . . (REGT)   1 July

2000

Wordley, Mark Richard hcsc psc Born 9/12/55 . . . . (ATC)   1 Jan
Barnes, Laurence Julian Franklin MSc psc Born 4/7/51 . . . . (REGT)   1 July
Denholm, Ian Thomas MBE BSc jsdc qs Born 13/7/54 . . . . (INT)   1 July
Gordon, Nicholas Jonathan MBE MBA FCIPD psc qab qwi(AD) Born 8/6/59 . . . . (FC)   1 July
Middleton, Ian Sidney MBA BA psc Born 12/4/57 . . . . (ATC)   1 July
Todd, David MBE BSc jsdc qs Born 13/5/50. . . . . (FC)   1 July

2001

Abbott, Steven MPhil BA jsdc G(a) qs Born 5/2/56. . . . . (REGT)   1 July
Ashwell, Mark Lawrence MBE BSc nadc psc Born 4/2/59 . . . . (FC)   1 July
Gimblett, Walter John BSc qab qs Born 17/9/50 . . . . (INT)   1 July

Group Captains

2001—contd

Stenson, James Philip MBE BSc qs Born 15/12/52 . . . . (ATC)   1 July

2002

Davie, Alexander OBE MA MBA psc Born 21/11/48 . . . . (REGT)   1 July

Wing Commanders

1985

Roberts, D. jsdc qwi
qs   (FC)   1 Jan

1990

Parker, J. E. psc   (FC)   1 Jan
Rodford, J. D. BSc G(a)
qs   (REGT)   1 Jan
Hooker, M. R. MCMI
qs   (REGT)   1 July
Shepherd, P. jsdc
qs   (FLTOPS)   1 July

1992

Hunter, P. R. OBE jsdc
qab   (FC)   1 July

1993

Hutchinson, N. osc(Fr)
qab i*   (FC)   1 Jan
Knowles, D. W. MBA
BA qs   (REGT)   1 July
Whiteway, H. A. qs (FC)   1 July

1994

Cornwell, B. A. BSc
ARCS qab qs   (FC)   1 Jan
Crofton, D. N. qs (INT)   1 July
Hamilton, D. B. nadc
qs   (INT)   1 July
Leckey, J. jsdc qs (FC)   1 July
Romney, C. N. BSc
psc(j) qab   (FC)   1 July

1995

Scott, A. M. O. BA
qss   (INT)   1 Jan
Strong, M. C. G.
qs   (ATC)   1 Jan
Trevett, A. D. qab
qs   (FC)   1 Jan
Hill, C. D. MBE qs(ATC)   1 July

1996

Colgate, J. A. MBE BSc
qs   (INT)   1 Jan
Dipper, K. R. MA BSc
G(a) psc   (REGT)   1 Jan
Kennedy, P. A. M.
MCMI ACII qs (REGT)   1 Jan
Trundle, C. C. psc(ATC)   1 Jan
Walker, D. J. qs (INT)   1 Jan
Wilkins, R. A. W.
qs   (INT)   1 Jan
Greatorex, M. psc (FC)   1 July
Smith, F. J. P. BEd nadc
qs   (ATC)   1 July
Strickland, K. N.
qss   (REGT)   1 July

1997

Batchelor, A. B.
qs   (INT)   1 Jan
Bunting, B. E. qs (ATC)   1 Jan
Clark, J. jsdc qs (ATC)   1 Jan
Dziuba, M. S. qs (ATC)   1 Jan
Hill, E. J. R. qss   (FC)   1 Jan
Minns, T. qs   (ATC)   1 Jan
Rimmer, M. qab qs(FC)   1 Jan
Steele, A. H. MPhil BA
PGCE psc(j)   (REGT)   1 Jan
West, C. M. BSc G(a)
qs   (REGT)   1 Jan
Williams, R. N.
qs   (ATC)   1 Jan
Balshaw, K. S.
psc(j)   (REGT)   1 July
Buist, S. L. psc(j) (FC)   1 July
Greville, P. J.
psc(j)   (ATC)   1 July

1998

Chambers, P. qs   (FC)   1 Jan
Galbraith, A. G.
qs   (REGT)   1 Jan
Peart, C. J. qs   (ATC)   1 Jan
Proudlove, A. MBA qab
qs   (REGT)   1 Jan
Stewart, P. D. T. MBE
MA AMBCS psc(j)
adp   (INT)   1 Jan
Tyrrell, I. R. BSc qtm
qs   (INT)   1 Jan
Chambers, M. A.
qs   (ATC)   1 July
Crayford, M. K.
psc(j)   (FC)   1 July

Lynch, R. D. MA BA
CDipAF psc(j) (REGT)   1 July
Peters, N. P. psc(j) (FC)   1 July

1999

Burt, P. MA G(a)
psc(j)   (REGT)   1 Jan
Green, B. C. qss   (FC)   1 Jan
Hemsley, R. J. T. BA
psc(j) qab   (FC)   1 Jan
Kirk, J. N. psc(j) (REGT)   1 Jan
La Forte, R. W. MBE BA
psc(j)   (REGT)   1 Jan
Osborne, T. E. jsdc cfs
qs   (FLTOPS)   1 Jan
Pearson, G. J. BA
psc(j)   (INT)   1 Jan
Ronaldson, A.
psc(j)   (FC)   1 Jan
Stevens, P. F. qab
qs   (FC)   1 Jan
Tolman, N. J.
psc(j)   (ATC)   1 Jan
Worrall, J. A. qs (ATC)   1 Jan
Beckwith, D. M.
qs   (REGT)   1 July
Clegg, J. A. qs   (FC)   1 July
Day, P. N. G(a)
qs   (REGT)   1 July
Driver, M. N. BSc(Eng)
MRAeS psc(j)
G(a)   (REGT)   1 July
Eaton, J. G. MBE MDA
BSc psc(j)   (REGT)   1 July
Foster, C. A. qs   (ATC)   1 July
Gorman, C. J.
psc(j)   (REGT)   1 July
Heath, M. A. BSc
MCIPD G(a)
qs   (REGT)   1 July
Loader, J. P. MBE
qss   (INT)   1 July
Millington, W. J. MA
psc(j) asq   (FC)   1 July
Mills, A. R. M. BA
psc(j)   (ATC)   1 July
Naworynsky, M. P.
psc(j)   (ATC)   1 July
Rogerson, M. MBE MA
MBA psc(j)   (ATC)   1 July
Williams, D. A. K.
psc(j)   (REGT)   1 July
Wragg, S. G. BSc
psc   (ATC)   1 July

Wing Commanders

2000

Barrowcliffe, I.
  qss   (INT)   1 Jan
Burchett, C. R. qs (INT) 1 Jan
Griffiths, B. M. MBA
  BSc MCMI G(a)
  qs   (REGT) 1 Jan
Hill, N. BSc qs   (INT) 1 Jan
Jones, P. A. BSc
  qs   (ATC) 1 Jan
Kay, A. qs   (FC) 1 Jan
Knapman, C. S. psc(j)
  qab   (FC) 1 Jan
Mitchell, G. I. qss (ATC) 1 Jan
Ormerod, C. A. MBE
  qs   (REGT) 1 Jan
Wilmshurst-Smith, J.
  D. qs   (FC) 1 Jan
Woosey, D. C. qab
  qs   (INT) 1 Jan
Balaam, D. C. MBE qab
  qtm qs   (INT) 1 July
Catmull, T. P. MA psc(j)
  fc   (FC) 1 July
Cox, P. H. psc(j) (FC) 1 July
Embleton, S. N.
  qss   (REGT) 1 July
Garston, R. J. L. MSc
  qs   (REGT) 1 July
Jobling, C. qs (FC) 1 July
Jones, R. W. qab
  qs   (FC) 1 July
Lainchbury, D. I.
  qs   (ATC) 1 July
Luton, M. qs (REGT) 1 July
Morton, M. A. BA
  psc(j)   (ATC) 1 July
Rapson, A. D.
  psc(j)   (ATC) 1 July
Roberts, A. J. BSc
  psc(j)   (ATC) 1 July
Watson, R. M.
  psc(j)   (ATC) 1 July

2001

Alexander, J. MBA BA
  qab G(a) qs (REGT) 1 Jan
Atkinson, P. W. BA
  psc(j)   (FC) 1 Jan
Barber, D. BA
  psc(j)   (ATC) 1 Jan
Bray, N. psc(j)
  qab   (REGT) 1 Jan

Bush, D. A. BSc qab
  qs   (ATC) 1 Jan
Buttery, P. A. MRAeS
  asq qs   (FC) 1 Jan
Cole, J. M. qs (INT) 1 Jan
Duncan, J. C. qs (ATC) 1 Jan
Harrison, E. C. MBE
  qss   (ATC) 1 Jan
Hewett, G. BEd qab
  qs   (FC) 1 Jan
Hodgson, J. W.
  qss   (ATC) 1 Jan
Hutchinson, F. N. MCMI
  qs   (REGT) 1 Jan
Jones, P. C. MBA qab
  qtm qs   (INT) 1 Jan
McCombe, A. B.
  qs   (REGT) 1 Jan
Payne, T. BSc G(a)
  qss   (REGT) 1 Jan
Todd, C. R. BSc
  psc(j)   (ATC) 1 Jan
White, J. P. BSc
  qs   (REGT) 1 Jan
Bartlett, A.   (FC) 1 July
Chalmers, J. E. BA
  psc(j)   (ATC) 1 July
Corbett, A. S. MBE BA
  psc(j)   (INT) 1 July
Downs, G. D. qs (INT) 1 July
Edwards, P. qs (INT) 1 July
King, A. J. qab qs (FC) 1 July
Marsh, R. J. L. BSc
  qs   (FLTOPS) 1 July
McLintic, P. J. qs (FC) 1 July
Mullings, N. W. BSc
  qs   (FC) 1 July
Preston, G. A. qab
  qs   (FC) 1 July
Smith, N. C. qs (REGT) 1 July
Stokes, P. M. MBE
  qs   (REGT) 1 July
Strachan, P. D.
  qs   (REGT) 1 July
Taylor, C. BA qab
  qs   (FLTOPS) 1 July
Thornber, S. R. BSc
  qs   (INT) 1 July

2002

Allan, D. qab qtm
  qs   (INT) 1 Jan
Chapman, N. A. MSc
  BA qs (INT) 1 Jan
Holland, D. A. qs (INT) 1 Jan
Paige, J. M. qss (ATC) 1 Jan
Quin, A. K. qs (ATC) 1 Jan
Bell, I. N. qs (ATC) 1 July

Bradnam, S. W. BSc
  qab qs (REGT) 1 July
Hall, A. J. MBE qab
  qs   (REGT) 1 July
Jones, D. K. qs (FC) 1 July
Loveday, N. J. BSc
  qs   (FC) 1 July
Newman, N. J. MPhil
  qs   (REGT) 1 July
Pound, M. G(a)
  qs   (REGT) 1 July
Roper, M. L. BA qs (FC) 1 July
Spencer, J. D. BSc
  qs (FLTOPS) 1 July
Todd, I. S. psc(j)
  G(a)   (REGT) 1 July
Tomaney, D. A.
  qs   (ATC) 1 July
Winstanley, D. qs (ATC) 1 July

Squadron Leaders

1981

Hunter, G. qs   (INT)   1 Jan

1982

Comina, P. S. C.
qss   (REGT)   1 Jan
Williams, M. qss   (FC)   1 July

1984

Jasinski, N. Z. R.
qs   (REGT)   1 July

1985

Stokes, R. K. MBE
qss   (REGT)   1 Jan

1987

Clough, G.   (FC)   1 Jan
Thompson, C. P. C.
qs   (FC)   1 July

1988

Chalklin, R. MBE
qs   (REGT)   1 Jan
George, A. M. MBE qs
i   (ATC)   1 Jan
Ingham, J. A.
qs   (REGT)   1 Jan
Smith, A. R.   (ATC)   1 Jan
Tester, D. J. MA
qs   (INT)   1 Jan
Tully, K. F. qs   (ATC)   1 Jan
Littlehales, M. P. G.
qs   (FC)   1 July

1989

Franklin, C. J.   (FC)   1 Jan
Gresham, J. W.   (ATC)   1 Jan
Revell, C. qs   (ATC)   1 Jan
Smith, P. R. qab qs (FC)   1 Jan
Sutherland-Scott, R.
MBE BSc qs   (ATC)   1 Jan

Ainslie, I. McP.
qss   (ATC)   1 July
Hammett, G. G.
qss   (INT)   1 July
Howells, L. qss   (ATC)   1 July
Hurry, A. J. qs   (REGT)   1 July
McManus, S. J. qss (FC)   1 July
Tolley, S. G. BSc qab
qwi qwi(T) qs   (FC)   1 July

1990

Campbell, I. M.
qss   (ATC)   1 Jan
Fryer, R. P. qs   (ATC)   1 Jan
Perkins, A. D. qs (ATC)   1 Jan
Yarnold, J. G. T.
qss   (REGT)   1 Jan
Bateman, J. C.
qwi(AD) qs   (FC)   1 July
Child, J. A. BSc MMar
adp qss   (FC)   1 July
Hallett, C. qab qss (FC)   1 July
Kiely, C. T. qs   (ATC)   1 July
Merryweather, D. V.
qss   (ATC)   1 July

1991

Challenor, G. B. BA
qs   (ATC)   1 Jan
Coggon, M. G. qss (FC)   1 Jan
Cross, H. C.   (REGT)   1 Jan
Abbott, C. J. qs (REGT)   1 July
Day, F. B. W. E.
qs   (FLTOPS)   1 July
Hann, K. MBE qwi
qs   (FC)   1 July
Hidden, C. J. BSc
qs   (REGT)   1 July
Powe, M. J. BSc qs (FC)   1 July
Stoner, N. B. qs   (ATC)   1 July
Thomas, N. A. qs (ATC)   1 July
Ware, I. H. qs   (REGT)   1 July

1992

Duffus, A. A. qs   (FC)   1 Jan
Evans, N. qs   (REGT)   1 Jan
Mellor-Jones, R. A. BSc
qab qs   (FC)   1 Jan
Oxley, J. P. qss   (FC)   1 Jan
Gray, R. W. qs   (FC)   1 July

1993

Beck, J. MSc BA
qs   (INT)   1 Jan
Christie, D. J. qs i (FC)   1 Jan
George, B. D. qss (ATC)   1 Jan
Nott, R. E. qs   (ATC)   1 Jan
Nuttall, S. V. qtm
qs   (INT)   1 Jan
Adey, E. J. BA
qs   (REGT)   1 July
Morrison, D. qss (ATC)   1 July
Robinson, A. qs (ATC)   1 July
Wylde, J. D. BA qss (FC)   1 July

1994

Bartlett, S. E. BSc
qs   (INT)   1 Jan
Bennett, P. G. BA qab
qss   (INT)   1 Jan
Chapman, M. A.   (ATC)   1 Jan
Cookson, J. D. BEM
qs   (ATC)   1 Jan
Fearon, J. B. BSc asq
qss   (FC)   1 Jan
McLean, B. J. MCMI
qs   (FC)   1 Jan
Nicolson, J. A.
qss   (ATC)   1 Jan
Ward, G. F. qs   (FC)   1 Jan
Dewar, N. A. qab   (FC)   8 Jan
Kreft, S. N. MBA BA
qs   (INT)   17 June
Dickson, G. L. BA qab
qs   (ATC)   1 July
Hyett, S. D. qs   (ATC)   1 July
McLean, A.   (INT)   1 July
Presley, M. A. MBA
MCMI qab qs   (FC)   1 July
Rayfield, P. H. qs (FC)   1 July
Smith, H. G. BA qab
qss   (ATC)   1 July
Steel, C. S.
qab qs   (INT)   1 July
Boe, B. M. C. (FLTOPS)   17 Oct

1995

Anthistle, P. qs   (ATC)   1 Jan
Davies, J. B. qs   (INT)   1 Jan
Dowling, F. K.
qs   (FLTOPS)   1 Jan
Drake, D. J. BA
qs   (ATC)   1 Jan
Hazelgreaves, G. BA
qs   (ATC)   1 Jan
Mackay, I. T.   (ATC)   1 Jan

141

Squadron Leaders

1995—contd

Prevett, W. S. qs (ATC) 1 Jan
Price, I. R. MCMI qab
  qwi(AD) qs   (FC) 1 Jan
Saunders, R. J. qab
  qs   (FC) 1 Jan
Maguire, P. J. BA
  qs   (FC) 1 July
Varley, G. A. qs (ATC) 1 July

1996

Brown, R. P. C. qs (INT) 1 Jan
Oldfield, C. I. qs (INT) 1 Jan
Raine, D. W. qs (ATC) 1 Jan
Reid, L. M. qs   (FC) 1 Jan
Taylor, W. S. MBE MSc
  BSc MCMI qs (REGT) 1 Jan
Tottman, M. BSc qs(FC) 1 Jan
Austen, D. J. qs (ATC) 1 July
Coffey, J. fc qs   (FC) 1 July
Heyworth, T. C. BSc
  qs   (REGT) 1 July
King, W. N. MDA BA
  MCIPD qs (REGT) 1 July
Martin, K. L. qss (ATC) 1 July
McCallum, A. qs (FC) 1 July
Park, A. R. qs   (FC) 1 July
Parsons, B. L.   (ATC) 1 July
Ryan, M. J. MCIPD
  MCMI qs (REGT) 1 July
Thorner, M. A. BA
  qs   (INT) 1 July
Wells, A. J. qs (ATC) 1 July
Woodward, R. G. G.
  qs   (REGT) 1 July

1997

Archer, J. P. qs (REGT) 1 Jan
Bainbridge, A. S.
  qss   (ATC) 1 Jan
Barnes, R. W.
  qs   (REGT) 1 Jan
Blake, F. J. qs (INT) 1 Jan
Burt, M. J. MCIPD
  MCMI G(a) qs(REGT) 1 Jan
Fitzmaurice, A. F. N.
  St.J. qs   (FC) 1 Jan
Gildersleeves, J. P. V.
  qs   (FC) 1 Jan
Gill, A. C. qs (ATC) 1 Jan

Kendall, E. S. G(a)
  qs   (REGT) 1 Jan
Kitt, A. P. BA qs (REGT) 1 Jan
Lawrence, R. J.
  qs   (ATC) 1 Jan
Millington, S. BA qab
  qs   (REGT) 1 Jan
Oliver, B. A. qss (ATC) 1 Jan
Osman, A. J. qs(REGT) 1 Jan
Owens, T. J. L. qs(ATC) 1 Jan
Smith, I. R. qs (REGT) 1 Jan
Todd, J. D. qs (REGT) 1 Jan
Turner, J. A. G(a)
  qss   (REGT) 1 Jan
Bailey, R. qab qs (INT) 1 July
Beckley, C. P. BSc(Econ)
  qs   (REGT) 1 July
Bird, M. R. MBE
  qs   (REGT) 1 July
Brunt, L. B. qab
  qs   (REGT) 1 July
Clifford, R. F. J.
  qs   (REGT) 1 July
Coleman, M. S. P.
  qs   (FC) 1 July
Gibson, C. R. qwi (FC) 1 July
Lackey, E. W. M. BSc
  qs   (ATC) 1 July
Madden, M. R. BSc
  MILT MIL G(a)
  qs   (REGT) 1 July
McFarland, S. S. qab
  qss   (REGT) 1 July
Portlock, J. B. qab
  qs   (FC) 1 July
Barling, N. R.
  qs   (FLTOPS) 1 Oct

1998

Belfield, F. D. MBE BSc
  qs   (FC) 1 Jan
Daisley, R. M. BSc
  qs   (FC) 1 Jan
Devoy, D. A. qab
  qs   (REGT) 1 Jan
Divver, T. J. qs (FC) 1 Jan
Dobson, A. P. BEng
  qs   (REGT) 1 Jan
Grayson, K. J.
  qss   (REGT) 1 Jan
Heaselgrave, D. R.
  qs   (ATC) 1 Jan
Jones, S. L. qs (FC) 1 Jan
Myers-Hemingway, A.
  P. BSc qs (INT) 1 Jan
Ploutarchou, A. P.
  qs   (ATC) 1 Jan
Rossiter, G. qs (ATC) 1 Jan

Speedy, P. P. BSc
  qs   (FLTOPS) 1 Jan
Wann, G. B. D.
  qss   (ATC) 1 Jan
Ware, G. S. MBA qab
  qs   (FC) 1 Jan
Wilkins, A. J. qss (FC) 1 Jan
Alcock, N. J. BSc
  qs   (ATC) 1 July
Crompton, N. A. C.
  qs   (FC) 1 July
Gilroy, A. BA qs(REGT) 1 July
Griffiths, S. MISM
  qwi(SAW) qs (REGT) 1 July
Lamont, N. BA qs (INT) 1 July
MacLeod, E.   (ATC) 1 July
Meridew, E. J. qs (ATC) 1 July
Phillips, D. C. qab
  qs   (ATC) 1 July
Read, D. J. BA
  qs   (REGT) 1 July
Scott, P. qs (REGT) 1 July
Thomson, I. A. BSc qab
  G(a) qs (REGT) 1 July
Walker, J. C. BSc qs(FC) 1 July
Wood, C. D. qs (ATC) 1 July

1999

Akehurst, P. L. MBE BSc
  qs   (ATC) 1 Jan
Cartmell, D. R. qs(ATC) 1 Jan
Dunstall, M. R. qs(ATC) 1 Jan
Ford, D. L. G(a)
  qs   (REGT) 1 Jan
Freeman, R. J. B. BA
  G(a) qs (REGT) 1 Jan
Gray, D. L. BA qs (FC) 1 Jan
Griffiths, D. J.
  qs   (REGT) 1 Jan
Hart, M. P. BA qab
  qs   (INT) 1 Jan
Henderson, G. S. BEd
  qss   (ATC) 1 Jan
Hughes, P. R. qs (INT) 1 Jan
Johnson, L. C. MVO
  qs   (ATC) 1 Jan
Knowles, A. G. BSc
  G(a) qab qs (REGT) 1 Jan
Lester, P. T. G. qab
  qs   (REGT) 1 Jan
Lewis, S. B. BSc
  qs   (INT) 1 Jan
Lindsey, D. E. qss(ATC) 1 Jan
Lockhart, N. L. qs(ATC) 1 Jan
MacKenzie, K. D.
  qs   (REGT) 1 Jan
Pope, M. S. BA
  qs   (REGT) 1 Jan

Squadron Leaders

1999—contd

Van Vogt, M. A.
qss   (ATC)   1 Jan
Williams, P. L. qs (INT)   1 Jan
Beasant, A. J.
qs   (REGT)   1 July
Coleman, C. W. T.
qs   (FC)   1 July
Doyle, J. M. qs (ATC)   1 July
Dyson, E. F. qs (REGT)   1 July
Hand, M. T. qs (REGT)   1 July
Jeffs, G. J. BA
qss   (ATC)   1 July
Keefe, D. B. qs (REGT)   1 July
Lloyd, A. T. BSc
qss   (INT)   1 July
MacLeod, G. M.
qs   (INT)   1 July
Marden, A. J. qs (ATC)   1 July
McCarney, E. S.
qs   (ATC)   1 July
McEvoy, J. J.
qs   (REGT)   1 July
McIntyre, A. E.
qss   (ATC)   1 July
Miller, S. M. qs (REGT)   1 July
O'Connor, S. K. qab
qs   (FC)   1 July
Pattinson, M.
qs   (REGT)   1 July
Scott, C. asq qss (FC)   1 July
Scott, C. W. qs (ATC)   1 July
Sharp, A. P. qss (ATC)   1 July
Walkerdine, I. M.
qs   (FC)   1 July
Watson, E. J. MSc qtm
qs   (INT)   1 July
Webster, A. J. E.
qs   (ATC)   1 July
White, A. A. F. MBA
DipMgmt qs (INT)   1 July

2000

Davies, A. J. qs (FC)   1 Jan
Garvey, K. qs (INT)   1 Jan
Gibbs, B. T. qs (FC)   1 Jan
Grimshaw, R. D. BSc
qab qs   (FLTOPS)   1 Jan
Hammond, G. B. T. BA
qs   (FC)   1 Jan
Hickson, P. R. BSc
qss   (REGT)   1 Jan
Jacob, R. G. BA
qs   (ATC)   1 Jan

James, P. M. qs (ATC)   1 Jan
Jones, A. D. BA
qs   (INT)   1 Jan
Kanhai, R. I. qss (ATC)   1 Jan
Kendall, W. J.
qs   (REGT)   1 Jan
Mackenzie, A. K.
qs   (ATC)   1 Jan
McAleer, A. S. qs (FC)   1 Jan
McKillop, J. A. BSc
qs   (ATC)   1 Jan
Nicholas, J. J. R. MCMI
qs   (ATC)   1 Jan
O'Dell, R. M. qs (FC)   1 Jan
Palmer, M. R. K. BSc
qs   (FC)   1 Jan
Payne, M. J. G(a)
qss   (REGT)   1 Jan
Pendleton, G. qss (ATC)   1 Jan
Povey, A. R. qs (ATC)   1 Jan
Pulling, B. S. qss (ATC)   1 Jan
Rutherford, A. qs (INT)   1 Jan
Sawyer, R. N. qab
qs   (REGT)   1 Jan
Sharp, J. C. BSc qs (FC)   1 Jan
Spence, S. qs (REGT)   1 Jan
Throsby, M. qss (ATC)   1 Jan
Turner, R. G. qs (FC)   1 Jan
Weaver-Smith, P. A.
qab qs   (REGT)   1 Jan
Beat, P. A. qss (ATC)   1 July
Benn, C. qs (FC)   1 July
Bolton, P. M. qss (FC)   1 July
Boyle, M. P. BSc
qss   (ATC)   1 July
Brabon, M. D.
qs   (REGT)   1 July
Brown, T. D. A.
qss   (FLTOPS)   1 July
Coleman, M. G.
qss   (ATC)   1 July
Connelly, R. qss (ATC)   1 July
Evans, P. W. BSc
qss   (FC)   1 July
Flanigan, R. qs (ATC)   1 July
Flint, C. D. qss (FC)   1 July
Green, I. qs (FC)   1 July
Green, P. J. qss (ATC)   1 July
Howes, D. J. G(a)
qss   (REGT)   1 July
Loveridge, S. M.
qss   (FC)   1 July
MacDonald, F. G.
qs   (ATC)   1 July
Nuttall, R. M. MBE
qs   (INT)   1 July
Owens, R. L. BSc
qs   (FC)   1 July
Patrick, S. N. BSc
qss   (ATC)   1 July

Pickering, J. D.
qs   (ATC)   1 July
Pollard, C. S. BSc
qss   (FC)   1 July
Powell, G. J. qss
   (REGT)   1 July
Sharples, S. P. BSc
qs   (REGT)   1 July
Shea-Simonds, P. J.
qs   (REGT)   1 July
Stirrat, S. S. BA
qs   (INT)   1 July
Stylianides, A. MBE
BSc qcc   (FC)   1 July
Tomkins, S. R.
qs   (REGT)   1 July
Walker, J. C. BSc
qss   (ATC)   1 July
Ryles, S. M. MBE (REGT) 12 Nov

2001

Bainbridge, D. J. F. BSc
G(a) qs   (REGT)   1 Jan
Beer, R. P. BSc asq
qs   (FC)   1 Jan
Birnie, R. E. R. BSc
qwi(AD) qss (FC)   1 Jan
Blake, I. R. qs (FC)   1 Jan
Brook, S. R. qss (ATC)   1 Jan
Clark, G. A. P.
qs   (REGT)   1 Jan
Cliff, C. H. G. qs (ATC)   1 Jan
Dyer, K. P. BSc
qss   (REGT)   1 Jan
Fountain, D. G(a)
qss   (REGT)   1 Jan
Glazebrook, A. J. C. BA
qs   (REGT)   1 Jan
Harrop, M. D. BEng
qs   (FC)   1 Jan
Howard-Vyse, C. A.
MBA BSc qtm
qs   (FLTOPS)   1 Jan
Jeffs, A. J. BSc
qss   (FLTOPS)   1 Jan
Kinnell, R. qss (REGT)   1 Jan
Liggat, A. K. S. G(a)
qss   (REGT)   1 Jan
Lowman, M. E. BSc
qss   (ATC)   1 Jan
Marshall, P. J. qs (ATC)   1 Jan
McGuigan, N. D. BSc
qs   (FLTOPS)   1 Jan
Miller, D. BSc qs (INT)   1 Jan
Owen, D. J. qss (INT)   1 Jan
Pickett, G. R. qss (FC)   1 Jan
Ratcliffe, P. A. BSc
qss   (FC)   1 Jan

Squadron Leaders

2001—contd

Riley, P. J. BA qss(ATC)		1 Jan
Rooney, W. J.		
qs	(REGT)	1 Jan
Sinclair, A. D.		
qss2	(ATC)	1 Jan
Stansby, A. W. qs	(FC)	1 Jan
Tait, J. D. BSc qs	(FC)	1 Jan
Thorpe, C. P. BSc		
qs	(FC)	1 Jan
White, J. P. qss	(REGT)	1 Jan
Young, C. A. MEd BSc		
qs	(FC)	1 Jan
Banbrook, J. M.		
qs	(REGT)	1 July
Bardell-Cox, T. A. MBA		
BSc(Econ) MCMI		
qs	(INT)	1 July
Barnes, T. J. qss	(ATC)	1 July
Breedon, C. J. qss	(FC)	1 July
Breeds, P. W. qss1	(INT)	1 July
Bruce, C. I. D. qcc	(INT)	1 July
Chappell, M. R. qss	(FC)	1 July
Derbyshire, J. G. BA		
qwi(SAW) qs	(REGT)	1 July
Eason, A. S. BA		
qss	(ATC)	1 July
Hodgson, R. qtm		
qss	(INT)	1 July
Jackson, J. A.	(REGT)	1 July
Jago, M. qss	(FC)	1 July
Jay, P. A. MSc BSc		
qss	(INT)	1 July
Johnson, M. R. BSc		
qwi(AD) qss	(FC)	1 July
Knight, D. qss1	(FC)	1 July
Larry, S. qss2	(FC)	1 July
Lawrence, P. qs	(REGT)	1 July
Lee, A. J. BA PGCE		
qs	(REGT)	1 July
Moore, C. D. qss	(INT)	1 July
Purse, M. A. qs	(INT)	1 July
Quigley, T. L. LLB		
qss2	(INT)	1 July
Sackley, D. P. qwi(AD)		
qss	(FC)	1 July
Simpson, J. C. D.		
qss1	(REGT)	1 July
Smart, K. qcc	(ATC)	1 July
Smeath, M. J. MBE		
qs	(REGT)	1 July
Snellock, C. D. BSc qtm		
qs	(INT)	1 July
Taylor-Powell, C. L.		
qss	(ATC)	1 July

Thickett, A. B. M.		
qcc	(INT)	1 July
Watkins, D. M.		
qss	(REGT)	1 July
Wilkinson, A. C. BSc		
qwi(SAW) qs	(REGT)	1 July

2002

Bellworthy, A. J.		
qss1	(ATC)	1 Jan
Benham, T. M.		
qss	(ATC)	1 Jan
Bennett, A. R. BA		
qs	(REGT)	1 Jan
Bishop, C. A. M. BA		
qss	(REGT)	1 Jan
Brooks, D. J. qss	(FC)	1 Jan
Brooks, J. qwi(AD)		
qss	(FC)	1 Jan
Brown, G. P.		
qss	(REGT)	1 Jan
Callander, A. D.		
qss	(REGT)	1 Jan
Catterall, C. qss	(FC)	1 Jan
Clyburn, N. P. qs	(ATC)	1 Jan
Cockin, M. D. qss	(FC)	1 Jan
Collins, S. E. qss	(INT)	1 Jan
Cumming, J. D.		
qcc	(REGT)	1 Jan
Cyster, J. L. qss	(INT)	1 Jan
Dallas, A. W.		
qss	(REGT)	1 Jan
Day, P. A. BSc qtm		
qss	(INT)	1 Jan
Dick, G. J. qss	(FC)	1 Jan
Dickson, J. C. qss(ATC)		1 Jan
Donoghue M. P. J.		
qss	(REGT)	1 Jan
Eden, J. J. BSc		
qss	(REGT)	1 Jan
Gray, F. J. LLB		
qss	(INT)	1 Jan
Greenwood, A. BA		
qss	(FC)	1 Jan
Hartle, N. J.	(FLTOPS)	1 Jan
Hellard, G. P.		
qss	(REGT)	1 Jan
Hewson, N. qwi(AD)		
qss2	(FC)	1 Jan
Hill, A. A. PhD BSc		
qss	(FC)	1 Jan
Hughes, D. L.		
qss	(ATC)	1 Jan
Jackson, A. D.		
qss	(FLTOPS)	1 Jan
Langley, P. H. qss (ATC)		1 Jan
McLucas, R. I.		
qss1	(REGT)	1 Jan

Miller, D. W. A. qs	(FC)	1 Jan
Reid, A. G. M. qss	(FC)	1 Jan
Rowntree, C. W.		
qss	(FC)	1 Jan
Scott, P. A. BA PGCE		
qs	(REGT)	1 Jan
Sinclair, S. J. qcc (ATC)		1 Jan
Sutton, J. P.		
qss2	(REGT)	1 Jan
Taylor, L. B. BA		
qwi(SAW)		
qss2	(REGT)	1 Jan
Thayne, A. G.		
qs	(REGT)	1 Jan
Wiggans, I. R.		
qss	(ATC)	1 Jan
Williams, A. G.		
qss	(REGT)	1 Jan
Wood, P. MBE		
qwi(SAW)		
qss	(REGT)	1 Jan
Armstrong, J. T.		
qss	(REGT)	1 July
Bond, C. N.		
qss1	(REGT)	1 July
Boundy, R. A. qwi(AD)		
qss2	(FC)	1 July
Bourton, M. J. W.		
qss	(ATC)	1 July
Burchill, G. M.		
qcc	(REGT)	1 July
Carpenter, P. J. BSc		
qs	(FC)	1 July
Cox, M. qcc	(FC)	1 July
Daisley, L. S. BSc		
qwi(AD) qss	(FC)	1 July
Davison, A. B. qwi(AD)		
qss	(FC)	1 July
Eden, R. E. qss (ATC)		1 July
Formby, M. R.		
qss	(REGT)	1 July
Fraser, P. D. qss	(INT)	1 July
Hadden, P. qss	(ATC)	1 July
Hope, N. qss	(ATC)	1 July
Hughes, J. L. BSc		
qwi(AD) qss	(FC)	1 July
Langley, R. I.		
qcc	(REGT)	1 July
Lewis, P. E. qss	(ATC)	1 July
Mayers, M. S. BSc		
qss	(ATC)	1 July
McCarney, N. C.		
qss2	(ATC)	1 July
Morley, W. J. qss (ATC)		1 July
Noone, J. M. qss (ATC)		1 July
Parkinson, J. H.		
qss	(REGT)	1 July
Philip, G. A. qcc	(FC)	1 July
Radnall, M. M.		
qcc	(REGT)	1 July

Squadron Leaders

2002—contd

Stewart, A. E.
qss2   (INT)   1 July
Stowers, M. J.
qs   (REGT)   1 July
Uren, T. E. BSc G(a)
qss   (REGT)   1 July
Varley, S. E. qcc (ATC)   1 July
Williams, D. K.
qss   (REGT)   1 July
Wymer, R. J. MCMI
qss   (ATC)   1 July

Flight Lieutenants

1974

Don, J. BSc qss (ATC)   10 Oct

1975

Wright, A. R.   (ATC) 10 May
Thomson, B. R.
qss   (REGT)   1 Oct

1977

Hill, M. qss   (ATC)   4 Aug

1978

Trist, S. N.
qss   (FLTOPS) 21 Mar
McClelland, D. M.(ATC) 29 June
Hartley, P. S.
qss   (FLTOPS) 16 Sept

1979

La Roche, R.   (ATC) 10 Nov

1980

Harrison, J. W.
qss   (ATC)   28 Apr
Haughie, J. R. qss (FC)   28 Apr
Ripley, G.   (FC) 11 May
Montgomerie, H. C. A.
qss   (FC) 29 June
Harrison, D. P.   (ATC) 13 Dec

1981

Broadway, S. J. H.
qss   (FC) 17 Jan
Reading, A. M.   (FC) 27 Sept

1982

Perry, R.   (ATC) 28 June
Nickles, R. C. BSc(ATC) 14 Nov
Williams, M. J. (ATC) 24 Dec

1984

Williams, P. F.
qss   (ATC) 18 Apr

1985

Purchase, S. P. MSc
BSc qss1   (INT) 25 Feb
Tyas, S. P. J. MBE
        (ATC) 23 May
Taylor, J. F. BSc asq
qss   (FC) 18 July
Brightman, P. S.(REGT) 8 Sept
Gemmill, T.   (FC) 19 Nov
Jones, M. P.   (ATC) 15 Dec

1986

Gamble, N. (FLTOPS)   3 Jan
Shaw, P. A. qss (ATC) 29 Jan
Millar, H. E.   (ATC) 18 Feb
Faulkner, H. M. BSc asq
fc qss   (FC) 11 June
Townshend, D. P.
qss   (FC) 13 June
Horne, I. qss   (ATC) 24 July
Summers, G. S. BA
qss   (FLTOPS) 17 Oct
Burke, D. G.   (ATC) 20 Dec

1987

Goatham, J. MSc BSc
PGCE qss (FLTOPS) 15 Jan
Williams, S. B. BSc
qss1   (ATC) 31 Jan
Wilson, S. C. BA
qss   (ATC) 22 Apr
Tape, S. F.   (FC)   4 July
Cothey, P. qss (FC)   5 Aug
Giles, A. M.
qss   (FLTOPS)   5 Aug
Hamilton-Bing, S. P. E.
qs   (ATC) 22 Aug
Iddles, J. A. D. qss (FC) 19 Sept
Sutton, A. J. qss (ATC) 6 Nov
Philipson, R. M. fc
qss   (FC)   5 Dec
Green, A. J. BSc
qcc   (ATC) 10 Dec

1988

Preedy, J. A. qss (ATC)   4 Mar

145

Flight Lieutenants

1988—contd

Mullan, P. M. BSc
   qss   (FC) 14 Apr
Johnson, A. W. qwi
   qss   (FC) 26 May
Tunaley, M. A. qss (FC) 26 May
Davies, I. D. qss   (FC) 29 May
Clarke, A. C. qss   (FC)   8 Oct
Whitehead, N. qcc (FC) 15 Oct
Smith, R. F. DPhil BA
   PGCE qss   (INT)   8 Nov
Ortyl, R. I. MCGI asq
   qss   (FC) 20 Nov
Gillott, S. M. BSc
   qss   (FC) 26 Nov

1989

Arber, R. C.
   qcc   (FLTOPS) 17 Jan
Pontefract, J. C.
   qss   (FLTOPS) 29 Jan
Coleman, A. J. BSc
   qwi(SAW) qss(REGT) 18 Feb
Gibson, G. J.   (FC) 28 Feb
Upton, M. N. qcc (FC) 23 Mar
Rodgers, M. P.
   qss   (FLTOPS) 20 Apr
Brown, A. M. qss (INT) 10 May
Kennedy, A. G. MA
   G(a)   (REGT)   7 June
Bingham, J. D.   (ATC)   4 July
Sumal, I. S. qss   (FC)   4 July
Dowie, C. H. BSc
   qss   (FC) 16 Aug
Heron, P. M. qss (ATC) 27 Aug
Barmby, C. S. BSc qtm
   qss   (INT) 30 Sept
Clayton, K. R. BSc
   qss   (REGT) 30 Sept
Elsegood, M. J.
   qss   (FLTOPS)   8 Oct
Jackson, D. qss (ATC)   3 Dec

1990

Nicholson, G. B.
   qss   (ATC)   3 Mar
Brooks, D. P. qab
   qss   (FLTOPS) 11 Apr
Mason, C. R. MPhil BSc
   qss   (FLTOPS) 11 Apr

Webb-Dicken, R.
   qss   (FLTOPS) 11 Apr
Sneddon, S. R. BSc
   qss   (INT)   7 June
Barrett, M. S. qss (ATC)   8 June
Ross, J. qss   (FC) 19 June
Disdel, C. A. H. BSc
   qss1   (FC)   8 July
Baker, D. A. qss (ATC) 28 July
Tilley. E. J. qss (FC)   1 Sept
Bartlett, S. M.
   qss   (ATC) 12 Sept
Richardson, F. S.
   qss   (REGT) 15 Sept
Tuite, P. F. qss   (FC) 15 Sept
Payne, S. M. qss (ATC)   2 Nov

1991

Clarke, J. qss   (ATC) 27 Jan
Trown, N. J. qab
   qss1   (REGT)   1 Mar
Allen, M. R. L.
   qss1   (REGT)   6 Mar
O'Neill, S. G. P.
   qss   (FC) 30 Mar
MacLennan, S. W. qab
   qwi(AD)
   qss   (FLTOPS) 11 Apr
Liston, M. J. (FLTOPS) 11 May
Buchanan, J. W.
   qss   (ATC) 15 May
Atchison, J. D. BA
   qss   (FC)   3 July
Kendall, R. A.   (ATC) 17 July
Steele, R. C. qss1 (ATC) 17 July
Ewen, G. P. MA
   qss   (ATC) 14 Aug
Wrenn, M. J.
   qss1   (ATC) 28 Aug
Thorpe, J. A. BA
   qss   (FC) 27 Sept
Hall, W. P. BS qss(ATC)   8 Nov
Lewis, J. H. BSc
   qss   (ATC) 14 Nov
Balfour, J. R. S. G(a)
   qss   (REGT) 23 Nov
Hunter, D. T. qss (ATC) 23 Nov
Currie, P. W. qss (FC) 10 Dec
Curtis, T. B. qss (ATC) 12 Dec
Collier, A. S. MSc BSc
   BSc FRGS qcc (INT) 19 Dec

1992

Kirkby, I. G. qss (FC)   4 Jan
Lorraine, A. G. qss (FC)   4 Jan

Laker, C. R. BA
   qss   (REGT) 15 Jan
Willingham, Y.
   qss   (ATC) 20 Jan
Craven, J. S. qwi(AD)
   qss1   (FC) 22 Jan
Istance, M. qss (ATC) 12 Feb
Scott, S. J.
   qss   (FLTOPS) 15 Feb
Maple, P. D. BA qss(FC) 25 Mar
Rickard, J. E. BSc
   qss   (INT) 25 Mar
Cooper, R. A. qss (INT) 29 Mar
Treacy, S. M. MSc BA
   qss   (FC)   1 Apr
Cooper, A. J.   (ATC) 30 Apr
Taylor, D. BSc qss (FC)   6 May
White, J. J. qss   (FC)   7 May
Rogerson, D. M. BSc
   qcc   (ATC)   8 July
Carter, T. J. FISM
   MILT   (FLTOPS) 19 Aug
Farmer, R. N. BA
   qss2   (INT) 19 Aug
Gunn, J. H.   (REGT)   3 Sept
Higgins, R. F. qss (ATC) 27 Sept
Harris, J. C. BSc
   qss   (REGT)   2 Oct
Vine, A. P. qss   (ATC)   8 Oct
Elks, S. J. qcc   (ATC) 11 Oct
Skipp, T. A. qss (ATC) 26 Oct
Bayley, N. J. qss (INT)   8 Nov
Blockley, S. A. qwi(AD)
   qss   (FC)   8 Nov
Oughton, M. D.
   qss   (FLTOPS)   8 Nov
Leatham, C. qss (ATC) 10 Dec
Attewell, D. J.   (ATC) 13 Dec
Hampson, J. R.   (ATC) 15 Dec
Crompton, D. A.
   qcc   (FLTOPS) 19 Dec
Dinsley, R. M. qcc (FC) 19 Dec
Ticehurst, J. qss (FC) 19 Dec
Walton, K. G. qss (FC) 19 Dec
Chick, A. J.   (FLTOPS) 20 Dec
Berners, P. R.
   qss   (FLTOPS) 21 Dec
Davis, C. D. (FLTOPS) 25 Dec

1993

Parrott, M. A. qss (INT) 11 Jan
Carter, S. J. BEng
   qss   (REGT) 15 Jan
Clark, A. B. BSc
   qss   (ATC) 15 Jan
Ferguson, E. J. BEd
   qss   (ATC) 15 Jan

Flight Lieutenants

1993—contd

Martin, D. A. BSc
  qss   (FC)   15 Jan
Axford-Hawkes, I. A.
  qss   (ATC)   7 Feb
Walker, J. M. L. qcc(FC)   1 Mar
Bullock, S. T. qcc (ATC)   5 Mar
MacKay, G. E.(FLTOPS) 11 Mar
Robinson, C. qcc (FC) 14 Mar
Burr, S. J. MILT
  qss   (FLTOPS) 16 Mar
Reid, G. S. BSc
  qss   (FLTOPS)   1 Apr
Clark, W. A.   (ATC) 23 Apr
Forrester, J. M. qss(FC) 23 Apr
Lindsay, G. H.   (ATC) 23 Apr
Swift, V. S. qss   (FC) 23 Apr
Box, R. C. qss   (FC) 25 Apr
Fraser, G. M. BSc
  qss   (FC) 11 May
Thomas, P. F. S.
  qss   (ATC) 23 June
Taylor, M. V. MSc BSc
  qss   (FLTOPS)   5 July
Mills, Z. G. BA qss(ATC)   7 July
Northam, M. P.
  qss   (ATC) 18 July
Prytherch, N. S.
  qss   (INT) 23 July
Watson, A. J.   (FC) 27 July
Allison, A. J. qss (FC) 29 July
James, D. W. qss (INT) 29 July
Seymour, K. L. qwi(AD)
  qss   (FC) 29 July
Hanby, D. J. qss (FC) 30 July
Douglas, I. J.
  qss1   (FLTOPS)   4 Aug
Lock, R. K.   (ATC)   5 Sept
Streeton, A. D.
  qss   (ATC)   5 Sept
Mason, M. I. qss
      (REGT) 12 Sept
Woolfson, C. A. qss(FC) 12 Sept
Cosway, D. P.
  qss   (FLTOPS) 15 Sept
Nixon, P. T.   (FC) 25 Sept
Riley, B. J. BSc
  qss   (INT) 30 Sept
Gibson, D. qss (FC) 23 Oct
Johnson, D. R.
  qss   (ATC) 23 Oct
Newton, K. V. qss (FC) 23 Oct
Morris, P. K. qss1 (FC) 27 Oct
Kelly, R. W. qss (INT)   7 Nov
Thomas, R. E. L.
  qss1   (ATC) 10 Nov

Burt, T. BA qss   (INT) 13 Nov
Dodds, M. A. qcc (ATC)   4 Dec
Durlston-Powell, C. A.
  qss2   (FLTOPS) 16 Dec
Jones, P. L. qcc (ATC) 19 Dec

1994

Robson, N. A. H.
  BSc(Econ) qss1 (ATC) 15 Jan
Sharland, R. E. qss (FC) 17 Jan
Walker, K. qss1 (FC) 17 Jan
Wilczek, D. S. E. P.
  qss   (FC) 17 Jan
Gratton, R. E. J. (ATC) 13 Feb
Rawsthorne, N. A. BSc
  qss   (REGT) 18 Feb
Whetnall, H. C. BA(ATC) 18 Feb
Kenning, J. B. BSc
  qss   (INT) 19 Feb
Owens, J. A. qss (ATC) 25 Feb
Duffy, P. J. qcc (REGT) 27 Feb
Millar, S. A.
  qss1   (REGT) 27 Feb
Sheppard, K. J.
  qss2   (ATC) 28 Feb
Bullement, H. M. BSc
  qcc   (ATC) 29 Mar
Goodchild, M. C. H. BA
  qss   (FLTOPS) 30 Mar
Taylor, M. R. BSc
  qwi(SAW) qss(REGT) 30 Mar
Caesar, I. R. qss (REGT)   8 Apr
Cox, J. L. qcc   (FC)   8 Apr
Craddock, G. A. qss(FC)   8 Apr
James, C. J. qss (ATC)   8 Apr
Rodger, A. L. (REGT) 23 Apr
Stride, K. J. BA
  qss   (ATC) 11 May
Preston-Whyte, P. A.
  qss   (ATC) 19 May
Robb, A. McE. (ATC) 19 May
Stevens, A. J. qss1 (FC) 19 May
Welling, S. C.
  qss1   (ATC) 19 May
Ballantyne, D. N.
  qss   (ATC) 22 May
Harvey, D. G. qcc (ATC) 25 May
Lutton, D. R. qss1(ATC) 22 June
Breddy, L. A. qcc (ATC) 30 June
Adamson, A. P. W. BSc
  AIL qss i* (FLTOPS)   5 July
Hughes, K. A. MA
  MISM MInstAM(Dip)
  qcc   (FLTOPS)   5 July
Church, J. E. A.
  qss1   (INT) 14 July
Hathaway, S. R. BSc
  qcc   (INT) 15 July

Boxell, D. M. qss (ATC)   2 Aug
Mclvor, N. J.
  qss   (REGT)   2 Aug
Dixon, N. R. A. qss (FC) 25 Aug
Gill, C. M. qss (ATC) 25 Aug
Horn, N. B.
  qwi(SAW) qss(REGT) 25 Aug
Hamer, P. qtm qcc (INT) 22 Sept
Johnston, M. J.
  qss1   (FC) 26 Sept
Moss-Rogers, N. B. BSc
  qss   (ATC) 30 Sept
Raper, S. P. qcc (ATC) 28 Oct
Beck, N. P. qss1 (FC)   5 Nov
Irvine, A. C. A.
  qss   (INT)   5 Nov
Ogden, M. R. qss (FC)   5 Nov
Tatters, S. D.
  qss1   (ATC)   5 Nov
Wheeler, S. C.
  qcc   (ATC)   5 Nov
White, A. J. qss (INT)   5 Nov
Ratcliffe, J. J. (REGT)   8 Nov
Hayter, G. qcc (ATC) 10 Dec
Mellings, I. M. qs (ATC) 10 Dec
Maxted, S. J. qcc (ATC) 11 Dec
Stamford, J. M.
  qss   (INT) 16 Dec
Atkinson, K. M. BSc
  qss   (INT) 23 Dec
Myatt, R. J. D. BSc
  qcc   (INT) 23 Dec
Hann, C. D. qss (FC) 24 Dec

1995

Grady, S. W. MA
  qcc   (ATC) 15 Jan
Metcalfe, J. H.
  qss1   (ATC) 18 Jan
Calame, A. B. G(a)
  qcc   (REGT) 28 Jan
Lunn, A. R. qtm
  qcc   (INT) 28 Jan
Otley-Doe, D. L. (ATC) 28 Jan
Kettle, T. M. qss (ATC) 11 Feb
Underhill, S. E. BSc
  qcc   (ATC) 18 Feb
MacLeod, F. D.
  qss   (ATC)   4 Mar
Prince, N. C. H.
  qss2   (REGT) 22 Mar
Tait, D. C. qss (REGT) 22 Mar
Carr, R. J. BSc
  qss   (ATC) 29 Mar
Gardner, S. MA MPhil
  BA qs (FLTOPS) 29 Mar
Graham, D. A. BA (FC) 29 Mar

147

Flight Lieutenants

1995—contd

Turner, J. P. BA
  qss   (FLTOPS) 29 Mar
Hixson, J. S. BSc qtm
  qss2   (INT) 8 Apr
Seaman, M. R. N.
  qss   (FC) 28 Apr
Astley-Jones, G. D.
  qss2   (REGT) 2 May
Biggs, A. J. qss1 (ATC) 2 May
Cranshaw, F. D. (REGT) 2 May
Hicks, P. M. qcc (ATC) 2 May
Hubbard, J. W. qcc (FC) 2 May
Kendrick, S. J. qss1(INT) 2 May
Leaman, M. J.
  qss2   (REGT) 2 May
Wilson, G. D. qss2 (ATC) 2 May
Biddlestone, A.
  (FLTOPS) 9 May
Greene, G. R. (INT) 9 May
Priddy, W. P. (ATC) 9 May
Tierrie-Slough, A. P.
  qss   (ATC) 17 May
Jackson, S. W. BSc
  qwi(SAW) qss1 (REGT) 6 June
Hamilton, G. A.
  qss2   (ATC) 15 June
McCall, W. L. BSc (FC) 5 July
Borley, W. D. qcc (ATC) 26 July
Gleeson, R. F. qss (FC) 26 July
Frost, M. L. qss (ATC) 29 July
Davies, R. A.
  qss1   (REGT) 2 Aug
Haselden, M. qss (INT) 16 Aug
Soanes, P. J. qss (ATC) 16 Aug
Whitworth, J. M.
  qss2   (ATC) 16 Aug
Moss, B. W.
  qss1   (REGT) 8 Sept
MacFarlane, A. BSc
  qss   (FC) 29 Sept
Phillips, P. R.
  qss   (FLTOPS) 29 Sept
Atherton, S. E.
  qss2   (ATC) 30 Sept
Dunbar, A. J. qss (ATC) 30 Sept
Franks, S. qss2 (ATC) 30 Sept
Hawtin, P. E.
  qss2   (REGT) 30 Sept
McEwan-Lyon, S. A.
  qss   (FC) 30 Sept
Middleton, A. J.
  qss2   (FC) 30 Sept
Oliver, S. J. qss (ATC) 30 Sept
Pickering, A. N.
  qss   (ATC) 30 Sept

Wylor-Owen, R. G.
  qss   (REGT) 30 Sept
Charlton, S. C. qss1
  (INT) 12 Oct
Laing, S. F. (ATC) 28 Oct
Gagnon, F. Y. BA qs (FC) 5 Nov
Macintyre, A. J. M. BSc
  qss   (REGT) 6 Nov
Lowman, S. (ATC) 7 Nov
Cockram, L. qtm
  qss   (INT) 11 Nov
Fone, S. qtm qss1(INT) 11 Nov
Lee, R. P. G. qcc (ATC) 11 Nov
Merrick, D. qss (REGT) 11 Nov
Short, N. P. qss (FC) 11 Nov
Jones, T. E. (ATC) 12 Nov
Hall, R. A. qss (ATC) 8 Dec
Maddocks, D. (ATC) 19 Dec
Davies, M. qss (FC) 22 Dec
Dimbleby, A. M.
  qcc   (FC) 22 Dec
Mayhew, S. M. (ATC) 22 Dec

1996

Cartwright, C. D. BSc
  qss   (FC) 15 Jan
Lamb, P. R. J. BTh
  qss   (FC) 15 Jan
Mansell, L. D. C. BSc
  qcc   (FC) 15 Jan
Western, S. M.
  qss2   (INT) 19 Jan
Holcroft, S. J.
  qwi(SAW)
  qss2   (REGT) 27 Jan
Capel, D. K. S.
  qss1   (REGT) 3 Feb
Endruweit, D. J.
  qss   (FC) 10 Feb
Hyde, E. A. MSc BSc
  qcc   (INT) 11 Feb
Sexton, S. R. BEng qtm
  qcc   (INT) 16 Feb
Jones, A. N.
  qcc   (REGT) 24 Feb
Darling, S. J. qss2 (ATC) 17 Mar
King, N. S. qss (ATC) 24 Mar
Bradley, A. C. qcc (ATC) 28 Mar
House, D. qss1 (ATC) 28 Mar
McDowell, I. G.
  qcc   (ATC) 28 Mar
Davies, R. E. BSc
  qcc   (ATC) 10 Apr
Cooke, G. B. BSc
  qcc   (FC) 11 Apr
Stowers, S. M. LLB
  qss2   (FLTOPS) 11 Apr
Palmer, M. A. (ATC) 7 May

Goodall, V. L. BSc
  qcc   (ATC) 6 June
Martin, K. M. BA
  qss2   (FC) 6 June
Muir, G. qss1 (FC) 15 June
Barclay, A. J. qcc (ATC) 21 June
Cargill, R. J.
  qss1   (REGT) 21 June
Marshall, K. L.
  qss1   (ATC) 21 June
Thompson, E. C.
  qss2   (INT) 21 June
Johnson, R. O. (REGT) 28 June
Stockbridge, E. (FC) 1 July
Lawson, A. J. BA (FC) 6 July
Harrison, T. G. S.
  qcc   (REGT) 27 July
Antrobus, A. E. BA
  qss2   (FC) 14 Aug
McGregor, D. A. S. BSc
  qss1   (REGT) 14 Aug
Tomlyn, I. M. BSc
  qcc   (FC) 14 Aug
Bendell, S. A.
  qss   (FLTOPS) 15 Aug
Dudman, T.
  qss2   (FLTOPS) 15 Aug
Ewer, R. P.
  qss2   (FLTOPS) 15 Aug
Finney, P. A. J.
  qcc   (INT) 29 Sept
Ibbetson, N. qcc (ATC) 29 Sept
Rosier, M. P.
  qcc   (FLTOPS) 29 Sept
Watts, D. L. qcc (INT) 29 Sept
Duncan, B. J.
  qss2   (ATC) 6 Oct
Trott, J. S. BEng
  qss2   (FC) 10 Oct
Dalton, M. J. qss2 (FC) 10 Nov
Gillespie, C. R. qss (FC) 10 Nov
Keighley, D. L. qcc (FC) 10 Nov
Smith, A. P. qcc (ATC) 10 Nov
Stead, A. A. qcc (FC) 10 Nov
Wilson, A. (REGT) 10 Nov
McCune, D. qcc (INT) 1 Dec
Burgess, G. S. (ATC) 15 Dec
Keenan, S. L. qcc (ATC) 15 Dec
Robinson D. M.
  qss2   (ATC) 15 Dec
Wilson, N. J. qss (ATC) 15 Dec
Lofthouse, G. D. J.
  qss2   (ATC) 21 Dec
McIntyre, S. asq
  qcc   (FC) 21 Dec
Robinson, P. D. qcc(FC) 21 Dec
Roylance, J. A.
  qcc   (REGT) 21 Dec

Flight Lieutenants

1997

Booth, J. A. BSc
  qcc (FC) 15 Jan
Doney, M. J. BA
  qcc (FC) 15 Jan
Hateley, P. B. BA
  qwi(SAW) qcc(REGT) 15 Jan
Honeybun-Kelly, C.
  L. (ATC) 2 Feb
Parfitt, J. E. qcc (ATC) 2 Feb
Forster, I. (REGT) 9 Feb
Fairburn, M. R.
  qss (FLTOPS) 11 Feb
O'Brien, S. J. (ATC) 11 Feb
O'Neill, R. K. (ATC) 11 Feb
Wood, M. J. qcc (FC) 20 Feb
Burton, M. J. J.
  qss1 (ATC) 17 Mar
Brown, A. qss2 (REGT) 26 Mar
Sills, M. R. qcc (ATC) 26 Mar
Walker, G. R. qtm
  qcc (INT) 26 Mar
Wallace, J. M. qtm
  qss (INT) 26 Mar
Payne, A. J. MA BA
  (INT) 21 Apr
Cowieson, K. S.
  qcc (FC) 30 Apr
Ingamells, S. E.
  qcc (ATC) 4 May
Street, G. E. qss1 (ATC) 8 May
Drummond, D. R.
  qss (FC) 10 May
Strefford, A. D. MSc
  BEng (INT) 13 May
Martin, A. P. qcc (FC) 8 June
Gavars, J. M.
  qss1 (REGT) 20 June
Jochum, C. W.
  qss1 (ATC) 20 June
Powell, M. S.
  qcc (REGT) 20 June
McCamley, D. S.
  qcc (ATC) 26 June
Greenwood, P. M. (REGT) 28 July
Hooper, J. A. qss (INT) 28 July
Reeves, A. J. qcc (INT) 28 July
Towell, J. BA (ATC) 12 Aug
Berryman, C. W.(REGT) 15 Aug
Bellworthy, C. J.
  qss2 (ATC) 17 Aug
Tomlinson, K. S. (ATC) 13 Sept
Richings, E. K. L.
  qcc (FLTOPS) 26 Sept
Harris, G. P. C. qss2(FC) 28 Sept

Jacklin, M. J.
  qcc (REGT) 28 Sept
Jacques, E. (FC) 28 Sept
Lain, D. P. J. qss2 (INT) 28 Sept
Richings, H. BA
  qcc (ATC) 9 Oct
Barber, A. J. BEng(INT) 10 Oct
Gilvary, D. R. F. BA
  qcc (FLTOPS) 10 Oct
Keer, M. BA qcc (ATC) 10 Oct
Nichols, J. M. BA qtm
  qss (INT) 10 Oct
Pegg. R. MSc qss(ATC) 10 Oct
Terry, G. BA
  qss (FLTOPS) 10 Oct
Walton, K. J. BSc
  qcc (ATC) 10 Oct
Lyttle, R. B. M.
  qtm (INT) 12 Oct
Griffiths, J. A.
  qss (REGT) 13 Oct
Henley, N. R. qss2 (FC) 9 Nov
Holland, P. T. W.
  qcc (REGT) 9 Nov
Howard, A. R. J.
  qcc (INT) 9 Nov
Pieroni, M. L. qss2 (FC) 9 Nov
Hickton, K. N. BEng(FC) 11 Nov
Morton, D. T. qcc (ATC) 13 Nov
King, C. J. (ATC) 28 Nov
Gilmore, S. T. (FC) 20 Dec
Kotlarchuk, S. J.
  qcc (FC) 23 Dec

1998

Walford, S. qcc (ATC) 4 Jan
Threlfall, N. E. BSc
  qcc (FC) 15 Jan
Janssen, P. C. qcc (FC) 29 Jan
Paddison, P. qss1(ATC) 29 Jan
Shea, K. Y. qcc (ATC) 29 Jan
Smith, M. C. (FLTOPS) 29 Jan
Greentree, D. W. MA
  BA (INT) 13 Feb
Brown, M. J. BSc
  qss (FC) 14 Feb
Davison, P. F. BA
  qcc (FC) 14 Feb
Garner, N. BSc qcc
  (INT) 14 Feb
McGlynn, S. BA (ATC) 14 Feb
Niven, R. J. BSc
  qss2 (FC) 14 Feb
Webb, S. F. BA qss (FC) 14 Feb
Wilson, R. J. BEng
  qwi(SAW)
  qcc (REGT) 14 Feb
Lindsay, C. J. qcc (ATC) 25 Feb

Aslett, J. R. qcc (ATC) 7 Mar
Deane, C. C. qcc (ATC) 7 Mar
Crosby, A. P. qcc (FC) 26 Mar
Hugall, J. J. qtm (INT) 26 Mar
Lumb, R. P. qs (REGT) 26 Mar
Shave, R. J. qss1 (INT) 26 Mar
Smith, M. W.
  qss2 (INT) 26 Mar
Clark, R. J. BA
  (FLTOPS) 8 Apr
Payne, D. V. BSc
  qss1 (FC) 8 Apr
Hall, I. D. BSc
  qss1 (INT) 9 Apr
Hughes, F. J.
  BEng (INT) 9 Apr
Sibley, V. E. BA (INT) 9 Apr
Williams, G. D. BSc
  qcc (INT) 9 Apr
Alborough, R. A.
  qcc (ATC) 11 Apr
Crooks, S. qcc (ATC) 11 Apr
Moss, G. W. qcc (ATC) 11 Apr
Woods, H. L. qcc (ATC) 11 Apr
Nott, J. M. BSc (ATC) 27 Apr
Brown, T. J. qcc (FC) 7 May
Rait, P. M. BSc
  qss (REGT) 16 May
Downey, C. P. L. (ATC) 19 June
Hall, A. J. qss1 (ATC) 19 June
Hindley, A. M.
  qss (FLTOPS) 19 June
Hunt, P. J. BSc qcc (FC) 19 June
Johnson, L. qss1 (FC) 19 June
Mount, G. J. L. qtm
  qcc (INT) 19 June
Parker, E. J. qcc (ATC) 19 June
Muir, C. E. BSc
  qcc (ATC) 11 Aug
Nelson, A. B. BEng
  qwi(SAW) (REGT) 11 Aug
Shaw, I. S. BSc (REGT) 11 Aug
Paul, S. L. S. BA (INT) 12 Aug
Lutman, A. J. qcc(ATC) 13 Aug
Lambton, N. W. J. qtm
  qcc (INT) 16 Sept
Bolton, C. L. (ATC) 28 Sept
Booth, S. qss (REGT) 3 Oct
Bottrill, M. qcc (REGT) 3 Oct
France, J. A. qcc (ATC) 3 Oct
Laing, R. P. MA (INT) 7 Oct
Lloyd-Jones, S. A. BA
  qss (INT) 7 Oct
Turner, S. G. BSc
  qcc (FLTOPS) 7 Oct
Hart, J. A. BSC (INT) 9 Oct
Stott, D. B. BEng
  qcc (ATC) 9 Oct
Ballantyne, W. A. (ATC) 31 Oct
Iveson, S. J. qcc (ATC) 31 Oct

Flight Lieutenants

1998—contd

Sweeney, M. P. C.		
qss1	(ATC)	31 Oct
Tunstall, M. S. R.		
qcc	(FLTOPS)	31 Oct
Williams, D. B. BSc		
qss	(FLTOPS)	1 Nov
Armstrong, A. M. R.		
qss2	(FLTOPS)	7 Nov
Garwood, F. D.		
qss2	(REGT)	7 Nov
Roberts, V. C. qss2 (FC)		7 Nov

1999

Morgan, R. L. BSc		
qcc	(REGT)	15 Jan
Wienburg, E. F.		
qcc	(INT)	30 Jan
Worthington, D.		
qwi(AD) qcc	(FC)	30 Jan
Wright, C. qss2	(INT)	30 Jan
Lavis, R. J.	(ATC)	6 Feb
Graham, F.	(FC)	9 Feb
Davies, B.	(REGT)	10 Feb
Brown, E. E. BA	(INT)	11 Feb
Robinson, N. C.		
MA	(ATC)	11 Feb
Smith, D. A. BSc		
qcc	(FC)	11 Feb
Wood, V. BSc (FLTOPS)		11 Feb
Bradley, T. J. BA		
qcc	(REGT)	13 Feb
Kirkpatrick, A. M. BA		
qcc	(REGT)	13 Feb
Meadows, E. E. MA		
qcc	(FLTOPS)	13 Feb
Andrews, G. P.		
	(FLTOPS)	14 Feb
Cairns, E. J.	(FLTOPS)	14 Feb
Clabby, M. J. FInstLM		
MILT LCGI	(FLTOPS)	14 Feb
Gray, J.	(FLTOPS)	14 Feb
Hinkley, R. W.	(REGT)	14 Feb
Lay, P. C.	(ATC)	14 Feb
Murray, A.	(FLTOPS)	14 Feb
Trangmar, J. M.	(ATC)	14 Feb
Gerrard, A. L.	(FC)	25 Feb
Jackson, A. M.	(FC)	24 Mar
Jermyn, S. M.		
qss2	(FC)	24 Mar
Phelps, D. L.	(FC)	24 Mar
Dendy, P.	(FLTOPS)	3 Apr
Lane, R. J.	(REGT)	3 Apr

McCarthy, P. G. J.		
qcc	(REGT)	3 Apr
Thorpe, G. K.		
qcc	(FLTOPS)	3 Apr
Underwood, S. J. (ATC)		3 Apr
Hollin, R. T. D. MA BSc		
qss	(INT)	6 Apr
Magee, S. MSc BSc		
qss1	(REGT)	8 Apr
Openshaw, S. BSc		
qwi(SAW) qcc (REGT)		8 Apr
Stedman, R. D. BSc		
qss1	(ATC)	8 Apr
Moreton, E. A.		
qcc	(FLTOPS)	21 Apr
Thomas, C. M.		
qcc	(REGT)	6 May
Hesketh, D. G.	(ATC)	16 May
Ling, J. J.	(FLTOPS)	21 May
Andrews, S. J.		
qs	(FLTOPS)	29 May
Barnes, D. M. qtm		
qss1	(INT)	29 May
Jones, R. C.		
qss1	(FLTOPS)	29 May
Sparrow, K. A.		
qcc	(FLTOPS)	29 May
Wilshaw Rhead,		
M. P.	(ATC)	20 June
Dunn, K.	(ATC)	7 July
Corner, A. G. qcc (ATC)		24 July
Derrick, A. M. (FLTOPS)		24 July
Flood, A. qcc (FLTOPS)		24 July
Heenan, J.	(ATC)	24 July
Irving, K. G.	(FLTOPS)	24 July
Parker, S. R.	(ATC)	24 July
Sproston, J. A.		
qtm	(INT)	24 July
Davies, J. C.		
qwi(SAW)	(REGT)	28 July
Gaskin, L. A.		
qss	(REGT)	28 July
Ackroyd, R. D. BA		
	(ATC)	9 Aug
Allen, D. T. BSc qss (FC)		9 Aug
Bailey, M. N. MA BSc		
qcc	(INT)	9 Aug
Hall, N. J. MA BSc		
qss	(INT)	9 Aug
Hancock, L. BSc		9 Aug
Crowther, N. R. BSc		
qcc	(ATC)	11 Aug
Dargan, R. J. qcc (ATC)		11 Aug
Elias, R. A. BSc		
qss1	(ATC)	11 Aug
Fruish, S. O. BSc		
qss1	(ATC)	11 Aug
Hill, A. G. BA	(ATC)	11 Aug
Hillier, V. A.	(ATC)	11 Aug

Hinde, M. R. BSc		
qcc	(FC)	11 Aug
Norton, E. M. BSc		
qss	(FC)	11 Aug
Shirley, G. J. qcc (ATC)		11 Aug
Thorpe, A. D. BSc (INT)		11 Aug
Wilkinson, M. G.		
BA	(INT)	11 Aug
Nicholls, K. P.		
qss1	(REGT)	28 Aug
McConnell, S. D.	(INT)	11 Sept
Duffield, P. J.	(FC)	2 Oct
Greenham, P. M.		
qcc	(ATC)	2 Oct
Hawker, S. M.	(ATC)	2 Oct
Ackland, E. C. MSc		
	(INT)	6 Oct
Bentley, S. A. BA		
qss	(FC)	6 Oct
Brown, P. N. BA	(INT)	6 Oct
Craig, M. D. BSc		
	(FLTOPS)	6 Oct
Duhan, J. P. BA (REGT)		6 Oct
Graham, M. R. MEng		
qcc	(FC)	6 Oct
Mason, P. M. BA		
	(REGT)	6 Oct
Neeson, C. G. MA		
	(ATC)	6 Oct
Ratnage, P. D. BA		
	(REGT)	6 Oct
Christian, S. M. BSc		
qss	(FC)	7 Oct
Coomber, A. M. BA		
	(INT)	7 Oct
Cressy, K. P. BEng		
qcc	(REGT)	7 Oct
Deakin, M. R. BSc (FC)		7 Oct
Hall, G. E. BA (FLTOPS)		7 Oct
Parr, H. M. BA (REGT)		7 Oct
Stellitano, D. W.		
BA	(REGT)	7 Oct
Fleckney, M. J.	(FC)	24 Oct
Cannon, S. M.		
qss	(ATC)	27 Nov
Dodd, R. M.	(REGT)	27 Nov
Harrop, G.	(FLTOPS)	27 Nov
King, A. G.	(FLTOPS)	27 Nov
McGhee, W. J.	(REGT)	27 Nov
Solomon, G. E.		
qss	(FLTOPS)	27 Nov
Allen, C. M.	(REGT)	28 Nov
Hetterley, A. D. BA		
qtm	(INT)	1 Dec
Parker, S.	(ATC)	3 Dec
Ramsden, C. D.		
qss	(REGT)	28 Dec

Flight Lieutenants

2000

Thorp, J. M. BSc		
qss1	(REGT)	15 Jan
Barnes, P.	(REGT)	16 Jan
Burns, B.	(FLTOPS)	16 Jan
Copsey, L. J.	(REGT)	16 Jan
Pryce, P. G.	(INT)	16 Jan
Robinson, R. F. A.		
	(FLTOPS)	16 Jan
Gregory, K. J. qss2		
	(ATC)	28 Jan
Grun, A. B.		
qcc	(FLTOPS)	28 Jan
Harvey, G. B.	(FC)	28 Jan
Rennie, S. D. qss	(FC)	28 Jan
Bruce, A. S. BA		
qss	(INT)	10 Feb
Quayle, G. E. BA		
	(REGT)	10 Feb
Roberts, B. W.		
BEng	(REGT)	10 Feb
Smith, E. M. BA		
	(FLTOPS)	10 Feb
Timms, D. L. BA	(FC)	10 Feb
Beck, N. J. BA qss(INT)		11 Feb
Beldon, V. L. BA		
qss	(INT)	11 Feb
Fitzsimon, J. P.		
BEng	(REGT)	11 Feb
Garwood, T. S. BSc(FC)		11 Feb
Hodgson, J. BA	(ATC)	11 Feb
Liston, J. H. BSc		
qss	(REGT)	11 Feb
Robbins, N. H. BSc		
qss	(FLTOPS)	11 Feb
Westbrook, A. L.		
BSc	(FC)	11 Feb
Whiteley, N. O. M.		
BSc	(INT)	11 Feb
Huyton, A. D. qss(ATC)		19 Mar
Black, D.	(REGT)	4 Apr
Conn, A. BSc (FLTOPS)		5 Apr
Wiseman, S. T. BEd		
	(REGT)	5 Apr
Galbraith, M. A.		
BSc	(FLTOPS)	6 Apr
Iveson, P. R. BTh (ATC)		6 Apr
Jones, C. R. M. BA (FC)		6 Apr
Khan, S. B. BSc		
qss	(FLTOPS)	6 Apr
Murphy, R. M.		
BEng	(FC)	6 Apr
Siddall, A. J. BA		
qtm	(INT)	6 Apr
Parker, J. C. S. BSc		
	(INT)	20 Apr

Kiff, H. J. qss (REGT)		28 Apr
Graham, J. M. qcc		
	(REGT)	2 May
Hawkins, T. R. A.		
	(FLTOPS)	2 May
Would, C. BSc		
	(FLTOPS)	4 May
Jones, R. M.	(REGT)	8 May
Ashcroft, J. A.	(ATC)	28 May
Lansdell, S. M. qss		
	(FLTOPS)	28 May
McGrath, B. L.	(FC)	28 May
Smith, S. M.	(ATC)	28 May
Adrain, J. M. BSc		
	(REGT)	1 June
Davenport, D. A.		
BSc	(FC)	1 June
Marshall, A. S. MLitt		
BA	(REGT)	1 June
Parker, J. P. F.		
BMus	(FC)	1 June
Smith, A. P. BA (REGT)		1 June
Marini, T. A. BSc (ATC)		16 June
Atkin-Palmer, C. M.		
qcc	(FLTOPS)	2 July
Wheeler, J. E.	(ATC)	13 July
Brockless, K. M.		
	(FLTOPS)	23 July
Chapman, R. A.		
	(FLTOPS)	23 July
De-Vry, J. R. (FLTOPS)		23 July
Denison, M. W.		
	(FLTOPS)	23 July
McLaughlin, K. J.		
	(FLTOPS)	23 July
Slark-Hollis, T. J.(REGT)		23 July
Sullivan, C. T. qcc		
	(FLTOPS)	23 July
Butterfield, A. J.		
BSc	(ATC)	8 Aug
Latimer, J. A. BEng		
	(ATC)	8 Aug
Miller, J. BEng (ATC)		8 Aug
Stewart, A. H. BSc (FC)		8 Aug
Warren Rothwell, P. P.		
BSc	(INT)	8 Aug
Campbell, J. L. BA		
	(FLTOPS)	9 Aug
Finley, E. T. BA qcc		
	(ATC)	9 Aug
Williams, M. BA		
qss	(REGT)	9 Aug
Williamson, J. S. BSc		
qcc	(INT)	9 Aug
Middleton, I. qcc (FC)		10 Aug
Wraith, J. A.	(INT)	27 Aug
Hoult, J. J.	(INT)	4 Sept
Hodgson, N. H.		
BA	(ATC)	1 Oct
Rowe, J. R. BA (REGT)		5 Oct

Madden, H. M. BSc(FC)		6 Oct
Parker, C. M. BSc PGCE		
qss	(INT)	6 Oct
Ratnage-Black, H. M.		
BA	(FLTOPS)	6 Oct
Sloley, R. BSc	(INT)	6 Oct
Waddilove, C. qcc		
	(FLTOPS)	23 Oct
Briggs, J. J. BSc (ATC)		30 Nov
Robinson, J. B. MA		
	(ATC)	30 Nov
Bennett, A. M. LLB		
qss	(INT)	1 Dec
Booker, C. J. BSc (INT)		1 Dec
Chambers, S. C. BA		
	(FC)	1 Dec
Finch, D. R. BA (REGT)		1 Dec
Stead, E. J. BSc (INT)		1 Dec
Stewart, J. D. BA		
	(REGT)	1 Dec
Philpott, V. Y.	(ATC)	14 Dec

2001

Parsons, M. S.	(ATC)	4 Jan
Donovan, G.	(REGT)	14 Jan
Duffy, M. R.	(ATC)	14 Jan
Jones, S. M. W.	(ATC)	14 Jan
Kilner, A.	(INT)	14 Jan
Rudland, P. H.	(ATC)	14 Jan
Buckle, J. V. BA		15 Jan
Ritchie, C. C. BEng (FC)		15 Jan
Tindale, A. R. BSc (FC)		15 Jan
Grant, T. L. qcc (ATC)		16 Jan
Gray, S. A.	(FC)	28 Jan
Edmond, S. M.	(ATC)	4 Feb
Wells, J. R. BEng		4 Feb
Brunton, M. J. BA (FC)		10 Feb
Lynn, C. J. BA (REGT)		10 Feb
Robinson, J. L. BA		
	(INT)	10 Feb
Slark-Hollis, R. L. S.		
BSc	(FLTOPS)	10 Feb
Stellitano, R. L. BA		
	(INT)	10 Feb
Wyatt, P. D. BSc (INT)		10 Feb
Hodgson, N. E. (ATC)		16 Feb
McWilliam, S. qss		
	(FLTOPS)	21 Mar
Posnett, G. A.	(FC)	1 Apr
Carter, M. K. BEd		
	(REGT)	4 Apr
Eayrs, J. BSc	(N)	4 Apr
Pattison, E. BA	(ATC)	4 Apr
Ryan-Goldstraw, S. M.		
BA	(ATC)	4 Apr
Atkins, N. O. BSc (FC)		5 Apr
Clegg, M. K. GRSM(FC)		5 Apr

Flight Lieutenants

2001—contd

Crook, D. J. P. BA (REGT)	5 Apr
Davies, J. M. E. BSc (INT)	5 Apr
Picken, T. J. BA qtm qss (INT)	5 Apr
Sewell, A. J. BSc (FLTOPS)	5 Apr
Sproule, G. A. BSc	5 Apr
Binks, P. E. L. (ATC)	6 Apr
O'Sullivan, K. J. (FC)	6 Apr
Greene, M. P. qcc (FLTOPS)	8 Apr
Dallimore, W. L. (ATC)	21 Apr
Brady, D. A. (FLTOPS)	8 May
Morton, C. (INT)	18 May
Page, T. C. (ATC)	21 May
Ferguson, G. R. (ATC)	27 May
Hughes, D. B. (ATC)	27 May
McCann, P. M. (REGT)	27 May
Owen-Hughes, M. T. (FLTOPS)	27 May
Boreham, D. P. (ATC)	29 May
Bowen, M. A. (REGT)	29 May
Cook, M. J. qss1 (REGT)	29 May
Hughes, M. I. (ATC)	29 May
Meacham-Roberts, D. A. M. (FC)	29 May
O'Flaherty, T. D. BA (ATC)	29 May
Smith, C. M. BSc (FC)	29 May
Cripps, E. A. BSc (REGT)	30 May
England, S. D. (FC)	30 May
Holden, E. A. BSc (INT)	30 May
Hook, J. L. BSc (REGT)	30 May
Misiak, C. L. BSc (FC)	30 May
Paine, R. J. BSc (INT)	31 May
Coomer, D. L. (ATC)	8 July
Buxton, F. N. (INT)	22 July
Dodsworth, S. J. (INT)	22 July
Drew, C. A. qcc (FLTOPS)	22 July
Gill, S. A. (FLTOPS)	22 July
Jones, M. E. R. (Sec)	22 July
Leadbeater, A. H. BSc (ATC)	22 July
Nickson, N. R. (ATC)	22 July
Quigley, I. P. J. (ATC)	24 July
Sweeney, P. F. qcc (INT)	24 July
Pearson, C. BA (REGT)	7 Aug
Adamson-Drage, M. N. BA (FC)	8 Aug
Bulmer, M. G. BA (FC)	8 Aug

Bush, R. J. BSc qtm (INT)	8 Aug
Cockram, R. E. BSc (FLTOPS)	8 Aug
Fisher, J. LLB (FC)	8 Aug
Hammerton, G. R. BSc (FC)	8 Aug
Hole, M. C. BA (ATC)	8 Aug
Nelson, D. LLB (REGT)	8 Aug
Paton, I. S. BSc (FC)	8 Aug
Shurmer, M. A. BSc (ATC)	8 Aug
Whiteley, D. J. BSc (FC)	8 Aug
Williams, S. D. R. BA (INT)	8 Sept
Smith, R. M. (FLTOPS)	29 Sept
Imrie, J. (ATC)	30 Sept
Kane, J. M. (FC)	30 Sept
Lapsley, J. M. (ATC)	30 Sept
Newman, A. C. (ATC)	30 Sept
Watkin, E. D. D. (FLTOPS)	30 Sept
Willingham, J. C. (ATC)	30 Sept
Mennell, G. R. (FC)	3 Oct
Tobin, M. D. A. MSc BSc met (FC)	4 Oct
White, L. L. BSc (FC)	4 Oct
Daniel, R. C. BA (ATC)	5 Oct
Lorriman, M. D. BSc (INT)	5 Oct
McCullough, C. L. BA (FC)	5 Oct
Milburn, R. M. LLB (FC)	5 Oct
Stevens, R. A. BSc (INT)	5 Oct
Martin, J. P. (ATC)	1 Nov
Auchterlonie, A. J.	25 Nov
Betley, M. A. J. BSc (REGT)	30 Nov
Hey, N. S. BSc PGCE (FC)	30 Nov
Hodges, M. S. BA (INT)	30 Nov
Ivings, A. P. BEng (FC)	30 Nov
McFall, J. M. BSc (REGT)	30 Nov
O'Brien, J. P. MTh MA (INT)	30 Nov
O'Donnell, S. J. BA (INT)	30 Nov
Price, C. A. BA (FLTOPS)	30 Nov
Smith, M. J. BA (FC)	30 Nov
Walton, A. R. BA (FC)	30 Nov
Macpherson, D. S. (ATC)	6 Dec
Leverton, D. (FC)	27 Dec

2002

Davidson, L. A. (INT)	13 Jan
Silvey, C. E. P. (FLTOPS)	13 Jan
Vance, G. J. (INT)	13 Jan
Hargreaves, K. L. BEng (FC)	15 Jan
Mankowski, M. K. L. BSc (REGT)	15 Jan
Priest, J. P. BSc (REGT)	8 Feb
Dixon, R. L. BA (INT)	9 Feb
Goodwin, H. J. BSc	9 Feb
Graham, J. H. LLB (INT)	9 Feb
Greenwood, E. C. BSc (ATC)	9 Feb
Huxley, J. C. F. BA (REGT)	9 Feb
Lofts, M. S. BA (INT)	9 Feb
Payton, S. J. BSc (ATC)	9 Feb
Wood, A. N. BEng (INT)	9 Feb
Martin, V. M. (ATC)	30 Mar
Osborne, A. K. (ATC)	30 Mar
Gee, M. P. J. BSc (ATC)	3 Apr
Pawson, C. L. MSc (ATC)	3 Apr
Quinn, S. D. MEng (REGT)	3 Apr
Glendinning, R. D. BA (REGT)	4 Apr
Johnson, M. A. BA (ATC)	4 Apr
Kemeny, C. J. BSc (FC)	4 Apr
Pattinson, G. J. BSc (ATC)	4 Apr
Pilkington, R. C. (FLTOPS)	5 Apr
Thomson, A. M. (REGT)	5 Apr
Dixon, S. J. qcc (FLTOPS)	13 May
Biggin, S. J. C. BA (INT)	25 May
Field, A. J. (REGT)	25 May
Horlock, J. M. (FC)	25 May
Alcock, F. BA (FC)	28 May
Kroyer, M. A. BA (REGT)	28 May
Reynolds, M. G. (ATC)	28 May
Swann, A. D. BA (REGT)	28 May
Dewar, M. A. S. BSc (REGT)	29 May
Dykes, C. BSc (ATC)	29 May
Garratt, J. S. LLB (FC)	29 May
Gill, D. J. BEng (ATC)	29 May
Makepeace, P. A. BSc (ATC)	29 May
Phipps, M. J. BSc (INT)	29 May

Flying Officers

1994

Pridding, I. J. BSc (INT)   26 Dec

1996

Gregory, J. M.	(REGT)	15 Feb
Griffin, P. R.	(ATC)	27 Feb
Goncalves-Collins, D. J.	(FC)	14 Apr
Seale-Finch, S.	(FLTOPS)	22 Apr
Streames, D. J.	(INT)	9 Oct
Weeks, R. A.	(FLTOPS)	13 Dec
Bastiani, M. P.	(FLTOPS)	24 Dec

1997

Beresford, S. A.	(FLTOPS)	21 Feb
Reed, M. L.	(ATC)	21 Feb
Needham, C. P.	(ATC)	13 Mar
Surman, K. J.	(FLTOPS)	31 Mar
Smith, M. G.	(ATC)	13 Apr
Flockhart, E.	(FLTOPS)	9 June
Lemin, C. J.	(ATC)	14 June
Morrell, J. M. BMus	(ATC)	16 June
Artus, T. BSc	(FC)	18 July
Leavesley, D.	(REGT)	18 July
Ramsay, A. G. BA	(INT)	7 Aug
Moran, K. A.	(FLTOPS)	25 Nov
Martland, C. J.	(FLTOPS)	22 Dec

1998

Dowen, K. J.	(ATC)	13 July
Gilroy, N. S.	(ATC)	23 July
Lomax, D. qcc	(FLTOPS)	23 July
Smith, D. O. BEng qcc	(FLTOPS)	23 July
Walker, D. J. qss	(REGT)	23 July
Fitzgerald, N. E. MEng	(FC)	6 Aug
Gilmore, M. A. BEd	(FC)	6 Aug
Arnall, J. V. BSc	(FC)	7 Aug
Beckett, S. M. BA	(ATC)	7 Aug
Doney, T. M. BA	(FC)	7 Aug

Evans, R. C. BA	(REGT)	7 Aug
Foy, A. K. BSc	(FC)	7 Aug
Raimondo, M. J. P. BA	(REGT)	7 Aug
Ridgway, M. K. BA	(INT)	7 Aug
Vine, S. L. qcc	(ATC)	8 Aug
Ashley, S. N.	(REGT)	2 Sept
Potts, B. D. BSc	(FC)	2 Oct
Anstey, J. S. qcc	(FLTOPS)	3 Oct
Coormiah, J. P. BSc	(FC)	4 Oct
Dunn, C. S. BSc	(FC)	4 Oct
Gibbons, R. L. BEng	(FC)	4 Oct
Hamilton, S. BSc	(REGT)	4 Oct
Holmes, J. K. BSc	(FLTOPS)	4 Oct
Massingham, G. J. BSc	(REGT)	4 Oct
Pape, J. C. BA	(FC)	4 Oct
Scott, T. E. BSc	(INT)	4 Oct
Sharp, D. R. BA	(FC)	4 Oct
Todd, D. BSc	(INT)	4 Oct
Wynne, R. J. BSc	(REGT)	4 Oct
Higgs, L. V.	(ATC)	14 Nov
Capleton, R. J. BSc	(REGT)	28 Nov
Furlong, G. BA	(REGT)	28 Nov
Smathers, D. BSc	(FC)	28 Nov
Briggs, S. J. LLB qtm	(INT)	30 Nov
Tack, C. P. BSc	(FC)	30 Nov
Cronin, P. J.	(REGT)	3 Dec
Amos, M. D.	(FLTOPS)	18 Dec

1999

Barnes, C. C. BSc	(REGT)	15 Jan
Stoneman, N. T. BA	(INT)	15 Jan
Brown, S. M.	(FLTOPS)	25 Jan
Cleaver, J. C.	(ATC)	25 Jan
Harrild, P. E. qss1	(FC)	25 Jan
Croxford, A. V.	(ATC)	27 Jan
Kelson, M. J.	(FLTOPS)	30 Jan
Hewson, C. I.	(INT)	3 Feb
Courtnadge, S. E. BSc	(INT)	6 Feb
Bagnall, C. A. BEng	(FC)	8 Feb
Battersby, N. J. BSc	(ATC)	8 Feb
Boyson, A. BSc(Econ)	(FC)	8 Feb
Burton, C. D. BSc	(FC)	8 Feb

Checksfield, G. BSc	(FC)	8 Feb
Fieldhouse, K. A. BSc(Econ)	(FLTOPS)	8 Feb
Frame, J. D. BSc	(REGT)	8 Feb
Gardner, D. M. BA qtm	(INT)	8 Feb
Gillespie, J. L. BSc PGCE	(ATC)	8 Feb
Green, S. F. BSc	(ATC)	8 Feb
Hurry, M. J. BSc	(REGT)	8 Feb
Logan, I. J. BSc	(INT)	8 Feb
Morris, H. P. BA	(REGT)	8 Feb
Smith, P. J. BSc	(FC)	8 Feb
Snoswell, J. C. BSc	(ATC)	8 Feb
Tye, A. B. BSc	(ATC)	8 Feb
Vamplew, S. BSc	(FC)	8 Feb
Wilthew, J. A. BA	(INT)	8 Feb
French, H. M. BA	(FLTOPS)	1 Apr
Harley, E. R. MEng	(FLTOPS)	1 Apr
Lazarus, A. L. BA	(ATC)	1 Apr
Bone, A. M. BSc	(INT)	3 Apr
Clark, P. W. BSc	(FC)	3 Apr
Day, J. BA	(REGT)	3 Apr
Glass, S. J. BSc	(FLTOPS)	3 Apr
Inglis, A. J. C.	(ATC)	3 Apr
Jack, M. V. BSc	(FC)	3 Apr
Plowden, M. A. BSc	(ATC)	3 Apr
Rhodes, E. J. BA	(FLTOPS)	3 Apr
Smithson, S. L. BSc	(FC)	3 Apr
Tennant, B.	(FC)	3 Apr
Phillips, J. S.	(FLTOPS)	5 Apr
Wood, G. M.	(REGT)	6 Apr
Mason, D. S.	(FC)	9 May
Humphrey, M. R.	(INT)	11 May
Reevell, S. J. MPhil BSc	(FC)	26 May
Gater, C. A.	(FLTOPS)	27 May
Lennie, J. P.	(REGT)	27 May
Leonce, A. J.	(FLTOPS)	27 May
Spark, T. L.	(FLTOPS)	27 May
Boreland, J. M. BA	(FC)	28 May
Dinnen, A. L. BAcc	(REGT)	28 May
Essex, A. J. BSc	(INT)	28 May
Fisher, K. H. BSc	(ATC)	28 May
Hamilton, P. T. BA	(REGT)	28 May
Hill, D. C. BSc	(FC)	28 May
McMinn, M. G. BSc	(REGT)	28 May
Parton, C. A. BSc	(ATC)	28 May

Flying Officers

1999—contd

Shave, S. J. BSc (ATC) 28 May
White, D. A. BSc
    (REGT) 28 May
Barker, J. R. L.
    (FLTOPS) 9 June
Hainsworth, M. A.
    (REGT) 22 July
King, J. R. (FLTOPS) 22 July
Vick, B. D. (REGT) 22 July
Secker, M. C. qss
    (REGT) 25 July
Machin, R. J. BSC (FC) 4 Aug
Tester, P. A. BA (FC) 4 Aug
Bate, M. J. BSc
    (FLTOPS) 6 Aug
Butcher, J. N. (ATC) 6 Aug
Fordyce, D. P. BSc (FC) 6 Aug
Hunt, T. E. BSc (ATC) 6 Aug
Meikle, M. E. (ATC) 6 Aug
Middleton, Y. J. qss(FC) 6 Aug
Mullen, E. H. qcc
    (FLTOPS) 6 Aug
O'Gorman, R. C.
    BA (ATC) 6 Aug
Robinson, C. L. D. PhD
    BA (FC) 6 Aug
Sedgwick, F. J. BSc(FC) 6 Aug
Seymour, E. BSc (FC) 6 Aug
Smith, A. M. A. BSc(FC) 6 Aug
Tripp, B. R. M. BA (INT) 6 Aug
Whitfield, M. R.
    BSc (FC) 6 Aug
Beckett, S. C. (ATC) 24 Aug
Malbon, A. S. (FLTOPS) 1 Oct
Turner, A. R. BSc (INT) 1 Oct
Blackett, S. L. BA (ATC) 2 Oct
Burdekin, D. A. BSc
    PGCE (FC) 2 Oct
Francis, D. J. T.
    BSc (ATC) 2 Oct
Fuchter, K. E. J.
    BSc (INT) 2 Oct
Jamieson, M. BA (INT) 2 Oct
McMurdo, K. M.
    BSc (REGT) 2 Oct
Moylan, T. F.
    BMus (REGT) 2 Oct
Roper, J. C. BSc (ATC) 2 Oct
Smith, J. G. BSc
    (REGT) 2 Oct
Trethowan, L. E.
    BSc (FLTOPS) 2 Oct
Wright, A. P. T.
    LLB (FLTOPS) 2 Oct
Yates, A. E. BSc (REGT) 6 Oct

Reynolds, R. C. BSc(FC) 27 Nov
Anspack-Logan, H. A.
    LLB (INT) 28 Nov
Hutchinson, A. M.
    BA (REGT) 28 Nov
Jordan, C. BSc (REGT) 28 Nov
Olive, A. J. BA (ATC) 28 Nov
Reeve, J. A. BSc (INT) 28 Nov
Richardson, P. D.
    BA (FC) 28 Nov
Smyth, W. G. L.
    MA (REGT) 28 Nov
Bland, R. G. qss (FC) 29 Nov
Chandler, K. (ATC) 29 Nov
Harris, S. (FC) 29 Nov
Jones, D. M. (REGT) 29 Nov
Percival, J. D. (ATC) 30 Nov

2000

Parker, J. T. S.
    BCom (FLTOPS) 15 Jan
Rice, A. M. BSc (ATC) 15 Jan
Wilkinson-Cox, P. M.
    A. (FC) 24 Jan
Dixon, P. N. (ATC) 1 Feb
Aspden, E. R. BSc
    (ATC) 6 Feb
Bastow, C. K. BSc (FC) 6 Feb
Beeston, N. C.
    BSc (REGT) 6 Feb
Burton, S. D. BSc (FC) 6 Feb
Hind, T. A. (INT) 6 Feb
Hutchinson, I. M.
    BA (ATC) 6 Feb
Johnstone, C. BSc
    (REGT) 6 Feb
Lewis, I. P. BA (FC) 6 Feb
Lynham, J. J. BA
    (REGT) 6 Feb
Naidoo, D. P. BA (INT) 6 Feb
Roberts, S. J. BSc (FC) 6 Feb
Sharpe, J. A. BSc (FC) 6 Feb
Cole, C. BSc (ATC) 12 Feb
Topping, M. C. BA
    (ATC) 12 Feb
Hobbs, R. S. (FC) 27 Mar
Bell, L. D. BSc (FLTOPS) 1 Apr
Broomhead, M.
    BSc (FC) 1 Apr
Cade, T. R. BSc (REGT) 1 Apr
Clinton, A. M. BSc (FC) 1 Apr
Ellis, J. D. BSc (ATC) 1 Apr
Large, B. W. BSc (FC) 1 Apr
Newell, T. J.
    BSc (REGT) 1 Apr
Simmons, K. J.
    BSC (FLTOPS) 1 Apr
Stevens, P. BA (REGT) 1 Apr

Currie, G. J. J. (ATC) 2 Apr
Hull, M. J. (FC) 2 Apr
Marshall, D. W. L. (INT) 2 Apr
McDonnell, C. (INT) 2 Apr
Willis, A. L. (ATC) 2 Apr
Woodbourne, M. F.
    (REGT) 2 Apr
Armit, G. N. (FLTOPS) 3 Apr
Smith, M. A. (FLTOPS) 6 Apr
Hammerton, R. S.
    BEng (ATC) 7 Apr
Powell, G. D.
    MPhys (FC) 7 Apr
Thomas, C. L. BSc
    (ATC) 7 Apr
Toothill, I. A. (ATC) 10 May
Cochrane, J. G. P. (INT) 25 May
Paul, S. R. (REGT) 25 May
Walters, R. M. (ATC) 25 May
Duke, C. P. BSc (FC) 26 May
Gauld, K. D. MA(REGT) 26 May
Read, G. E. BSc (INT) 26 May
Sessions, G. D. BSc
    (FC) 26 May
Taylor, M. J. P. BSc
    (ATC) 26 May
Clayton, D. L. (FC) 27 May
Danso, K. G. (REGT) 27 May
Howell, W. S. (REGT) 20 July
Morley, M. J. (REGT) 20 July
Paffett, C. (REGT) 20 July
Rhodes, D. P. (ATC) 20 July
Bird, K. A. BA (INT) 4 Aug
Burns, R. G. BA (FC) 4 Aug
Cooper, E. R. BA (ATC) 4 Aug
Corry, E. A. LLB (FC) 4 Aug
Dickson, G. G. BSc
    (REGT) 4 Aug
Jessup, T. BA
    (FLTOPS) 4 Aug
Johnston, P. R. BA
    AIL i* (INT) 4 Aug
Miu, E. J. K. BEng
    (ATC) 4 Aug
Powell, G. D.
    BEng (REGT) 4 Aug
Walker, J. A. BA (ATC) 4 Aug
Westlake, A. C. BSc
    (ATC) 4 Aug
Williams, E. A. BSc
    (FC) 4 Aug
Williams, E. C. MA
    PGCE (FC) 4 Aug
Wright, S. BSc (ATC) 4 Aug
Berry, N. J.
    (FLTOPS) 5 Aug
Hopkins, M. J.
    (FLTOPS) 5 Aug
Stanley, J. P. (FC) 5 Aug
Ward, G. (FLTOPS) 5 Aug

Flying Officers

2000—contd

Jackson, S. B.	(ATC)	11 Sept
Robinson, R. L.	(FLTOPS)	12 Sept
Worth, S.	(FLTOPS)	28 Sept
Adcock, T. W. PhD	(FC)	1 Oct
Edwards, G. M. J. BSc	(ATC)	1 Oct
Hough, I. J. BA	(FLTOPS)	1 Oct
Tubb, R. S. BA	(ATC)	1 Oct
Hawthorne, V. J.	(ATC)	2 Oct
Howard, K. E. L.	(ATC)	2 Oct
McIntyre, A. J.	(ATC)	2 Oct
Reeve, M. W.	(FC)	2 Oct
Bishop, F. S.	(ATC)	4 Oct
Gibbins, A. M.	(ATC)	8 Oct
Pope, D. J. BA	(FC)	27 Nov
Warner, P. R. BSc	(FC)	27 Nov
Weston, J. A. BSc	(INT)	27 Nov
Yates, B. J. BA	(FLTOPS)	27 Nov
Green, A.	(ATC)	28 Nov
Kinnear, M. R.	(FLTOPS)	28 Nov
Murray, E. A.	(ATC)	28 Nov

2001

Baker, L. M. BA	(ATC)	15 Jan
Ford, N. BSc	(REGT)	16 Jan
Thornton, L. J.	(FC)	16 Jan
Russell, B. M.	(FC)	20 Jan
Berryman, A.	(ATC)	23 Jan
Bresher, A. D.	(ATC)	23 Jan
Cooper, J. P.	(REGT)	23 Jan
Errington, J. N.	(FLTOPS)	23 Jan
McNish, J. P.	(REGT)	23 Jan
Weekes, J. R.	(REGT)	23 Jan
Darby, S. J. K.	(ATC)	31 Jan
Robinson, E. A.	(ATC)	31 Jan
Constant, A. C. BSc	(REGT)	12 Feb
Davies, J. M. BSc	(FC)	12 Feb
Davies, P. E. BA	(ATC)	12 Feb
Ford, D. R. BSc	(REGT)	12 Feb
Frogley, T. M. BSc	(ATC)	12 Feb
Gaskell, A. P. BSc	(REGT)	12 Feb
Herring, A. W. BSc	(ATC)	12 Feb
Hindson, K. G. BSc	(FC)	12 Feb
Kennerley, E. L. MA	(INT)	12 Feb
Lennie, C. G. BA	(FC)	12 Feb

Maloney, R. C. BSc	(ATC)	12 Feb
Stewart, E. W. MA	(ATC)	12 Feb
Wake, C. L. LLB	(FC)	12 Feb
Byford, S. C.	(ATC)	17 Feb
Piper, A. J.	(ATC)	21 Feb
Neame, J. P.	(REGT)	1 Apr
Sefton, N. C.	(INT)	1 Apr
Wright, D.	(REGT)	1 Apr
Dalziel, S. BA	(FC)	7 Apr
Edgecombe, A. C. BSc	(ATC)	7 Apr
Gerrard, S. BSc	(FLTOPS)	7 Apr
Harrison, S. L. BA	(ATC)	7 Apr
Hicks, M. C. H. BEng	(REGT)	7 Apr
Mortimer, D. S. BSc	(FC)	7 Apr
Oakley, A. L. BA	(ATC)	7 Apr
Ponting, J. A. BSc	(INT)	7 Apr
Stallard, R. J. BSc	(ATC)	7 Apr
Trott, V. E. K. BSc	(ATC)	7 Apr
Edwards, P. J.	(FC)	24 May
Nicholls, G.	(INT)	24 May
Sheeran, J. A. M.	(REGT)	24 May
Norry, P. A.	(REGT)	26 May
Walker, O. H.	(REGT)	26 May
Passman, L. J.	(ATC)	9 June
Anderson, P. T.	(ATC)	19 July
Crook, P. J.	(REGT)	19 July
Hardaker, M. G.	(ATC)	19 July
Lambert, D. M.	(FC)	19 July
Pickett, D. MBE	(FLTOPS)	19 July
Sockell, J. I.	(INT)	19 July
Gleeson, R. J.	(FLTOPS)	4 Aug
Goodwin, M. R.	(FLTOPS)	30 Sept
Bhatia, L. R.	(ATC)	18 Oct
Harpham, A. Y.	(ATC)	24 Oct
Wood, L. A.	(ATC)	25 Oct
Fox, P. A.	(ATC)	10 Nov
Kirkman, J. M.	(REGT)	26 Nov

2002

Cressy, J. H.	(ATC)	22 Jan
Lindsell, A.	(ATC)	22 Jan
Marsh, S. B.	(REGT)	22 Jan
McLaughlan, A.	(INT)	22 Jan
Thomas, S. J.	(REGT)	22 Jan
Mulvihill, S.	(ATC)	24 Jan
Morris, M. A.	(REGT)	22 Mar
Cooper, A. G. P.	(FC)	30 Mar
Llewellyn, A. J.	(ATC)	30 Mar
McGregor, M. S.	(REGT)	30 Mar
McKinley, D. J.	(REGT)	30 Mar
Nickless, J.	(FC)	30 Mar

Undrell, H. R. BSc	(FLTOPS)	7 Apr
Antoniou, A. M.	(REGT)	25 May
Moore, A.	(FC)	25 May
Pirt, J. W. G.	(REGT)	25 May
Shackleton, R. M.	(FLTOPS)	25 May
Goodwin, M. R.	(FLTOPS)	30 Sept

Pilot Officers

1998

Jux, A. T.	(FLTOPS)	8 Aug

1999

Bates, A. M.	(FC)	29 Nov

2000

Abrutat, D. J.		
BSc	(REGT)	6 Feb
Rooke, D. I.	(ATC)	19 May
Richards, J. A.	(FLTOPS)	25 May
Flach, A. N.	(REGT)	3 Aug
Haith, D.	(FC)	3 Aug
Page, C. D.	(INT)	3 Aug
Skorge, P. G.	(REGT)	3 Aug
Littlewood, P.	(FC)	4 Aug
Culley, P. J. A.	(REGT)	30 Sept
Hobbs, S. C.	(REGT)	30 Sept
Neal, R. J.	(REGT)	30 Sept
Redhead, J.	(FC)	30 Sept
Concarr, M. D.	(REGT)	25 Nov
Geuter, E. C.	(REGT)	25 Nov
Huntley, S. P.	(FC)	25 Nov
Conniss, R. C.	(ATC)	22 Dec

2001

Belham, R. J.	(REGT)	20 Jan
Martens, H.	(ATC)	20 Jan
Mitchell, L. P.	(REGT)	20 Jan
Chambers, M. A.	(ATC)	28 Mar
Knight, C. M.	(ATC)	28 Mar
Macdonald, J. A.	(INT)	28 Mar
Saxon-Jones, N. J.	(FC)	28 Mar
Burton, H.	(INT)	23 May
Cosslett, K. P.	(REGT)	23 May
Donald, M. S.	(REGT)	23 May
Durnin, P. A.	(ATC)	23 May
Evans, S. R.	(FC)	23 May
Kinsman, J. L.	(ATC)	1 Aug
Linton, K. E.	(INT)	1 Aug
Coleman, B. E.	(REGT)	29 Sept
Ricks, A. L. BSc	(INT)	7 Oct
Rowlands, D. M.		
BA	(REGT)	7 Oct
Wilson, J. BSc	(REGT)	7 Oct
Enock, C. E.	(FC)	24 Nov
Lee, T. M.	(REGT)	24 Nov
Lucisano, P.	(FLTOPS)	24 Nov
Smith, J. N.	(REGT)	24 Nov
Stewart, K.	(FC)	24 Nov
Druce, P. M. BA	(ATC)	2 Dec
Ellis, J. E. BA	(ATC)	2 Dec
Kemp, R. J. BA	(INT)	2 Dec
Sharp, N. BSc	(FLTOPS)	2 Dec
Towers, N. A.		
BEng	(INT)	2 Dec

2002

Shelley, L. R.	(FC)	19 Jan
Turner, G. J.	(ATC)	19 Jan
Wiggin, G. M.	(ATC)	19 Jan
Cross, J. B. BSc	(ATC)	10 Feb
Denmead, P. S. BA	(INT)	10 Feb
Jones, C. M. BA	(ATC)	10 Feb
Oakley, M. I. BA	(INT)	10 Feb
Short, A. P.		
BSc	(FLTOPS)	10 Feb
Tricklebank, A. J.		
BA	(ATC)	10 Feb
Atkins, G. M.	(REGT)	4 Apr
Cobb, D. R.	(ATC)	4 Apr
Costello, P. N.	(REGT)	4 Apr
O'Malley, K. J.	(FC)	4 Apr
Page, J. B.	(ATC)	4 Apr
Riley, D. T.	(ATC)	4 Apr
Bridger, G. D. BSc	(INT)	7 Apr
Cribb, B. BA	(ATC)	7 Apr
Crow, G. M. BSc	(FC)	7 Apr
Dickinson, T. BA	(FC)	7 Apr
Eames, C. M. BSc	(ATC)	7 Apr
Edgley, J. E. R.		
BA	(FLTOPS)	7 Apr
Gething, D. P. G.		
BSc	(INT)	7 Apr
Gurr, K. P. BA	(ATC)	7 Apr
McDonald, H. M.		
BA	(ATC)	7 Apr
Perkins, S. L. BSc	(ATC)	7 Apr
Phelps, R. J. BA	(INT)	7 Apr
Smith, H. J. M. BSc	(FC)	7 Apr
Taylor, J. P. MSc		
BA	(INT)	7 Apr
Thomas, H. B. M. MSc		
BA	(FC)	7 Apr
Ball, A. C.	(FLTOPS)	29 May
Jones, S. P.	(REGT)	29 May
Shaw, A. E. J.	(FC)	29 May

Acting Pilot Officers

2002

Beazley, N. J. A.	(REGT)	7 Feb
Yarnall, E. R.	(FC)	7 Feb
Hames, R. P.	(FC)	4 Apr
Langrish, S. W.	(FC)	4 Apr
May, R. A.	(REGT)	4 Apr
Parker, G. D.	(FC)	4 Apr

ENGINEER BRANCH

Group Captains

1991

Lampard, Christopher John BSc(Eng) CEng MRAeS ACGI psc amec Born 22/3/46 . . (M) 1 July

1992

Samuel, Edmond George BSc CEng MIMechE psc amec Born 25/11/48 . . . . . (M) 1 July

1994

Badcock, Peter Charles MBE jsdc semc qs Born 15/12/46 . . . . (EI) 1 July
Paterson, Graham Austin BSc CEng FIEE FRAeS FCMI jsdc ae Born 29/5/48 . . . . (EI) 1 July

1996

Chitty, Jonathan Paul OBE MA BSc(Eng) CEng FRGS FRAeS ACGI psc Born 4/8/53 . . (M) 1 Jan

1997

Capps, Julian John BSc psc ae Born 4/3/49. . . . . (M) 1 Jan
Stevenson, John Graham MSc BSc CEng FIEE psc ae Born 7/5/49 . . . . . . (EI) 1 Jan
Verdon, Andrew Martin BTech CEng FRAeS psc semc Born 14/12/52 . . . . . . (M) 1 Jan
Benstead, Bruce Graham MBE BSc CEng FIEE jsdc ae Born 11/1/53 . . . . . . (EI) 1 July
Cole, Geoffrey MBA CEng MIMechE psc Born 5/3/48 . . . . (M) 1 July
Stevens, Mark Christopher BSc psc semc Born 2/12/54 . . . . (M) 1 July

1998

Burrell, Leslie James ADC BEng CEng FRAeS psc Born 19/9/56 . . . . (M) 1 Jan
Kurth, Nicholas Julian Eugene OBE MA MBA CEng FRAeS FRGS rcds psc Born 13/9/55 (M) 1 Jan
Sims, Stephen Ronald OBE BSc CEng MRAeS DLUT psc ae Born 1/3/52. . . . . (M) 1 July
Suckling, Christopher Alan MBE BSc CEng MIEE jsdc adp qs i Born 1/3/48 . . . . (EI) 1 July

1999

Akehurst, Peter Basil LVO OBE BTech CEng MRAeS jsdc semc qs Born 31/1/51 . . . (M) 1 Jan
Allan, Robert Ian OBE MSc BSc ACGI psc ae Born 4/9/55 . . . . (EI) 1 Jan
Britten-Austin, Harold Gerald MSc BSc CEng FIEE psc ae Born 3/2/48 . . . . . (EI) 1 Jan
Deytrikh, Alexander BSc CEng FRAeS psc Born 15/5/57 . . . . (M) 1 Jan
Harvey, Bryan David BSc psc semc qs Born 24/3/51 . . . . (EI) 1 Jan
Kiralfy, Richard John Charles MSc BSc CEng FIEE FCMI psc ae Born 13/9/50 . . . (EI) 1 Jan
Lane, Paul Leonard MSc BSc jsdc nadc semc qs Born 6/9/54 . . . . (M) 1 Jan
Watson, Graham Mcneill BSc CEng MIMechE semc psc Born 24/11/49 . . . . . (M) 1 Jan
Watson, Robert MBA BA psc Born 22/5/55 . . . . 1 Jan
Church, Frederick Murray MBE BSc psc semc Born 20/9/54 . . . . (M) 1 July
Evans, Graham Sinclair MA MSc CEng FRAeS psc Born 25/12/50. . . . . . . (M) 1 July

Group Captains

1999—contd

Gammon, Neil William MA MSc BSc CEng FRAeS MCMI psc semc Born 23/7/54	(M)	1 July
Kirby, Trevor MBE jsdc semc qs Born 5/2/51		1 July
Lewis, Anthony Luther BSc ae psc i Born 20/8/50	(EI)	1 July
Montagu, Christopher Bernard MSc BSc CEng MIMechE psc ae smc Born 18/5/50	(M)	1 July
Ottridge, Stephen Douglas BSc CEng MIEE MBCS jsdc semc Born 23/2/52	(EI)	1 July
Pigott, John Irwin MSc BSc CEng MIEE psc(n) ae semc Born 19/10/53	(EI)	1 July
Thorne, Ian David OBE BSc jsdc qs Born 6/7/53	(M)	1 July

2000

Ashenhurst, Ralph MSc BSc CEng MRAeS psc Born 29/3/52	(M)	1 Jan
Bollom, Simon John BSc CEng MIMechE jsdc qs Born 22/1/60		1 Jan
Ebdon, Andrew Kevin BA CEng MRAeS jsdc semc qs Born 30/5/53	(M)	1 Jan
Goody, Allan John MA BSc(Eng) CEng FRAeS ACGI nadc psc semc Born 31/8/55	(M)	1 Jan
Heard, Philip John MBE MSc BSc CEng FIMechE FRAeS psc(n) ae Born 5/6/57		1 Jan
Young, Julian Alexander OBE MDA BSc psc ptsc Born 18/12/61		1 Jan
Atkinson, Ian Christopher BSc CEng MIMechE DLUT jsdc ae qs Born 27/11/49	(M)	1 July
Pickerill, Roy Anthony OBE MA BSc CEng MIMechE MBCS psc Born 10/2/57	(M)	1 July

2001

Parker, Stephen Henry MSc BSc(Eng) CEng MRAeS ACGI jsdc ae semc Born 26/4/53	(M)	1 Jan
Parrish, Adrian James MA MSc BSc CEng MRAeS MCMI psc Born 28/4/55	(EI)	1 Jan
Dean, Trevor Philip MSc BSc MRAeS jsdc ae Born 13/8/52	(EI)	1 July
Field, Clive Frank MSc BSc jsdc ae qs Born 25/3/54	(EI)	1 July
McElroy, George Edgar MDA BSc CEng MRAeS psc Born 15/8/57		1 July
Simpson, Ronald Carmont Ross MSc MBCS MCMI adp qs Born 22/6/49.	(M)	1 July

2002

Baber, George Albert OBE BSc CEng psc semc Born 18/7/57	(M)	1 Jan
Cossar, Alexander Kirk MSc BSc(Eng) CEng MIEE ae semc qss Born 2/12/48	(EI)	1 Jan
Edwards, Charles Redvers MSc BA CEng MIEE ae qss Born 16/8/50		1 Jan
Gray, Barrie Leslie BSc IEng FIIE jsdc semc qs Born 20/7/54		1 Jan
Major, Ashley Charles MSc BTech CEng MRAeS psc(j) semc Born 18/1/55	(M)	1 Jan
Vaughan-Smith, Nigel Vaughan BSc CEng MIEE MRAeS jsdc semc qs Born 20/5/48	(EI)	1 Jan
Clark, Martin Adrian MBA BSc(Eng) CEng MIEE psc Born 17/2/61		1 July
Driver, Peter John BSc(Eng) psc Born 30/5/53	(M)	1 July
Green, Christopher Hugh MA BSc CEng MRAeS jsdc psc(j) Born 20/1/59		1 July
Mackenzie, Kenneth MA MSc CEng MRAeS psc ae Born 9/7/55	(M)	1 July
Shearer, Richard Andrew MA BSc CEng MRAeS MIEE MCMI psc semc Born 20/8/58		1 July

Wing Commanders

1987

Hockley, C. J. MBE
CEng MRAeS df
semc psc (M) 1 Jan
Pearce, M. S. BSc CEng
MIEE amec qs (EI) 1 July

1988

Patel, M. R. OBE BSc
CEng MRAeS psc
semc (M) 1 Jan
Nelson, B. J. R. qs (EI) 1 July

1989

Gilbert, P. N. BSc CEng
MRAeS semc qs (M) 1 Jan
Johncock, D. A. qs (EI) 1 July
O'Neill, A. G. MSc
CEng MIEE semc
qs (EI) 1 July
Woods, C. J. MSc
BSc(Eng) CEng
MIMechE MRAeS
qs (M) 1 July

1990

Clark, T. R. semc qs (M) 1 Jan

1991

Brown, J. BA jsdc semc
qs (M) 1 Jan
Willenbruch, A. G. MA
(Eur Ing) CEng
MIMechE MRAeS
MCMI jsdc ae (M) 1 Jan
Harris, R. M. BSc CEng
MIEE semc qs (EI) 1 July
McCormick, D. W. BSc
nadc semc qs (M) 1 July
Phillips, R. A. BSc ae
semc qs (EI) 1 July
Robinson, D. J. MA
IEng MIIE psc
semc (EI) 1 July
Salter, M. G. MBE MBA
BA CEng MRAeS
semc qs (M) 1 July

Turner, C. D. MSc BSc
qs (EI) 1 July
Wilson, D. G. MBE BSc
CEng MIMechE
qs (M) 1 July

1992

Kilshaw, M. J. OBE
MSc BSc(Eng) CEng
MRAeS jsdc qs (M) 1 Jan
Turvill, P. A. BSc CEng
MIMechE psc (M) 1 Jan
Chalmers, G. M. BSc
CEng psc semc (M) 1 July
MacLean, D. F. BSc
CEng MIMechE
psc (M) 1 July
Secker, J. C. psc (EI) 1 July

1993

Pickavance, D. MSc
BSc(Eng) psc (M) 1 Jan
Lawrence, C. H. BSc
CEng MRAeS psc
semc (M) 1 July
Smith, D. R. MSc BSc
CEng MRAeS jsdc ae
qs (M) 1 July

1994

Dyson, G. W. BSc CEng
MIMechE semc
qss (M) 1 Jan
Foster, J. A. MSc BSc
CEng MIEE CDipAF
ae semc qss (EI) 1 Jan
Munday, R. W. semc
qss (E) 1 Jan
Richardson, K. MSc
BSc(Eng) qs (M) 1 Jan
Smith, R. P. BSc(Eng)
CEng MIEE jsdc semc
qs (EI) 1 Jan
Barnes, A. J. BSc
qs (EI) 1 July
Fisher, F. E. MBE BSc
CEng MRAeS qs (M) 1 July
Wheatcroft, J. G. MSc
BSc(Eng) CEng MIEE
qss (EI) 1 July

1995

Caffell, A. N. MSc BSc
CEng MInstD MIEE
MRAeS psc(n) ae
semc (EI) 1 Jan
Little, N. G. BSc CEng
MIEE semc qs (EI) 1 Jan
Welburn, S. MA MSc
BSc CEng MRAeS
psc semc (M) 1 Jan
Spencer, J. W. C. MSc
BSc CEng MIMechE
qs (M) 1 July

1996

Brown, P. M. D. BSc
CEng MRAeS MCMI
semc qs (M) 1 Jan
Tanner, D. J. qs 1 Jan
Ward, A. J. MSc BSc
CEng MRAeS MCMI
jsdc 1 Jan
Ward, D. A. R. BSc
CEng MIEE qs (EI) 1 Jan
Welburn, M. slmc
qss 1 Jan
Binfield, G. H. qss 1 July
Hickman, C. H. BSc
CEng MRAeS
psc 1 July
Render, M. E. J. MA
MBA MSc BSc CEng
MRAeS psc (M) 1 July
Taylor, S. J. MBE MSc
CEng MIEE MCMI
nadc ae qs (EI) 1 July
Thomas, V. E. MA BSc
CEng MRAeS
psc 1 July
Wishart, G. K. MA MSc
BSc CEng MIMechE
psc(j) ae 1 July
Wynne, C. A. MBE
qss (M) 1 July

1997

Gale, S. BSc semc
qss (EI) 1 Jan
Harris, G. H. MA MBA
BSc(Eng) CEng
MIMechE MCMI
psc(j) semc (M) 1 Jan
Martin, G. C. psc 1 Jan
Pallister, I. BSc semc
qs (M) 1 Jan

Wing Commanders

1997—contd

Pharaoh, P. J. MSc BSc
qab qs   (EI)   1 Jan
Richards, E. W. MA
MSc LLB BSc(Eng)
CEng MIEE DIC LTCL
ACGI psc qsb   1 Jan
Ryder, R. S. MSc BSc
psc(j) gw   1 Jan
Thomson, I. W. MSc
BSc(Eng) qss   (M)   1 Jan
Ward, M. M. MDA BSc
MIL MCMI osc(Ge)
semc i*   1 Jan
Witney, J. W. MSc
MPhil BSc CEng
MIEE MCMI qs   (EI)   1 Jan
Wrigley, M. J. MSc BSc
qss   (EI)   1 Jan
Abbott, J. D. F. BSc
CEng MIMeche
psc   1 July
Betteridge, R. MSc BSc
ARCS semc qss (EI)   1 July
Boyle, A. MSc BSc
psc(j) slmc   1 July
Brandt, I. T. G. MA MSc
BSc CEng MIMechE
psc(j)   1 July
Burke, T. C. MSc BSc
psc(n) slmc   1 July
Carlin, G. M. semc qs   1 July
Collins-Bent, N. MDA
BTech CEng MRAeS
psc   1 July
Dipper, A. L. psc   1 July
Fulford, M. A. MSc
MBA BSc CEng MIEE
semc qss   (EI)   1 July
Kinder, S. J. MBE MSc
BSc jsdc semc
qss   (EI)   1 July
Lewis, A. P. qss   1 July
Maciver, J. slmc
qss   1 July
Neal, M. F. OBE IEng
FIIE osc(UK) semc
qs   1 July
Parker, J. S. MBE MBA
BSc CEng MRAeS
semc qss   (EI)   1 July
Phelps, S. M. BTech
CEng MIMechE semc
qs   (M)   1 July

Rigby, J. C. OBE MA
MSc BSc CEng MIEE
psc(j) ae   1 July
Wilson, A. slmc qss   1 July

1998

Barwell, R. J. BSc CEng
MRAeS psc
semc   (M)   1 Jan
Bishop, T. L. J. OBE
MSc BSc CEng MIEE
psc(j)   1 Jan
Burgess, C. A. R. MSc
jsdc semc qss   1 Jan
Dixon, M. D. BSc slmc
psc(j)   1 Jan
Gale, D. J. MBE MA
MDA BSc CEng MIEE
psc(j) slmc   1 Jan
Russell, G. M. MA BSc
psc(j)   1 Jan
Tudor, D. C. qss   1 Jan
Whittaker, D. A. MDA
BSc psc   1 Jan
Wiltshire, J. qs   1 Jan
Ashraf, M. A. BSc
psc(j)   1 July
Bushell, C. R. MA BSc
CEng MIMechE
psc(j)   1 July
Ewen, P. R. jsdc qs   1 July
Ridge, P. C. BSc
psc(j)   1 July
Short, P. BSc qs   1 July
Walker, W. F. IEng MIIE
semc qs   1 July
Winwood, C. D. L. BSc
CEng MIEE psc(j)   1 July

1999

Bailey, S. J. psc(j)   1 Jan
Bland, G. J. BSc CEng
MIEE psc   1 Jan
Charnock, S. MSc BSc
BSc(Eng) CEng
MIMechE MRAeS
CDipAF jsdc ae
qs   1 Jan
Dubock, I. M. BEng
qs   (EI)   1 Jan
Farnell, G. P. OBE MA
MBA BSc CEng
MRAeS psc(j)   1 Jan
Mawston, A. N. BSc
psc(j)   1 Jan

Sibley, M. A. psc
slmc   1 Jan
Smith, M. D. pcs(j)   1 Jan
Abra, J. E. MBE semc
qs   (EI)   1 July
Aleandri, M. P. BSc
psc(j)   1 July
Arnold, A. J. qs   1 July
Bromehead, J. M. BSc
psc(j) slmc   1 July
Canning, G. M. BSc
psc(j) slmc   1 July
Cartwright-Terry, L. G.
G. MBE BA semc
qs   (M)   1 July
Chantry, J. S. MDA BSc
CEng MRAeS qs   1 July
Christensen, C. K. MBE
MSc CEng DipEE
MIEE ae semc qs (EI)   1 July
Cox, B. W. MBE slmc
qs   1 July
Crocombe, M. MIIE
qss   1 July
Davis-Poynter, S. P. MA
MA MSc CEng
MRAeS psc(j) ae   1 July
Donohoe, H. G. MDA
BSc CEng MRAeS
psc(j)   1 July
Eckersley, R. B. MBE
MSc BSc CEng
qs   1 July
Edgar, J. D. BSc CEng
MRAeS qs   1 July
Farr, A. J. R. BA qs   1 July
French, M. J. MBE BSc
CEng MRAeS MCMI
AIL psc(j) slmc i*   1 July
Gill, C. A. BSc
psc(j)   1 July
Gould, C. slmc qs   1 July
Greenbank, A. R. MSc
CEng MIEE MIProdE
MCMI semc qs   1 July
Griffiths, D. K. MSc
MRAeS MCIPS semc
qs   1 July
Harsley, S. J. MA MBA
MRAeS psc(j)
slmc   1 July
Hicks, P. G. MBE BSc
qs   1 July
Hutchinson, R. P. W.
MA BSc CEng
MRAeS psc(j)
semc   1 July
McTeague, R. B. BSc
semc qs   1 July

Wing Commanders

1999—contd

Moody, S. C. MA BSc psc(j)	1 July
Mowat, I. semc qs	1 July
Parton, N. MDA MA BSc CEng MRAeS psc(j)	1 July
Reid, W. McK. PhD BSc qs	1 July
Scotchmer, N. J. BSc qs	1 July
Smith, C. J. L. semc qss (M)	1 July
Tulloch, R. D. A. MBE BSc qs (M)	1 July
Weaver, C. B. MBA MSc BSc CEng MRAeS MCMI ae qs (M)	1 July
West, S. P. MA MSc ae qss (M)	1 July

2000

Barton, T. R. slmc qs	1 Jan
Beange, P. MA psc(j)	1 Jan
Brunning, G. MSc BSc CEng MRAeS ae qss (M)	1 Jan
Bunting, M. E. MSc BSc CEng MIEE psc(j) ae	1 Jan
Fletcher, G. J. MA MSc BSc CEng DMS MIEE psc(j) ae	1 Jan
Garner, A. S. BSc CEng MRAeS psc	1 Jan
Gingell, C. E. MBE scc qs	1 Jan
Hamilton, C. W. MSc BSc CEng MIMechE ae qs (M)	1 Jan
Henwood, C. M. MA MSc BSc CEng MIMechE psc(j)	1 Jan
Johnston, J. B. MBE MA BSc psc(j)	1 Jan
Mercer, B. P. BSc CEng MRAeS MCMI qs	1 Jan
Powell, A. L. MSc BSc CEng MIEE slmc qs	1 Jan
Wingrove, G. E. MSc BSc slmc qs	1 Jan
Barker, P. semc qss	1 July
Cocksey, J. K. MSc BSc CEng MRAeS qs	1 July

Cox, N. J. BSc CEng MIMechE psc slmc	1 July
Dunn, J. F. PhD MBA MSc BSc CEng MIEE MIMechE slmc qs	1 July
Goslin, I. P. MSc BSc CEng MIEE qs	1 July
Kirkwood, I. McI. A. MSc BSc CEng MIEE psc(j)	1 July
Leitch, D. O. S. semc qs	1 July
Martin, P. MSc BSc CEng MIEE ae qs	1 July
Miller, R. L. BSc CEng MIMechE qs	1 July
Moss, S. A. MBE MSc BSc CEng MIEE MRAeS psc(j) ae	1 July
Orme, D. J. MSc BSc CEng MIEE MCMI qs (EI)	1 July
Rigby, R. P. BSc CEng MIEE psc(j)	1 July

2001

Daykin, C. P. BEng CEng MIMechE psc(j)	1 Jan
Gray, S. C. MSc BSc CEng MIEE psc(j)	1 Jan
Guy, T. J. BEng psc(j)	1 Jan
Hargrave, R. J. BSc CEng MRAeS psc(j)	1 Jan
Harris, S. J. psc(j)	1 Jan
Hill, K. W. M. MSc BSc CEng MIMechE psc(j)	1 Jan
Hobbs, M. H. psc(j)	1 Jan
James, R. D. MA qss	1 Jan
Martin, J. PhD MSc qs	1 Jan
Pearce, K. N. MSc BSc CEng MIMechE qs	1 Jan
Phillips, N. J. MBA IEng MIIE psc(j)	1 Jan
Smith, C. R. M. BSc psc(j)	1 Jan
Stead, J. R. MSc BSc qab qs	1 Jan
White, P. J. IEng FIIE qs	1 Jan
Williams, G. psc(j)	1 Jan
Willis, M. E. MSc IEng MIIE LCGI qs	1 Jan
Barclay, I. G. qs	1 July
Box, A. P. R. BSc psc(j)	1 July
Devlin, T. D. MBA BSc IEng MIIE MCMI psc(j) slmc	1 July

Dixon, Q. L. MA MSc BSc CEng MIEE psc(j) ae	1 July
Evans, B. R. BEng CEng MIMechE psc(j)	1 July
Friend, R. qs	1 July
Gatenby, G. J. BSc qss (M)	1 July
Gray, A. BSc CEng MRAeS slmc qs	1 July
Grinsted, P. J. MRAeS DipMgmt psc(j)	1 July
Hesketh, R. L. MA MSc qs	1 July
Humphries, L. J. MSc BA CEng MRAeS gw qss	1 July
Jenkins, M. R. MBE BA IEng MCMI AMRAeS semc qss	1 July
Land, A. IEng MIIE qss	1 July
Leech, D. W. MSc BA BEng CEng MIEE qs	1 July
Lindsay, P. F. MBE qss	1 July
Lovell, G. J. MSc MRAeS MCMI slmc qs	1 July
McHale, J. MDA BSc CEng MIEE MCMI semc qs	1 July
Parkinson, S. J. qs	1 July
Powell, K. BSc CEng MIMechE slmc qs	1 July
Richards, S. R. qs	1 July
Roberts, J. D. BSc slmc qs	1 July
Sarjeant, A. P. qs	1 July
Shears, A. J. MBE qss	1 July
Small, M. K. MSc BSc ae qs	1 July
Taylor, A. J. BSc CEng MRAeS slmc qs	1 July
Thomas, K. L. MBA MSc BEng CEng MIEE MCMI qss	1 July
Thompson, A. J. qss	1 July
Thompson, T. A. qss	1 July
Underhill, G. P. BSc CEng MIEE slmc qs	1 July
Walsh, J. MDA BSc CEng MRAeS qs	1 July
Webb, C. MBA BSc CEng MIMechE MRAeS slmc qs	1 July
Williamson, M. B. BSc CEng MIEE MCMI qs	1 July
Wynne, M. qs	1 July

Wing Commanders

2002

Appleton, D. P. MSc BSc (Eur Ing) CEng MIMechE psc(j)	1 Jan
Barnes, O. R. J. MSc BSc CEng MIMechE psc(j)	1 Jan
Bradshaw, N. T. BEng psc(j)	1 Jan
Clouth, P. J. MSc BEng CEng MIEE psc(j)	1 Jan
Elliott, V. P. MSc BSc CEng MIEE slmc qs	1 Jan
Fyffe, J. C. N. MSc BSc slmc gw qs	1 Jan
Gilbert, C. N. R. MSc BEng ae qss	1 Jan
Kevan, G. J. qs (E)	1 Jan
Liley, S. qss	1 Jan
Liston, G. D. MSc BSc slmc qs	1 Jan
Melhuish, R. T. K. MSc BEng CEng MIMechE psc(j)	1 Jan
Muir, A. G. BSc CEng MRAeS psc(j) qsb	1 Jan
Page, J. M. MBA BSc CEng MIMechE MCMI qs (M)	1 Jan
Payne, T. A. R. MSc BA CEng MIEE qs	1 Jan
Pickavance, R. MSc BSc CEng MIEE ae qss (EI)	1 Jan
Quigley, M. psc(j)	1 Jan
Richardson, S. A. BSc CEng MRAeS psc(j)	1 Jan
Tolometti, G. R. BTech CEng MRAeS qs	1 Jan
Venner, R. MBA IEng AMRAeS qss	1 Jan
Warmington, M. A. BSc qss	1 Jan
Wilkinson, S. R. MDA BSc CEng MRAeS MCMI psc(j)	1 Jan
Wood, N. C. MBE BSc qs	1 Jan
Bray, B. A. J. BSc qs	1 July
Cook, D. R. D. MSc BSc CEng MRAeS qs	1 July
Derbyshire, I. MBE MSc BA CEng MInstP MIEE ae qs (EI)	1 July
Edmondson, S. J. BSc CEng MIEE qss	1 July
Hands, S. J. MDA BSc CEng MRAeS psc(j)	1 July
Jones, F. B. IEng MIIE qs	1 July
Kerry, C. J. BSc semc qss	1 July
Myers, I. A. qs	1 July
Waring, M. S. BSc qs	1 July
Williams, T. B. MSc BSc CEng MIEE qs	1 July

Squadron Leaders

1978

Fleckney, C. F. MSc BSc DIC qs	(M)	18 Mar

1983

Bakewell, G. BSc(Eng) CEng MIMechE MRAeS semc qs	(M)	1 July
Seviour, C. D. BSc qss	(EI)	1 July

1984

Hulland, G. R. qss	(M)	1 Jan
Deane, S. T. MSc CEng MIMechE qss	(M)	1 July

1985

Chappell, D. IEng MIIE MCMI qss	(EI)	1 Jan
Rutter, A. S. BSc CEng MRAeS semc qss	(M)	1 Jan
Slater, I. M. MSc BSc CDipAF semc qs i	(EI)	1 Jan
Webster, D. M. semc qss	(EI)	1 Jan
Ayers, R. S. semc qss	(E)	1 July
Dunkley, P. R. IEng MIIE qs	(M)	1 July
Keen, P. J. BA semc qs	(EI)	1 July
Peterson, G. K. CEng MRAeS qs	(M)	1 July
Ruskell, C. M. BSc semc qss	(EI)	1 July

1986

Costello, M. E. MSc BSc CEng MIMechE MCMI semc qs	(M)	1 Jan
Ladds, R. G. BSc CEng MBCS adp	(M)	1 Jan

Squadron Leaders

1986—contd

Stanhope, M. F. BSc
qs   (M)   1 July

1987

Daniels, S. R. BSc ae
slmc qs   (M)   1 Jan
Denham, R. L. MSc BSc
CEng MIEE semc
qs   (EI)   1 Jan
Elsom, J. BSc CEng
MRAeS ae semc
qss   (M)   1 Jan
Gow, P. J. MSc BSc
CEng MIEE slmc
qs   1 Jan
Howell, A. J. MBE
BSc(Eng) CEng
MRAeS ACGI qs (M)   1 Jan
Humphrey, P. G. IEng
MIIE   (EI)   1 Jan
Jones, G. B. BSc CEng
FIMechE qss   (M)   1 Jan
Adams, R. M. MBE MSc
BSc CEng MRAeS
MCMI qss   (M)   1 July
Dean, P. IEng MIIE
semc qss   (EI)   1 July
Denwood, V. R. MBE
amec   (EI)   1 July
Goff, N. J. BSc CEng
MRAeS semc
qss   (M)   1 July
Matthews, T. J. BSc
qs   (EI)   1 July

1988

Chadwick, G. H. CEng
MRAeS semc qs (M)   1 Jan
Harris, P. R. BSc(Eng)
MRAeS qss   (M)   1 Jan
Marshall, D. MBE slmc
qss   1 Jan
Parfit, G. R. BA semc
qs   1 Jan
Priestley, S. D. BSc
CEng MIEE qs   (EI)   1 Jan
Dixon, M. F. MSc BSc
qss   1 July
Jennings, R. W.
qss   (M)   1 July

Ruddlesden, D. N. BA
CEng MRAeS qs (M)   1 July
Tillbrook, R. E. qss   1 July

1989

Butterfield, M. qss   1 Jan
Crookston, J. MSc
CEng MIMechE
qs   (M)   1 Jan
Durling, R. A. R. MSc
BSc ae semc qs   1 Jan
Harding, M. BSc CEng
MIMechE MCMI
qs   (M)   1 Jan
Hardwick, M.   (M)   1 Jan
Hopton, C. H. MSc BSc
(Eur Ing) CEng MIEE
MRAeS ae slmc
qss   (EI)   1 Jan
Woodhouse, I. P. MBE
BSc CEng MRAeS
MCMI semc qs (M)   1 Jan
Fillingham, D. BSc
CEng MIEE semc
qs   (EI)   1 July
Twine, N. E. semc   1 July

1990

Adams, R. C. qs   1 Jan
Bees, A. R. IEng MIIE
qss   1 Jan
Buckland, A. J. MA (Eur
Ing) CEng MIEE
qss1   (EI)   1 Jan
Cardy, T. IEng AMRAeS
semc qs   1 Jan
Childs, D. R. MSc BSc
CEng FBIS MRAeS ae
qs   (M)   1 Jan
Drake, D. W. qs   1 Jan
Dreier, S. A. IEng qs   1 Jan
Eagles, M. E. BA BSc
semc qs   (M)   1 Jan
Goodall, J. P. qs   1 Jan
Gooden, R. qs   1 Jan
Martin, M. L. MCMI
qss   1 Jan
Musselwhite, M. N.
MBE IEng MIIE
qs   (EI)   1 Jan
Peers, J. MSc BSc ae
slmc qss   1 Jan
Readman, N. E. BSc
IEng AMRAeS semc
qs   1 Jan

Stephenson, I. MSc BA
gw   (EI)   1 Jan
Thompson, M. J.
qs   1 Jan
Walton, J. IEng qss   1 Jan
Wilson, S. J. MSc BSc
gw qs   1 Jan
Wray, C. F. BSc CEng
MRAeS slmc qs   1 Jan
Codling, A. semc
qs   1 July
Helliwell, D. MSc BSc
CEng MRAeS qs   1 July
James, A. R. MSc BSc
CEng MRAeS ae
qss   1 July
Kelly, W. J. R. BSc CEng
MIMechE adp
qss   1 July
Robinson, J. C. P. BSc
CEng MRAeS qss   1 July
Webber, S. semc
qs   1 July

1991

Allen, R. J. BSc CEng
MIEE qs   1 Jan
Bottomley, S. D. G. BSc
qss   1 Jan
Brown, A. qss   1 Jan
Cottam, S. BSc CEng
MIEE qs   1 Jan
Davidson, M. C. F. MDA
MSc BSc CEng
MRAeS MCMI qs   1 Jan
Flowers, P. A. qs   1 Jan
Foran, P. J. qs   1 Jan
Gransden, A. W. MBE
BSc CEng MBCS
qs   1 Jan
Hughes, G. J. MSc ae
qss   1 Jan
Leach, R. L. F. BSc
MInstNDT slmc
qss   1 Jan
Millington, N. G. IEng
FIIE   1 Jan
Moran, M. qss   1 Jan
Pappa, M. R. qss   1 Jan
Roads, C. BSc CEng
MRAeS qss   1 Jan
Skinner, M. W.   1 Jan
Storey, R. N. MSc BSc
CEng MIEE slmc
qs   1 Jan
Lindsay, J. R. qss   (EI)   1 July
Pearce, A. J. qss   1 July

Squadron Leaders

1991—contd

Stammers, M. O.
qs   1 July
Wren, C. A. MSc
BSc(Eng) ae qs   1 July

1992

Bush, V. R. MSc IEng
MIIE ae qs   1 Jan
Hawley, A. B. MSc BSc
ae slmc qs   1 Jan
Moore, A. W. BSc slmc
qs   1 Jan
Nicholls, P. slmc qs   1 Jan
Ousby, R. T. MSc BSc
ae qs   1 Jan
Rickwood, S. R. qss   1 Jan
Roughsedge, E. IEng
MIIE qs   1 Jan
Straw, K. BSc CEng
MIEE qs   1 Jan
Thorne, P. A. MSc BSc
CEng MIMechE
qs   1 Jan
Verth, J. W. MSc BA
CEng MRAeS MIEE
DIC qss   1 Jan
Woodland, C. R. qss   1 Jan
Bole, L. T. qss   1 July
Lean, P. A. BSc IEng
MIIE slmc qs   1 July
Smith, J. J. MSc
MRAeS slmc qs   1 July

1993

Martindale, I. qss   1 Jan
Surtees, I. BSc adp
qs   1 Jan
Voss, M. G. BSc CEng
MIEE slmc qss   1 Jan
Billings, P. A. qs   1 July
Evans, M. A. BA MCMI
qs   1 July
Nidd, D. A. BSc adp
qss   1 July
Powell, D. McA. BSc
semc qss   1 July
Sirs, R. C. MSc ae
qs   1 July
Turner, R. M. BSc
qs   1 July

Wade, R. A. MA MSc
CEng MIMechE
qs   1 July
Williams, J. D. BSc
qss   1 July

1994

Clark, D. R. qs   1 Jan
Dalley, S. L. IEng   1 Jan
Pennycook, J. A. R.
semc   1 Jan
Aunger, D. J. MSc BSc
qs   1 July
Croft, P. J. MSc BSc ae
slmc qs   1 July
Dunn, G. J. BSc CEng
FIIE MRAeS qss   1 July
Izard, B. S. MSc BSc
CEng MIMechE
qs   1 July
Jones, R. A. semc
qss   1 July
Lansbury, D. BA qs   1 July
McMillen, W. R.   1 July
Singleton, C. M. slmc
qs   1 July
Spencer, R. M. J. MBA
IEng MIIE qs   1 July
Stewart, W. J. MSc BA
CEng MIIE MRAeS
qss   1 July
Tarbitten, C. M.
BSc(Tech) qss   1 July
Terrett, J. D. qss   1 July
Whitaker, J. qss   1 July

1995

Bingham, G. K. MSc
BSc ae qss   1 Jan
Butler, A. J. qs   1 Jan
Keeton, P. MBA BSc
CEng MRAeS slmc
qs   1 Jan
Marshall, K. A. BSc
CEng MIMechE
qs   1 Jan
McDermid, B. D. MBA
MSc BEng CEng
MRAeS ae qs   1 Jan
Newby, M. A. MSc BSc
ae qs   1 Jan
Baird, M. J. MSc BSc ae
qs   1 July
Brodie, G. E. BSc CEng
MIMechE qs   1 July

Clark, T. J. MSc BSc
CEng MIEE ACGI
qs   1 July
Dangerfield, M. J. BSc
qss   1 July
Donald, P. W. qs   1 July
Featherstone, C. J. MSc
BSc CEng MIEE
psc(j)   1 July
Headey, G. E. qss   1 July
Hollis, M. BSc CEng
MRAeS slmc qs   1 July
Jones, C. G. IEng MIIE
qss   1 July
McCloskey, P. W. J.
qss   1 July
Moody, D.   1 July
Moore, C.   1 July
Peet, K. MSc MDA
BEng CEng MIEE
MInstD slmc qs   1 July
Perry, L. K. IEng
MIExpE MIIE
AMRAeS slmc
qss   1 July
Rawcliffe, A. P. qss   1 July
Scott, D. P. P.
MInstBE   1 July
Turner, N. J. BSc qs   1 July

1996

Annal, P. D. BSc CEng
MIMechE qss   1 Jan
Conant, A. J. BSc
qs   1 Jan
Evans, D.   1 Jan
Howitt, M. G. qs   1 Jan
Johnstone, A. K. MSc
BSc CEng MIMechE
MRAeS qs   1 Jan
March, A. P. BSc qs   1 Jan
Murray, N. qs   1 Jan
Russell, S. M. IEng MIIE
MCMI qs   1 Jan
Turner, T. N. MPhil MSc
BSc AMIMechE slmc
qs   1 Jan
Walder, C. L. MSc
qss   1 Jan
Ambrose, I. D. qss   1 July
Bartlett, N. G. IEng MIIE
qs   1 July
Brown, A. S. E. qss   1 July
Ho, M. Y. K. MBE
BSc(Eng)   1 July
Mann, T. S. BSc CEng
FIMechE qs   1 July
Marshall, J. qss   1 July

Squadron Leaders

1996—contd

McAlpine, P. W. MSc
BSc CEng MRAeS ae
qs   1 July
Moss, M. S. BEM BA
qss   1 July
Patel, P. MSc IEng FIIE
qs   1 July
Simpson, A. C. IEng
MIIE slmc qs   1 July
Taylor, K. R. IEng MIIE
qss   1 July
Thompson, C. M. BSc
qs   1 July

1997

Bradbeer, P. A. qs   1 Jan
Bradbury, N. J. BSc
CEng MIMechE
qs   1 Jan
Cottrell, N. IEng MIIE
qs   1 Jan
Donald, M. H.   1 Jan
Ham, G. qss   1 Jan
Horrocks, M. MSc BSc
ae qss   1 Jan
Horton, M. qs   1 Jan
Nesbitt, R. C. slmc
qss   1 Jan
Northcote-Wright, A.
psc(j)   1 Jan
Orton, D. G. BSc CEng
MIEE qsb qs   1 Jan
Satchell, V. J. qs   1 Jan
Stewart, S. MSc BSc ae
qs   1 Jan
Stubbs, M. R. MSc
BSc(Eng) qs   1 Jan
Tait, A. G. BSc(Eng)
CEng MRAeS
AMIMechE qs   1 Jan
Wood, A. qs   1 Jan
Armitage, S. R. MSc
BEng CEng MRAeS
qs   1 July
Benford, C. BSc qs   1 July
Booth, G. A. qs   1 July
Burgess, C. M. IEng
MIIE qs   1 July
Deacon, R. qs   1 July
Delaney, R. H. MSc
qs   1 July
Gasson, B. R. qs   1 July

Gilbert, M. R. BSc IEng
AMRAeS qs   1 July
Gill, J. R. MSc BEng
MRAeS qss   1 July
Holmes, C. N. BSc
qs   1 July
Hughes, R. G. MBA BSc
CEng MIEE qs   1 July
Jarvis, K. E. MSc BEng
qss   1 July
Johnson, R. M. MSc
BSc ae qs   1 July
Keeley, R. F. MSc slmc
qs   1 July
Mitchell, P. MSc BEng
CEng MRAeS qs   1 July
Murphy, T. G. BEng
slmc qs   1 July
Pearce, P. MBA BSc
CEng MRAeS CDipAF
qs   1 July
Pettitt, S. J. BSc CEng
MRAeS qs   1 July
Read, A. B. BSc CEng
MRAeS psc(j)   1 July
Rogers, D. E. IEng MIIE
qs   1 July
Rose, P. S. MSc BEng
ae qs   1 July
Sainsbury, N. M. IEng
AMRAeS qs   1 July
Taylor, C. BSc CEng
MIEE qss   1 July
Wariner, J. P. BSc CEng
MIEE psc(j)   1 July
Wilkes, J. G. IEng MIIE
qss   1 July
Wilson, I. A. MSc BEng
ae qs   1 July
Wilson, P. MRAeS
qss   1 July
Young, A. G. BEng
qs   1 July

1998

Andrews, D. L. qss   1 Jan
Axelsen, M. IEng
AMRAeS qss   1 Jan
Brook, D. J. BSc CEng
MRAeS psc(j)   1 Jan
Burn, R. IEng AMRAeS
qs   1 Jan
Currie, A. J. A. MSc
BEng CEng MIEE
qs   1 Jan
Davies, M. R. BSc
qss   1 Jan

Day, A. P. MSc BSc ae
qs   1 Jan
Edge, A. D. MSc BSc
MIMechE qs   1 Jan
Evers, M. C. MSc
qs   1 Jan
Gowing, A. R. IEng
MIIE qss   1 Jan
Grainger, R. MBA
BSc(Eng) CEng
MIMechE slmc
qs   1 Jan
Hand, J. A. IEng MCMI
AMRAeS qs   1 Jan
Hartley, N. J. BSc CEng
CPhys MIEE MInstP
slmc qs   1 Jan
Hurst, I. M. MSc CEng
BSc MIEE qs   1 Jan
Kelsey, D. BSc qs   1 Jan
Knott, S. BSc qs   1 Jan
Legg, A. R. MSc BEng
gw qs   1 Jan
Manger, M. J. MSc
BEng CEng MIEE ae
qs   1 Jan
Nicholls, A. P. BEng
qss   1 Jan
Northover, M. J. MBE
BEng qs   1 Jan
Powell, N. R. BSc qsb
slmc qs   1 Jan
Rhimes, D. M. qs   1 Jan
Roberts, H. MSc BSc
CPhys MInstP qsb
qs   1 Jan
Sansom, A. M. MSc
BEng CEng MRAeS
ae qs   1 Jan
Smith, F. E. A. BEng
qs   1 Jan
Tyrell, A. J. MSc BEng
qss   1 Jan
Ward, I. BSc qs   1 Jan
Webster, S. M. J.
qs   1 Jan
Weston, A. J. BEng
qs   1 Jan
Wray, S. W. BEng
qss   1 Jan
Turner, S. BSc slmc   14 Jan
Arnold, D. B. BSc
qs   1 July
Balderstone, A. W. MSc
BEng qs   1 July
Bell, A. S. MSc BSc ae
qss   1 July
Bethell, K. H. R. qs   1 July

Squadron Leaders

1998—contd

Birkenhead, G. B. MSc
BSc CEng MIEE
qs 1 July
Borthwick, S. P. MDA
BA BEng MRAeS
MCMI qs 1 July
Brown, M. A. MSc
CEng MRAeS
qss 1 July
Buckland, P. J. qs 1 July
Coleman, M. J. IEng
MIIE qs 1 July
Edwards, M. A. BSc
qs 1 July
Ewbank, T. D. qs 1 July
Firby, N. qss 1 July
Freer, G. W. MSc BSc
ae slmc qs 1 July
Gilligan, M. MSc BSc
gw qs 1 July
Graham, H. MSc BSc
qss 1 July
Green, N. B. MBA BA
qs 1 July
Greenway, A. M. MSc
BEng CEng MIEE
qs 1 July
Greenwood, R. J. IEng
AMRAeS qs 1 July
Gunn, T. J. BSc IEng
MRAeS DipMgmt
qs 1 July
Hands, C. J. MSc BEng
ae qss 1 July
Hawley, G. A. qss 1 July
Holmes, A. G. K. qs 1 July
Hughes, G. K. BSc
qss 1 July
Jemmett, R. C. MSc
BSc CEng ae qs 1 July
Johnson, C. N. qs 1 July
Kimber, A. J. MSc ae
qs 1 July
MacRury, D. G. qs 1 July
Machray, R. G. MSc
BEng ae qs 1 July
McCann, N. F. BEng
qs 1 July
Nelson, A. R. MSc
BEng CEng MRAeS
ae qss 1 July
Parlett, R. B. qss 1 July
Pye, C. D. BEng qss 1 July

Rowsell, M. A. BEng
CEng MIMechE
qs 1 July
Saunders, D. BEng
CEng MIMechE
qs 1 July
Slee, P. BEng CEng
MIEE adp qs 1 July
Starr, P. G. 1 July
Tremaine, J. MSc BEng
CEng MIEE qss 1 July
Watts, D. J. BSc CEng
MIEE qs 1 July
Wells, M. C. BEng
MRAeS qs 1 July
Williams, P. L. MSc BSc
CEng MIEE qss 1 July

1999

Allison, P. B. BEng
CEng MRAeS
qss1 1 Jan
Armitage, G. V. R. BSc
qs 1 Jan
Bannister-Green, G. M.
BSc CEng MIEE
qs 1 Jan
Beresford, I. M. MBE
qs 1 Jan
Bolton, G. I. BEng
qs 1 Jan
Carleton, R. K. MSc
BEng CEng MIEE
qss 1 Jan
Chapman, M. A.
qss 1 Jan
Edwards, C. J. MSc
BEng (Eur Ing) CEng
MIEE qss 1 Jan
Ellard, S. D. MSc BSc
CEng MRAeS MBCS
ae qs i* 1 Jan
Ellis, S. C. MBE IEng
MIIE qs 1 Jan
Flather, N. qss 1 Jan
Hammond, J. BSc
qs 1 Jan
Higson, D. W. MSc
BEng qss 1 Jan
Hubert, I. L. BSc
qss 1 Jan
Jack, S. A. BEng CEng
MIEE qs 1 Jan
Knighton, R. J. MA
CEng MIMechE
qs 1 Jan
Kyte, G. M. BSc CEng
MIEE qs 1 Jan

Lea, N. J. MSc BEng
qs 1 Jan
Lee, P. B. T. BEng CEng
MIMechE qs 1 Jan
Lloyd, N. J. BSc qsb
qs 1 Jan
Lockhart, P. MBA
DipMgmt qs 1 Jan
Martin, N. R. BSc
qs 1 Jan
Marvell, C. B. BEng
CEng MIEE qs 1 Jan
McCann, C. T. BSc
qss 1 Jan
Mitchell, J. MSc BEng
CEng MRAeS
qss 1 Jan
Paris, C. A. BEng
qss 1 Jan
Rose, P. M. BEng CEng
MIEE qs 1 Jan
Senior, K. S. MSc
BSc(Eng) CEng
FIMechE qs 1 Jan
Shields, R. G. qs 1 Jan
Stace, C. J. BEng CEng
MIEE qs 1 Jan
Taylor, I. J. MSc BEng
CEng MRAeS qs 1 Jan
Thomas, D. M. MSc
BEng CEng MRAeS
qs 1 Jan
Ward, S. K. MBA BA
MCMI MRAeS
qss 1 Jan
Wheeler, P. G. MSc BSc
CEng MRAeS
qss 1 Jan
Wilcock, S. J. MSc
BEng CEng MRAeS
gw qs 1 Jan
Wright, J. M. qss 1 Jan
Akerman, C. MBA
qs 1 July
Barratt, P. L. MA MSc
BEng ae qs 1 July
Barrington, M. P. B.
qs 1 July
Burke, J. G. MBA
DipMgmt qss 1 July
Campbell, A. J. BEng
qss 1 July
Campbell-Perrett, B. J.
BA BSc CEng MRAeS
qss 1 July
Chalmers, G. MSc IEng
MIIE AMIEE qss 1 July
Chowns, D. A. BEng
CEng MRAeS qs 1 July

Squadron Leaders

1999—contd

Clarke, N. MBE IEng MIIE qs	1 July
Clarkson, D. BSc qss	1 July
Cockram, J. D. BEng CEng MRAeS qs	1 July
Cooper, A. J. qss2	1 July
Cooper, I. R. qs	1 July
Cummins, N. J. IEng MIIE qs	1 July
Dryden, I. BEng slmc qs	1 July
Elsy, K. MSc BEng CEng MIEE qss	1 July
Fryer, D. MSc BEng CEng MIEE qss	1 July
Harrop, J. M. MSc BSc CEng MRAeS qss	1 July
Hegharty, D. BSc(Eng) qss	1 July
Hellard, S. M. BEng slmc qss	1 July
Hill, G. W. BEng qss	1 July
Hill, J. J. MBE	1 July
Hopkins, D. J. BEng CEng MIEE qss	1 July
Hopkins, M. J. IEng MIIE qss	1 July
Jamieson, J. IEng MIIE qss	1 July
Jeffrey, D. W. R. BSc CEng MIMechE qss	1 July
Johnson, J. S. BEng qs	1 July
Kennedy, M. H. IEng MIIE qs	1 July
Khan, J. M. BEng AMIEE qs	1 July
Kilbride, D. M. IEng MIMechE qss	1 July
Knight, A. J. BEng qs	1 July
Lomas, M. MBE IEng AMRAeS qss	1 July
MacDonald, A. T. qss	1 July
Marshall, T. A. MSc BSc CEng MIMechE gw qs	1 July
Owen, M. J. qss	1 July
Panton, A. BSc qss	1 July

Peacock, J. C. slmc qss	1 July
Philliban, J. qsb qs	1 July
Pye, G. A. BEng CEng MRAeS qs	1 July
Ramsey, S. A. BEng AMIEE slmc qss	1 July
Rees, P. A. BSc CEng MRAeS qs	1 July
Riddell, J. G. MSc BSc CEng MRAeS qss	1 July
Salmon, R. E. BSc qss	1 July
Sansome, E. A. BEng qs	1 July
Skinner, M. D. IEng MIIE qss	1 July
Spencer, P. M. IEng MIIE qs	1 July
Terrill, N. S. MSc BEng qss	1 July
Vella, R. A. BSc MIEE qss	1 July
Willis, A. S. BSc qs	1 July

2000

Adams, A. D. qs	1 Jan
Allan, R. M. BSc qsb qs	1 Jan
Atkins, A. R. qss	1 Jan
Baldwin, P. J. qs	1 Jan
Bareham, D. M. MSc BEng CEng MRAeS LCIPD qs	1 Jan
Brown, D. P. MSc BEng CEng MIEE qss	1 Jan
Carter, S. J. asq qss	1 Jan
Croxford, K. C. A. qss	1 Jan
Dabrowski, M. R. MSc BSc qss	1 Jan
Daulby, P. R. BEng slmc qss	1 Jan
Dove, E. L. BEng qss1	1 Jan
Dunnett, R. D. IEng qss1	1 Jan
Empson, J. G. MSc MSc BEng CEng MIEE qcc	1 Jan
Evans, M. P. MSc qs	1 Jan
Goddard, M. R. BSc qs	1 Jan
Harvey, S. D. BSc qs	1 Jan

Hurst, T. M. BSc qss2	1 Jan
Johnson, P. E. C. BEng CEng MRAeS qs	1 Jan
Jones, A. S. MSc BSc ae qss	1 Jan
Jones, L. J. BSc (Eur Ing) CEng MRAeS slmc qs	1 Jan
King, J. qss	1 Jan
Kirk, J. qcc	1 Jan
Mason, D. G. J. BSc qsb slmc qss	1 Jan
McGregor, W. R. BSc CEng MRAeS qs	1 Jan
Miller, P. L. MSc BEng CEng MIEE qs	1 Jan
Mitchell, I. J. BEng qs	1 Jan
Molle, D. C.	1 Jan
Palk, R. A. MSc BEng CEng qs	1 Jan
Pemberton, A. J. MSc qsb qs	1 Jan
Poole, G. J. MDA BEng CEng MRAeS qs	1 Jan
Robinson, I. M. MSc qcc	1 Jan
Rowland, D. J. BEng CEng MIEE qs	1 Jan
Seaton, G. R. BSc CEng PGCE MRAeS qss	1 Jan
Seymour, W. S. MBA BEng CEng MIEE qss	1 Jan
Shears, P. M. BEng MRAeS qs	1 Jan
St John-Crees, D. MSc MSc BSc (Eur Ing) CEng MRAeS qss	1 Jan
Streatfield, G. P. BEng qs	1 Jan
Tanfield, I. F. qss	1 Jan
Tudor, N. J. MSc BEng CEng MIEE qss	1 Jan
Vernoum, K. G. qss	1 Jan
Vicary, S. R. MDA BEng CEng MIMechE qs	1 Jan
Welberry, J. BEM	1 Jan
Woods, R. A. BSc qs	1 Jan
Anderson, D. qss	1 July
Beckett, W. B. M. qss1	1 July
Beken, D. C. qs	1 July
Brudenell, J. P. qs	1 July

Squadron Leaders

2000—contd

Challonder, A. S. qss — 1 July
Childs, C. BEng CEng MIEE qss — 1 July
Dickinson, P. W. BSc CEng MRAeS qss — 1 July
Dodding, S. D. BSc qss — 1 July
Elder, R. P. BSc CEng MIEE qss — 1 July
Ellen, R. A. BEng qss — 1 July
Gay, M. A. MSc BEng qcc — 1 July
Goodfellow, R. C. BEng CEng MIEE qs — 1 July
Green, A. R. BA qs — 1 July
Greenstreet, D. M. BSc CEng MRAeS qss — 1 July
Gudgeon, A. C. MSc BSc CEng MIEE qs — 1 July
Halliday, S. J. BEng CEng MIEE qss — 1 July
Hanley, R. D. MSc BEng qss1 — 1 July
Hartland, P. A. MSc BEng CEng MIEE qss2 — 1 July
Haywood, S. J. BEng qs — 1 July
Herbert, G. S. R. BSc qsb qs — 1 July
Houghton, A. P. slmc qcc — 1 July
Johnson, J. A. MSc BEng CEng MIMechE qss — 1 July
Ladbrook, P. R. IEng MRAeS qss — 1 July
Long, C. E. BEng CEng MIMechE qs — 1 July
Losh, S. slmc qss — 1 July
Marsh, R. E. MSc MEng MBA CEng MIMechE MRAeS CDipAF qs — 1 July
Martin, D. V. BEng qss — 1 July
McKevitt, M. MBE BEM qss — 1 July
Middlewood, M. L. BSc IEng qss — 1 July

Moore, C. J. BEng qcc — 1 July
Moran, R. F. qss — 1 July
Owen, R. M. qss — 1 July
Pawsey, A. R. BSc adp qss — 1 July
Pipe, A. J. MBA IEng MIIE MCMI qs — 1 July
Rawes, R. A. qss — 1 July
Rillie, I. MIIE qss — 1 July
Rogers-Jones, A. MDA BEng CEng MIEE qss — 1 July
Rule, S. Z. BSc qss — 1 July
Sadler, A. R. BSc slmc qss — 1 July
Sallis, B. A. MBE qss — 1 July
Stanley, M. BEng qs — 1 July
Stanway, N. A. MSc BEng CEng MRAeS qss — 1 July
Thompson, A. G. AMRAeS qss2 — 1 July
Timoney, M. J. BSc CEng MRAeS qs — 1 July
Wilby, S. K. qss — 1 July
Wilkinson, S. N. MSc BSc CEng MRAeS ae qss — 1 July
Wilson, M. R. BSc qs — 1 July
Wilson-Smith, G. K. IEng MIIE qs — 1 July

2001

Abbs, M. R. qss — 1 Jan
Bales, S. J. qss1 — 1 Jan
Bateman, G. J. IEng AMRAeS qs — 1 Jan
Berrecloth, P. C. BSc qss — 1 Jan
Broderick, C. A. BEng qss2 — 1 Jan
Brown, M. G. BEng qsb qss — 1 Jan
Burke, S. BEng AMIEE qss2 — 1 Jan
Connelly, J. A. BEng qss2 — 1 Jan
Cudlipp, R. M. — 1 Jan
Dalton, G. BEng CEng MIEE qss2 — 1 Jan
Dearing, S. L. MSc BEng qcc — 1 Jan
Docherty, C. IEng AMRAeS slmc qs — 1 Jan

Eaton, K. P. qcc — 1 Jan
Eccleston, A. M. MEng CEng MIEE qcc — 1 Jan
Edwards, G. D. BSc qss — 1 Jan
Elford, S. B. qss — 1 Jan
Exley, M. A. IEng MIIE qss — 1 Jan
Farrow, P. W. qss1 — 1 Jan
Grimsley, D. T. A. BSc qs — 1 Jan
Hill, C. V. BEng CEng MRAeS qs — 1 Jan
Jones, J. G. — 1 Jan
Jones, J. P. BEng qss2 — 1 Jan
Kelsey, C. M. MSc BSc ae qss — 1 Jan
Lloyd, P. H. MDA BEng CEng MIMechE qss2 — 1 Jan
Lunan, I. BEng qss2 — 1 Jan
Marshall, R. S. BA qss — 1 Jan
McKeown, I. D. BEng qss — 1 Jan
McNeill, A. D. BEng qcc — 1 Jan
Mitchell, A. BTech IEng MRAeS qss — 1 Jan
Partridge, M. A. MDA IEng MIIE qss2 — 1 Jan
Payne, D. E. BEng qss2 — 1 Jan
Pearce, G. C. MIMIME qss — 1 Jan
Pickard, M. J. BEng qsb qs — 1 Jan
Poulton, J. C. qss1 — 1 Jan
Praag, A. N. qss2 — 1 Jan
Press, J. R. qss — 1 Jan
Saul, P. M. BEng qss2 — 1 Jan
Simmonite, A. J. BEng qss2 — 1 Jan
Smeaton, J. P. R. BEng CEng MIEE qss2 — 1 Jan
Thompson, T. M. BEng qss — 1 Jan
Treloar, B. C. qss — 1 Jan
Watkins, G. D. BEng CEng qss — 1 Jan
Whittingham, R. C. MBE qss — 1 Jan
Winfield, R. J. qss — 1 Jan
Wootten, M. J. qs — 1 Jan
Aitchison, D. F. qss — 1 July
Allan, C. J. qss — 1 July

Squadron Leaders

2001—contd

Armstrong, A. D. MSc BEng qss	1 July
Bailey, A. P. BEng MRAeS	1 July
Baldwin, B. F. qss	1 July
Carlton, D. qss	1 July
Carroll, J. H. qss2	1 July
Carroll, M. W. MDA BEng MRAeS qss	1 July
Coleby, T. B. MSc BEng CEng MRAeS ae qss	1 July
Cook, C. M. IEng MIIE qsb qss	1 July
Crowe, J. A. MBE BSc qcc	1 July
Dalton, G. S. qss	1 July
Darby, C. A. M. IEng AMRAeS qs	1 July
Evans, M. S. BEng qss	1 July
Ford, A. J. qss	1 July
Goodfellow, A. M. BEng CEng MIEE qss2	1 July
Hill, I. R.	1 July
Howard, J. C. E. qss	1 July
Lainchbury, I. M. BEng CEng MIEE qss	1 July
Lucie-Smith, E. R. BSc CEng MRAeS qss	1 July
MacLennan, A. R. IEng MIIE qss	1 July
Mackay, D. J. BSc IEng AMRAeS qss	1 July
Martin, G.	1 July
Martin, P. L. MSc BEng CEng qss	1 July
McCleary, D. P. BSc CEng MIMechE qss	1 July
McDermott, D. qss	1 July
Mills, J. B. BEng qss	1 July
Newton, C. H. qss2	1 July
Newton, M. D.	1 July
Nicholson, E. H. J. MBE BSc CEng qss	1 July
Parker, G. H. qss	1 July
Parker, R. M. MA MSc ae qs	1 July

Parry, D. T. IEng MIIE MCMI	1 July
Payne, N. G. BSc qs	1 July
Phillips, J. S. MSc BEng CEng qss	1 July
Powlson, M. D. BEng qss2	1 July
Pullen, M. P. BEng CEng MIEE qs	1 July
Ramsden, G. P. BEng CEng MIEE qs	1 July
Shelley, J. M. qss	1 July
Stevens, J. E. MSc MSc BEng CEng MIEE qss	1 July
Twine, A. N. H. qss	1 July
Tyler, P. MBE IEng MIIE qss	1 July
Walker, R. J. BEng qss	1 July
Wallis, A. D. BSc CEng MRAeS qss	1 July
Waters, P. J. qss	1 July
Williams, D. J. LLB IEng AMRAeS qss	1 July
Williams, W. J. A. BA	1 July
Wright, K. M.	1 July

2002

Alcock, A. BEng CEng MRAeS qss	1 Jan
Austen, R. G. slmc qss	1 Jan
Baldaro, J. L. BEng CEng qss2	1 Jan
Bilney, M. BEng qss	1 Jan
Bolt, A. T. BEng qsb qss	1 Jan
Briggs, S. V. MSc BEng CEng MIEE qss2	1 Jan
Cooksley, A. P. MSc BSc CEng MIEE qss	1 Jan
Dawes, D. P. BEng qss2	1 Jan
Edmondson, E. A. BEng CEng MIMechE qss	1 Jan
Egan, C. J. BEng qcc	1 Jan
Fitzpatrick, J. D. BEng CEng MRAeS qss	1 Jan
Forbes, G. S. qss	1 Jan

Gilroy, J. R. BEng qss2	1 Jan
Harris, S. BEng qcc	1 Jan
Haynes, P. D. BEng qss2	1 Jan
Hesketh, S. J. BEng CEng MRAeS qss	1 Jan
Hewitt, A. K. MSc BEng CEng MIMechE qss	1 Jan
Hodge, M. BEng qss2	1 Jan
Hutchison, H. G. MSc BEng CEng MIMechE qss	1 Jan
Iles, A. D. G. qss2	1 Jan
Knights, S. A. BEng qcc	1 Jan
Lilly, P. D. BEng qs	1 Jan
McCarthy, J. A. MSc BEng qss	1 Jan
McLaughlin, S. BEng qsb qcc	1 Jan
McNair, G. W. BEng qs	1 Jan
McQuillan, S. D. V. MSc BEng CEng MIMechE qss	1 Jan
Mockford, A. D. qss	1 Jan
Osborne, J. B. BEng qcc	1 Jan
Parry, R. M. BEng qss	1 Jan
Parry, S. A. BEng qss2	1 Jan
Potts, M. J. BEng qss	1 Jan
Prentice, P. R. BEng qcc	1 Jan
Roberts, L. P. BEng qs	1 Jan
Russell, J. qss2	1 Jan
Sadler, B. qss1	1 Jan
Simpson, S. M. BEng qss2	1 Jan
Slaven, D. R. BEng CEng MIEE qcc	1 Jan
Smith, L. F. BEng CEng MIMechE qss1	1 Jan
Souter, W. G. BEng qss1	1 Jan
Tucker, C. D. BEng qcc	1 Jan
Watford, I. R. IEng AMRAeS qss	1 Jan
Watson, B. J. BEng qss	1 Jan

169

Squadron Leaders

2002—contd

Watson, N. MSc BEng
  BSc CMath MIMA ae
  qss   1 Jan
Williamson, S. C. BEng
  qss2   1 Jan
Wilson, A. G. A. BEng
  CEng MIEE qss   1 Jan
Wilson, C. J. qss   1 Jan
Wincott, S. M. BEng
  qss   1 Jan
Withers, R. M. BEng
  qcc   1 Jan
Woodfine, D. S. BEng
  CEng MIEE qss   1 Jan
Wray, P. M. BEng
  qss   1 Jan
Beech, G. qs   1 July
Blogg, D. O. qss   1 July
Bowden, J. T. IEng
  AMRAeS qss   1 July
Bowland, J. E. qcc   1 July
Bradley, I. M. BEng
  CEng MIEE qss2   1 July
Bradshaw, S. J. MEng
  MSc qss   1 July
Eames, D. P. MSc
  BEng   1 July
Ellis, G. BEng CEng
  MRAeS qss   1 July
Espie, D. W. qss1   1 July
Frew, D. M. BEng
  qss   1 July
Gee, S. MSc BEng
  qss   1 July
Hale, R. J. BEng
  qcc   1 July
Hawkins, F. P. BEng
  CEng MIEE qss   1 July
Heath, S. T. MSc BEng
  CEng MRAeS ae
  qss   1 July
Hillary, N. P. slmc
  qss   1 July
Huby, G. M. BEng CEng
  MRAeS qss2   1 July
Jones, A. J. MSc BEng
  CEng MIEE qs   1 July
Killick, A. J. qs   1 July
Krauze, I. A. MSc BEng
  CEng MIEE ptsc ae
  qss2   1 July
Lander, D. S. BEng adp
  qss2   1 July
Lawrence, G. BSc CEng
  qss   1 July

Leyland, T. J. W. BSc
  qss   1 July
Martin, J. W. R. MSc
  BEng AMIEE qss   1 July
McLoughlin, A. J.
  qcc   1 July
McQuillin, K. F. BSc
  CEng MRAeS
  qss   1 July
Paling, J. J. IEng   1 July
Parsons, C. J. qss   1 July
Paul, J. C. BEng
  qss2   1 July
Pease, C. T. qss   1 July
Waring, S. J. BSc
  qss   1 July
Warr, S. A. BEng
  qss   1 July
Watt, K. G. BEng CEng
  MIEE qss   1 July
White, A. J. BEng
  qcc   1 July

Flight Lieutenants

1983

Kohli, R. D. S. BSc qss 13 July

1985

Perry, A. T. BSc qss   20 Oct
Jones, K. C. BSc IEng
  MIIE   26 Oct

1987

Roberts, T. M. C. BSc
  CEng MIEE qss   17 Jan
Palmer, G. R. A. BSc
  qss   15 Oct

1988

Jones, C. H. BSc
  qss   25 Mar
Haggarty, E. MSc BSc
  qss   11 Apr
Chapman, P. G. H.
  BSc   20 Aug

1989

Ellis, T. J. R. BSc CEng
  MRAeS MIExpE qtm
  qss   15 Jan
Burgess, M. K.   17 Jan
Norton, B. K.   17 Jan
Kinsey, A. T. qss   27 Aug
Reese, N. P. BSc ae   3 Oct
Martland, J. R. BSc
  qss   17 Oct
Way, C. S. BSc qss   7 Dec
Frieland, C. A. qss   19 Dec

1990

Swinney, R. W. MSc
  MSc BSc MIEE
  qcc   11 Jan
Anderson, M. G. MSc
  CEng MISM MRAeS
  ae qss   19 Jan
Butt, N. J. MSc BSc
  qss2   15 Mar

Flight Lieutenants

1990—contd

Chandler, J. H. BEM BSc qss	27 Mar
Clark, F. S. BSc(Eng) qss	15 Apr
Stott, I. R. qss	26 Apr
Hockley, S. P. qss	5 May
Shelton-Smith, C. A. BEng CEng MRAeS qss	27 May
Bowles, K. N. qss	28 July
Booth, D. M. C. qss	31 July
Pawson, P. T. qss	31 July
Upton, D. J.	31 July
Houghton, I. BSc CEng MIEE qss2	19 Sept
Leadbitter, S. J. IEng AMRAeS	22 Nov

1991

Milwright, D. T. P. BSc CEng MIEE qss	15 Jan
Savage, S. J. MSc BEng CEng MIEE qss	15 Jan
Tapson, I. R. BEng qss	15 Jan
James, T. R. BEng qss	12 Apr
Ashcroft, K.	4 June
O'Connell, S. T. BEng qss	8 July
Clarke, K.	17 July
Saldanha, R. C.	17 July
Morgan, D. W. MEng CEng qss	19 Aug
Oglesby, D. H. MSc BEng CEng MIEE ae qss	25 Aug
Robbins, C. J.	27 Aug
Nimick, P. G. BEng qcc	7 Sept
Callaghan, J. BEng CEng MIMechE qss	2 Oct
Robinson, D. A. MBE qss	14 Dec
Studley, G. S. qss	21 Dec
Hill, C. M. BEng qss	25 Dec

1992

Walsh, T. J. BSc	15 Jan

Bradgate, J. K. MSc BEng CEng MIEE qss	27 Feb
Gordon, B.	5 May
Stellitano, W.	5 May
Williams, M. J. BEng qss	6 May
Grace, J. C. BEng CEng qss	12 May
Murphy, C. J. qss2	15 June
Peters, C. E. MSc qss	21 June
Hood, M. G. H. qss2	2 July
Marshall, P. S. BEng BSc CEng MIEE	13 July
Legge, G. P. E. BEng qcc	15 July
McLaughlin, W. MSc BEng qss	15 July
Still, W. BEng qss	15 July
Stockton, N. A. BEng qss	15 July
Jones, C. A. qss	2 Aug
Miller, S. BEng qss	23 Aug
Bailey, C. P. IEng qss	26 Sept
Barraclough, R. BEng qss	2 Oct
Sanderson, A. M. BSc CEng qss	2 Oct
Peck, R. BEng qcc	23 Oct
Freeman, G. J. BSc IEng AMRAeS qss	2 Nov
Hoyton, D. G. BSc qcc	7 Nov
Boardman, L. D. qss	8 Nov
Paice, N. J. qss	8 Nov
O'Brien, P. F. J. Ing EurEta IEng MIIE qss1	26 Nov
Brown, M. H. qss	15 Dec
Phillips, M. E.	15 Dec

1993

Bell, J. R. BEng BA qss1	15 Jan
Di Nucci, S. MSc BEng qss	15 Jan
Hutchison, P. B. MSc BEng qss	15 Jan
McEwing, M. F. BEng qss	15 Jan
Thurrell, W. M. BEng qcc	15 Jan

Jack, J. A. BEng qss	28 Mar
Burgess, P. D. C. MSc BEng CEng MIEE ae qcc	1 Apr
Morris, P. D. MBA BEng CEng MIMechE	1 Apr
Mitchell, J. C. BEng qss	2 Apr
Oram, G. BEng CEng MIEE qss	20 Apr
Mammatt, J. E. BEng qss2	7 May
Smith, P. J.	11 May
Trimble, I. C.	11 May
Hart, S. J. MSc BEng CEng MRAeS ae qss	12 May
Scantlebury, P. J. MSc BEng ae qss	12 May
Blackmore, N. J. BEng qss	25 May
Evans, D. J. qss	25 June
Connor, S. P. BEng qcc	15 July
Godbolt, S. D. BEng qcc	15 July
Lefley, R. MSc BEng ae	15 July
Reed, S. J. MSc BEng CEng MIEE ptsc qss	15 July
Woodgate, A. M. BEng adp qcc	15 July
Hall, D. A. qss	14 Aug
Arnold, J. G. qss	12 Sept
Blake, C. BEng qcc	27 Sept
Horsley, D. R. BEng CEng qss	23 Oct
Arnold, N. J. BEng qcc	29 Oct
Sussex, P. S. BEng qss	4 Nov
Crosby, C. P. qss	9 Nov
Gibson, G. V. MSc BSc IEng MIIE CertEd qss1	19 Dec
Scott, M. D. BSc qss1	19 Dec
Wilkins, M. E. IEng MIIE qss2	19 Dec
Gibbs, P. qss	21 Dec
O'Callaghan, P. J.	21 Dec
Gillespie, W. M. BEng qss1	22 Dec
Taylor, C. M.	26 Dec

Flight Lieutenants

1994

Beverley, S. J. BEng qss	15 Jan
Brennan, M. F. BEng qss2	15 Jan
Ford, R. J. BEng qss	15 Jan
Hallam, A. J. BEng CEng MRAeS qs	15 Jan
Leeks-Musselwhite, M. MSc BSc CEng MRAeS AMIEE qss	15 Jan
Owen, P. E. BSc qss2	15 Jan
Thompson, J. P BEng qcc	15 Jan
McCreary, C. M. BSc	2 Feb
Burke, R. T. qss2	13 Feb
Moore, S. N. qss1	13 Feb
Dodds, F. K.	15 Feb
Duncan, J.	15 Feb
Rickards, T. J.	15 Feb
Shatford, W. F.	15 Feb
Villiers, P. BEng qcc	25 Feb
Worth, N. P. qss	29 Mar
O'Brien, M. C. BEng	21 Apr
Beasley, S. G. qss	7 May
Meeghan, P. qcc	7 May
Cruikshanks, R. W. qss1	10 May
Hollins, D. G.	10 May
Moinet, A. N.	10 May
Potterill, S. M. BSc qcc	11 May
McMurtrie, S. R. J. BEng qss	31 May
Cannon, S. A. IEng qss	16 June
Gidda, G. S. MBA qcc	16 June
Channon, M. P. qss	21 June
Gray, G. H.	21 June
Johnson, T. P. qss1	21 June
Piaggesi, G. P. qss	21 June
Ricketts, J. M. MSc qcc	21 June
Clapham, D. L. BEng qss1	15 July
Dunne, A. J. BEng qcc	15 July
Ingleson, M. S. BEng qss	15 July

Maxwell, I. D. BEng qcc	15 July
Rosbotham, K. BEng qss2	15 July
Ross, F. G. BEng	15 July
Southall, R. C. BEng qcc	15 July
Bailey, P.	2 Aug
Tanner, A. J. IEng MIIE MInstLM	2 Aug
Goldsworthy, J. H.	26 Sept
Greenfield, J. M.	26 Sept
Hamilton, E. S. qss	26 Sept
Pick, K.	26 Sept
McKenzie-Orr, A. BSc qss2	29 Sept
Khan, F. MEng	9 Oct
Cunliffe, P. BEng qss	22 Nov

1995

O'Kane, S. J. BEng qcc	10 Jan
Bradley, M. R. BEng CEng MIMechE qcc	15 Jan
Dart, P. G. BEng qss2	15 Jan
Heath, P. A. MSc BEng ae qcc	15 Jan
Ross, J. M. BEng qss	15 Jan
Woods, S. B. MSc BEng CEng MIEE qcc	15 Jan
Walker, M. B.	28 Jan
Collie, P. D.	31 Jan
Jones, D. M. qss2	2 Feb
Musk, T. S. qss	11 Feb
Dourish, G. A.	14 Feb
Pullen, J. R. E. qcc	16 Feb
Smeaton, C. A. BEng CEng MRAeS qss	18 Feb
Mepham, K. D. BEng (Eur Ing) CEng MIEE qss	22 Feb
Watkins, S. C. BEng qcc	21 Mar
Mannall, D. M. qss	28 Mar
Pybus, K. W.	28 Mar
Simpson, I. BEM	28 Mar
Skirving, D. J. BEng qss2	29 Mar
Smith, I. T. G. BEng qss	4 Apr
Noon, A. R. BEng qss	5 May
McCann, A. M. MBE qss	9 May
Davies, S. R. qss	13 May
Tempest-Roe, R. M.	17 May
Breslin, P. G. qss1	20 June

Doughty, R. qss	20 June
Kellaway, E. M. MSc BEng qs	5 July
Chapman, P. M. BEng qss2	15 July
Hussain, Z. BEng qcc	15 July
Lacey, L. J. BEng qcc	15 July
Longden, R. D. BEng qcc	15 July
Smith, R. L. BEM BEng MRAeS qss1	15 July
Stanley, A. K. BEng qcc	15 July
Robinson, B. qss1	28 July
Turner, J. qcc	28 July
Bradley, R. N. qss	29 July
Moss, A. R. BEng	30 July
Zakary, P. C. BSc CEng MIMechE MIEE MIMarE MCIWEM	2 Aug
Stanley, R. M. BEng qcc	12 Aug
Keen, K. M. MSc MEng qss	14 Aug
Lowry, W. M. IEng MIET qss1	26 Sept
Walton, J. R.	26 Sept
Orme, D. I.	10 Oct
Blyth, I. qss	7 Nov
Cann, C.	7 Nov
Cole, M. E. IEng	7 Nov
Roberts, W.	7 Nov
Russell, S. J. qss1	7 Nov
Stevens. C. N.	7 Nov
Wild, J. R.	7 Nov
Wilson, P.	17 Nov
McGhie, D. C. P.	19 Dec

1996

Barton, S. D. MEng qcc	15 Jan
Baxter, D. M. BEng CEng MRAeS qss2	15 Jan
Chappell, J. L. BEng qss1	15 Jan
Donnellan, S. J. BEng qss	15 Jan
Downey, E. A. BEng qss1	15 Jan
Fell, A. T. BEng CEng MRAeS qss	15 Jan
Green, A. S. BEng CEng MIEE qss1	15 Jan
Ley, E. R. J. BEng CEng MRAeS qss2	15 Jan

Flight Lieutenants

1996—contd

Lindsay, D. R. BEng qss1	15 Jan
Lloyd, R. A. BEng qcc	15 Jan
Matthew, J. H. MSc BSc qcc	15 Jan
Morley, P. M. BEng qss	15 Jan
Plant, B. M. BEng qcc	15 Jan
Ross, I. A. BEng qss1	15 Jan
Warren, J. BEng qcc	15 Jan
Wilson, J. W. I. BEng qss	15 Jan
Hopwell, I. J. qcc	10 Febl
Regan, P. E. BEng qss1	17 Feb
Brodie, S. BEng qss2	28 Feb
Harrison, A. R. BEng qcc	8 Mar
Doherty, B. D. BEng AMIEE qss	13 Mar
Tapping, J. G. C.	26 Mar
Creber, D. J. PhD BEng PGCE	6 Apr
Wright, R. BEng qcc	11 Apr
Streatfield, P. J. BEng qcc	30 Apr
Elliott, A. H. qss	7 May
Munroe, G. M. BEng qss	12 May
Pinckney, N. J. BEng qcc	6 June
Higham, N. P. BEng qcc	24 June
Barr, R. P. BEng qcc	15 July
Calder, A. P. J. BEng qcc	15 July
Davies, H. B. BEng	15 July
Gadney, A. D. BEng qcc	15 July
Kent, S. E. R. BEng qcc	15 July
Kilday, I. BEng	15 July
Kirk, N. H.	15 July
Russell, S. I. BEng	15 July
Tomlinson, G. G. BEng CEng MIEE qss1	15 July
Tomlinson, J. I. M. BEng qcc	15 July

Young, J. N. BEng qcc	23 July
Harmer, N. J. BEng qss2	14 Aug
Shipley, J. M. BEng qcc	13 Sept
Fielder, R. BEng qcc	16 Sept
Wood, B. D. A. BEng qcc	29 Sept
Blevins, P. R. qcc	6 Oct
Green, J. R. qcc	6 Oct
Hodge, C. F. BEM qcc	6 Oct
Johnson, T. W. R. S. qss	6 Oct
Bye, D. D. BSc CEng MRAeS qss2	10 Oct
Graham, K. B. BEng qss	10 Oct
Howard, N. A. BEng qcc	27 Oct
Mercer, G. F. BEng qcc	2 Nov
Wild, J. E.	13 Dec

1997

Bradbury, S. P. BEng qss2	15 Jan
Green, C. D. BEng CEng MIMechE qcc	15 Jan
Hampson, M. C. BEng qss2	15 Jan
Joly, R. B. BEng CEng MRAeS qss2	15 Jan
Kelly, P. BEng qss2	15 Jan
Rolf, J. MA MRAeS qss2	15 Jan
Shipp, A. M. MSc BEng ae qcc	15 Jan
Smith, R. L. S. BEng qcc	15 Jan
Tozer, D. J. BEng qcc	15 Jan
Wilkinson, P. J. BEng qss2	15 Jan
Longley, C. I. BEng qcc	6 Feb
Rayner, K. S. BEng qcc	10 Feb
Copeland, A. W. W. qss	11 Feb
Daly, C. T. BEng qcc	14 Feb
Casey, T. J. BEng qss1	15 Feb
Storer, K. A. BEng qcc	15 Feb

Harris, R. C. MEng CEng MIEE	20 Feb
Crook, L. D. BEng qcc	1 Mar
Bedding, S. J. qcc	29 Mar
Hunt, M. BEng CEng MIMechE qss2	10 Apr
Seddon, J. W. BEng CEng MIMechE qcc	10 Apr
Waggitt, R. D. BEng qss2	10 Apr
Brydon, M. F. qss	14 May
Croft, P. BEng qcc	2 June
Corfield, G. M. PhD BEng (Eur Ing) CEng MIMechE MIChemE MIM DIC	3 June
McLeod, A. C. BEng qcc	13 July
Cowie, I. BEng	15 July
Greenland, S. J. BEng qcc	15 July
Hall, G. J. BEng	15 July
Hatten, G. A. BEng qcc	15 July
Lawson, D. M. BEng	15 July
Mayo, P. R. BEng qss1	15 July
Nadin, M. A. BEng qss	15 July
Russell, P. J. BEng	15 July
Swanson, J. BEng qcc	15 July
Wright, M. S. BEng	15 July
Bradshaw, N. J. qcc	28 July
Pridmore, B. J. BEng CEng MRAeS qcc	4 Aug
Clapp, S. E. BEng qcc	8 Aug
Hawley, M. R.	16 Aug
Powley, S. K. BEng qss	16 Aug
Todd, B. S. BEng qcc	23 Aug
Stephens, D. A. BEng	9 Oct
Lewis, D. A. BEng qcc	10 Oct
Gibson, M. A. BEng qcc	11 Nov
Hope, M. A. BEng qss	2 Dec

Flight Lieutenants

1998

Ankers, J. R. BEng	15 Jan
Bobbin, A. J. BEng qcc	15 Jan
Browning, J. L. W. MSc BEng ae qcc	15 Jan
Carter, K. BEng qcc	15 Jan
Collins, L. BEng qcc	15 Jan
Hamilton, D. M. BEng	15 Jan
Handley, D. A. MEng	15 Jan
Neal-Hopes, T. D. MSc BEng qcc	15 Jan
Richards, R. P. MEng qs	15 Jan
Frazer, S. R. BSc	30 Jan
Harrop, D. G. qss	8 Feb
Paris, G. D. qss1	8 Feb
Brown, R. N. BEng qcc	13 Feb
Goodchild, S. P. BEng	13 Feb
Bellamy, S. J. BEng qcc	14 Feb
Hamilton, C. J. BSc qss	14 Feb
Limb, N. P. BEng	14 Feb
Morris, B. D. BEng qss	6 Mar
Greenwood, P. qcc	4 Apr
Salter, A. R. qcc	4 Apr
Warren, M. C. BEng	5 Apr
Barker, M. A. BEng qss1	9 Apr
Carter, D. J. BEng qss2	9 Apr
Stone, J. D. BEng qcc	9 Apr
Iddon, J. N. BEng qcc	12 May
Robertson, D. BEng	12 May
Collett, T. G. BEng qss2	13 May
Pullen, C. L.	4 July
Brooker, P. A. BEng	15 July
Checkley, C. C. T. BEng	15 July
Clarkson, J. E. BEng	15 July
Dixon, J. BEng	15 July
Dyke, S. J. BEng AMIEE	15 July

Keeling, A. C. BEng	15 July
Nash, J. S. BEng	15 July
Ponting, R. D. BEng	15 July
Taylor, S. M. BEng	15 July
Walker, G. J. BEng	15 July
Williams, E. D. BEng	15 July
Leech, A. H. qss2	25 July
Lusty, R. O. D.	25 July
Peeters, G. A.	25 July
Keir, R. H. BEng	5 Aug
Watson, J. D. BSc qss1	11 Aug
Burnham, R. E. BEng qcc	12 Aug
Cooke, A. J. BSc	12 Aug
James, P. BEng qcc	12 Aug
Beagle, T. qss2	3 Oct
Calder, F. J. qcc	3 Oct
Lowe, D. P.	3 Oct
Austin, P. R. BEng	7 Oct
Bremner, S. D. BEng	7 Oct
Stocks, M. C. MSc BEng	7 Oct
Thorley, L. D. BEng qcc	9 Oct
Mews, J. E. qsb qss2	10 Oct
Franklin, J. A. R. BEng	20 Oct
Harding, M. BEng	3 Nov

1999

Green, D. H. BEng qcc	15 Jan
Rodley, C. I. MEng qss	15 Jan
Sumner, L. D. BEng qcc	15 Jan
Whyte, E. BEng CEng MIEE qcc	15 Jan
Cooke, P. A. BEng	8 Feb
Goddard, A. P.	9 Feb
Hull, P.	14 Feb
Lamb, J. D.	14 Feb
Colledge, G. G.	3 Apr
Collis, P. H. qss	3 Apr
Dunn, B. J.	3 Apr
Higton, C. N. BEng	3 Apr
Place, M. J.	3 Apr
Potter, A. K. IEng MIIE qss2	3 Apr
Shrewsbury, T. J. qss1	3 Apr
Strachan, T. R. A. qcc	3 Apr
Styles, G. T. qcc	3 Apr

Sinclair, A.	4 Apr
Bolton, P. J.	6 Apr
Hartley, S. E. BEng	6 Apr
McBain, R. BEng qcc	6 Apr
Morfee, J. P. qss	6 Apr
Whitehouse, S. qss	6 Apr
Baker, A. J. BEng	8 Apr
Catt, M. S. BEng qss	8 Apr
Chappell, D. C. BEng	8 Apr
Crichton, I. A. B. BEng	8 Apr
Curzon, N. A. BEng qcc	8 Apr
Hansford, J. E. BEng qcc	8 Apr
Race, S. C. BEng qcc	8 Apr
Ralph, S. BEng PGCE ACGI qcc	8 Apr
Robinson, N. M. BEng qcc	8 Apr
Vickers, L. R. BSc	8 Apr
Peach, B. J. qss	5 May
Watkins, T. C. S. BEng qss1	13 May
Carrier, P. A. qss1	29 May
Rogers, A. qcc	29 May
Wood, A. J.	29 May
Waters, A. N. BEng	30 June
White, E. P. BSc	7 July
Barry, R. J. BEng	15 July
Chesworth, I. D. BEng	15 July
Hicks, A. B. BEng	15 July
Hutcheon, R. BEng	15 July
Jackson-Soutter, P. B. BEng	15 July
Jones, D. L. BEng	15 July
Kennedy, D. M. BEng	15 July
Lipscomb, P. R. BEng	15 July
Millne, P. E. BEng	15 July
Nicholson, M. S. qss1	24 July
Newman, I. J. BSc	26 July
Atkins, I. E.	28 July
Grigglestone, C. M. qcc	28 July
MacNaught, R. L. F. IEng MIIE qss	28 July
Timms, T. G.	28 July
Balls, R. J. BEng	9 Aug
Bradbrook, D. M. BEng	9 Aug
Neasham, S. BEng	9 Aug

Flight Lieutenants

1999—contd

Pescott, K. J. BEng qss1	9 Aug
Brett, S. J. BEng qss1	11 Aug
Moody, I. P. BEng qss1	11 Aug
Sidney, R. BEng qcc	11 Aug
Middleton, G. R. BEng	15 Aug
Attwood, J.	6 Sept
Neasham, M. A. BEng	8 Sept
Ellis, S. qss	2 Oct
Gellini, M. qcc	2 Oct
Greenslade, L. A.	2 Oct
Schoner, A. L. qcc	2 Oct
Skelton, P. J.	2 Oct
Tinsley, I. K. qcc	2 Oct
Ward, A. L. qcc	2 Oct
Williams, N. P. qss	2 Oct
Gilbert, A. MEng qss	6 Oct
Armstrong, N. BEng qss1	7 Oct
Coles, J. R. BSc	7 Oct
Dickinson, M. J. BEng	7 Oct
Gow, A. BEng qcc	7 Oct
Keenan, S. N. BEng qss1	7 Oct
Hayton, J. R. B Eng	24 Oct
Kirby, S. qss	4 Nov
Birchall, S. T.	27 Nov
Cox, B. N.	27 Nov
Ditton, R. J. qcc	27 Nov
Hill, S. W. qss	27 Nov
Jackson, D. R.	27 Nov
James, M. H.	27 Nov
Lambert, T. T. A.	27 Nov
Ratcliffe, J. D. K.	27 Nov
Rowdon, S. C. BEng CEng MRAeS qcc	1 Dec
Townsend, D. J. BEng AMIEE	17 Dec

2000

Follows, M. W. L. MEng	15 Jan
Rose, L. J. MEng BA	15 Jan
Anderson, B. M.	16 Jan
Taylor, M.	16 Jan

Bertie, J. J. E. MSc BEng	9 Feb
Fashade, O. A. BEng qss	10 Feb
Fawcett, P. W. MEng qcc	10 Feb
Young, S. E. MEng qss	10 Feb
Joy, S. D. BEng qss	11 Feb
Peters, C. J. BEng CEng MRAeS qcc	11 Feb
Staveley, M. D. BEng qcc	11 Feb
Trollone, S. M.	2 Mar
Francis, T.	4 Mar
Leighton, P. M. MSc	8 Mar
Dodwell, J. E. BEng	16 Mar
Barrett, J. E. B.	2 Apr
Bent, C. G.	2 Apr
Blenkinship, D.	2 Apr
Corn, J. A.	2 Apr
Elliott, E. J.	2 Apr
Garrad, J.	2 Apr
Holmes, D. P.	2 Apr
Jones, C.	2 Apr
Keen, S. D.	2 Apr
Rudge, W.	2 Apr
Searle, P. J.	2 Apr
Woods, D. K.	2 Apr
Flett, D. P.	4 Apr
Harding, N. qss	4 Apr
Haygarth, M. qss1	4 Apr
Parkes, D. W. qss	4 Apr
Day, S. P. BEng	5 Apr
Anderson, R. D. BEng	6 Apr
Harle, J. E. BEng qss	6 Apr
Newcombe, L. A. BEng	6 Apr
Radford, H. L. BEng	6 Apr
Adam, P.	28 May
Bell, S. J.	28 May
Hays, S.	28 May
Jones, R. E.	28 May
Lester, M. D.	28 May
Mullen-Cragg, A. K.	28 May
Palfrey, S. qcc	28 May
Patterson, M.	28 May
Simmonds, G. T.	28 May
Smith, B. J.	28 May
Smith, R. D.	28 May
Reid, D. G. BEng qss	30 May
Rose, P. M. BEng qcc	1 June
Baskerville, G. D.	23 July
Higgins, J. qss	23 July
Hawthorn, N. R. qss	25 July
Macalister, S. J.	25 July
Wright, H. L. BSc qss	8 Aug
Middleton, T. J. BEng	9 Aug
Bryant, G. J. BEng qss	1 Sept
Willis, R. L. BEng	25 Sept
Ahmed, M. A. qss	1 Oct
Steel, R. N.	1 Oct

Sweatman, G. G.	1 Oct
Malcolm, N. I. BEng	5 Oct
Martin-Jones, P. D. BEng qss	6 Oct
Mason, M. I. P. BEng qss	6 Oct
Clarke, S. D.	16 Oct
Barley, N. D.	26 Nov
Bartley, L. D.	26 Nov
Bryan, T. J. qss	26 Nov
Deakin, M. J.	26 Nov
Greensill, K. B.	26 Nov
Gundry, D.	26 Nov
Matthews, P. H. IEng MIIE	26 Nov
McKay, I. J.	26 Nov
Parr, L. C.	26 Nov
Reid, R. V.	26 Nov
Taylor, R. A.	26 Nov
Taylor, R. M.	26 Nov
Tuckwood, G.	26 Nov
Walton, S. T.	26 Nov
Black, D. C. S. BEng	30 Nov
Weekes, S. A. BSc	1 Dec

2001

Forsdyke, M. J.	12 Jan
Edy, S. M.	14 Jan
Grieves, A.	14 Jan
Bleakley, T. J. MEng BA	15 Jan
Edmondson, S. W.	15 Jan
Johnson, H. M. BEng	15 Jan
Lowe, M. C. MEng BA	15 Jan
Penter, D. A. MEng	15 Jan
Ruben, R. BEng	15 Jan
Tillyard, M. S. BEng	15 Jan
Ball, G. P.	4 Feb
Chapman, S. BEng	4 Feb
Johnston, D. J.	4 Feb
Bennett, N. P. BEng	10 Feb
Osselton, R. G. S. BEng qss	10 Feb
Hart, R. J. E.	24 Feb
Willis, S. G. BEng	8 Mar
Bevan, N. A.	1 Apr
Cox, J. E.	1 Apr
McMahon, J. D. BEng	1 Apr
Rushton, J. R.	1 Apr
Andrews, I. D. BEng	4 Apr
Price, N. E. S. MEng	4 Apr
Braybrook, R. E. BSc	5 Apr
Hide, A. K. BSc	5 Apr
Overthrow, J. T. Q. BEng	5 Apr
Sach, J. L. BEng qss	5 Apr
Pinder, K. BSc	27 May
Turner, J. S.	27 May

Flight Lieutenants

2001—contd

Critchley, N. J. MEng	29 May
Hayes, M. I. qss1	29 May
Pearce, S. C. BEng	29 May
Richardson, C. J.	28 June
Fitton, R. J. BSc	2 July
Madden, G. J. P. BEng	2 July
Rhymer, S. J. MSc BSc	13 July
Bolger, D. J.	22 July
Bright, I. G.	22 July
Brown, M. A.	22 July
Bryant, J. S. M.	22 July
Curran, P. A.	22 July
Fraser, P. J. IEng MIEE	22 July
Garth, M. A.	22 July
Gorringe, D. J.	22 July
Hoyle, M. E.	22 July
Nealon, R. H.	22 July
Quinn, C. A.	22 July
Cole, T. M.	24 July
Farrell, D. M.	24 July
Oughton, P.	24 July
Plumley, R. K.	28 July
Blackie, J. R. BEng	8 Aug
Evans, B. BEng AMIEE	8 Aug
Heard, G. A. BEng	8 Aug
Smith, N. D. BEng	10 Aug
McKenna, B.	25 Aug
Birchenall, R. P.	1 Sept
Burnage, S. P.	30 Sept
Chadwick, A.	30 Sept
Cowan, J.	30 Sept
Curran, D. A.	30 Sept
Elliott, P. G.	30 Sept
Flynn, S. T.	30 Sept
McAllister, D. J.	30 Sept
Munroe, I. J.	30 Sept
Pettit, M. B.	30 Sept
Riding, P. E.	30 Sept
Bath, G. J. MSc BEng	4 Oct
Crimin, M. J. BEng	4 Oct
Ellis, D. G. MEng	4 Oct
Thorley, J. O. BEng	4 Oct
Ede, J. A. BSc	5 Oct
Mustoe, K. J. BEng PGCE	5 Oct
Slater, J. H. BSc	5 Oct
Dark, G. D.	6 Oct
Hake, B. D.	6 Oct
Williams, R. J.	13 Oct
Cashmore, S. P.	25 Nov
Creighton, J.	25 Nov
Croson, S. A.	25 Nov
Dix, G. M.	25 Nov
Howells, G.	25 Nov
Kelham, L. J.	25 Nov

Podmore, J. V. R.	25 Nov
Rees, K. A.	25 Nov
Schofield, W. D.	25 Nov
Wood, M. R.	25 Nov
Hall, J. R. BEng	30 Nov
Latham, A. N. BEng	30 Nov
Smith, R. S. MEng	30 Nov
Fortune, J. H.	1 Dec

2002

Cooke, G. B. M.B.E.	13 Jan
Lynskey, M. F. BEM	13 Jan
Downing, A. M. BEng	15 Jan
Quick, M. D.	19 Jan
Akehurst, M. J.	3 Feb
Aldridge, J.	3 Feb
Carruthers, R. W.	3 Feb
Cawrey, S.	3 Feb
Cockerton, P. D.	3 Feb
Deakin, P. I. BSc IEng AMRAeS	3 Feb
Naylor, S. W. BEng AMIEE	3 Feb
Scott, P. A.	3 Feb
Clark, B. J. MEng	8 Feb
Cook, M. C. BEng	9 Feb
Lane, M. A. BEng	9 Feb
Ward, J. C. V. BEng	9 Feb
Arthur, P. R.	30 Mar
Barlow, J. R.	30 Mar
Mateer, J. E.	30 Mar
Welchman, S. J.	30 Mar
Worker, R. D.	30 Mar
Scott, M. N. BEng	2 Apr
Batch, S. M. MEng	3 Apr
Homsey, K. G. MEng	3 Apr
McKenna, J. BEng	3 Apr
Pearce, S. R. BEng	3 Apr
Smith, N. R. BEng	3 Apr
Winter-Goodwin, G. C. BEng	3 Apr
Wood, A. BEng	3 Apr
Budden, N. BSc	4 Apr
Gates, R. D. J. BEng	4 Apr
Parsons, C. BEng	4 Apr
Taylor, E. R. BEng	4 Apr
Mould, J. S.	24 Apr
Main, A. J.	1 May
Cokayne, I. M.	25 May
Cosbie-Ross, N. A.	25 May
Hill, M. D. C.	25 May
Jessel, B.	25 May
Lisle, S. J. BA	25 May
Parker, J. C.	25 May
Sweet, M. I.	25 May
Wheeler, J. J.	25 May
Bullerwell, K. V. BEng	28 May

Dexter, A. W. IEng AMRAeS	28 May
Ghataora, M. S. BEng	28 May
Parker, A. F.	28 May
Williams, Y. D. MSc BEng	28 May
Ashbridge, T. BEng	29 May
Jones, H. B. BEng	29 May

Flying Officers

1991

Dale, S. C.	17 Mar

1992

Quant, B. A.	17 Apr
Mackenzie, J. N.	2 Aug
Catlett, A. J. BSc	9 Sept
Lashbrook, A. A.	14 Sept
Large, A. J.	1 Oct
Smith, M. J.	2 Oct
Wilson, A.	27 Nov

1993

Thorne, M. A.	17 Jan
West, M. A.	22 Jan
Alden, M. D.	21 Feb
Sharp, P. R.	22 Feb
Edwards, M. D. BSc	4 Mar
Lewis, M. A. BSc IEng	13 Mar
McLoughlin, D. M.	6 June
Evans, J. R.	10 July
Sedgley, J. I.	26 July
Foulkes, S. J.	19 Aug
Cryer, S. M.	23 Aug
McAllister, N. J.	6 Sept
Conway, K. T. G.	16 Sept
Oughton, D. W.	1 Nov
Dunson, G. J. W.	25 Dec
Phillips, A. J.	31 Dec

1994

Griffin, A. R.	12 Jan
Smith, P. J.	20 Jan
Bell, C. G.	22 Jan
Monk, G. A.	31 Jan
Garriock, J. M.	27 Feb
Edgeworth, B. I.	30 Mar
Poley, C. A.	30 Mar
Williams, D. B.	3 Apr
Hedge, G.	4 Apr
Gilfillan, S.	14 Apr
Fisher, K. J. BSc	28 Apr
Jones-Lofting, D. J.	9 May
Forrester, D. M.	21 Aug
Smith, B. J. E.	25 Aug
Resoli, A. R.	11 Sept
Haddon, P. J.	15 Sept
Douglas, G.	29 Sept
Climie, A. J.	30 Oct

Finnigan, B. A.	10 Nov
Boll, K.	13 Nov
Ball, M. D.	16 Nov
Stocken, R. G.	20 Dec
Lewis, A. J.	29 Dec

1995

De-Vaal, A. G.	8 Jan
Morris, S. G.	4 June
Lilly, S. J.	24 June
Dixon, S.	27 June
Allen, I. BSc	8 Aug
Wright, D. C.	29 Aug
Lipscomb, R. J.	3 Oct
Whitecross, Y. E.	16 Oct
Roberts, M. A.	22 Oct
Doney, M. L.	1 Nov
Adamson, M. F. BEng	7 Dec
Wood, H. A.	11 Dec

1996

Hudson, S. P.	1 Jan
Thompson, R. L.	21 Jan
Grant, P. J.	24 Jan
Frost, D. A.	11 Feb
Spalding, E.	16 Feb
Lyons, C. J. BSc	13 Mar
Sanders, L. J.	18 Mar
Hillman, J. P.	12 Apr
Peel, A.	6 May
Kerswill, J. M. J.	26 May
Deith, S. P.	27 June
Bennett, I. J.	9 Aug
Thompson, D. M.	16 Aug
Woodward, S. P. T.	1 Sept
McCarthy, K.	27 Oct
Kerrison, D. S.	28 Nov
McGowan, T. R.	2 Dec
Darley, T. J.	14 Dec

1997

McIntyre, P. D.	28 Feb
Dingle, A.	29 Mar
Judson, R. H.	7 Apr
Gould, S. C.	15 Apr
Bull, J.	22 May
O'Sullivan, S. D.	26 June
Sanderson, A. J.	4 Aug
Wright, I. C.	4 Aug
Hannan, O. S.	11 Aug
Sweetlove, S. F.	4 Oct
Cudlipp, A. M.	16 Oct
Paton, B.	26 Oct
Anderson, L. M.	23 Nov

Eskdale, C. I.	30 Nov
Cameron, I.	9 Dec

1998

Marshall, D. A.	11 Jan
Shepherd, I. P.	8 Feb
Priday, R.	15 Feb
North, D. S.	19 Feb
Thompson, C. A.	16 Mar
Pearson, M. D.	29 Apr
Curson, D. C. BEng	29 May
Fortune, S. D. M.	3 June
Jones, I. J.	23 July
Warner, A. M.	23 July
Free, V. M.	7 Aug
Higgins, C. A. BEng	7 Aug
Sherry, J. N.	24 Sept
Askew, D. BSc	2 Oct
Pamplin, I. R. MA MEng BA	2 Oct
Kirk, A. I. C. BEng	4 Oct
Thrower, R. B. BEng	4 Oct
Belcher, I. C.	11 Oct
Joyce, T. M. BSc	28 Nov
Miller, D. C. BEng	28 Nov
Slack, R. A.	29 Nov

1999

Askew, T. BEng	15 Jan
Butterworth, M. C.	15 Jan
Feeney, C. H. MEng	15 Jan
Trapnell, B. P. MEng	15 Jan
Watson, C. S. BEng	15 Jan
Vogel, D. W.	21 Jan
Greenhill, K. J. MEng	6 Feb
Hornsby, D. MEng	6 Feb
Lively, J. P. MEng	6 Feb
Burgess, G. A. BEng	8 Feb
Hart, R. A. BEng	8 Feb
James, I. M. Z. BEng	8 Feb
Fenn, C. R. MEng	1 Apr
Hyatt, A. L. MEng	1 Apr
Robinson, J. BEng	1 Apr
Leigh, D. J. BEng	3 Apr
Reynolds, C. J. BEng	3 Apr
Salmon, J. J. MEng	26 May
Scott, A. BEng	26 May
Gorse, P.	27 May
Audus, A. M.	31 May
Downer, R. E.	22 July
Willmott, G. J. MSc BEng	1 Aug
Hadland, J. R. MEng	4 Aug
Jones, J. N. BEng BCom	4 Aug
Khan, S. L. BSc	6 Aug

177

Flying Officers

1999—contd

Williams, S. P.	8 Aug
Scully, K. N.	16 Sept
Vaughan, J. A. MSc BSc	27 Sept
Minshull, K. N.	30 Sept
Webber, K. A. BSc	30 Sept
Rowley, S. R. BEng	1 Oct
Dunn, S. A. BSc	2 Oct
Gambon, I. D. BEng	2 Oct
Mathew, J. M. BEng	2 Oct
Oatley, D. J.	26 Oct
Smith, P. K.	5 Nov
Barber, K. S. BEng	27 Nov
Forsyth, K. L. D.	29 Nov

2000

Banks, L. A. BEng	15 Jan
Clarke, M. J. MEng	15 Jan
Flynn, E. J.	15 Jan
Phillips, S. W. MEng	15 Jan
Price, R. J. MEng	15 Jan
Evans, C. L. BEng	6 Feb
Fitton, M. BSc	6 Feb
Harvey, D. J. BEng	6 Feb
Okwara, A. G. L. BEng	6 Feb
Roe, D. BEng	6 Feb
Wedlake, G. D. BEng	6 Feb
Calver, B. J.	10 Feb
Beynon, J. A. MEng	12 Feb
Cooper, L. M. M Phys	12 Feb
Matthews, L. MEng	12 Feb
Wheadon, W. J.	17 Feb
Sturcke, S. B.	22 Feb
Price, J. G.	24 Feb
Gibb, C. G. W. BEng	12 Mar
Chester, E. R. BEng	1 Apr
Hollings, I. P. BEng	1 Apr
Hollingworth, J. MEng	7 Apr
Lomas, S. J. MEng	7 Apr
Murphy, M. T. BEng	7 Apr
Pasfield, B. G. BEng	7 Apr
Raichura, A. K. MEng	7 Apr
Roden, I. R. BEng	7 Apr
Beirne, J. P. BSc	25 May
Cranswick, K. R. MSc	25 May
Sapsford, M. R.	25 May
Smith, G. C.	25 May
Stephens, J. R.	25 May
Humble, R. BEng	26 May
Armstrong, G.	20 July
Creppy, R. W.	20 July
Crowe, J. A.	20 July
Forster, D. T.	20 July

Frazer, R.	20 July
Hylands, R. P. BSc	20 July
Morrison, J. B.	20 July
Robson, P. A.	20 July
Wanklin, T. J.	20 July
Johnson, J. A. BSc	4 Aug
Lee, S. D. BEng	4 Aug
Norris, M. R. BSc	4 Aug
Way, N. A. BEng	4 Aug
Robertson, B. A. BEng	12 Aug
Croson, C. T.	28 Sept
White, M. J.	28 Sept
West, M. J. BEng	1 Oct
Pitelen, R. W.	11 Oct
Gaylard, C. J.	23 Nov
Sheldon, J. A. BEng	27 Nov
Batson, P. C.	30 Nov

2001

Shapowal, K. BEng	15 Jan
Nettleton, T. J. C.	25 Jan
Awoniyi, I. O. MEng	12 Feb
Burnett, A. W. BEng	12 Feb
Cummins, J. S. BEng	12 Feb
Dass, K. A. BEng	12 Feb
Hanson, D. M. BEng	12 Feb
Mackley, P. J. BEng	12 Feb
Raja, H. R. BEng	12 Feb
Symes, D. M. T. BEng	12 Feb
Riches, K. M.	8 Mar
Newcombe, C.	22 Mar
Holt, A. F. L.	29 Mar
Collingwood, A. S. BEng	7 Apr
Hasbury, R. S. BEng	7 Apr
South, R. BEng	7 Apr
Taylor, L. BEng	7 Apr
Venables, N. R. A. BEng	7 Apr
Wilson, M. A. C. BEng	7 Apr
Preece, M. G.	17 Apr
Done, A. J.	21 May
Fleming, A. J.	24 May
Skoyles, J. G.	24 May
Smith, B. M.	24 May
Lavender, J. J. D.	28 May
Martin, I. D.	19 July
Philip, C. L.	19 July
Waters, P. BSc	19 July
Robson, D.	4 Oct

2002

Barstow, C. D.	1 Apr
Boyd, J. R. BSc	1 Apr
Hayward, P. J.	27 May

Pilot Officers

1999

Potton, F. H. BSc	6 June

2000

Trundle, V. MEng	15 July
Pemberton, R. J.	20 Aug

2001

Goddard, S. W. H. MSc BEng PGCE	10 Nov
Brooks, L. J.	2 Dec
Brown, D. M. MEng	2 Dec

2002

Allinson, D. BEng	10 Feb
Bradford, L. P. BEng	10 Feb
Clarke, M. P. R. BEng	10 Feb
Cowdry, D. R. BSc	10 Feb
Eckersley, M. I.	10 Feb
Whitehead, A. T. BEng	10 Feb
Mayhew, J. J. BEng	7 Apr
Neal, R. P. BEng	7 Apr
Peel, G. M. BEng	7 Apr
Pink, J. MEng	7 Apr

SUPPLY BRANCH

Group Captains

1995

Armstrong, John Christopher MCIPS psc ssc Born 10/11/46 . . . . 1 Jan
Gaskin, Peter Patrick Victor OBE psc Born 23/10/47 . . . . 1 July
Morton, Glenn MCIPS psc ssc Born 2/12/47 . . . . 1 July

1996

Tripp, Robert Jonathan BSc MCMI psc Born 15/3/49 . . . . 1 Jan
Ovens, Allan Jefferson OBE BSc psc ssc Born 12/2/52 . . . . 1 July

1997

Cannon, Donald Bernard MSc BSc MCIT MILT psc ts Born 1/12/53 . . . . . . 1 Jan
Bernard, David Charles MBE FRAeS MILT MCMI psc qab ssc Born 19/7/47 . . . . 1 July
Miles, Philip Mark BSc MCIPS MCMI rcds psc Born 18/4/53 . . . . 1 July

1998

Thompson, Julian Howard MSc BA MBCS jsdc im Born 11/3/54 . . . . 1 Jan
Page, Brian Stephen psc Born 6/11/48 . . . . 1 July

1999

Babington, Jeremy Paul BA jsdc ssc qs Born 3/4/50 . . . . 1 Jan
Cromarty, Neil William psc ssc Born 28/4/58 . . . . 1 Jan
Wiles, Matthew John Gethin MBA MILT psc ssc Born 9/2/61 . . . . 1 Jan
Foster, David John MSc BSc psc(j) im qab Born 19/11/53 . . . . 1 July

2000

Blore, David John MSc BSc MRAeS psc ts ssc Born 29/9/59 . . . . 1 Jan
Simpson, Frank Michael BA MIL MRAeS ALCM odc(Ge) qs i* Born 16/1/53 . . . . 1 Jan
Williams, Robert Adrian OBE MA BA psc Born 16/8/59 . . . . 1 Jan
Humphries, Andrew Stephen MBA FCMI MIMIS psc ssc Born 2/6/49 . . . . . . 1 July
Knights, Jeremy Charles FRGS psc ssc Born 2/8/53 . . . . 1 July

2001

Belmore, Donald Sydney MBE MCIPS jsdc qs Born 6/9/57 . . . . 1 Jan
Leonard, Richard Graham OBE psc ssc Born 23/7/52 . . . . 1 Jan
Davenport, Anthony James Richard psc Born 7/4/54 . . . . 1 July
Faulconer, Edwin Jonathan MA BSc psc Born 24/2/53 . . . . 1 July

Group Captains

2002

Armitage-Maddox, Susan Elizabeth MBE qs Born 11/11/56 . . . . 1 Jan
Howard, Graham John MA MCIT MILT MCMI psc(m) ssc Born 29/8/60 . . . . 1 Jan
Primett, Martin Nicholas MA psc Born 24/3/58 . . . . 1 Jan
Archer, Derek Franklin MBE MSc MCIPS jsdc ssc qs Born 14/6/48 . . . . 1 July
Sheppard, Neil Allan MCIPS MRAeS psc Born 30/11/53 . . . . 1 July
Warne, Ashley Peter MA BA psc(j) Born 2/9/59 . . . . 1 July

Wing Commanders

1988

Thomas, J. A. ssc
qs   1 Jan

1989

Bolton, B. N. psc   1 July

1990

Hay, B. D. T. MCIT MILT
MRAeS qs   1 July
Hollands, S. A. MCMI
ssc qs   1 July

1991

Rushmere, P. A. MCMI
psc   1 July

1992

Grimson, P. MInstPet
MRAeS psc   1 July
Thompson, D. R.
qss   1 July
Thompson, R. V. MSc
MILT psc im ssc
qs   1 July

1993

Howlett, E. B. psc   1 Jan
Bennett, J. B. ssc
qs   1 July
Bushby, R. D. MDA BA
MInstPet MCIT MILT
ssc qs   1 July
Oldaker, R. W. BSc
psc   1 July

1994

Caunt, S. F. qs   1 Jan
Mahon, W. E. BA
psc(m) ssc   1 July

Norris, M. W. MInstPet
MRAeS qss   1 July

1995

Mason, A. J. MA jsdc
ssc qs   1 July
Patch, T. J. MSc BA
CDipAF psc(m)
ssc   1 July
Steiner, P. H. MILT ssc
qs   1 July

1996

Brierley, M. BA MILT
jsdc qs   1 July
Hicks, C. P. qs   1 July
MacLeman, R. BSc ssc
qss   1 July
Markey, C. R. psc   1 July
Martin, I. M. MPhil LLB
MCIT MILT MRAeS
CDipAF jsdc ssc
qs   1 July
O'Dea, K. L. MA MRAeS
MCMI psc(j)   1 July
Rowney, P. J. ssc
qs   1 July
Thomas, J. M. MSc BA
ts qss   1 July
Towler, A. J. psc
ssc   1 July
Veale, R. M. MDA BA
qs   1 July
Waldegrave, R. A. ssc
qss   1 July

1997

Palmer, M. W. BSc psc
slmc   1 Jan
Vose, W.L. ssc qs   1 Jan
Ashford, R. R. qss   1 July
Henson, S. W. jsdc
qs   1 July
Hewat, C. J. S. MBE qss   1 July
Moore, M. C. C. qs   1 July
Thompson, S. P. BSc qs   1 July
Williams, G. T. BA MCIT
MILT MRAeS qs   1 July

1998

Cannock, P. J. BSc
psc   1 Jan

Gell, A. T. MBA MA BA
BSc MCIT MILT
psc(j)   1 Jan
Thorogood, P. J. MA
MRAeS MILT psc(j)
semc ssc   1 Jan
Atherton, R. L. A. psc(j)
ssc   1 July
Forshaw, K. H. MSc BSc
MCIT MILT psc(j)
ts   1 July
Hubble, P. N. MSc BSc
MCMI psc(j)   1 July
Smith, R. S. MA BSc
psc(j) slmc   1 July

1999

Beanland, A. K. BA
psc(j)   1 Jan
Cooke, S. C. BA psc(j)
qab   1 Jan
Pike, J. MSc qs   1 Jan
Arnold, N. MA MInstPet
psc(j)   1 July
Bagnall, A. R. BSc ACA
ssc qs   1 July
Buckingham, A. E. MILT
ssc qs   1 July
Hadnett, D. T. J. qss   1 July
Laws, D. L. MBE MSc
BA DESEM MCIT
MILT MIL ts ssc qs
i*   1 July
Rice, P. BA ssc qs   1 July

2000

Attrill, M. P. ssc qs   1 Jan
Doherty, L. A. MBE
psc(j)   1 Jan
Hardwick, M. C. MA
MCIT MILT psc(j)
slmc   1 Jan
Luter, B. A. psc(j)   1 Jan
Parr, N. H. E. MCIPS
qss   1 Jan
Anderson, K. W. qs   1 July
Ayers, D. L. OBE qs   1 July
Baxter, A. D. M. qs   1 July
Dobson, G. A. qss   1 July
Farnsworth, A. D. MSc
MCIPS slmc qss   1 July
Finnegan, R. M. J. MDA
BSc ssc qs   1 July
Flippant, P. J. MA MSc
qs   1 July

Wing Commanders

2000—contd

Green, J. W. M. BA slmc qs i* i	1 July
Grimson, A. S. BA qss	1 July
Heaton, S. M. slmc qss	1 July
Higgins, P. MA BA psc(j) slmc	1 July
Hornsby, R. C. MDA BH MCIT MILT MCMI qs	1 July
Hughes, J. I. MSc BSc MCIPS MILT ssc qs	1 July
Kime, A. G. qs	1 July
Lester-Powell, D. M. BSc psc(j) slmc	1 July
Old, R. C. MCIPS slmc qs	1 July
Orr, D. J. slmc qs	1 July
Paterson, P. F. B. qss	1 July
Roberts, O. J. slmc qs	1 July
Selby, G. M. C. BA MIL DipEurHum ssc qs i	1 July
Simmonds, A. slmc qs	1 July
Thomas, H. qs	1 July
Weber, E. R. MSc BA MILT ssc qs	1 July

2001

Bessell, J. C. psc(j)	1 Jan
Harpum, S. P. MSc BSc MILT psc(j) ts	1 Jan
John, D. H. LLB BA psc(j) slmc	1 Jan
Maddox, A. J. M. qsb qs	1 Jan
Nichol, H. R. BSc psc(j) slmc	1 Jan
Boyce, C. L. MBE MIL slmc qs	1 July
Crockatt, S. H. ssc qs	1 July
Fitness, P. M. BSc qss	1 July
Green, M. D. qss	1 July
Hickey, S. D. MCMI qs	1 July
Hornett, M. C. G. BSc slmc qs	1 July

Huxtable, R. D. slmc qs	1 July
Jones, C. L. MCMI slmc qs	1 July
Laurent, C. L. T. qss	1 July
Morris, W. B. slmc qs	1 July
Palmer, D. J. ssc qs	1 July
Peacock, E. BA slmc qs	1 July
Russell, I. R. qs	1 July
Stark, J. P. MSc BSc ts qs	1 July
Swift, A. B. ssc qs	1 July
Thomson, D. B. psc(j) slmc	1 July

2002

Cook, P. G. qs	1 Jan
Honeyman, D. J. M. BSc qs	1 Jan
Mickleburgh, A. S. MSc BSc qs	1 Jan
Organ, J. W. slmc qs	1 Jan
Osman, M. R. psc(j) slmc	1 Jan
Picton, D. M. BSc MCIPS psc(j)	1 Jan
Serrell-Cooke, P. J. psc(j) slmc	1 Jan
Smith, R. D. BA qs	1 Jan
Stevens, N. W. H. BA psc(j)	1 Jan
Thomas, G. D. qs	1 Jan
Watson, C. W. MBE MSc MCIPS MInstPet ppetc qsb qs	1 Jan
Bleeker, J. D. MBA BA BSc MCIPS qs i*	1 July
Craib, B. L. MBA BSc qs	1 July
Gordon, R. G. H. slmc qs	1 July
O'Keefe, R. J. qs	1 July
Thomson, A. H. W. slmc qs	1 July

Squadron Leaders

1979

Storey, R. R. BSc im ssc qs	1 Jan

1981

Pickles, T. ssc qs	1 Jan

1984

Garstin, J. C. BSc ssc qs	1 Jan
Bolton, G. E. qs	1 July

1985

Bevan, D. L. ssc qss	1 Jan
Powling, B. F. E. BA im qs	1 July

1986

Thompson, D. A. qs	1 July
Williams, D. R. MSc BSc im qs	1 July

1988

Bentley, N. L. qs	1 Jan
Drake, I. P. BA ssc qs	1 Jan

1989

Beverley, I. M. MDA BA MCIPS qs	1 Jan
Fulker, M. D. qs	1 Jan
Henry, L. H. ssc qs	1 Jan
Morgan, A. J. qss	1 Jan

1990

Moody, D. B. qss	1 Jan
Parker, R. J. qs	1 Jan
Phillips, I. R. BA MCIPD ssc qs	1 Jan
Thompson, M. J. MILT ssc qss	1 Jan

Squadron Leaders

1990—contd

Gannon, D. M.	1 July

1991

Bacon, D. R. qss	1 Jan
Berry, P. W. MBE qss	1 Jan
Ward, V. H. slmc qss	1 Jan
Heslin, T. MBE MBA ssc qs	1 July
Watton, R. J. MILT slmc qss	1 July
Vincenti, M. N. MBE MDA BSc MCMI	11 Dec

1992

Coward, M. J. BA qs	1 Jan
Craib, J. A. MDA BSc(Econ) qs	1 Jan
Ford, M. S. MSc MPhil qs	1 Jan
Newstead, T. J. qs	1 Jan
Grogan, P. ssc qs i	1 July
Hall, S. D. B. slmc qss	1 July
Hannaway, P. MA qss	1 July
Howard, R. M. ssc	1 July
Payne, P. J. MSc BA slmc qs	1 July

1993

Dabin, N. R. S. ssc qs	1 Jan
Haywood, P. R. BSc ssc qs	1 Jan
Hardman, A. N. slmc qs	1 July
Smith, N. A. MDA BSc MILT slmc qs	1 July

1994

Beresford, M. J. slmc qs	1 Jan

Coller, A. J. MPhil BA MILT MCIPS MCMI slmc qs	1 Jan
Joseph, J. D. MSc MPhil BA MIEMgt MCIPD df qs	1 Jan
Sexton, G. MBE qsb adp qs	1 Jan
Treanor, B. G. qs	1 Jan
Arkle, N. BSc qss	1 July
Barbour, S. R. A. MSc BA MIL slmc qss	1 July
Gough, P. M. MSc BSc MILT ts slmc qs	1 July
Hill, C. M. J. MCIT MILT qs	1 July
Howlett, D. J. qss	1 July
Stone, T. MSc FCIT FILT MCIPS MRAeS im qs	1 July
Topley, N. E. A. MILT qs	1 July

1995

Gill, E. A. MSc BSc MILT MCMI CDipAF qs	1 Jan
Watts, D. BA MIL slmc qs i*	1 Jan
Young, M. P. MCIT MILT slmc qs	1 Jan
Brown, A. G. qs	1 July
Halliday, D. G. MBE	1 July
Hunter, J. M. MCIT MILT qs	1 July
Pey, P. G. DipMgmt qs	1 July
Phillips, A. B.	1 July

1996

Firth, H. V. qss	1 Jan
Fletcher, S. P. qs	1 Jan
Jones, K. S. qss	1 Jan
Ainsworth, A. M. MCMI DipMgmt qs	1 July
Berry, T. I. BSc slmc qss	1 July
Cole, D. qs	1 July
Dack, J. R. adp qss	1 July
Goss, C. H. MA MILT slmc qss	1 July
Hardcastle, O. E. qs	1 July
Hudson, P. A. MSc MCIPS qs	1 July
Pearson, J. M. BSc slmc qs	1 July

Sargent, B. BA MIL MILT MCMI qss i* i*	1 July
Woodward, M. F. qss	1 July
Wright-Cooper, S. J. F. MBA BSc MILT MCMI qs	1 July

1997

Clempson, P. qss	1 Jan
Colpus, M. R. MDA BSc MCIPS qs	1 Jan
Elworthy, B. J. DMS qs	1 Jan
Haseltine, S. J. MCIT MILT qss	1 Jan
Lee, R. G. MSc BSc MILT qs	1 Jan
McMillan, N. J. MSc MILT qs	1 Jan
Munday, S. P. qss	1 Jan
Mutton, P. A.	1 Jan
Porter, J. D. BSc AKC qss	1 Jan
Rolfe, A. W. MDA BSc MCIT MILT qs	1 Jan
Widger, W. J. MBA MILT MCMI slmc qss	1 Jan
Cowie, G. BSc qs	1 July
Dolan, M. C.	1 July
Ellis, J. slmc qs	1 July
Fogden, R. qs	1 July
Hughes, M. A. qs	1 July
Jones, S. D. BSc qss	1 July
Lory, G. I. BSc qs	1 July
Mitchell-Gears, S. BSc slmc qs	1 July
Poppe, A. N. BSc MILT slmc qs	1 July
Read, S. G. MBA MCIT MILT qs	1 July
Tranter, P. BA qss i* i*	1 July
Vincent, M. S. E. BA qs	1 July

1998

Barclay, E. J. A. MSc BSc slmc qs	1 Jan
Curtis, A. R. qs	1 Jan
Dunn, M. K. qs	1 Jan
Flint, R. MSc MILT qs	1 Jan
Hale, R. J. BSc qs	1 Jan

Squadron Leaders

1998—contd

Hill, R. MCIT MILT qs	1 Jan
Otley-Doe, C. E. slmc qs	1 Jan
Perryman, J. G. qs	1 Jan
Roberts, R. W. qss	1 Jan
Sharpe, S. J. A. slmc qs	1 Jan
Tempest-Roe, C. B. slmc qs	1 Jan
Henderson, T. A.	1 Apr
Crighton, M. BSc qss	1 July
Dainton, S. D. qsb qs	1 July
Duncan, A. W. BA	1 July
Grieves, D. J. MCIT MILT slmc qss	1 July
Howard, R. E. BA qs	1 July
Ogden, S. qs	1 July
Paulson, J. D. slmc qs	1 July
Smith, C. R. BA slmc qs	1 July
Sutton, R. A. qs	1 July
Tripp, I. M. slmc qs	1 July
Walsh, P. MSc BA MCIT MILT MCIPS slmc qss	1 July

1999

Bell, N. E. BA qs	1 Jan
Binns, S. M. BSc qs	1 Jan
Carlton, M. R. MSc BA qs	1 Jan
Killey, A. H. MDA BSc DMS slmc qs	1 Jan
MacPherson, C. J. qs	1 Jan
Allen, R. D. qs	1 July
Atkinson, N. F. MBE qs	1 July
Corby, K. S. MCIT MILT LCGI qss	1 July
Etches, T. J. slmc qs	1 July
Fisher, S. MA MDA qss	1 July
Flint, T. D. MSc MCIT MILT ts qsb qs	1 July
Jones, P. G. MCIT MILT qs	1 July

Musselwhite, J. BSc MILT qs	1 July
Tomkinson, P. qss	1 July
Turner, M. J. qss1	1 July
Williams, S. K.	1 July

2000

Barley, M. J. qss	1 Jan
Bowtell, C. MILT qs	1 Jan
Brewer, G. P. BEM qss	1 Jan
George, E. R. MBE MILT qss2	1 Jan
Hermon, E. L. qsb qs	1 Jan
Hutchinson, P. D. BSc qss	1 Jan
Large, M. L. qs	1 Jan
Morgan-Frise, F. T. qs	1 Jan
Mulholland-Fenton, L. G. ACMA qss	1 Jan
Wilson, K. J. qss	1 Jan
Barth, R. O. qs	1 July
Bewsher, J. E. S. MSc qs	1 July
Brambles, J. P. qs	1 July
Bridgman, P. J. MCIT MILT qss	1 July
Comfort, J. L. qs	1 July
Coughlan, J. R. MILT qs	1 July
Dathan, C. H. BA slmc qss	1 July
Dungate, J. MILT qs	1 July
Gannon, A. S. BSc qss2	1 July
Garnham, A. J. BSc qs	1 July
Harrop, D. J. BEd MInstPet qs	1 July
Heath, P. J. qs	1 July
Ireland, D. qss1	1 July
Jacobs, D. E. qss	1 July
Jinadu, A. O. qsb qs	1 July
Laurie, J. K. qss	1 July
Potts, D. J. qs	1 July
Talbot, D. J. qss	1 July
Vine, A. J. slmc qs	1 July
Wilkins, D. E. qss	1 July
Wright, S. Mck. qs	1 July

2001

Alexander, D. R. BSc qss2	1 Jan
Cole, E. J. qcc	1 Jan
Hawker, A. M. qss	1 Jan
Lloyd, A. R. qs	1 Jan
Morgan, S. J. BSc qss	1 Jan
Perkins, S. N. qs	1 Jan
Rowland, E. M. BA qss2	1 Jan
Shields, P. L. qss	1 Jan
Smith, G. N. qss	1 Jan
State, A. J. qs	1 Jan
Sykes, I. J. qss	1 Jan
Taylor, A. C. qss	1 Jan
Tomlinson, C. M. A. qss	1 Jan
Warwick, P. J. qss2	1 Jan
Wood, M. J. MInstPet	1 Jan
Adams, I. M. qss	1 July
Carroll, P. J. qss	1 July
Evans, R. D. MILT qsb qss	1 July
Licence, J. R. qss	1 July
Mahon, M. C. qss	1 July
Maple, G. C. MSc BA ts qss	1 July
Merrison, K. L. MInstPet qs	1 July
Newland, D. J. MCIPS qss1	1 July
Page, A. C. qs	1 July
Parry, D. W. qsb qss	1 July
Smith, D. P. BSc qss	1 July
Turner, C. R. qss	1 July

2002

Alford, S. L. qss	1 Jan
Burn, R. qss	1 Jan
Cooper, D. A. qss	1 Jan
Crossman, M. L. BEd qss	1 Jan
Dorsett, P. qss1	1 Jan
Duffy, S. J. qss2	1 Jan
Green, N. MCIT MILT qcc	1 Jan
Harrington, J. M. H. qss	1 Jan
Lansdown, M. L. E. A. qss	1 Jan
Larkin, P. J. BA qss	1 Jan
Lendon, G. D. C. qss	1 Jan

Squadron Leaders

2002—contd

Pratley, R. D. MA qss2	1 Jan
Reynolds, I. D. qss2	1 Jan
Waterworth, G. K. BSc qcc	1 Jan
Webb, W. M. qss2	1 Jan
Beeby, S. C. qss2	1 July
Burrows, T. MILT qss	1 July
Clare, P. E. BA qss	1 July
Davidson, N. qss	1 July
Durke, J. MILT qss	1 July
Hulls, A. P. MCIT MILT qss	1 July
Jones, K. A. qss	1 July
Keith, A. K. BSc qcc	1 July
MacKenzie, E. G. MILT qcc	1 July
Pratt, T. F. qss	1 July
Sawyer, G. T. qcc	1 July
Thurston, P. L. BA qs	1 July
Twose, S. J. qss	1 July
Valentine, W. A. qcc	1 July
Wilson, L. M. qss	1 July

Flight Lieutenants

1985

Hardingham, P. qss	15 June
Cope, P.	11 July

1986

Wilson, A. J. O. MILT AMCIPD	30 Aug

1987

Innes, A. G. BSc qss	31 Jan

1988

Bullers, P. M. BA qss	2 Mar

1989

Stanford, P. G. MILT qss	26 Mar
Dean, M. J.	26 Sept

1990

Caldara, S. BEng qcc	15 Jan
Aldhous, R. R. qss	21 Jan
Scire, J. P. qss	20 Apr
Sharples, V. C. BA qss	7 Dec

1991

Duffy, G. J. M. qss	21 Jan
Whitwham, M. D. qss	23 Jan
Grice, G. B. qss	6 Feb
Marshall, M. L. qss	11 Apr
Power, R. W. MSc BSc qss1	14 May
Christison, D. S. W. qss	28 Aug
Redgwick, C. D. MSc BA qss	12 Nov

1992

Almond, M. BSc MILT qss	14 Feb
Cumberland, M. J. MBA BSc MILT qss	15 Feb
Hale, S. L. BSc	5 May
Beach, T. E. BEd qss	12 May
Marshall, A. R. MILT qss	28 May
Grimwood, M. P. MILT	16 June
Tyre, G. J. B. BA qss	7 July
Davidson, R. B. qss	3 Aug
Rowlands, J. W. MDA BSc MCIT MILT ARCS qss	19 Aug
Burman, C. W. qss	27 Sept
Norman, G. J. BSc qss	2 Oct
Little, R. A.	2 Nov

1993

Gossow, S. D.	4 Jan
Sendell, C. W. J. qss	28 Feb
Bathgate, A. qss	31 Mar
Barclay, I. D. qss	26 Apr
Biggs, P. R.	11 May
Williams, M. R. qcc	11 May
Ward, J. L. BA qss	12 May
Forshaw, N. de C. qss	4 June
Cameron, J. D. BA qss1	7 July
Jones, G. R. qss	29 July
Johnson, K. qss	15 Aug
Lee, S. W. MILT	12 Sept
Wilcox, R. J. qss2	26 Sept
Bowsher, S. J. qss1	21 Oct
Udy, J. G. qss	23 Oct
Winks, K. MCIT MILT qss	7 Nov

1994

Rose, J. R. qss	13 Mar
Tissington, B. R.	29 Mar
Curry, R. J. BA qss	30 Mar
Alexander, G. C. qss	8 Apr
Louca, J. C. LLB qss	14 May

Flight Lieutenants

1994—contd

Farmer, R. M. L. MCIT MILT qss	16 June
Wober, D. U. BA qss	6 July
Bowen, S. M. qss	17 Aug
Heaton, D. C. BSc qss2	17 Aug
Smith, B. J. BSc qcc	30 Sept
Duguid, R. K. qss1	30 Oct
Davies, M. L. qss2	5 Nov
Jarvis, D. J. MBE qcc	10 Nov

1995

Veitch, C. C. DipTechEd qss	7 Jan
Jackson, I. A. MSc BSc MILT qss	15 Jan
Moss, T. S. BSc qcc	15 Jan
Wardle, S. J. H. MDA BA MILT qcc	15 Jan
Young, C. BA qss2	18 Feb
Prime, R. J. qss	22 Mar
Roberts, R. J. BA qss2	29 Mar
Giles, M. R. MDA FInstLM MILT qss	2 May
Rockliffe-Fidler, G. N.	17 May
Arnold, P. J. BSc qsb qss	6 June
Chilas, A. BSc qcc	6 June
Lambe, P. A. qss	21 Aug
Stutters, G. A. MILT	26 Sept
Logan, M. J. BSc qss	29 Sept
Smith, M. G. qcc	1 Oct
James, P. A. H. qcc	11 Nov
Matthews, L. A. MILT DipHE qss2	11 Nov
Ward, D. N.	11 Nov
Jones, N. A. qss	22 Dec

1996

Florey, I. BSc qss2	16 Feb
Mahony, P. A.	18 Feb
Reed, G. W.	26 Mar
Simpson, M. qss2	28 Mar
Randerson, A. qcc	23 May
Dant, A. C. qss1	9 June

Binns, J. S. MCIT MILT	23 June
Drummond-Hay, R. N. qcc	24 June
Henry, D. G. qcc	28 July
Robinson, J.	24 Sept
Topley, D. C. qcc	29 Sept
Campbell-Wood, J. S. MCIPS qcc	6 Oct
Hart, R. J. qcc	6 Oct
Fairgrieve, J. A.	10 Nov

1997

Rowlands, M. A. qss	6 Jan
Stepney, M. J. BA qcc	15 Jan
Williams, C. R. BSc qcc	15 Jan
Baxter, K. D. qcc	22 Jan
Nash, R. A. J. qss1	9 Feb
Doyle, P. J. BSc qcc	14 Feb
Collingswood, P. D. qss1	19 Mar
Frain, I. K. qss	26 Mar
Leckie T. M. qcc	8 May
Alford, T. E. qss	16 June
Curnow, J. D. qcc	28 July
Garnon-Cox, D. G. MInstPet MILT qcc	28 July
Thorne, C. J. qss	28 July
Brown, C. G. J. BSc qss2	13 Aug
Stewart, S. J. BSc qss2	13 Aug
Stuart, P. G.	14 Aug
McGowan, J. qss1	5 Sept
Casey, G. A. qcc	5 Oct
Haggett, P. J. qcc	5 Oct
Crewe, J. C. BA qcc	9 Oct
Lindsay, H. D. BSc	9 Oct
Rands, S. M. qcc	9 Nov

1998

O'Neill, A. J. qss1	4 Jan
Wilson, J. P. MA qcc	15 Jan
Wiseman, F. qsb qss	15 Jan
Munden, B. qss1	29 Jan
Corriette, R. H. qcc	8 Feb
Hampton, D. J.	8 Feb
Ingram, G. J. qss2	8 Feb
Kinloch, S. MSc BSc PGCE qss1	13 Feb
Taylor, D. C.	13 Feb
Crabtree, J. A. E. BA qs	14 Feb
Holmes, S. L. BSc qcc	14 Feb
Manwaring, C. A. BSc qss1	14 Feb
Ling, S. J. qss	4 Apr
Vaughan, S. M. P. qcc	4 Apr

Hodge, M. BA qcc	9 Apr
Rooke, J. P. qcc	7 May
Pook, E. A. qcc	29 May
Hamilton, D. qcc	19 June
Keith, C. S.	19 June
Langfield, G. qcc	19 June
Connor, P. MBE	6 Aug
Roberts, R. J. qss	6 Aug
Rogers, S. H. qcc	6 Aug
McGrath, T. E. BSc qcc	11 Aug
Yarwood, S. N. BA qcc	12 Aug
Andrews, N. J.	26 Sept
McComisky, E.	26 Sept
Morrison-Smith, S. BSc	7 Oct
Atkinson, V. L. BA qcc	9 Oct
Bullard, G. L. BA qcc	9 Oct
Hubbick, D. J. BA qcc	9 Oct
Stoneley, I. S. BA qss1	9 Oct
Bell, Q. L. qcc	11 Dec
Knight, S. R. qcc	13 Dec

1999

Hall, T. G. BSc(Econ) qcc	15 Jan
Baker, A. M. BA qcc	11 Feb
Chappell, S. J. BSc qss1	11 Feb
Sharp, D. J. W. MA qss	11 Feb
McGeary, G. P. BA	13 Feb
Presly, A. D. BSc qcc	13 Feb
Reece, L. P. BEng	13 Feb
Leigh, R. A.	14 Feb
Abbott, P. K.	20 Mar
Cane, P. J. qcc	24 Mar
Stewart. A. G. qss1	24 Mar
Hale, S. L. BA qss	6 Apr
Wheeler, P. J. qss	6 Apr
Barnes, G. A. BSc qcc	8 Apr
Benjamin, T. M. BA	8 Apr
Turnbull, J. K. BA qss1	8 Apr
Clulo, M. J. qcc	6 May
Craig, P. S. A. qss1	6 May
Atack, J. E. qss	29 May
Coughlin, K. BEng	11 Aug
Evans, D. B. L. BSc	11 Aug
Knight, C. O. M. BA qcc	11 Aug
Toye, S. E. BA qcc	11 Aug
Kane, I. F. qs	14 Aug
Eastham, J. F. A. qcc	19 Aug
Cameron, R. C. BSc qcc	7 Oct
O'Brien, P. J. BA qcc	7 Oct
Lindley, J. E. BSc	8 Oct
Fountain, M. J.	27 Nov
Jones, A. D. qcc	27 Nov
Brennan, C. BA	1 Dec

Flight Lieutenants

2000

Edgeworth, J. R.	16 Jan
Kirton, W. S.	16 Jan
Miller, J. J. MInstPet	
ppetc qcc	28 Jan
Baker, G.	5 Feb
Bayley, N. J. BSc qcc	10 Feb
Griffiths, R. G. BA	10 Feb
Brabner, D. J. BEng qcc	11 Feb
Davies, F. BSc(Econ)	
qss	11 Feb
Symons, J. A. BSc	11 Feb
Watkinson, S. J. BSc	11 Feb
Brown, D. D. MA	5 Apr
Clarke, P. J. BSc	6 Apr
Gregory, S. J. E. BSc	6 Apr
Grist, A. W. J. BSc	6 Apr
Smith, P. D. BA qss1	6 Apr
Sigsworth, N.	28 May
Smith, J. P. qss	28 May
Stait, T. C. qss	28 May
Harris, R. A. F. BA	1 June
Brown, S. J. B. BA	8 Aug
Stevenson, T. L. BSc	8 Aug
Gray, A. R. BA	9 Aug
Rogers, P. D. BSc	9 Aug
Fell, J.	10 Aug
Brooks, S. S.	1 Oct
Reed, M. MSc BSc	5 Oct
White, N. D. BSc	5 Oct
Doncaster, J. C.	7 Oct
Wilson, L. J.	26 Nov
Cruse, S. R. BEng	30 Nov
Barker, R. J. BA	1 Dec
Burcher, G. S.	28 Dec

2001

Males, A. C. BSc	15 Jan
Batey, T. J. BA	10 Feb
Whitnall, M. G. BA qsb	10 Feb
Fothergill, S. R. BSc	5 Apr
Moss, S. J. R. BSc	5 Apr
Tribble, J. L. BA	5 Apr
Grant, A. N. qcc	6 Apr
Huntley, N. J. A. qcc	6 Apr
Sheehan, J.	2 May
Buxton, P. G.	22 July
Degg, A. R.	22 July
Thomson, K. E.	30 July
Sadler, G. M. BA	8 Aug
McLuskie, T. A.	9 Aug
Lamb, A. L. BA	5 Oct
Priestley, J. B. BSc	5 Oct
Sadler, L. K. qcc	6 Oct

Jackson, C. J.	25 Nov
Organ, J. D. BA	30 Nov

2002

Moore, S. M. BSc	15 Jan
Whelan, G.	28 Jan
Spiridigliozzi, D. BSc	8 Feb
Gledhill, H. M. BSocSc	9 Feb
Shilvock, A. L. BSc	9 Feb
Tose, A. BA	9 Feb
Hall, V. C. J. LLB qcc	4 Apr
Cresswell, N. P.	25 May
Hainsworth, S. BSc	25 May
Steele-Benny, C.	25 May

Flying Officers

1995

Bell, J. H. D. BSc qss1	24 Nov

1996

Banstead, G. M.	7 June
Shelley, J. L.	15 June

1997

Taylor, P. S.	17 Mar
Millar, H.	15 Apr

1998

Unsted, S. R. BA	7 Aug
Kingsman, M. P.	8 Aug
Houghton, C. D. MMath	2 Oct
Scaife, N. MSc BSc	2 Oct
Higgins, J. M.	4 Oct
Clark, M. D. BSc PGCE	30 Nov

1999

Wheildon, M. B.	13 Jan
Jones, E. A. BA	15 Jan
Matthias, M. L. Q.	15 Jan
Oliver, S. J. BSc	15 Jan
Windridge, J. L. BSc	15 Jan
Motley, J. A. K.	25 Jan
Elliott, H. BSc	8 Feb
Emmett, D. T. BA	8 Feb
Evitt, S. L. BSc	8 Feb
Francis, G. M. BSc	8 Feb
Magenty, D. BA	8 Feb
Pratley, D. H. BA	8 Feb
Pugh, A. J. BA	8 Feb
Sardesai, S. S. LLB	8 Feb
Taylor, E. L. BSc	8 Feb
Caves, B. D. BA	3 Apr
Watts, S. D. BSc	3 Apr
Simpkin, P. R. BSc	26 May
Castle, A. M. BA	28 May
Myers, D. BA	28 May
Brooke, J. C. A.	6 Aug
Lobbedey, J. C. BA	1 Oct
Whitehead, C. J. BSc	1 Oct
Arnall, S. J. MSc BSc	2 Oct
Blackwood, A. R. BSc	2 Oct
Fletcher, T. H. BSc	2 Oct
Howell, R. T. BSc	2 Oct

Flying Officers

1999—contd

Matthews, R.	3 Oct
Ryder, E. W.	7 Nov
Staunton-Lambert, D. P.	19 Nov
Walker, V. L. BA	27 Nov
Allen, C. S. BA	28 Nov
Branton, J. A. BA	28 Nov
Maton, A. K.	29 Nov

2000

Alexander, S. M. BA	15 Jan
Stone, G. L. MILT	24 Jan
Hall, S. W. BSc	6 Feb
Bloomer, S. M. N. BA	1 Apr
Farrell, K. L. BSc PGCE	1 Apr
Luker, A. J.	1 Apr
Ross, V. A. L. BA	1 Apr
Holden, N. J. BSc	26 May
Braddick, B. G.	5 June
Hick, R. G.	20 July
Fielder, D. J. BSc	4 Aug
Jessup, S. BA	4 Aug
Burns, H. MSc BSc	1 Oct
Buttling, M. J. BA	1 Oct
Marshall, C. BSc	1 Oct
Bailey, O. T. BSc	27 Nov
Membry, H. M. A. BSc PGCE	27 Nov
Wharam, D. C. BA	27 Nov
McGeehan, G. L.	28 Nov
Watson, P. J.	28 Nov

2001

Capps, F. L. BSc	15 Jan
Baily, C. L. BSc	12 Feb
Chater, E. C. BSc	12 Feb
Cleland, S. E. J. BA	12 Feb
Middleton, R. E. BSc	12 Feb
Screech, R. M. BSc	12 Feb
Summers, M. J. H. BA	12 Feb
Wheatley, E. C. MA BA	12 Feb
Winters, B. E. O. BA	12 Feb
Wright, L. M. BA	12 Feb
Collins, R. A. BA	7 Apr
Davey, L. M. BA	7 Apr
Sharrock, M. R. BSc	7 Apr
Parker, R. L.	26 Apr
Merritt, P.	19 July

Pilot Officers

2000

Coombe, R. J.	21 Feb
Blair, G. J.	2 June
Wise, S. C.	16 June

2001

Jones, C. J.	1 Aug
Chudleigh-Warren, S. J. BA	2 Dec
Hills, E. A. BA	2 Dec

2002

Hamilton, A. J. D.	19 Jan
Bell, G. BSc	7 Apr
Claridge, D. P. BSc	7 Apr
Collis, C. S. BSc	7 Apr
Hale, A. R. BSc	7 Apr
Penwill, A. P. BA	7 Apr
Hubbard, A. K.	29 May

Acting Pilot Officer

2002

Croft, R. J.	4 Apr

ADMINISTRATIVE BRANCH

Group Captains

1995

Harris, Andrew BSc psc Born 12/8/50	(Trg)	1 July
Ingham, David Andrew OBE BSc qs Born 22/3/50	(Sec)	1 July

1996

Sherit, Kathleen Louise MA MSc CEng FCIPD MInstMC rcds jsdc ae qs Born 1/10/53 .	(Trg)	1 July

1997

Turner, Philip David James BSc FCMI FCIPD rcds jsdc Born 7/5/53	(Sec)	1 Jan
Bruton, Ian Frank BA jsdc qs Born 8/11/50	(Sec)	1 July
Evans, Christopher David OBE qs Born 4/4/48	(Sec)	1 July
Randall, Helen Mary jsdc psc Born 10/4/52	(Sec)	1 July

1998

Lilley, Stephen Patrick John MA psc Born 3/10/57	(Sec)	1 Jan

1999

Amroliwala, Feroze Fredoon OBE ADC MA MBA rcds psc Born 23/12/59.	(Sec)	1 Jan
Hibberd, Peter James BA psc Born 1/8/57	(Sec)	1 Jan
Leatt, Michael Trevor BSc psc Born 27/2/55.	(Trg)	1 Jan
Maxwell, Alistair Rennie psc Born 30/10/52	(Sec)	1 Jan
Urquhart, Morag Marjory Anne qs Born 26/6/49	(Sec)	1 Jan
Barton, David George BSc jsdc qs Born 20/5/55	(Sec)	1 July
Brzezicki, Michael Paul MPhil MIL qs i* Born 21/2/56	.(ProvSy)	1 July
Hodcroft, Peter Gerald Hugh BSc MBCS psc Born 14/7/53.	(Sec)	1 July
MacEachern, Ian James Ogilvie OBE MSc MBA BSc BA CEng CMath FIMA FCIPD		
FCMI MBCS CDipAF jsdc qs Born 8/9/52	(Trg)	1 July
Pearson, David Alastair Weech MHCIMA psc Born 6/4/49	(Cat)	1 July
Ware, Geoffrey qs Born 7/2/51	(Sec)	1 July

2000

Doel, Martin Terry OBE MA BEd psc(j) Born 21/11/56	(Sec)	1 Jan
Harding, Richard Anthony MA MDA BA FCIPD psc Born 20/6/57	(Sec)	1 Jan
Pollock, Alison Jane ADC jsdc qs Born 7/10/58.	(Sec)	1 Jan
Wheeler, Jonathan Kim OBE BA FBIFM MCMI psc Born 7/7/57	(Sec)	1 Jan
Davidson, Christopher Sinclair MA MLitt jsdc qs Born 13/7/55	(Sec)	1 July
Harvey, Ian BSc qs Born 27/5/53.	(Sec)	1 July
Scaplehorn, Edward John OBE BA MMar qs Born 21/9/51	.(ProvSy)	1 July
Wardill, Timothy Colin qs icc Born 30/1/48	.(ProvSy)	1 July

Group Captains

2000—contd

Waring, Martin Richard MA BSc FCIPD psc Born 2/3/56 . . . . (Trg) 1 July

2001

Hughesdon, Paul Jonathan FInstD FCMI psc Born 27/12/60 . . . . (Sec) 1 Jan
Innes, Ray Russell OBE MCMI CDipAF qs Born 6/12/52 . . . . (Sec) 1 Jan
Murray, The Honourable David Paul OBE FCMI MBIFM psc Born 8/4/60 . . . . . (Sec) 1 Jan
Paterson, Ross OBE BSc jsdc qs Born 1/6/61 . . . . (Trg) 1 Jan
Smith, Vincent MSc MBA BEd MCIPD MCMI AMBCS psc Born 27/2/58 . . . . . (Trg) 1 Jan
Blackburn, Stewart MBE jsdc qs Born 10/2/51 . . . . (Sec) 1 July
Heaton, Patricia psc Born 6/1/54. . . . . (Sec) 1 July

2002

Bale, Neil Trevor MLitt BSc MCMI qs Born 13/12/52 . . . . (Sec) 1 Jan
Cruickshank, Joan Mary odc(Aus) qs Born 9/8/56 . . . . (Sec) 1 Jan
Hollin, Michael Arthur MBE MInstD psc Born 24/8/58 . . . . (Sec) 1 Jan
Lackey-Grant, Robin James BSc scc qs Born 7/7/55 . . . .(ProvSy) 1 Jan
Nash, Paul OBE BSc psc(j) Born 22/12/55 . . . . (Sec) 1 Jan
Williams, Michael Anthony jsdc pfc qs Born 27/1/59 . . . . (Sec) 1 Jan
Gillingham, Nigel Kenneth OBE BEd qs Born 16/1/53 . . . . (PEd) 1 July
Knight, Stephen Colin MA FCIPD MCMI psc(j) Born 13/4/60 . . . . (Sec) 1 July
Ross, Jack Gregory MSc FCMI CDipAF qs Born 22/1/51 . . . . (Sec) 1 July

Wing Commanders

1987

Edgar, S. MHCIMA
qss (Cat) 1 July

1988

Shore, I. D. L. MIMIS
adp qs (Sec) 1 July

1989

Lindley, R. B. MCMI
psc (Sec) 1 Jan
Medford, A. W. BSc
qs (Sec) 1 July
Parkhurst, C. R.
qs (Sec) 1 July

1990

August, G. I. BA
osc(Fr) qs (Sec) 1 Jan
Codgbrook, M. A. C.
BSc psc(j) qab (Cat) 1 Jan
Salisbury, D. StJ.
psc (Sec) 1 July
Sharma, D. C. qs (Sec) 1 July

1991

Burdett, R. F. BA
qs (Sec) 1 Jan
Gracie, S. A. MA BA psc
i* (Trg) 1 Jan
Jones, M. H. OBE
qs (Sec) 1 Jan

1992

Bolam, S. F. MHCIMA
AInstAM(Dip) qs(Cat) 1 Jan
Harrison, R. J. BA
MCMI DPhysEd
CertEd psc (PEd) 1 Jan
Hayward, D. J. jsdc
qs (Sec) 1 July
Hill, C. J. FISM MCMI
qss (Sec) 1 July

1993

Spearpoint, A.
MCMI (Sec) 1 Jan

1994

Fox, L. MA psc (Sec) 1 Jan
Poyntz, S. J. qss (Sec) 1 Jan
Wood, S. C. MCMI
qs (Sec) 1 Jan
Bessant, L. R. E.
MHCIMA psc (Cat) 1 July
Britton, C. A. MCIPD
qs (Sec) 1 July
Codd, M. L. F. BEd
MREC qss (Sec) 1 July
Moore, G. J. P. BSc
DipEurHum
DipAppSS jsdc qab
qs (ProvSy) 1 July
Murray, C. A. OBE
qs (Sec) 1 July
Roberts, C. I. BSc(Econ)
MCMI qs (Sec) 1 July
Wilkinson, N. W. R. BA
BSc PGCE FCIPD
FCMI qs (Trg) 1 July

1995

Winstanley, T. MA MSc
psc (Trg) 1 Jan
Burkinshaw, D. A. MEd
nadc qs (Trg) 1 July
Parker, R. G. BA
qss (Sec) 1 July

1996

Castle, R. A. J. MDA BA
jsdc qs (Sec) 1 Jan
Mayne, J. P. BSc
qss (Trg) 1 Jan
Beaumont, B. J.
CDipAF qs (Sec) 1 July
Campbell, C. B. BSc
ACIS pfc qss (Sec) 1 July
Cato, N. A. S. BA
DipEurHum
qs (ProvSy) 1 July
Jermy, G. A. OBE
qs (Sec) 1 July
Taylor, M. W. BSc
qss (Sec) 1 July
Walker, B. J. qss (Sec) 1 July

Williams, G. A. OBE
psc (Sec) 1 July

1997

Andrews, J. R. MA jsdc
qs (Sec) 1 Jan
Barnes, N. J. BSc jsdc
qs (Trg) 1 Jan
Beet, N. P. MA BA
psc(j) (Sec) 1 Jan
Leggat, J. G. MA FCMI
psc(j) (ProvSy) 1 Jan
Melhuish, P. qs (Sec) 1 Jan
Taylor, C. M. FBIFM
MCMI DipMgmt
qs (Sec) 1 Jan
West, M. E. qss (Sec) 1 Jan
Bake, A. T. MDA BSc
qs (Sec) 1 July
Berridge, A. J. MA
psc(j) (Sec) 1 July
Cooper, B. OBE
psc(j) (Sec) 1 July
Dingle, A. G. FHCIMA
qs (Cat) 1 July
Fairbrother, D.
qss (ProvSy) 1 July
Harris, P. G. qs (Cat) 1 July
Hereford, P. J. OBE
(Sec) 1 July
Howard, S. P. FHCIMA
FCMI qs (Cat) 1 July
Leggett, A. E. MDA BA
FInstAM qs (Sec) 1 July
Milburn, M. J. BEd
qs (PEd) 1 July
Sagar, P. J. MBE jsdc
qs (Sec) 1 July
Wilson, P. A. qs (Sec) 1 July

1998

Bonell, S. E. BA ACIS
pfc qss (Sec) 1 Jan
Coombes, D. C. OBE
GradDipMS FInstAM
MBIFM MCMI
psc (Sec) 1 Jan
Harrison, J. MA
psc(j) (Sec) 1 Jan
Ogg, D. I. BSc
psc(j) (Sec) 1 Jan
Opie, G. A. MA MDA
BSc psc(j) (Sec) 1 Jan
Smith, C. L. MBE
psc(j) (Sec) 1 Jan

Wing Commanders

1998—contd

Archer, T. D. BEd
  qs   (Trg) 1 July
Branston, N. G. MBE
  BA FInstAM MIL
  MCMI psc i* i* (Sec) 1 July
Bray, P. L. BEd qs (Sec) 1 July
Court, S. J. MBE
  qss   (ProvSy) 1 July
Egerton, A. J. MA MBA
  psc(j)   (Sec) 1 July
Forte, C. B. qs   (Cat) 1 July
Greenwood, S. D. MDA
  MInstAM(AD) ACII
  qs   (Sec) 1 July
McCafferty, D. A.
  psc(j)   (Sec) 1 July
McMillan, R. MA MSc
  qs   (Trg) 1 July
Milroy, W. H. MA PhD
  BTh MCIPD MBIFM
  qss   (Sec) 1 July
Oxland, C. J. OBE ACIS
  qs   (Sec) 1 July

1999

Clark, J. J. qs (Sec) 1 Jan
Faulkes, J. J. MA
  psc(j)   (Cat) 1 Jan
Gammage, R. D. MA
  MSc BSc PGCE
  psc(j)   (PEd) 1 Jan
Haywood, M. W. MBE
  MA MDA BA
  MInstAM(AD)
  MCMI psc(j) (Sec) 1 Jan
Lee, G. MSc MDA BSc
  qs   (Sec) 1 Jan
Login, B. MA ACIS
  psc(j)   (Sec) 1 Jan
Page, M. L. GradDipMS
  psc   (Sec) 1 Jan
Parr, R. M. P. MDA BA
  qs   (Sec) 1 Jan
Pollitt, I. S. MBE MA
  MDA psc(j) (Sec) 1 Jan
Schollar, J. S. B. MDA
  MInstAM MCMI
  psc(j)   (Sec) 1 Jan
Tomlin, J. S. BA
  psc(j)   (Trg) 1 Jan
Fletcher-Smith, R. D.
  BSc qss   (Trg) 1 July

Horscroft, G. D. MA
  MSc BSc psc(j)
      (ProvSy) 1 July
Lewis, M. P. D. MSc
  MSc MSc BSc CEng
  MIEE CMath MIMA
  qss   (Trg) 1 July
Mellor, D. B. MA DMS
  CertEd pji qss (PEd) 1 July
O'Donnell, T. K. BSc
  FHCIMA qs (Cat) 1 July
O'Sullivan, M. P. BA
  qs   (Trg) 1 July
Roberts, C. S. MA MSc
  BSc psc(j) (Trg) 1 July
Roberts, R. W. qs (Sec) 1 July
Shackleton, M. J. BSc
  psc(j)   (Trg) 1 July
Simpson, C. BA pji
  qs   (PEd) 1 July
Thomas, A. M. MA
  qs   (Trg) 1 July
Tindall, P. D. BSc
  qss   (Trg) 1 July
Waygood, S. A. MSc
  BSc psc(j) (Sec) 1 July
Webster, M. K. qss
      (Sec) 1 July
Williams, P. R. B. qs
      (Sec) 1 July

2000

Caddick, R. P. MA
  psc(j)   (Sec) 1 Jan
Campbell, P. A. BSc
  qs   (Sec) 1 Jan
Cowell, R. J. psc(j)
      (Sec) 1 Jan
England, J. D. L. MBE
  LLB MCIPD qs (Sec) 1 Jan
Gibson, D. A. MA MA
  MIL MCMI psc(j)
  i*   (Sec) 1 Jan
Haughton, S. E. MBE
  BA psc(j) (Sec) 1 Jan
Hedley-Smith, P. C. W.
  PhD MBA BSc
  psc(j)   (Sec) 1 Jan
Hill, D. J. MA psc(j)
      (Sec) 1 Jan
Lyttle, R. E. MCMI
  qs   (Sec) 1 Jan
Pepper, M. S. MSc adp
  qs   (Sec) 1 Jan
Tomany, M. P. BEd
  psc(j)   (Sec) 1 Jan
Whitfield, K. H. MA adp
  psc(j)   (Sec) 1 Jan

Bale, M. A. BA adp
  qss   (Sec) 1 July
Dean, S. P. BA FICPD
  MInstAM qs (Sec) 1 July
Everall, N. D. qs
      (ProvSy) 1 July
Fidgett, J. G.
  MIISec (ProvSy) 1 July
Galloway, A. H. qs
      (Sec) 1 July
Johnston, A. qs
      (ProvSy) 1 July
Lacey, S. M. qab
      (ProvSy) 1 July
Lindsay, A. J. BA
  qss   (Sec) 1 July
Lindsay, S. M. MA BSc
  qss   (Trg) 1 July
Marden, V. J. A. BA
  qss   (Sec) 1 July
Marley, T. J. BSc
  qss   (Sec) 1 July
Martin, D. L. BSc
  qss   (Sec) 1 July
McDevitt, P. M. qs (Sec) 1 July
McLean, J. F. MA BA
  MBIFM psc(j) (Sec) 1 July
Peters, S. G. MCIPD
  qss   (Sec) 1 July
Reith, R. G. MA
  psc(j)   (Sec) 1 July
Shay, S. P. qss (Sec) 1 July
Townsend, P. A. qs
      (PEd) 1 July
Turner, D. J. qss (Cat) 1 July
Ulhaq, Z. BA FCMA
  qs   (Sec) 1 July
Whitmell, J. W. qs
      (ProvSy) 1 July
Wolton, A. J. qs (Sec) 1 July

2001

Chubb, M. A. MA BSc
  MCMI qs (Sec) 1 Jan
Flynn, K. G. M. BSc
  FCMA MCMI qs (Sec) 1 Jan
Good, J. BSc psc(j)
      (Cat) 1 Jan
Hill, A. R. FBIFM
  psc(j)   (Sec) 1 Jan
Johnston, S. J. MBE
  MA MREC qss (Sec) 1 Jan
Smith, C. M. psc(j)
      (Sec) 1 Jan
Spencer, K. A. BH
  psc(j)   (Sec) 1 Jan
Stretton, C. J. H. MSc
  BSc qs (ProvSy) 1 Jan

Wing Commanders

2001—contd

Taylor, P. A. BSc MBCS
adp qss   (Sec)   1 Jan
Tolfts, I. R. MA
psc(j)   (Sec)   1 Jan
Bate, P. N. qs   (PEd)   1 July
Bown, T. V. qs   (PEd)   1 July
Davies, J. A. BA
qs   (Trg)   1 July
Davies, J. C. BSc
DipAppSS qs
   (ProvSy)   1 July
Field, T. W. J. psc (Sec)   1 July
Heffron, M. D. MCMI
osc(Ge)   (Sec)   1 July
Lloyd, P. J. qs   (Sec)   1 July
Montellier, C. A. MCMI
psc(j)   (Sec)   1 July
Mountain, P. W. MSc
BSc CEng MRAeS
CertEd qs   (Trg)   1 July
Rabagliati, R. O. ACIS
MInstAM qs   (Sec)   1 July
Röver-Parkes, S. N.
MCMI qs   (Sec)   1 July
Smith, D. M. BA qs
   (PEd)   1 July
Spence, S. J. psc(j)
   (Sec)   1 July
Waterfield, B. J. FCIPD
qs   (Sec)   1 July

2002

Bray, C. M. qs   (Sec)   1 Jan
Bruce, G. J. MBE
psc(j)   (Sec)   1 Jan
Chadwick, S. P.
psc(j)   (Sec)   1 Jan
Godfrey, P. M. BSc
qs   (Trg)   1 Jan
Hunter, A. J. BA
psc(j)   (Sec)   1 Jan
Mackenzie, D. P.
qs   (Sec)   1 Jan
Radcliffe, A. J. MA
psc(j)   (Sec)   1 Jan
Tunnicliffe, G. MA BA
psc(j)   (Sec)   1 Jan
Williams, M. qs (Sec)   1 Jan
Clayton, C. A. M.
qs   (Sec)   1 July
Coombes, R. E.
qs   (ProvSy)   1 July

Evans, M. G. MEd
qss   (Trg)   1 July
Evans, M. W. BSc
MCMI psc(j)   (Trg)   1 July
Firth, M. H. MBA BA
MIL qs i*   (Sec)   1 July
Griffiths, S. C. BA
psc(j)   (Trg)   1 July
Holden, T. I. MA
psc(j)   (Sec)   1 July
McCafferty, P. qs (Sec)   1 July
Tench, I. R. PhD BA
qs   (Trg)   1 July
Vizoso, A. F. BSc
qss   (Sec)   1 July

Squadron Leaders

1980

Leech, T. MHCIMA
MCMI qs   (Cat)   28 Aug

1984

McBurney, A. E. qs
   (Sec)   1 July

1985

Gunn, D. C. E. MCMI
qs   (ProvSy)   1 July

1986

Donnelly, P. P. MA
qs   (Sec)   1 Jan
Makin, B. G. qss (Sec)   1 Jan
Melvin, I. BSc adp
qs   (Sec)   1 July
Walton, P. MSc BSc
ae   (Trg)   1 July

1987

Browning, C. J. BA
   (Sec)   1 Jan
Chown, B. A. qs (Sec)   1 Jan
Devlin, D. BSc CEng
MBCS ARSM qss
   (Sec)   1 Jan
Wright, E.   (Cat)   1 Jan
Asher, D. R. LLB MCIPD
qs   (Sec)   1 July
Johnston, C. W. H.
   (Sec)   1 July
Wood, C. R. LLB qs
   (Sec)   1 July

1988

Burton, A. J. MSc
MPhil BEd DIC
AMCIPD qs   (Trg)   1 Jan
Learner, P. F. G. MCMI
qss   (Sec)   1 Jan
Morris, P. J. qs (Trg)   1 Jan
Roberts, S. E. BSc
qs   (Sec)   1 Jan

Squadron Leaders

1988—contd

Smith, S. qss   (Cat)   1 Jan
Kenrick, M. C. BSc
  qs   (Sec)   1 July
Sharpe, J. H. MBE
  MRAeS MCMI qs
     (Sec)   1 July

1989

Ashton, D. C. MSc BSc
  qs   (Trg)   1 Jan
Bartlett, G. D. BSc
  qs   (Trg)   1 Jan
Brooke, R. BSc qs (Sec)   1 Jan
Erwich, K. M. adp
  qss   (Sec)   1 Jan
Muir, J. N. qs   (Sec)   1 Jan
Potter, D. N. R. MPhil
  BEd df qss   (Sec)   1 Jan
South, A. A. MBE
  DPhysEd qss   (PEd)   1 Jan
Rawe, C. J.   (Sec)   1 July

1990

Cowdrey, M. A. BA
  qss   (Sec)   1 Jan
Daughtrey, P. S. qs
     (Trg)   1 Jan
Green, M. D. BSc MMS
  ACIS pfc qss   (Sec)   1 Jan
Johnston, I. A. B.
  qs   (Sec)   1 Jan
Powell, J. B. qss (Sec)   1 July

1991

Brooks, D. R. BSc
  qs   (Trg)   1 Jan
Mackie, E. D. qss (Sec)   1 Jan
Ritchie, N. D. BA
  MCIPD   (Sec)   1 Jan
Walker, A. qs (ProvSy)   1 Jan
Wilmers, D. H. qss
     (Sec)   1 Jan
Banks, P. A. BSc qs
     (Sec)   1 July
Clews, P. J. MEd BSc
  qss   (Trg)   1 July
Finlow, B. H. BSc
  qss   (Cat)   1 July

Guthrie, J. M. BSc
  FInstAM FInstLM
  qss   (Sec)   1 July
Renshaw, S. MSc BSc
  qss   (Trg)   1 July
Swatkins, I. R. BA
  qs   (Sec)   1 July

1992

Brown, A. M. MSc
  qss   (Trg)   1 Jan
Clarke, D. C. qss
     (ProvSy)   1 Jan
Grant, K. F. MA MEd
  qs   (Trg)   1 Jan
Hermon, C. C. qs (Sec)   1 Jan
Kelly, P. G. qss   (Sec)   1 Jan
McIntosh, J. A. K.
  qs   (Sec)   1 Jan
Neal, N. J. MSc MSc
  BSc qs   (Trg)   1 Jan
Wookey, C. K. MHCIMA
  qs   (Cat)   1 Jan
Bacon, D. T. qs   (Sec)   1 July
Bellars, B. P. qab qs
     (Sec)   1 July
Cambrook, I. D. MBE
  MDA BA qss   (Sec)   1 July
Evans, B. N. qss   (Sec)   1 July
Harker, J. qss   (Sec)   1 July
Lee, M. K. MBE   (PEd)   1 July
Slade, J. P. MA BA qsb
  qs   (Sec)   1 July
Tyrer, S. qs   (Sec)   1 July

1993

Burton, A. J. MEd BA
  qs   (Trg)   1 Jan
Donald, R. qs   (Trg)   1 Jan
Warwick, N. C. qs (Sec)   1 Jan
Bryne, A. M. BA MCIPD
  qs   (Trg)   1 July
Harrison, J. MHCIMA
  qss   (Cat)   1 July
Leech, G. BA CertEd
  ACIPD qs   (Trg)   1 July
Williams, G. D. V. MBE
  qs   (Cat)   1 July

1994

Campbell, A. qs   (Sec)   1 Jan
Griffin, M. J. MA BSc
  PGCE MCIPD qs (Trg)   1 Jan
Heath, R. A. BA   (Sec)   1 Jan

Henderson, G. G.
  qss   (Sec)   1 Jan
Hutchison, B. BA
  qs   (ProvSy)   1 Jan
Jones, T. A. qss   (Sec)   1 Jan
McLintock, I. MSc BSc
  CDipAF qs   (Sec)   1 Jan
Ralston, W. MSc qs
     (Trg)   1 Jan
Sumner, E. C. DMS
  MInstAM MCMI
  qss   (Sec)   1 Jan
Tagg, P. MCMI qs (Sec)   1 Jan
Williams, D. V. BA
  PGCE MCIPD qs
     (Sec)   1 Jan
Williamson, I. D. qs
     (Sec)   1 Jan
Blanchard-Smith, R. M.
  BSc CertEd qss (Sec)   1 July
Chaplin, C. P. FInstLM
  MBIFM MCMI
  qss   (Sec)   1 July
Collinson, D. P. BSc
  DipAppSS qs   (Sec)   1 July
D'Ardenne, P. J.
  qss   (ProvSy)   1 July
Dean, S. MSc BSc
  qs   (Trg)   1 July
Exeter, D. W. BA
  qss   (Trg)   1 July
Forde, D. J. C. BA
  qs   (Cat)   1 July
Harvey, J. C. MA MIL qs
  i*   (Trg)   1 July
Hockley, S. J. E. MBA
  BSc CBiol MIBiol
  MInstD CertEd
  qs   (Trg)   1 July
Hopkin, R. A. BEd
  qs   (Trg)   1 July
Horton, P. qss   (Sec)   1 July
Jerrard, P. E. BSc
  qs   (Sec)   1 July
Kerr, R. A. qs   (Sec)   1 July
Lamb, J. A. qss   (Cat)   1 July
Lyons, D. E. MSc BA
  qss   (Sec)   1 July
MacTaggart, R. A. McL.
  qss   (Sec)   1 July
McCullough, D. McC.
  qss   (Trg)   1 July
Mitra, A. R. qs   (Sec)   1 July
Moos, F. J. BSc MBCS
  adp qss   (Sec)   1 July
Neild, J. R. qss   (Sec)   1 July
Perks, R. J. FCIS
  qss   (Sec)   1 July
Surr, R. A. BA qss
  i*   (Trg)   1 July

Squadron Leaders

1994—contd

Wallis, H. M. BA MCIPD		
qss	(Sec)	1 July
Walsh, A. W. qss	(Sec)	1 July
Young, M. qs	(Sec)	1 July
Youngs, R. A. DMS		
qs	(Sec)	1 July

1995

Atkinson, R. D.		
qss	(Sec)	1 Jan
Harris, K. A. qs	(Sec)	1 Jan
Little, C. BEd qs	(Sec)	1 Jan
Parkinson, W. N. MA		
BSc CEng MIMechE		
MCIPD qs	(Trg)	1 Jan
Reed, D. J. BA PGCE		
qss	(Trg)	1 Jan
Bain, D. D. BSc qs	(Trg)	1 July
Cobley, L. W. G. BSc		
qs	(Trg)	1 July
Kinvig, G. A. qs	(Sec)	1 July
Leadbeater, N. C. LLB		
qs	(Sec)	1 July
Mahoney, N. G. A. BSc		
qs	(Sec)	1 July
McGuigan, M. P. BA		
qs	(Sec)	1 July
Organ, M. J. BEd		
qs	(Sec)	1 July
Patching, C. BSc		
qss	(Sec)	1 July
Riseley-Prichard, J. M.		
BSc qs	(ProvSy)	1 July
Seymour, P. S. AIB		
qs	(Sec)	1 July
Warby, D. A. J. MBE		
MSc BEd MCMI pji		
qss	(PEd)	1 July

1996

Carver, L. BA qss	(Trg)	1 Jan
Collett, T. G. BA qs		
	(Cat)	1 Jan
Crowder, S. J. qs	(Sec)	1 Jan
Flatt, H. BSc MCIPD		
qs	(Sec)	1 Jan
Garwood, M. qs	(Sec)	1 Jan
Gough, A. A. MSc BEd		
qs	(Trg)	1 Jan

Highmore, R. A. icc		
qs	(ProvSy)	1 Jan
Mahoney, P. J. BA		
qs	(Sec)	1 Jan
McKiernan, C. J. BA		
MBIFM qs	(Sec)	1 Jan
Nicholson, A. S. qs		
	(Sec)	1 Jan
Read, R. C. MBA FCIS		
qs	(Sec)	1 Jan
Selway, K. qs	(Sec)	1 Jan
Stanfield, J. W. MA BA		
qs	(Sec)	1 Jan
Stewart, A. G.	(Sec)	1 Jan
Walker, A. BA qs	(Sec)	1 Jan
Weight, M. J.	(Sec)	1 Jan
Atkins, S. qss	(ProvSy)	1 July
Barlow, P. E. qs	(Sec)	1 July
Bowen, S. J. FIL qs		
i	(Sec)	1 July
Brinkworth, D. A.		
qs	(Cat)	1 July
Chant, T. J. qs	(Sec)	1 July
Clarke, P. K. BEd		
qs	(PEd)	1 July
Dickinson, C.	(Sec)	1 July
Erskine, J. W. icc		
qs	(ProvSy)	1 July
Fuller, M. A. qss	(Sec)	1 July
Kellachan, P. A. BSc		
qs	(Trg)	1 July
Lawlor, A. E. M.		
MHCIMA	(Cat)	1 July
Lock, D. M.	(Sec)	1 July
MacLean, D. A. qss		
	(Sec)	1 July
Reynolds, R. G. MBA		
BA MCMI qs	(Sec)	1 July
Roberts, O. D. BEd pji		
qs	(PEd)	1 July
Robins, P. D. BA		
qss	(Sec)	1 July
Webster, J. T. qs	(Sec)	1 July
Willox, K. W. qs	(Cat)	1 July

1997

Bolton, G. BA AdDipEd		
qss	(Trg)	1 Jan
Bulman, C. G. MBE		
qss	(Sec)	1 Jan
Chapman, P. W. BSc		
qss	(Sec)	1 Jan
Cornish, C. S. qs	(PEd)	1 Jan
Evans, M. A. BA qs		
	(Sec)	1 Jan
Jewsbury, M. R. MSc		
BSc MCIPD qss	(Trg)	1 Jan

Keetley, A. E.		
psc(j)	(Sec)	1 Jan
Kindell, H. D. BA		
qs	(Trg)	1 Jan
Lawson, E. BSc icc		
qs	(ProvSy)	1 Jan
Leighton, G.	(Trg)	1 Jan
Lunan, M. qs	(ProvSy)	1 Jan
Pearson, A. qs	(PEd)	1 Jan
Salway, J. E. BA		
qs	(Trg)	1 Jan
Tracey, M. A. BA ACIS		
qs	(Sec)	1 Jan
Wilkinson, K. BA		
qs	(Sec)	1 Jan
Williams, B. V. H. BA		
psc(j)	(Sec)	1 Jan
Cairns, S. L. BSc MCMI		
qs	(Sec)	1 July
Cunliffe, R. P. BEd		
qs	(PEd)	1 July
Curry, D. BA qs	(Sec)	1 July
Elliott, D. J. McC		
BA	(Sec)	1 July
Louth, J. P. W. BSc		
qss	(Sec)	1 July
McCracken, T. S.	(Sec)	1 July
Mulready, C. P. qs	(Sec)	1 July
Palmer, I. L. qs	(Sec)	1 July
Paul, R. J. BA qs	(Sec)	1 July
Prescott, K. qs	(Sec)	1 July
Seabright, A. J. MA BA		
qs	(ProvSy)	1 July
Sugden, G. H. B. MSc		
FIISec qs	(ProvSy)	1 July
Vincent, H. J. C. qs		
	(Sec)	1 July
Wheeler, M. qss		
	(ProvSy)	1 July

1998

Aderyn, A. A. MA		
qss	(Sec)	1 Jan
Anderson, P. W. MSc		
adp qs	(Sec)	1 Jan
Ashworth, D. R.		
MDefStud psc	(Sec)	1 Jan
Ball, L. P. qss	(Sec)	1 Jan
Beaton, J. E. BA		
qss	(Sec)	1 Jan
Bruff, K. J. qss	(Sec)	1 Jan
Daniels, J. C. BSc		
qs	(Sec)	1 Jan
De Soyza, N. A. qss		
	(Sec)	1 Jan
Fane de Salis, H. J. A.		
BA qs	(Sec)	1 Jan
Fiddy, P. C. qs	(ProvSy)	1 Jan

Squadron Leaders

1998—contd

Gracey, D. G. T. BSocSc
qss   (ProvSy)   1 Jan
Hobkirk, C. A. qs (Sec)   1 Jan
Hollingsworth, M. J.
qs   (Sec)   1 Jan
Isaac, S. A. BSc qs
             (Trg)   1 Jan
Jackson, P. A. FCIPD
qs   (Sec)   1 Jan
Jennings, R. MBE (Sec)   1 Jan
Morgan, A. N. MSc BEd
qab qss   (Trg)   1 Jan
Palomeque, A. G. BA
MHCIMA DipAT
qss   (Cat)   1 Jan
Peoples, S. F. MSc BSc
qs   (Trg)   1 Jan
Riches, A. W. MA
qs   (Trg)   1 Jan
Todd, C. W. BA
qs   (Sec)   1 Jan
Tudor, R. I. C. MA MEd
BA MCMI qs   (Trg)   1 Jan
Turner, M. J. qs (Sec)   1 Jan
Martin, M. J.   26 Jan
Ainsworth, M. S. A.
qs   (Sec)   1 July
Bell, N. J. D. qss (Sec) 1 July
Black, P. BA qab qs
             (ProvSy)   1 July
Carten, J. B. qs (Sec)   1 July
Doubleday, S. BA
qs   (Sec)   1 July
Dryburgh, D. S. MSc
BSc qs   (Trg)   1 July
Ellis, R. A. BA CertEd
qss   (Sec)   1 July
Gorman, N. R. BEd pji
qs   (PEd)   1 July
Johnstone, S. C. BEd
qs   (PEd)   1 July
Jones, A. qss (Sec)   1 July
Khepar, B. S. qs (Sec)   1 July
Loxton, W. T. BEd qab
pji qs   (PEd)   1 July
Marshall, P. J. qs (Sec) 1 July
McCord, A. A. BA
MCMI adp qs   (Sec)   1 July
McGill, A. qs   (Sec)   1 July
Mennie, B. G. qs (Cat)   1 July
Mitchell, J. K. H. qs
             (Sec)   1 July
Page, M. R. qs (ProvSy)   1 July
Potts, D. A. BA qss
             (Sec)   1 July

Stewart, D. E. M. (Sec) 1 July
Trollen, A. F. ACIS
qs   (Sec)   1 July
Wain, W. J. qss (Sec)   1 July
Wilson, A. R. BA qs
             (Sec)   1 July
Wood, T. H. P. qs (Sec)   1 July
Young, C. MHCIMA
qs   (Cat)   1 July
Butler, S. J.   (Trg)   12 July

1999

Bland, M. qss (ProvSy)   1 Jan
Coton, C. C. qs (Sec)   1 Jan
Doherty, J. N. qs (Sec)   1 Jan
Jones, W. A. qs (PEd)   1 Jan
Lamb, R. A. qss (PEd)   1 Jan
Loader, P. C. BEd
qss1   (Trg)   1 Jan
Mandley, C. J. BA RGN
qs   (Sec)   1 Jan
Mathieson, P. BSc
qs   (Sec)   1 Jan
Morris, I. J. MBE
CertFE   (Sec)   1 Jan
Newcombe, E. P. MA
CertFE qs   (Trg)   1 Jan
O'Shea, P. F. A. MBA BA
qs   (Sec)   1 Jan
Ousby, S. E. BSc qs
             (Trg)   1 Jan
Palmer, W. V. qss (Sec)   1 Jan
Parry, J. A. MA BSc
qs   (Trg)   1 Jan
Perkins, J. M. BA
qs   (Sec)   1 Jan
Petty, M. J. qss1 (Cat) 1 Jan
Sanderson, J. M. BSc
qcc   (Sec)   1 Jan
Smith, P. A.   (Sec)   1 Jan
Sunderland, S. J. E.
BSc qs   (Trg)   1 Jan
Sutherland, W. D.
qss   (Sec)   1 Jan
Wadsworth, S. E. BA
qs   (Trg)   1 Jan
Wright, N. D. qs
             (ProvSy)   1 Jan
Allcock, G. BA pji
qs   (PEd)   1 July
Bamford, R. qs (Sec)   1 July
Bell, P. N. BA qs (Sec)   1 July
Brooks, G. S. MSc BA
FRGS ACMA qss
             (Sec)   1 July
Brown, H. J. qs (Sec)   1 July
Bunce, A. R. BA qs
             (ProvSy)   1 July

Carter, S. G. qs   (Sec) 1 July
Cottew, T. A. J. ACMA
adp qs   (Sec)   1 July
Couzens, M. C. A.
qs   (ProvSy)   1 July
Crennell, J. qss (Sec)   1 July
Forbes, L. MSc BSocSci
MCIPD qss   (Trg)   1 July
Hill, J. S. MSc BA
qs   (Trg)   1 July
Hyde, R. M. BMus
qs   (Trg)   1 July
Jackson, S. J. qs (Cat) 1 July
Kelly, J. A. C. qs (Cat) 1 July
Lavender, M. D. qs
             (Sec)   1 July
MacAlpine, A. T. MA
qss   (Sec)   1 July
Marsh, H. MBE BEd
qs   (PEd)   1 July
McCormack-White,
C.   (Cat)   1 July
McSherry, P. BSc
qss   (Sec)   1 July
Meal, R. G. qss
             (ProvSy)   1 July
Miles, F. W. J. qs (Sec) 1 July
O'Donnell, N.   (Sec)   1 July
Suggett, D. M. H.
qs   (Sec)   1 July
Trevey, S. G.   (Sec)   1 July
Vaughton, P. A. qs
             (PEd)   1 July
Wallace, P. J. qss (Sec) 1 July

2000

Battye, A. E. BSc
qs   (Trg)   1 Jan
Buchan, E. M. BEd
qs   (Sec)   1 Jan
Cooper, J. D. BSc
qss   (Trg)   1 Jan
Cowsill, J. R. pji qs
             (PEd)   1 Jan
Day, M. BSc qss (Trg)   1 Jan
Ditch, O. qss   (Cat)   1 Jan
Doughty, A. M.
qs   (ProvSy)   1 Jan
Fancourt, I. J.
qs   (ProvSy)   1 Jan
Forster, D. BA qs (Sec)   1 Jan
Godsland, M. BEd pji
qs   (PEd)   1 Jan
Gorton, A. P. BA qs
i   (Trg)   1 Jan
Harper, S. A. qs (Sec)   1 Jan
Harrison, I. M. qs (Sec) 1 Jan

Squadron Leaders

2000—contd

Holcroft, K. M. LLB		
qss	(Sec)	1 Jan
Jardim, M. P. MBE		
BA	(Trg)	1 Jan
Lynch, B. G. BA CertEd		
qs	(Trg)	1 Jan
Moore, C. qs	(Sec)	1 Jan
Mountain, A. R. qss		
	(Sec)	1 Jan
O'Neill, P. E. MCIPD		
qss	(Sec)	1 Jan
Pilkington, G. S.		
qss	(Cat)	1 Jan
Ripley, B. E. qs		
	(ProvSy)	1 Jan
Roberts, A. R. MInstAM		
CertEd qs	(Sec)	1 Jan
Sloan, N. P. qs	(Sec)	1 Jan
Willis, S. R. MSc BSc		
CDipAF qs	(Sec)	1 Jan
Alker, M. A. BA qs (Trg)		1 July
Ball, H. J. qss	(Cat)	1 July
Bauer, J. C. MA BA		
qss	(Trg)	1 July
Beanlands, S. M.		
MInstAM(Dip) MISM		
MCMI AInstBA		
qs	(Sec)	1 July
Boyes, H. R. BEM		
qs	(Sec)	1 July
Burbridge, J. M. BEd		
qs	(PEd)	1 July
Chauhan, A. R. BA		
qss	(Sec)	1 July
Clucas, A. W. BSc		
qs	(Sec)	1 July
Cooper, J. R. qss (Sec)		1 July
Cross, L. qss2	(Sec)	1 July
Cullen, H. R. MA qs		
	(Sec)	1 July
East, R. G. adp qs (Sec)		1 July
Eichenberger, M. T. BA		
qss	(Sec)	1 July
Elliott-Mabey, A. V.		
qs	(Sec)	1 July
Fairbrass, P. MInstAM		
qss	(Sec)	1 July
Fyfe, P. D. qs (ProvSy)		1 July
Gavin, M. K. qss (Sec)		1 July
Hamilton, I. G. BSc		
qcc	(Trg)	1 July
Harris, A. W. D. BA		
DipMgmt ALCM(Sec)		1 July
Hicks, D. A. BEd		
qss	(PEd)	1 July

Horne, S. R. BSc qs		
	(ProvSy)	1 July
Huddlestone, J. A. BEd		
qss	(Trg)	1 July
Hughes, A. M. qss (Cat)		1 July
Hunt, B. J. MSc qs		
	(Sec)	1 July
McCleery, S. BSc		
qs	(ProvSy)	1 July
Morris, D. S.	(Cat)	1 July
Newbould, H. C.		
qss	(Sec)	1 July
Owens, P. J. qss (Sec)		1 July
Painter, R. E. PhD BSc		
qss	(Trg)	1 July
Richards, N. M. BSc		
qss	(Trg)	1 July
Rothery, W. BA qs (Sec)		1 July
Rowntree, R. A. LLB		
qcc	(Sec)	1 July
Scott, S. H. qs	(Trg)	1 July
Sexton, M. S. BA		
qs	(ProvSy)	1 July
Stacey, A. M. qss (Sec)		1 July
Stewart, G. K.		
qss	(ProvSy)	1 July
Sykes, P. qss	(PEd)	1 July

2001

Alvey, M. J. qss	(Sec)	1 Jan
Ardron, A. qs	(Sec)	1 Jan
Beech, J. A. qs	(Sec)	1 Jan
Bettridge, A. V. R. MBE		
qs	(Sec)	1 Jan
Bon, D. A. BEd pji		
qss	(PEd)	1 Jan
Bushell, K. J. qss (Sec)		1 Jan
Churchman, N. J.		
qss	(Sec)	1 Jan
Clarke, I. P. qss2		
	(ProvSy)	1 Jan
Collins, M. A. qs	(Cat)	1 Jan
Cook, J. A. qss	(Cat)	1 Jan
Cusack, E. P. BSc PGCE		
qcc	(Sec)	1 Jan
Dharamraj, S. J. BSc		
qs	(Trg)	1 Jan
Dorsett, S. J. qs (Sec)		1 Jan
Eamonson, J. M.		
qss	(ProvSy)	1 Jan
Egglestone, M.		
qss1	(ProvSy)	1 Jan
Gaynor, J. qs	(Sec)	1 Jan
Gilroy, K. M. qss1 (Sec)		1 Jan
Harrison, A. G. BSc		
qss	(Sec)	1 Jan
Headland, G. C.		
qs	(Sec)	1 Jan

Heathcote, A. J.		
qss	(ProvSy)	1 Jan
Heathfield, A. J. BEd		
qss	(Trg)	1 Jan
Larter, M. H. qs (Sec)		1 Jan
Maskell, P. BEng PGCE		
qss	(Trg)	1 Jan
McWilliam, I. A. B.		
qss	(Sec)	1 Jan
Morin, R. A. BA DMS		
qs	(Sec)	1 Jan
Moss, D. S. MSc BA		
qs	(Trg)	1 Jan
Murphy, C. M. MBE		
pji	(PEd)	1 Jan
Nicholls, B. A. BEd		
qss	(PEd)	1 Jan
Parkinson, G. E. MA		
BSc qss	(Trg)	1 Jan
Purdom, C. J. BA		
qss	(Sec)	1 Jan
Ratcliff, P. M. de G. BSc		
MCIPD qs	(Sec)	1 Jan
Rowlands, D. C.		
qss2	(Sec)	1 Jan
Sharp, R. A. qs	(Sec)	1 Jan
Smith, M. I. qs	(Sec)	1 Jan
Turner, D. J. M. qs		
	(Sec)	1 Jan
Ward, M. A. BA	(Cat)	1 Jan
Ackroyd, C. A. qs (Sec)		1 July
Appleton, M. R. qs		
	(ProvSy)	1 July
Bailey, K. R. BA qs		
	(ProvSy)	1 July
Brake, C. R. BSc		
qss	(ProvSy)	1 July
Braun, S. P. MBE		
MInstAM qs	(Sec)	1 July
Brebner, R. A. qss (Sec)		1 July
Chadwick-Higgins, S. G.		
qss	(Sec)	1 July
Clarke, R. M. P. G. BEd		
qss	(PEd)	1 July
Dole, W. E. BA qs (Sec)		1 July
Draper, L. M. LLB		
qss	(Sec)	1 July
Fowler, J. D. BSc		
qs	(Sec)	1 July
Freak, D. C. BSc adp		
qss	(Trg)	1 July
Fuller, A. D. qss (Sec)		1 July
Gibson, E. A. qss (Sec)		1 July
Gibson, S. J. qss2 (Cat)		1 July
Gillies, J. R. C. BSc		
qss	(Trg)	1 July
Healey, J. R. qss (Cat)		1 July
Hewitt, S. L. qss		
	(ProvSy)	1 July
Hill, D. J. qcc	(Sec)	1 July

Squadron Leaders

2001—contd

Holden, R. P. MSc MBA
BSc PGCE MCIPD
qs   (Trg)   1 July
Incledon-Webber, P. D.
qss   (Cat)   1 July
Kearney, J. S. BSc
qss   (Sec)   1 July
MacInnes, A. J. E. BA
qss   (Sec)   1 July
Manktelow, A. J.
qss1   (Sec)   1 July
Mason, T. R. BA
qss   (Trg)   1 July
McEvoy, D. A. T.
qss2   (Sec)   1 July
Moorhouse, R. W.
qss   (Sec)   1 July
Morris, P. M. BA adp
qss   (Trg)   1 July
Nicholson, S. qss (Sec)   1 July
Overton, D. G. BA
CPhys MInstP
qss   (Trg)   1 July
Peel, D. B. qss   (PEd)   1 July
Penelhum, J. P. BA
qss   (ProvSy)   1 July
Rice, P. H. BA qs (Sec)   1 July
Richards, A. C.
qss2   (Sec)   1 July
Salmon, D. R. qss (Sec)   1 July
Smith, M. G. qs (Sec)   1 July
Snell, R. A. MBA qs
      (Sec)   1 July
Spiller, A. W. J. qcc
      (Sec)   1 July
Stalker, A. D. J. qss
      (Sec)   1 July
Taylor, I. B. BSc PGCE
qss   (Sec)   1 July
Tripp, K. M. BEd
qcc   (Trg)   1 July
Walters, J. MBE qs
      (Sec)   1 July
Williams, K. D. qss
      (ProvSy)   1 July

2002

Bill, N. J. BA GradIPD
qcc   (Sec)   1 Jan
Bowie, I. J. qss (Sec)   1 Jan
Cook, R. W. qs (Sec)   1 Jan
Cox, K. R. BSc
qcc   (Sec)   1 Jan

Curwen, D. J. MSc BSc
MRAeS MCIPD
CertEd qs   (Trg)   1 Jan
Dempsey, K. C. qs
      (Sec)   1 Jan
Dixon, S. A. qss (Sec)   1 Jan
Ellison, A. M. qss2
      (Sec)   1 Jan
Fox, D. A. BA qs
      (ProvSy)   1 Jan
Glendinning, P. J.
BSc   (Trg)   1 Jan
Gosling, V. P. BA
qcc   (Sec)   1 Jan
Hannaford, G. E. MBA
qss   (Sec)   1 Jan
Hunt, A. C. BEd pji
qss   (PEd)   1 Jan
Lushington, R. D. L. BA
qss2   (Sec)   1 Jan
Martin, J. W. qss (Sec)   1 Jan
McMillan, D. R.
qss1   (Sec)   1 Jan
Mellings, N. A. BA
qss2   (Sec)   1 Jan
Moore, T. BA   (Sec)   1 Jan
Morrow, A. M. H. BA
qss   (Sec)   1 Jan
Morton, J. E. BA
qss2   (Sec)   1 Jan
Norris, R. H. qss
      (ProvSy)   1 Jan
O'Donnell, P. K. qcc
      (Trg)   1 Jan
Overend, D. T. qss
      (Sec)   1 Jan
Parkhouse, T. E. BSc
qs   (ProvSy)   1 Jan
Petersen, C. J. BA
qss   (PEd)   1 Jan
Prichard, K. A. BSc
qss   (ProvSy)   1 Jan
Sanger-Davies. P. R. BA
qss2   (Sec)   1 Jan
Sayer, J. P. qss (Trg)   1 Jan
Shieber, K. J. qcc
      (ProvSy)   1 Jan
Tanner, D. B. qss2 (Cat)   1 Jan
Thomas, D. G. MSc BSc
qss   (Trg)   1 Jan
Tullock, E. P. qss (Sec)   1 Jan
Watt, A. W.   (Sec)   1 Jan
Young, R. BSc qss (Trg)   1 Jan
Young, S. R.   1 Jan
Ashmore, G. J. BEng
qss2   (Sec)   1 July
Barnes, S. A. K. qss
      (Sec)   1 July
Barratt, W. T. qss (Sec)   1 July

Bellingham, A. BSc
      (Cat)   1 July
Burston, K. A. D.
qss   (Sec)   1 July
Butler, I. qss2 (Sec)   1 July
Cheeseman, N. D.
qcc   (ProvSy)   1 July
Cockerill, G. S. MIL
qcc   (Sec)   1 July
Connolley, R. J. BA
GradIPD qss2 (Sec)   1 July
Cooper, M. qsb
qss2   (Sec)   1 July
Cowley, R. L. R. BA
qss   (Sec)   1 July
Dalton, S. M. qss
      (ProvSy)   1 July
Dean, P. N.
AInstAM(Dip) (Sec)   1 July
Dunn, R.   (Sec)   1 July
East, J. S. BA qss2
      (Sec)   1 July
Galway, N. K. BSc
qcc   (Trg)   1 July
Garnett, I. M. BSc
qss   (Sec)   1 July
Gwillim, J. M. D.
qss   (ProvSy)   1 July
Hamilton-Wilks, J. L.
BSc qss2 (Sec)   1 July
Hartley, N. A. qss2
      (Sec)   1 July
Hutchinson, L. J. BEd
qss   (Trg)   1 July
Jackson, M. L. BSc
qs   (Trg)   1 July
Lewis, D. L.
MInstAM(Dip)
qss   (Sec)   1 July
Lumsdon, M. BEng
MBIFM qcc (Sec)   1 July
Luton, S. BSc qss (Trg)   1 July
Lyons, N. J. qcc (Sec)   1 July
McNamara, A. J.
qcc   (Sec)   1 July
Miller, R. M. BA qss
      (Sec)   1 July
Nicholas, A. K. qs
      (ProvSy)   1 July
Quinn, A. M. qss
      (ProvSy)   1 July
Read-Jones, A. M.
qcc   (Sec)   1 July
Rimmer, L. F. BA
qss2   (Sec)   1 July
Rowlinson, D. I. MSc
BEd   (Sec)   1 July
Saunders, P. C. H.
qss   (PEd)   1 July

Squadron Leaders

2002—contd

Savage, J. E. BSc
  qss   (Sec) 1 July
Simmonds, A. BA
  qss   (Sec) 1 July
Simon, R. J. qcc (Sec) 1 July
Smith, D. B. MSc BSc
  PGCE CEng MIEE
  qss   (Trg) 1 July
Walker, R. S. qss (Sec) 1 July
Wood, S. M.
  qss   (ProvSy) 1 July
Worsfold, D. L.
  qss1   (Cat) 1 July

Flight Lieutenants

1976

Dickson, W. H. E.
  DPhysEd pji (PEd) 29 Aug

1982

Walling, G. MA BA
  PGCE MCIPD qss
          (Trg) 14 June

1983

Cassels, J. D. MISM
  MCMI qss (ProvSy) 16 Mar

1984

Wilkinson, K. MA BSc
  CertEd qss   (Trg) 3 July
Revell, M. FRSA FCIPD
  MCMI qss   (Sec) 17 July
Morgan, G. R.   (Trg) 3 Aug
Heathershaw, C. M. pji
  qss   (PEd) 17 Aug

1985

Jarvis, R. A. CertEd (Trg) 1 Feb
Barrett, J. BSc qss (Trg) 19 Feb
Denner, P. O. H. BA BSc
  PGCE qss   (Trg) 30 Apr
Kerr, R. J. gw   (Trg) 3 July
Merrick, R. E. MCIPD
  AIB qss   (Sec) 17 Oct

1986

Ashton, C. C. BA
  qss   (Trg) 30 Apr
Bullock, C. G. qss (Sec) 19 July

1987

Griffiths, M. A. BEd
  pji   (PEd) 4 Jan
Cannon, M. J. BSc
  PGCE CBiol MIBiol
  MCIPD   (Trg) 29 Mar

Hemingway, C. J.
  qss   (Sec) 31 May
Amis, S. A. qss
      (ProvSy) 4 July

1988

Kirman, C. K.   (Sec) 26 Apr
Stanyon, P. BSc CertFE
  qss   (Trg) 19 June
Shuttleworth, M. R.
  MSc BEd qss (PEd) 14 Sept
Colgan, A. J. BEd
  qcc   (PEd) 10 Nov

1989

Buchanan, N. J. BEd
  qss   (PEd) 7 Mar
Manders, N. R. BSc
  qss   (Trg) 21 Mar
Bailey, J. P. BSc
  CertEd   (Trg) 1 Apr
George, R. M. A. pji
  qss   (PEd) 1 Aug
Keane, C. BSc adp
  qss   (Trg) 1 Aug
Brown, G. BEd
  qss   (PEd) 18 Aug
Bateman, S. A. BH
  PGCE qss   (Trg) 7 Dec
Kendell, M. R. J. B.
      (Sec) 19 Dec

1990

Snape, C. J. S.
  qss1   (Sec) 3 Feb
Finneran, M. A.
  qs   (Sec) 4 Feb
Jarvis, S. N. P. BEd pji
  qss   (PEd) 14 Feb
Burns, P. BSc (Trg) 20 Feb
Paveley, D. J. BA
  qss   (PEd) 11 Apr
Rayfield, P. R. BA
  qss2   (Trg) 4 June
Bryce, S. BA pji qss
      (PEd) 8 July
Ward, J. M. MSc BSc
  PGCE qss   (Trg) 1 Dec
Potts, A. J. qss (Cat) 22 Dec

Flight Lieutenants

1991

Bissell, R. J. BA
  qss   (ProvSy) 8 Jan
Marshall, I. G. BSc
  qss   (Trg) 19 Jan
Taylor, S. qss (Sec) 19 Jan
Warren, D. R. qss (Sec) 19 Jan
Scott, S. C. W. MBA
  MHCIMA qss (Cat) 27 Jan
Conning, T. F. BA (Trg) 28 Feb
Adams, M. P. BSc (Sec) 1 Mar
Gillies, R. L. MA
  qcc   (Trg) 25 Mar
Williams, S. G. BA
  CertEd qcc (PEd) 12 May
Dyson, P. J. qss (Cat) 19 July
Jamieson, B. W. BSc
  qss   (Sec) 3 Aug
Dunn, J. J. BEd
  qss   (PEd) 27 Sept
Logsdon, C. L.
  MHCIMA qss (Cat) 7 Dec

1992

Dalby, R. P. BSc
  PGCE   (Trg) 19 Feb
Seaton, A. D. I. BSc
  PGCE qss   (PEd) 20 Feb
Wiener, J. S. adp (Sec) 29 Mar
Armstrong, B. L.
  qss   (Sec) 7 June
MacDonald, A. R.
  qss   (Sec) 22 June
Jones, M. G. BSc adp
  qss   (Trg) 6 July
Tribe, D. M. MInstAM
  MCMI DipMgmt
  qss   (Sec) 19 July
Pollock, D. M. (Trg) 12 Sept
Sharpe, S. R. MBA
  MCIPD MCMI (Trg) 27 Sept
Parker, K. L. MSc
  qss   (Trg) 10 Oct
Dickinson, K. (PEd) 2 Nov
Harwood, R. W. (Sec) 2 Nov
Ramsey, B. P. qss (Sec) 8 Nov
Jones, W. A. BEd
  qss   (ProvSy) 11 Nov
Heffer, R. J. MA (Trg) 13 Nov
Whitty, M. A. BA
  qss   (Sec) 14 Nov

1993

Balmer, M. T. qss (Sec) 24 Jan
Leckenby, D. BA
  qss   (Sec) 19 Feb
Barry, S. qss (ProvSy) 11 Mar
Johnston, G. A.
  qss   (ProvSy) 11 Mar
Rich, K. L. qss (Cat) 27 Mar
Ellis, M. J. BEd pji
  qss2   (PEd) 30 Mar
Norey, M. BA qs (Trg) 1 Apr
Parker, J. R. qss (Sec) 23 Apr
Halliday, R. J. qss (Sec) 9 May
Faulkner, N. (ProvSy) 11 May
Simmonds, J. R. MBA
  BA pji qss (PEd) 11 May
Booth, R. J. BEd pji
  qss   (PEd) 12 May
Wright, S. qss (ProvSy) 12 May
Davies, J. A. qcc (Trg) 27 June
Turner, K. A. BA
  qcc   (Trg) 6 July
McKeen, P. W. qss(Sec) 29 July
Oswald, N. G. pji
  qss1   (PEd) 29 July
King, I. D. qss (Sec) 21 Aug
Rossiter, G. A.
  qss   (Sec) 21 Aug
Yarwood, J. T.
  qcc   (ProvSy) 26 Aug
Wotton, R. E. qss (PEd) 28 Sept
Kay, C. J. BA (Trg) 30 Nov

1994

Sheppard, R. MA BA
  qss   (Trg) 8 Jan
Hebden, M. A. BA
  PGCE qss   (Trg) 18 Feb
McFetrich, M. S. BSc
  MCIPD MHCIMA
  qss2   (Trg) 18 Feb
Lawrence, C. S. BA
  qss   (ProvSy) 19 Feb
Turner, B. A. (ProvSy) 23 Feb
Thomson, W. J. BEd
  qcc   25 Feb
Rignall, A. J. (Sec) 7 Mar
Greaves, J. M. BA
  qss2   (Trg) 29 Mar
Parr, S. E. (Sec) 3 Apr
Wright, I. N. BSc
  qcc   (Sec) 10 May
Bogg, A. BSc qss (Trg) 11 May
Perry, K. W. BSc
  qss   (Sec) 11 May
Evans, T. J. qcc (Cat) 2 July

Hayes, M. J. BA
  qss2   (Sec) 5 July
Wardle, C. R. BSc
  qss2   (Cat) 5 July
Searles, S. M. qss (Sec) 30 July
Bayliss, D. G. (Sec) 2 Aug
McCormack-White, P.
  A.   (Cat) 2 Aug
Williams, D. BSc PGCE
  qss1   (Trg) 29 Sept
Marsh, D. W. R. BSc
  pji   (PEd) 30 Sept
Gerry, S. T. qss (Sec) 23 Oct
Dixon, M. C. qss
        (ProvSy) 30 Nov

1995

Bishop, J. N. qcc (Cat) 7 Jan
Cleary, D. J. BSocSc
  qss   (Sec) 15 Jan
Scott, A. E. M. qcc
        (Sec) 11 Feb
Peebles, L. D. BEd
  qcc   (Trg) 16 Feb
Burton, A. D. BSc
  qss   (Sec) 18 Feb
Chipperfield, G. A. BA
  qss   (Trg) 18 Feb
Taylor, D. A. qss (Sec) 8 Mar
Barnes, C. R. qss1
        (ProvSy) 19 Mar
Wyeth, G. L. BSc
  qss2   (Sec) 29 Mar
Ratcliffe, H. C. (Sec) 15 Apr
Rodrigues, V. E.
  BSc   (Trg) 29 May
Wannell, H. M. qcc(Sec) 9 June
Ricks, I. J. BA (Trg) 4 July
Jenkins, A. G. L.
       (ProvSy) 9 July
Gulliver, A. D. qss (Sec) 19 July
MacDonald, P. D.
  qss2   (Sec) 19 July
Dawling, R. I. RVM
        (Cat) 28 July
Gadbury, T. M. qcc
        (Sec) 28 July
Jones, A. G. qcc (Trg) 28 July
Marshall, A. P. (Cat) 28 July
Mitchell, P. W. (ProvSy) 29 July
McAlpine, R. D. BA
  qcc   (Trg) 8 Aug
Clayton, N. J. BSc
  qss1   (Sec) 14 Aug
Bell, A. qss (ProvSy) 18 Aug
Gange, D. K. pji
  qss1   (PEd) 26 Sept

Flight Lieutenants

1995—contd

Hindmarsh, H. C. BA
  DipEurHum qss (Sec) 30 Sept
Parlor, S M. (PEd) 4 Oct
Armitage, G. J.
  qss (Trg) 7 Oct
Myers, M. (Sec) 11 Nov
Wright, J. M. BSc
  qcc (Sec) 15 Nov
Brown, A. D. qss2 (Sec) 20 Dec
Logan, S. W.
  qss2 (ProvSy) 22 Dec

1996

Treweek, A. J. MSc
  qss1 (PEd) 2 Jan
Davies, J. A. qcc (Sec) 6 Jan
Schollar, A. D. B.
  qcc (ProvSy) 6 Jan
Gillespie, A. J. qss
  (ProvSy) 19 Jan
Bowditch, M. qss2
  (Sec) 27 Jan
Taylor, D. L. BA (Trg) 31 Jan
Gunther, J. C. BSc
  qss1 (Trg) 11 Feb
Pettit, B. W. qss (Trg) 12 Feb
Mitchell, A. K. BSc
  qcc (Trg) 16 Feb
Parker, C. qcc (Sec) 9 Mar
Best, M. C. (Sec) 15 Mar
Serrell-Cooke, T. BSc
  qcc (Sec) 2 Apr
Pruden, J. R. BA (Trg) 10 Apr
Welborn, J. M. BA
  qss1 (Sec) 10 Apr
Brittain, N. C. J. BA
  qss (Sec) 11 Apr
Corbett, G. BA qss1
  (Sec) 11 Apr
Stewart, D. E. BA ALCM
  qss2 (Sec) 12 Apr
Parkins, E. A. qss2
  (ProvSy) 26 May
McLafferty, G. BSc
  qcc (Sec) 6 June
Harrison, R. J. T.
  qcc (ProvSy) 21 June
Roulston, S. P. (ProvSy) 28 July
Phipps, K. H. BA (Sec) 1 Aug
Adams, J. E. BA
  qss1 (Sec) 14 Aug
Disley, J. BA (ProvSy) 14 Aug

Haskell, S. L. MBA BA
  DipMgmt qss1
  (ProvSy) 14 Aug
McEwan-Lyon, S. R.
  MBA BA (Sec) 14 Aug
Thacker, S. L. McD.
  qss2 (Sec) 15 Aug
Coombes, C. A. qcc
  (Sec) 29 Sept
Adey, D. D. qs (Sec) 6 Oct
Akred, R. L. qss1 (Sec) 6 Oct
Beer, P. qss2 (Sec) 6 Oct
Brickwood, R. P. (Trg) 6 Oct
Cross, N. G. qcc (Trg) 6 Oct
Hall, J. T. BEng qcc
  (Trg) 9 Oct
Brown, J. T. BA qcc
  (Sec) 10 Oct
Corbould, R. J. BA BA
  qcc (Sec) 10 Oct
Griffiths, N. R. BA
  qss2 (Ed) 10 Oct
Rea, S. K. BA qss2
  (Sec) 10 Oct
Sanger-Davies, C. J.
  BSc qcc (Trg) 10 Oct
Wilson, S. J. BA
  qss2 (Sec) 10 Oct
Michael, T. J. BSc (Sec) 29 Oct
Gillespie, A. L. qcc
  (Sec) 10 Nov
Blakeley, P. qss1 (Sec) 21 Nov
Barrett, M. E. MA (Trg) 30 Nov
Thompson, D. E. BA
  qcc (Trg) 7 Dec
Petticrew, G. A adp
  qcc (Sec) 21 Dec

1997

Alabaster, M. J. BSc
  qss2 (ProvSy) 15 Jan
Burns, A. S. BSc
  qss2 (Sec) 15 Jan
Havercroft, R. I. BSc
  qss (Sec) 15 Jan
Sharp, C. (PEd) 15 Jan
Cumberland, M. J.
  qcc (Sec) 23 Jan
Chan, D. C. BSc (Trg) 31 Jan
Sumner, G. BA (Trg) 10 Feb
Unsworth, A. BSc
  qss2 (Sec) 13 Feb
Moore, I. D. (Sec) 21 Feb
Brown, S. A. MECI
  qcc (Sec) 26 Mar
Bryden, L. P. qss2 (Sec) 26 Mar
Treharne, S. M.
  qcc (ProvSy) 26 Mar

Smith, C. A. qss2 (Sec) 29 Mar
King, D. R. qss2 (Sec) 31 Mar
Duffy, J. F. LLB
  qss1 (ProvSy) 6 Apr
Nichols, R. M. (Cat) 6 Apr
Riddell, J. W. qss1
  (Sec) 6 Apr
Stembridge-King, J. R.
  MBE qcc (Sec) 6 Apr
Mardon, P. D. BA
  qcc (Sec) 9 Apr
Heath, I. R. BA qcc
  (Trg) 31 May
Edwards, E. S. BA
  (PEd) 1 June
Jackson, T. I. (Sec) 3 June
Cartmell, G. H.
  qss2 (Sec) 20 June
Currie, K. D. L.
  qss2 (Sec) 20 June
Anstee, S. D. qcc (Sec) 28 July
Scott, J. B. qcc (Trg) 28 July
Whyborn, C. M.
  qss1 (ProvSy) 28 July
McClelland-Jones, M.
  A. BA (Sec) 1 Aug
Jenkins, G. S. BSc
  qcc (Trg) 6 Aug
Fall, J. J. H. BEng (Trg) 8 Aug
Neaves, M. G. BSc
  qss1 (Cat) 12 Aug
Knight, J. BSc
  qss (ProvSy) 13 Aug
Stephenson, A. BA
  qss (Trg) 11 Sept
Hornby, G. P. qcc (Sec) 28 Sept
Fothergill, M. A.
  BA (Trg) 4 Oct
McClurg, P. A.
  qss1 (Sec) 5 Oct
Doyle, E. M. BEM (Sec) 7 Oct
Heath, C. A. BA pji
  qcc (PEd) 9 Oct
Goodwin-Baker, J.
  BEng (Sec) 10 Oct
Palk, A. L. BA qcc (Sec) 10 Oct
Sharp, S. D. BSc
  qcc (Sec) 10 Oct
Jennings, R. S.
  qcc (Sec) 17 Oct
Baird, W. Y. qss2 (Sec) 20 Nov
Sandilands, A. P.
  qss (Sec) 20 Nov
Holder, D. M. BA pji
  qss (PEd) 11 Dec
Cowan, T. W. (Sec) 20 Dec
Jolliffe, G. J. R.
  qcc (Sec) 30 Dec

Flight Lieutenants

1998

Harland, D. P. MCIPD		
qss2	(Sec)	29 Jan
Kidd, P. D. qcc	(Sec)	29 Jan
Pitter, A. M.	(Sec)	29 Jan
Trotter, L. R. A.	(Sec)	12 Feb
Gibson, A. L. BSc PGCE		
qcc	(Trg)	13 Feb
Neasom, R. J. BSc		
qss1	(Trg)	13 Feb
Scott, S. L. BA qss2		
	(Sec)	13 Feb
Yates, J. A. BA qss		
	(Sec)	13 Feb
Allcock, S. A. BA		
qcc	(ProvSy)	14 Feb
Ogden, J. E. BSc		
qcc	(Sec)	14 Feb
Stoker, S. E. BA		
qss1	(Trg)	14 Feb
Jackson, R. A. qcc		
	(Sec)	26 Feb
Barnes, T. M. qss1		
	(Sec)	5 Mar
Ingram, A. qss2	(Sec)	5 Mar
Sturtridge, K. N.		
qcc	(Sec)	11 Mar
Brayshaw, J. P. MCIPD		
qss1	(Sec)	18 Mar
Ball, R. F. qcc	(Sec)	26 Mar
Clark, A. C. qss2	(Sec)	26 Mar
Harper, D. P. qcc	(Sec)	29 Mar
Pearce, H. E. BSc		
qcc	(Trg)	6 Apr
Pearson, K. W. BSc		
qcc	(Trg)	7 Apr
Dryburgh, J. S. BA		
qcc	(Trg)	8 Apr
Floyd, A. D. C. BEd pji		
qss1	(PEd)	8 Apr
Manvell, S. P. BSocSc		
qcc	(ProvSy)	9 Apr
Posthumus, L. C. BSc		
qcc	(Trg)	9 Apr
Priestnall, S. J. BSc		
qcc	(Sec)	9 Apr
Hobbs, M. K. qcc	(Sec)	7 May
Lloyd, E. R. qcc	(Sec)	7 May
Woolley, J. E. MInstAM		
MISM MCIPD	(Sec)	7 May
Reed, W. A. qcc	(Sec)	27 May
Buttery, M. J. qss2		
	(Sec)	19 June
Blake, A. G. qcc	(Sec)	29 June
Harrison, P. A.		
qcc	(Sec)	25 July

Smith, M. qcc (ProvSy)		25 July
Chalk, J. A. BA qcc		
	(PEd)	9 Aug
Collier, E. L. BA qcc		
	(Sec)	11 Aug
Miller, M. L. MA		
qcc	(Sec)	11 Aug
Finn, N. J. BA (ProvSy)		12 Aug
Graham, S. A. BA		
qcc	(Sec)	12 Aug
Armstrong, S. J.		
	(ProvSy)	13 Aug
Webber, P. N. qss2		
	(ProvSy)	16 Aug
Parry, H. L. qss	(Sec)	28 Aug
South, A. C. qcc	(Sec)	26 Sept
Tomlin, N. D. qcc	(Sec)	26 Sept
Harrison, C. A. qcc		
	(Trg)	3 Oct
Malone, M. qcc	(Sec)	3 Oct
Roberts, B. A.	(Trg)	3 Oct
Eley, S. qss	(Trg)	6 Oct
Palmer, K.	(Sec)	6 Oct
Brown, J. E. BA qcc		
	(Sec)	9 Oct
Craggs, J. V. BSc		
qss2	(Sec)	9 Oct
Paterson, C. P. BA		
qcc	(ProvSy)	9 Oct
Bown, M.	(Sec)	7 Nov
Boyle, M. qss2	(Sec)	7 Nov
Jones, N. A.	(ProvSy)	7 Nov
Orr, S. A. qcc	(Sec)	7 Nov
Pickering, A. K.		
qss2	(Sec)	7 Nov
Ramsden, M. Y.		
qss2	(Sec)	7 Nov
Rogers, E. qcc	(Sec)	7 Nov
Gudgeon, N. M.		
BEd	(Trg)	23 Dec

1999

Bettington, G. J. BA		
qcc	(Sec)	15 Jan
Lynam, N. C. BSc		
qcc	(ProvSy)	15 Jan
Davies, A. J.		
AInstAM(Dip)		
qcc	(Sec)	30 Jan
Hodder, M. A. qcc	(Sec)	30 Jan
O'Neill, K. M. qss		
	(ProvSy)	30 Jan
Phillips, K. M. qss		
	(Sec)	30 Jan
Allen, A. C. MIPR	(Sec)	9 Feb
Irwin, R. W.	(ProvSy)	9 Feb
Whiting, P. D. BEd pji		
qss	(PEd)	10 Feb

Lannie, F. P. BA qcc		
	(Trg)	11 Feb
Luxon, J. L. BA	(PEd)	11 Feb
McKee, C. BA	(Cat)	11 Feb
Razzaq, S. BA	(Sec)	11 Feb
Walker, G. M. BEd		
pji	(PEd)	11 Feb
Barnett, J. qcc	(Sec)	12 Feb
Foster-Jones, R. A. BA		
qcc	(ProvSy)	13 Feb
Fox-Wiltshire, C. A.		
BA	(Sec)	13 Feb
Newland, R. J. BA		
	(Sec)	13 Feb
Wilkinson, D. J. BA		
	(ProvSy)	13 Feb
Davidson, R. BSc MISM		
MCMI LicIPD	(Trg)	14 Feb
Lane, A.	(PEd)	14 Feb
Thom, I. BA MCIPD		
CertFE	(Trg)	14 Feb
Threlfall, M.	(PEd)	14 Feb
Walters, M.	(Sec)	14 Feb
Williams, N. E. BEM		
LicIPD	(Sec)	14 Feb
Hinton, S. BA		9 Mar
Dickens, P. BSc	(Trg)	1 Apr
Charlesworth, K. H.		
BSc	(Trg)	6 Apr
Mayes, T. M. BSc		
qcc	(ProvSy)	8 Apr
Morgan, P. J. BA		
adp	(Sec)	8 Apr
O'Carroll, N. D. BA		
qcc	(ProvSy)	8 Apr
Phillips, J. BSc		
PGCE	(Trg)	8 May
Northeast, D. E. J. MA		
BA PGCE		27 May
Aston, A. D. BSc		
DipMgmt qcc	(Sec)	29 May
Lovatt, I. M.	(PEd)	29 May
Wooler, D. V. qss	(Sec)	29 May
Lowe, P. S. BSc	(Cat)	1 June
Setters, E. P. BA	(Trg)	9 June
Owen, C. J. BSc	(PEd)	5 July
Brearley, J. F. qcc	(PEd)	24 July
Dear, R. A. qss	(Sec)	24 July
Dennis, J. L. qcc	(Sec)	24 July
Green, A. C. MBE BSc		
qcc	(Trg)	24 July
Meenan, K.		
qss	(ProvSy)	24 July
Baker, C. qss	(Sec)	28 July
Addison, D. BA	(Trg)	9 Aug
Allen, M. C. BSc	(Sec)	9 Aug
Discombe, S. N.		
MA	(Sec)	9 Aug
Drake, A. Y. BA		
qss	(ProvSy)	11 Aug

Flight Lieutenants

1999—contd

Elliott, D. R. BA qcc
(Sec) 11 Aug
Humphrey, G. D. BSc
qcc (Sec) 11 Aug
Martin-Smith, A. C.
BSc (Ed) 11 Aug
O'Donnell, S. J.
BSc (Sec) 11 Aug
Trasler, J. qcc (Sec) 11 Aug
Willis, S. C. BA
qss1 (Sec) 11 Aug
Hodder, B. qss1 (Cat) 14 Aug
Daly, B. J.
MInstLM (ProvSy) 20 Aug
Donoghue, P. (Sec) 20 Aug
Scheepers, J. C. BA
(Trg) 1 Sept
Pemberton, A. L.
BSc (Sec) 4 Oct
Bailey, S. E. BEng
adp (Trg) 7 Oct
Potter, M. S. A. BSc
qss1 (ProvSy) 7 Oct
Draper, T. C. qss2 (Sec) 8 Oct
Edwards, D. K.
qss2 (Sec) 8 Oct
Blockley, S. L. (Cat) 9 Oct
McLintic, D. E. BSc
(Sec) 11 Oct
Edwards, P. W. MIL
qss (Sec) 14 Oct
Kendall, J. M. qss (Sec) 24 Oct
Full, S. M. (Sec) 27 Nov
Johnstone, I. A. MSc
BSc (Trg) 27 Nov
Scott-Jeffs, M. A.
BA (Trg) 30 Nov
Goodwin, J. P. BEng
qss (Trg) 1 Dec
Jones, M. I. BA
qss (Sec) 1 Dec
Warwick, K. MA MSc
qss (Sec) 1 Dec

2000

Parr, J. N. BSc
qss (PEd) 5 Jan
Payne, R. B. BEng (Trg) 9 Jan
Westcott, S. J. BA
qcc (PEd) 15 Jan
Boissel, T. K. (Sec) 16 Jan
Brooks, C. BA (Trg) 16 Jan

Pritchard, R. D.
AFM (PEd) 16 Jan
Backus, T. W. qcc (Sec) 28 Jan
Boyle, M. M. qss2 (Sec) 28 Jan
Curzon, R. S.
qss2 (ProvSy) 28 Jan
Jeffery, C. R.
qss1 (ProvSy) 28 Jan
Rossi, C. A. S. (Sec) 28 Jan
Mould, D. A. BSc (Trg) 31 Jan
Sharman, N. J.(ProvSy) 31 Jan
Lynch, H. A. M. BA
qss (Sec) 10 Feb
Reeves, J. E. BA (Sec) 11 Feb
Rowdon, R. M. BSc
PGCE (Trg) 9 Mar
Kelly, M. F. BA (Cat) 31 Mar
Hall, A. F. BA CertEd
LCGI qcc (Trg) 2 Apr
Hannam, R. (Sec) 2 Apr
Warner, S. R. BSc
qcc (Trg) 2 Apr
Brown, A. J. BA (Cat) 5 Apr
Huntley, D. M.
MSci (ProvSy) 5 Apr
Larsson-Clifford, M.
BEd (Trg) 5 Apr
Matthews, K. L. BSc
adp (Trg) 5 Apr
Nesbitt, J. A. BA (Trg) 5 Apr
Radford, J. MA BA
(Trg) 5 Apr
Jelfs, R. J. BA qss
(Sec) 6 Apr
Slater, E. A. M. BSc
qss (Sec) 6 Apr
Dobbing, T. J. qss1
(Sec) 7 Apr
Chiles, G. N. (Trg) 28 May
Davies, G. B. H. BEd
pji (PEd) 30 May
Gillespie, S. G. BA
(Sec) 30 May
Williams, O. A. BA
(Trg) 30 May
Calame, L. M. LLB
qss (Sec) 1 June
Watkins, T. K. BA (Sec) 1 June
Nicholl, E. J. BEd (Trg) 2 June
Walls, J. A. BA (Sec) 8 July
McGuinness, W. A.
qcc (Trg) 23 July
Mulheron, J. (ProvSy) 23 July
Mansell, A. C. qss (Sec) 25 July
Du ross, S. J. BSc
(PEd) 7 Aug
Lomas, V. A. BA (PEd) 8 Aug
McDonnell, C. L.
BEd (PEd) 8 Aug

Tipping, C. J. BSc
qss (Trg) 8 Aug
Collinge, M. J. BA
qss (Sec) 9 Aug
Harris, K. R. BSc
qss (Sec) 9 Aug
Mordecai, S. LLB (Sec) 9 Aug
Gue, R. W. M. BSc
qcc (Sec) 10 Aug
Knox, A. J. qss1 (Cat) 13 Aug
Douglas-Sim, J. A.(Sec) 27 Sept
Bell, C. BA (Sec) 1 Oct
Howkins-Griffiths,
I. S. (Sec) 1 Oct
Morris, A. (Sec) 1 Oct
Simpson, D. J. (Sec) 1 Oct
Swanson, S. J. (Sec) 1 Oct
Howie, D. A. MBE
qss1 (PEd) 3 Oct
Miller, H. MSc (Trg) 4 Oct
Gleave, B. J. BA
qcc (Sec) 5 Oct
Scott, S. BA (Sec) 5 Oct
Bowles, S. J. BSc (Trg) 6 Oct
Bunce, N. J. E. BSc
(Sec) 6 Oct
Garratt, A. J. BA (Sec) 6 Oct
Sloan, M. A. BSc (Sec) 6 Oct
Rylatt, A. J. BEng 7 Oct
Davies, W. G. BSc
(ProvSy) 14 Nov
Wood, S. M. (Sec) 26 Nov
Caplan, R. A. BEd
(PEd) 29 Nov
Powell, P. J. BA qss 30 Nov
Reid, P. BA (Sec) 30 Nov
Appleby, R. I. BA
(ProvSy) 1 Dec
Barber, S. C. BA (Sec) 1 Dec
Floyd, S. BA qss (Sec) 1 Dec
King, N. A. BSc (Sec) 1 Dec
Macdonald, F. M.
BA (Sec) 1 Dec
Mills, D. L. BA (Sec) 1 Dec
Gray, S. E. BA (Trg) 4 Dec

2001

Percy, D. W. BEM (PEd) 14 Jan
Portlock, A. J. BSc
(Sec) 15 Jan
Popper, I. A. (Sec) 4 Feb
Carney, W. MA (Sec) 9 Feb
Smith, M. G. BEd
pji (PEd) 9 Feb
Cordock, M. A. L. BA
qcc (Cat) 10 Feb
Curtis, L. J. BA (Sec) 10 Feb

Flight Lieutenants

2001—contd

Hampson, M. D.		
BA	(Sec)	10 Feb
McIntosh, K. M. BA		
qcc	(Sec)	10 Feb
Smyth, A. S. J.		
BSc	(ProvSy)	10 Feb
Todd, P. M. BSc	(Sec)	10 Feb
Lovejoy, A. F.	(Sec)	11 Feb
Scott, D. J.	(Sec)	13 Mar
Clark, N. qss	(Sec)	1 Apr
Leeming, M. D.	(Sec)	1 Apr
Crossby, O. H. BSc	(Trg)	4 Apr
Lane, S. J. BA	(Trg)	4 Apr
Edensor, L.	(Cat)	5 Apr
Hiller, L. J. BA	(Sec)	5 Apr
Pilgrim-Morris, L. S.		
BA	(Sec)	5 Apr
Sinclair, R. A. BA	(Sec)	5 Apr
Rickard, M. W.	(Sec)	6 Apr
Straw, E. L.	(Sec)	6 Apr
Greenald, J. B. BSc		
PGCE	(Trg)	7 Apr
Emmett, S. J. MA		
PGCE	(Trg)	26 May
Darby, G. J.	(ProvSy)	27 May
Littlecott, M. BSc	(Trg)	27 May
Smith, T. D. G.	(ProvSy)	27 May
Travis, J. J. BSc	(Trg)	27 May
Wheeler, P. L.	(Sec)	27 May
Condren, M. A.	(PEd)	29 May
Fitzgerald, A. C.		
BSc	(Trg)	29 May
Hackett, J. N. BA	(Sec)	29 May
Scott, P. J. BA	(Trg)	29 May
Brown, A. J. BA	(Sec)	30 May
Cross, T. A. BA	(Sec)	30 May
Davis, A. G.		
BA	(ProvSy)	30 May
Gabb, N. BSc	(Sec)	30 May
Glover, T. M. BSc		
qss	(Sec)	30 May
Lawrence, D. J.		
BA	(Trg)	30 May
McCormack, W. J.		
DPhil BSc	(Trg)	30 May
Shaw, C. BSc PGCE		8 June
Griffin, L. BSc qcc	(Sec)	4 July
Maidment, S.	(Trg)	22 July
Noel, R. S. J.	(Sec)	22 July
Philip, R. M.	(Sec)	22 July
Scott, S. A.	(ProvSy)	22 July
Skillen, M. R.	(Sec)	22 July
Weavill, R. G.	(PEd)	24 July
Howarth, S. L. BA	(Sec)	7 Aug
Carrick, J. BSc	(ProvSy)	8 Aug

Dengate, N. S.		
BSc	(Sec)	8 Aug
Eason, R. M. BA	(Trg)	8 Aug
Jones, P. A.		
MA	(ProvSy)	8 Aug
Milledge, E. C. BA	(Sec)	8 Aug
Outteridge, G. J.		
BA	(ProvSy)	8 Aug
Park, C. S. BSc	(Sec)	8 Aug
Parker, L. V. LLB	(Sec)	8 Aug
Mahon, K. qcc	(Sec)	9 Aug
Hone, J. A. qcc	(Sec)	11 Aug
Hitt, M.	(Sec)	17 Aug
Thompson, P. BSc	(Sec)	30 Sept
Whelan, J. F.	(Sec)	30 Sept
Ireland, B. BEd	(PEd)	3 Oct
Farrelly, B. L.		
BSc	(ProvSy)	4 Oct
Lye, S. J. BA	(Sec)	4 Oct
Makinson-Sanders, J.		
BA	(Sec)	4 Oct
Parrott, T. A. BA	(PEd)	4 Oct
Waller, K. S. MA	(Sec)	4 Oct
Hinton, R. J. MSc BSc		
FRGS	(ProvSy)	5 Oct
Macinnes, F. C. L.		
BSc	(Trg)	5 Oct
Milburn, M. J. BA	(Sec)	5 Oct
Morefield, C. E. BSc		
qcc	(Trg)	5 Oct
Whitehead, N. H.		
BA	(Sec)	5 Oct
Moody, G. A.	(Sec)	6 Oct
Wood, N. M. qcc	(Sec)	6 Oct
Moss, R. M.	(Sec)	25 Nov
Priest, A. A. BSc	(Trg)	25 Nov
Carr, M. D. BA	(ProvSy)	30 Nov
Curran, N. W.		
BSc	(ProvSy)	30 Nov
Dempster, M. BA	(Trg)	30 Nov
Doney, M. J.		
BA	(ProvSy)	30 Nov
Mungroo, V. BEng		
BA	(Trg)	30 Nov
Gowans, N. M. BSc		
PGCE		4 Dec

2002

Marklew, M. J.	(Sec)	13 Jan
Stronach, J. W.	(Cat)	13 Jan
Hamilton, J. J.	(ProvSy)	28 Jan
Milnes, J. A. J.	(Regt)	28 Jan
Putland, K. A.		
MBE	(ProvSy)	5 Feb
John, A. M. BEng	(Sec)	6 Feb
Spencer, K. J. BA	(Sec)	8 Feb
Brocklebank, J. M.		
BSc	(Sec)	9 Feb

Edmond, R. W.		
BA	(Sec)	9 Feb
Hughes, V. L. BSc	(Sec)	9 Feb
Jennings, C.	(Cat)	10 Feb
Austin, S. J.	(Sec)	30 Mar
Harrison, S. W. P.	(Trg)	30 Mar
Parker, S. R.	(Sec)	30 Mar
Reeves, T.	(Sec)	30 Mar
Gray, A. BEng	(Trg)	1 Apr
Willday, C. L. BEd	(PEd)	1 Apr
Cornish, M. J. BSc		
PGCE	(PEd)	3 Apr
Dunning, P. A. BSc		
PGCE pji	(PEd)	3 Apr
Short, V. J. K. BA		
PGCE	(Sec)	4 Apr
Green, N.	(Sec)	5 Apr
Egan, J. N. MSc BSc		
PGCE	(Trg)	7 Apr
Sutton, D.	(ProvSy)	25 May
Barratt, D.	(Sec)	28 May
Forsman, V. L. BA	(Trg)	29 May
Gregory, S. A. BA	(Trg)	29 May
Hughes, P. B. BA	(Sec)	29 May
Lockwood, S. C.		
LLB	(Sec)	29 May
Whyte, A. C.		
BSc	(ProvSy)	29 May

Flying Officers

1991

Benham, L. A. S.
BSc   (Trg) 31 Mar

1993

Norton, V. C. MBA
PGCE   (Trg) 24 Mar
Brown, A. C.   (Trg) 16 Aug

1994

Graves, A. R.   (Trg) 22 May

1995

Jones, N. M.   (Trg) 27 Feb
Sinclair, G. S.   (Sec) 29 Aug

1996

Cookson, C. W. MRIPH
MHCIMA   (Cat) 11 Mar
Pascoe, D. J. (ProvSy) 22 Apr
Fopp, C. M. BSc (Sec) 9 Aug

1997

Steven, J. C.   (Sec) 4 Mar
Stuart, R. C.   (Sec) 7 Aug
Edwards, J.   (Sec) 21 Sept
Kinroy, R.   (Sec) 22 Nov
Whalley, K. A.   (PEd) 16 Dec

1998

Dean, L. J.   (Sec) 9 Jan
Harvey, S. M.   (Sec) 5 Feb
Formoso, K. L. BA(Sec) 9 Feb
Geary, S. A.   (Sec) 6 Mar
Scales, D. J.   (Sec) 26 Apr
Evans, A. J. qcc (Sec) 29 June
Dilley, P. M.   (PEd) 23 July
Newman, R. E.(ProvSy) 23 July
Elliott, C.   (Sec) 1 Aug
Gilmore, R. A. BA (Sec) 6 Aug
Law, C. A. BSc (Trg) 6 Aug
Betts, D. D. BSc (Sec) 7 Aug
Davis, A. J. BA (Sec) 7 Aug

Shearing, J. BA (Sec) 7 Aug
Williams, M. R.
BA   (ProvSy) 7 Aug
Mackintosh, A. J. (Sec) 1 Oct
Rackham, V. L. BA (Trg) 1 Oct
Bryson, M. J.
BMus   (Sec) 2 Oct
Houston, S. C.
BSc   (Sec) 2 Oct
Ireland, N. E. BSc (Trg) 2 Oct
Pike, R. P. BSc
PGCE   (PEd) 2 Oct
Cairns, S. L.   (Sec) 4 Oct
Carbutt, D. P. BA (Sec) 4 Oct
Marshall, T. A. BA(Sec) 4 Oct
Perrin, M. N. A. BA
PGCE   (Sec) 4 Oct
Partridge, I. P. (Sec) 13 Oct
Bird, S. A.   (Sec) 7 Nov
Macivor, K. S. (Trg) 30 Nov

1999

Muir, L. R.   (Sec) 23 Jan
Martin-Jones, A. L.
qss   (Sec) 25 Jan
Carter, C. M.   (Sec) 6 Feb
Coombes, D. J.
BA   (ProvSy) 8 Feb
Senescall, M. J. E. (Sec) 9 Feb
Roe, J. E.   (Sec) 18 Mar
Ward, A. J.   (Sec) 18 Mar
Fraser, I. P.   (Sec) 28 Mar
Pluckrose, A.   (PEd) 1 Apr
Rowland, L. M.
LLB   (ProvSy) 2 Apr
Curd, A. L. BSc (Trg) 3 Apr
Hetherington, J. (Sec) 3 Apr
Mann, D. D. qcc (Sec) 3 Apr
Morgan, Z. E.
BSc   (ProvSy) 3 Apr
Parsbo, S. R. BSc (Sec) 3 Apr
Steel, J. J. BA (Sec) 3 Apr
Hawkins, S. A. (Sec) 27 May
Taylor, M. A.   (Sec) 27 May
Calder, K. BA (Sec) 28 May
Pocha, C. LLB (Sec) 28 May
Teasdale, C. L.
BA   (ProvSy) 28 May
Hodgson, V. L. (Sec) 19 June
Hazelden, O. D. (Sec) 22 July
Pullin, M. J.   (Sec) 22 July
Sheehy, B. M. (Sec) 22 July
Lock, D. E. qcc (Sec) 29 July
Affleck, T. L. BEd (PEd) 4 Aug
Simpson, J. BA
PGCE   (PEd) 4 Aug
Cranston, L. L.
BSc   (ProvSy) 6 Aug

Norman, D. M.
BA   (ProvSy) 6 Aug
Tope, M. D. BA (Trg) 10 Aug
Van Halteren,
S. J.   (ProvSy) 26 Sept
Cawthray, J. A. BA
PGCE   (Sec) 2 Oct
Fagg, A. D. BSc (Trg) 2 Oct
Hoban, L. J. BSc (Sec) 2 Oct
McMillan, M. A. BA (Trg) 2 Oct
Mildon, A. C.
BA   (ProvSy) 2 Oct
McGuckin, S. J. (Cat) 4 Oct
Downs, S. M.
BA   (ProvSy) 7 Oct
Lunnon-Wood, D.
BEd   (PEd) 7 Oct
Homer, N.   (Sec) 15 Oct
Godwin, D. W. (Sec) 27 Oct
Brock, J. G.
BA   (ProvSy) 27 Nov
McKeown, S. J. BA (Trg) 27 Nov
Tenniswood, J. E.
BSc   (Trg) 28 Nov

2000

Parrack, C. E. BA (Sec) 15 Jan
Cooper, T. A. LLB (Sec) 6 Feb
Jones, R. D. L.
BSc   (Trg) 6 Feb
Kempster, M. J. (Sec) 6 Feb
Smith, M. L.
BA   (ProvSy) 6 Feb
Whiteman, E. J.
BA   (Sec) 6 Feb
Allen, M. R.
BA   (ProvSy) 12 Feb
Ellis, R. A. MA BA (Sec) 12 Feb
Freestone, N. LLM (Sec) 12 Feb
Lawrence, S. J. L.
qss   (Sec) 26 Mar
Hall, K. M. J.
LLB   (ProvSy) 1 Apr
Mackay, M. BSc (Sec) 1 Apr
Bryan, K. P. qss (Sec) 2 May
Gill, C. K.   (PEd) 25 May
Rahaman, A. P. (Sec) 25 May
Dudman, K. H. BA (Trg) 26 May
Joy, B.   (Sec) 27 May
Butler, J. R.   (Sec) 18 July
Johnson, G. O. (Sec) 18 July
Logan, J. C.   (Sec) 18 July
Beekman, S. G.(ProvSy) 20 July
Campbell, L. (ProvSy) 20 July
Cornell, M. C. (Cat) 20 July
Powell, L. J.   (Sec) 20 July
Woods, M. P.   (Cat) 20 July
Bicket, G. BSc (ProvSy) 4 Aug

Flying Officers

2000—contd

Hawthornthwaite, J. M.	(Sec)	4 Aug
Leeman, L. BSc	(ProvSy)	4 Aug
Jones, A. L.	(ProvSy)	5 Aug
Hunt, L. J. M.	(Cat)	8 Aug
Atkinson, M. M. BA	(Sec)	1 Oct
Lonsdale, A. C. LLB	(ProvSy)	1 Oct
Middleton, E. C. BSc	(Sec)	1 Oct
Ritchie, A. BSc	(Sec)	1 Oct
Hardiment, R. A. BA	(Sec)	27 Nov
Newbury, H. R. BA	(Sec)	27 Nov
Benson, C. E.	(Cat)	28 Nov
Long, R. F. qcc	(Sec)	28 Nov
Marshall, E. L.	(Sec)	29 Dec

2001

Jupp, C. A. BSc	(Sec)	15 Jan
Melmoth, D. A. C. BA	(Trg)	15 Jan
Skaife, C. R.	(Sec)	23 Jan
Williams, S. G.	(ProvSy)	23 Jan
Francis Smith, K. A. BSc	(ProvSy)	12 Feb
Garvin, J. D. BSc	(Sec)	12 Feb
Griffiths, C. E. BSc	(Sec)	12 Feb
Perrett, J. E. BA	(Sec)	12 Feb
Tolan, A. L. BA	(Sec)	12 Feb
Hard, K. BA	(Sec)	7 Apr
Henton, L. A. BA	(Sec)	7 Apr
Taylor, G. T. BSc	(Sec)	7 Apr
Smith, N. A.	(Sec)	4 May
Brealey, S. J.	(Sec)	7 May
Brunning, R. M.	(Cat)	24 May
Parker, A. J.	(Sec)	24 May
Provan, A. P.	(ProvSy)	24 May
Singh, M.	(Sec)	24 May
Skinner, D. W.	(PEd)	24 May
Thompson, J. M.	(PEd)	24 May
Yates, P. D.	(Sec)	7 July
Carvell, S. L.	(Sec)	19 July
Dodds, P. E.	(Sec)	19 July
Paton, G.	(Sec)	19 July
Purnell, S. F. BSc MBE	(ProvSy)	19 July
Davis, M. J. M.	(Sec)	4 Aug
Wells, L. A.	(Sec)	13 Aug
Fulcher, S. R.	(Sec)	4 Oct

Macdonald, C. H.	(Sec)	5 Nov
Morris, A. J.	(Sec)	19 Dec

2002

McCay, J. F. L.	(Sec)	19 Jan
Train, N. M.	(Sec)	19 Jan
Clark-Smith, K. J.	(Sec)	15 Mar
Heald, S. L.	(Sec)	25 May
Miller, J.	(Sec)	25 May

Pilot Officers

2000

Durows, J. R.	(ProvSy)	30 Sept

2001

Fields, L. S.	(Sec)	20 Jan
McNeice, A. L.	(Sec)	1 Feb
Brookes, A. J.	(ProvSy)	4 Feb
Readings, M. J.	(ProvSy)	28 Mar
Lloyd, B. J.	(ProvSy)	1 Aug
Card, N. J.	(ProvSy)	29 Sept
Credland, R. M. BA	(Sec)	2 Dec
Davies, D. BA	(ProvSy)	2 Dec
Doodson, C. L. MSc BSc	(ProvSy)	2 Dec

2002

Stone, M. J.	(ProvSy)	19 Jan
Davis, N. C. BA	(Trg)	10 Feb
Cope, C. R. BA	(ProvSy)	7 Apr

Acting Pilot Officer

2002

Collins, C. M. (ProvSy)   4 Apr

MEDICAL BRANCH

Air Vice-Marshal

2002

Pike, Warwick John QHP MSc MB BS MRCGP MRCS MFOM DRCOG DAvMed LRCP qss
Born 31/12/44 . . . . (F)   1 July

Air Commodores

1992

Cullen, Stephen Anthony QHS MB ChB FRCPath FRAeS DCP Born 18/7/39 . . . .   6 Apr

1996

Morgans, Brian Thomas QHP MB BCh FRCS(Glas) Born 31/5/43 . . . . 21 Aug
Rainford, David John MBE MB BS FRCP FFOM FRAeS MRCS Born 27/7/46 . . . . . 21 Aug

1997

Gibson, Terence Michael PhD MPhil MB ChB FFOM FRAeS DAvMed DDAM psc
Born 6/3/47 . . . . (F)   1 July

1998

Thornton, Eric John QHP MB ChB FCMI MFOM DAvMed rcds psc Born 24/8/48. . . (F)   1 Jan

1999

Merry, Robert Thomas George MB BS FRCP MRCPsych DRCOG Born 25/10/37 . . . . .   1 Feb

2000

Dougherty, Simon Robert Charles QHP MSc MB BS FFOM FCMI FRAeS DRCOG DAvMed
jsdc qs Born 26/2/49 . . . . (F)   1 Jan

2002

Mitchell, Ian Duncan QHS MDA BSc MB BS FRAeS MRCGP MHSM DRCOG DAvMed
AFOM psc Born 22/1/48 . . . . (F)   1 Jan

Group Captains

1995

Jones, John MSc MB BCh MRCPath DRCOG Born 15/4/48 . . . . (F) 11 Aug
Batchelor, Anthony John CBE QHS BSc MB BS FRCP FRAeS DRCOG DAvMed Born 27/6/47 (F) 30 Nov

1996

Coker, William John OBE MB ChB BA BSc LLB FRCP FRAeS DAvMed Born 28/8/46. . (F) 12 Mar
Laundy, Trevor John BSc MB BS FRCP DAvMed qss Born 11/4/48 . . . . . . 7 Oct

1997

Ranger, Michael QHS MB BS DAvMed AFOM MRAeS qss Born 23/8/49 . . . . . (F) 1 Jan 97

1998

Dharmeratnam, Rajkumar MB BS FRCR DCH Born 30/3/50 . . . . 20 June

1999

McConnell, David Leslie MSc MB ChB DObstRCOG DAvMed qss Born 23/12/49. . . (F) 1 July
Jones, David Wynford FRCP FISM MRCP(UK) MRCS(Eng) LRCP Born 4/12/47 . . . 14 Aug

2000

Morris, Christopher Brian MB BS DRCOG Born 5/3/52. . . . . (F) 1 Jan
Reid, Geoffrey Ewing MB ChB FRCPsych DAvMed MRAeS qs Born 28/7/48 . . . . (F) 1 Aug

2001

McManus, Francis Bernard MB BS MRCPsych qss Born 3/3/53 . . . . 10 Mar
Keatings, Brian Thomas MMedSci MB ChB MFOM DAvMed qs Born 11/12/53 . . . (F) 1 July
Watkins, Mark John Guy BA MB BChir FRCS(Edin) Born 4/4/53 Born 4/4/53 . . . . 30 Aug

2002

Evans, Christopher Paul Anthony MSc MB BCh DAvMed psc Born 20/12/54 . . . . (F) 1 July

Wing Commanders

1991

O'Connell, C. R. W. MB
BCh BAO
LLMRCP(Irel)
LLMRCS(Irel)   3 July

1993

Elphinstone, L. H. MSc
MB ChB MRCGP
MFPHM qs   15 Feb
Lenoir, R. J. MA MB
BChir FFARCS
DRCOG   10 May
Smyth, D. G. BA MB
BCh BAO   16 July
Skipper, J. J. MB BCh
FRCS(Ed) qss   1 Sept
Blake, D. C. S. BSc MB
ChB FFARCS   1 Nov

1994

Jenkins, D. I. T. MSc
BSc MB BS MRCGP
MFOM DRCOG
DAvMed MRAeS
qs   (F) 24 May
Marshall, D. N. F. MB
ChB MRCGP DRCOG
DAvMed qs   (F) 18 July
Reynolds, M. F. MB ChB
MRCGP DRCOG
qss   (F)   2 Aug
McGuire, N. M.
BMedSci BM BS   3 Aug
Macauley, S. J. BSc MB
BS   2 Sept
Kilbey, J. H. BSc MB
BS   28 Sept

1995

Peterson, M. K.   17 Feb
Mozumder, A. K. MB
BS MRCGP
MRCS(Eng) LRCP
DRCOG DTM&H
DAvMed qs   (F) 29 July
Anderson, A. M. MB
ChB MRCGP   (F)   1 Aug

Gradwell, D. P. PhD BSc
MB ChB FRAeS
DAvMed   1 Aug

1996

Scerri, G. V. G. J.
FRCS(Eng) LRCP   1 Feb
Green, A. D. MB BS
MRCPath
DTM&H   27 Feb
Broadbridge, R. J. M.
MB BS MRCGP
DRCOG DAvMed
DOccMed qs   (F)   1 Aug
Aitken, J. BSc MB ChB
DAvMed AFOM   (F) 13 Nov
Schofield, P. J. MB ChB
MRCGP DA(UK)
DAvMed qss   (F) 17 Nov

1997

Khan, M. A. MB BS
MRCP   19 May
Bell, I. F. MB ChB
qss   (F) 30 June
Whitbread, T. MB BS   4 July
Ryles, M. T. MSc MB
ChB MRCGP DRCOG
DAvMed   1 Aug
Wilcock, A. C. MSc MB
ChB MRCGP MFOM
DRCOG DAvMed
qs   (F)   1 Aug
Seddon, P. J. BSc MB
BS   15 Aug
Cousins, M. A. MB ChB
MRCGP qss   8 Oct
Webster, T. M. MB BS
MRCGP DRCOG
qs   (F) 16 Oct
Allison, G. E. MB
BS   (F) 17 Nov
Bone, C. E. MB ChB   25 Nov

1998

Gaffney, J. E. BSc MB
ChB MRCGP DCH
DRCOG DAvMed
psc(j)   (F) 11 Jan
Bhullar, T. P. S. MB BS
FRCPRCS(Glas)
FRCS(Edin)   12 Jan

Bruce, D. L. MBE MSc
MB BS FIMCRCS(Ed)
MRCGP DAvMed
AFOM MRAeS AKC
qss   (F)   1 Aug
Matthews, R. S. J. BSc
MB BS MRCGP
qs   (F) 19 Aug
Sheldon, K. J. MB ChB
DOccMed   9 Sept

1999

Wallace, V. J. MB ChB
MRCGP DRCOG
psc(j)   (F)   2 Mar
Kirkpatrick, R. B. J. MB
BS DAvMed   (F) 26 Apr
Reid, A. N. C. MB BS
MRCGP DRCOG
qss   27 June
Shapland, W. D. MB BS
MRCPsych DA
DRCOG   27 June
Greenish, T. S. MB BS
DAvMed qss   (F)   1 Aug
Farmer, D. J. MSc BSc
MB ChB FRSH
MRCGP DRCOG
DAvMed DPDerm
qss   6 Aug
Kilbey, S. C. MB ChB
MRCGP DRCOG
DAvMed DOccMed
qs   (F) 12 Aug
Amos, A. M. MB BCh
MRCGP DRCOG
DAvMed DOccMed
MRAeS qs   5 Sept

2000

Cartwright, J. MB BS
DAvMed qss   (F) 13 Jan
Dexter, D. MA BSc MB
ChB MRCGP DRCOG
DAvMed qs   (F)   1 Aug
Hurley, A. V. A. BA BM
DOccMed   (F)   1 Aug
Sargeant, I. D. MB BS
qs   1 Aug
Boden, J. G. MB ChB
qss   (F)   3 Aug
Ross, D. E. MB ChB
qs   (F)   4 Aug

Wing Commanders

2001

Archer, G. A. MB BS	1 Aug
Houghton, J. A. MB BS	1 Aug
Winfield, D. A. MSc BSc MB ChB MRCGP DCH DRCOG DCH DPhil ARCS qss	2 Aug
Hall, I. S. MB BS	27 Aug

2002

Scott, R. A. H. MB BS	26 Feb

Squadron Leaders

1994

Hutchinson, M. R. MB BS qss	(F)	1 Aug
Paish, N. R. MB BS		1 Aug
Carter, N. D. R. MB ChB		21 Aug
Connor, M. P. MB ChB		25 Aug
Hansford, N. G. MB ChB	(F)	27 Aug
Green, N. D. C. BSc MB BS		1 Sept

1995

Wright, P. MSc MB BCh BAO DAvMed qcc	(F)	25 Feb
Pathak, G. MB BS FRCS		22 Mar
Trudgill, M. J. A. MB BCh MRCGP DAvMed DiplMC MRAeS	(F)	1 Aug
Walton, C. S. BSc MB BS MRCGP DRCOG qs	(F)	1 Aug
Low, N. J. MB ChB		7 Aug
Bastock, J. M. MB ChB qss		26 Aug
Holdcroft, A. J. MB ChB MRCGP DRCOG	(F)	26 Aug
Lewis, M. E. MB BCh		18 Nov

1996

Maidment, G. MA BM BCh DAvMed MRAeS qss		24 Feb
Pandya, A. N. MB BS MS MCh(Plast) FRCSGlasg		24 Nov
Hodgson, J. MB ChB		1 Aug
McLoughlin, D. C. MB BCh BAO MRCGP DRCOG qs	(F)	1 Aug
Ruth, M. J. MB ChB		1 Aug
Timperley, A. C. BSc MB ChB		1 Aug
Lasrado, I. F. N. MB BS		24 Sept

Caldera, S. R. M. BSc MB BS FRCS	25 Nov

1997

Hill, K. P. MB BS qss1		1 Aug
Khan, R. MB BS		1 Aug
Stitson, D. J. MB BS		1 Aug
Thomson, N. J. MB ChB		1 Aug
Zaman, A. U. MB BS FRCS		11 Aug
Monnery, P. M. MB BS		27 Aug
McGrath, R. D. MB BCh		3 Sept

1998

Ampat, G. MB BS FRCS		18 June
Baker, J. E. MB BS qcc	(F)	1 Aug
Berry, R. D. BSc BM BS		1 Aug
Flucker, C. J. R. BSc		1 Aug
Geary, K. G. MB ChB		1 Aug
Hocking, G. MB ChB		1 Aug
Hughes, P. R. MB ChB		1 Aug
Williams, M. MB ChB		1 Aug
Withnall, R. D. J. MB BS MRCGP		1 Aug
Daborn, D. K. R. BSc MB BS MRCGP DRCOG DiplMC DOccMed qss		3 Sept

1999

Venkatachalam, S. MS MB BS FRCSRCPS(Glas)	6 Apr
Lewis-Russell, J. M. MB ChB	1 Aug
Smith, S. A. MB BCh MRCGP qss	1 Aug
Trimble, K. T. MB ChB MRCS(Eng)	1 Aug

Squadron Leaders

1999—contd

Nunn, N. K. BSc MB ChB DRCOG	23 Aug

2000

Sapsford, W. MA MB BChir FRCS	4 May
Evison, D. MB ChB	1 Aug
Birch, K. BM BSc FRCA MRCP DAvMed	2 Aug
Brown, D. J. G. MB ChB	2 Aug
McCombie, Y. M. BSc MB ChB	2 Aug
Naylor, J. R. MB ChB	2 Aug
Temple, M. J. MB ChB	2 Aug
Davies, G. W. MB BS MRCP(Irel)	6 Aug
Davies, M. T. BSc MB ChB qss1	7 Aug
Cabre, A.	23 Sept

2001

Timperley, J. MB ChB	7 Feb
Singleton, J. F. MB ChB	22 Feb
Talabi, A. O. MB BS	2 Mar
Paul, S. N. MB BS MRCP	28 Mar
Griffiths, J. S. MB BCh qss	1 Aug
Dalrymple, P. M. MB ChB	7 Aug
Grimmer, P. M. MB ChB	7 Aug
Pook, A. BSc MB BS	7 Aug
Whittle, C. L. MB BS	7 Aug
Woodcock, M. G. L. BM	8 Aug
Vaikunthanathan, R. S. MB BS	16 Aug
Chapple, S. A. MB ChB	1 Sept
Masterson, S. W. MB ChB	30 Sept

McGrath, M. M. MB ChB	14 Oct

2002

Covill, J. A. qcc	1 Jan
Ellis-Martin, P. qss	1 Jan
Harper, D. G. MB BCh MRCGP	6 Feb
Huntbach, J. A. BSc BA BChir	13 Feb
Court, P. G. BSc qcc	1 July

Flight Lieutenants

1997

Khan, J. MB BS MRCGP	16 May
Lewis, C. L. BM	1 Aug
Kendrew, J. M. MB BS	6 Aug
Tagg, C. E. MB BS	6 Aug
Haseldine, D. C. MB ChB	7 Aug
Bennett, A. N. MB ChB MRCP	1 Nov
Hope, A. J. BM	3 Dec

1998

Becker, G. W. MA MB BChir MRCS(Eng)	4 Feb
Sharma, D. M. MB BCh BAO	5 Apr
Okojie, E. I. MB BS	24 June
Hughes, S. N. BSc MB BS	5 Aug
Mollan, I. A. MB ChB	11 Sept
Harris, R. L. BM	15 Oct
Miles, H. C. MB ChB	31 Oct

1999

Houghton, L. J. MB ChB	4 Aug
Nicol, E. D. MB BS	4 Aug
Ostler, A. M. MB BS	4 Aug

2000

Smith, E. J. D. BA BM BCh	2 Feb
D'Arcy, J. L. MB ChB	2 Aug
Gourlay, S. I. G. MB ChB	2 Aug
Kendall-Smith, M. MB ChB	3 Aug
Tipping, R. D. MB BS	7 Aug
Gillen, P. MB BCh	17 Sept

Flight Lieutenants		Flying Officers		Pilot Officers	
2001		**1996**		**1999**	
Bradley, J. C. ChB	6 Feb	Tomlin, N. M.	7 Nov	Corbett, G. D.	19 July
O'Reilly, D. J. MB BCh	9 July			Cummings, I. M.	19 July
Hendriksen, D. A. BM				Wayne, C. G. BSc	19 July
BS	17 July	**1999**		Dewar, G. L.	29 Nov
Partner, A. M. MB BCh	19 July				
Davy, A. P. MB BS	27 July	Clarke, E. BA	2 Oct		
Mollan, S. P. MB ChB	27 July	Brian, T. C. BSc	28 Nov	**2000**	
Andrews, P. D. PhD BSc					
BM BS	28 July	**2000**		Adcock, C. J.	20 Mar
Shepherd, B. D. BSc				Baladurai, S.	17 July
MB ChB	28 July	Lynes, D. A. BA	10 Feb	Butterfield, S. A.	17 July
		Ramsay, L. M.	14 July	Cooper, H. R.	17 July
				Flutter, C. L.	17 July
				John, K. E.	17 July
		2001		Masterson, L. M.	17 July
				Richards, J. A.	17 July
		McCormack Fisher, L.		Spurrier, E. J.	17 July
		E. BEd	12 Feb	Looker, J. J.	20 Nov
		Manson, A. L. MB ChB	2 July	McMillan, K. G.	20 Nov
		Patterson, D. T. MB ChB	4 July	Patterson, C. M.	20 Nov
		West, S. L. MB BS	13 July		
		Brown, A. M. R. MB BS	15 July	**2001**	
		Ward, E. M. BSc MB BS	15 July		
		Caygill, S. J. MB ChB	17 July	Taylor, M. C. C.	19 Jan
		Craig, D. G. N. BSc	17 July	Lashbrooke, B. P.	5 July
		Harris, N. S. BSc MB		Austin, J. L.	3 Sept
		BCh	17 July	Chalmers, S. M.	3 Sept
		Jacobs, N. MB ChB	17 July	Davison, C. A.	3 Sept
		Ellison, D. R. BSc		Gardner, F. K.	3 Sept
		MBChB	19 July	Hindle, P.	3 Sept
		Than, R.	3 Sept	Hurst, K.	3 Sept
		Jones, R. E. W.	30 Sept	Maitland-Knibb, S. B.	3 Sept
				Rand, B. C. C.	3 Sept
				Sherwood, D. A.	3 Sept
				Wheble, J. L. C.	3 Sept
				Rimmer, J. E.	29 Oct
				Otobo, I. O.	5 Dec
				2002	
				Gelnar, J. A.	25 Mar
				Grieve, A. W.	25 Mar
				O'Neill, D. BSc	25 Mar

DENTAL BRANCH

Air Commodore

2000

Reid, John QHDS BDS MGDSRCPS(Glas) psc Born 11/9/46 . . . . 1 July

Group Captains

1987

Shepherd, Robert George BDS FDSRCPS LDSRCS MCMI qss Born 16/1/41 . . . . 29 July

1996

Amy, David James MSc BDS MGDSRCS(Ed) qss Born 17/6/50 . . . . 1 July
Armstrong, David Brian BDS MGDSRCS(Eng) DGDP(UK) LDSRCS Born 21/9/46. . . . . 1 July

1997

Richardson, Peter Sandiford MSc BDS MGDSRCS(Eng) MGDSRCS(Ed) LDSRCS(Eng)
   DDPHRCS(Eng) Born 29/9/48 . . . . 1 Jan

1998

Rees, David John MSc BDS MGDSRCS(Eng) qs Born 5/5/53 . . . . 1 July

1999

Cornthwaite, Peter William BDS MGDSRCS(Ed) qs Born 3/9/51 . . . . 1 July

2000

Gallagher, Peter Michael QHDS BDS BA MGDSRCS(Ed) qs Born 22/10/47 . . . . . . 1 Jan

Wing Commanders

1984

Knowles, R. C. BDS
LDSRCS   15 Dec

1992

Nottingham, J. A. BDS
MGDSRCS(Ed) qs   2 Apr
Mayhew, M. T. MSc
BDS DDPHRCS jsdc
qs   5 Dec

1994

Monaghan, A. M. BDS
FDSRCSEng qss   12 Jan

1995

McCarthy, D. MSc BDS
MGDSRCS(Eng)
DGDP(UK) LDSRCS
qss   21 Apr
Brown, R. T. M. BDS
MGDSRCS(Ed) psc(j)   18 June

1996

Knight, H. I. MSc BDS
MGDSRCS(Eng)
DDPHRCS
LDSRCS   30 Jan
Senior, N. J. MSc BDS
MGDSRCS(Eng)   31 July
Harper, K. A. MSc BDS
FDSRCSEng
MGDSRCS(Eng)
MRD qss   1 Aug
Bows, R. W. BDS BA
MGDSRCS(Ed) qss   22 Aug

1997

Gibbons, A. J. MA BDS
MB BChir FDSRCSEd
FRCS(Edin) LDSRCS
qss   16 Mar
Bambridge, D. E. BDS   5 Aug

1998

Birkett, A. C. BDS   2 Jan
Nelson, T. A. B. BChD
FDSRCSEng   3 Feb
Fleming, J. C. MSc BDS
MGDSRCS(Eng)
LDSRCS   4 Apr
Chadwick, A. R. BDS
MFDSRCPS(Glas)
qss   10 Sept
Duffy, S. BDS   29 Oct

1999

Cox, J. J. LDSRCS   1 Apr
Brooks, E. A. S. BDS   6 July
Hamshaw, G. BSc BDS   16 July
Boyle, L. M. BDS
MGDSRCS(Eng)
MFDSRCS   8 Sept
McDavitt, J. N. MSc
BDS
MGDSRCPS(Glas)
qss1   18 Dec

2000

Cook, C. BDS qss   4 Jan
Gowing, S. T. J. BDS
qss   4 Jan
Rhodes, C. E. LLM BDS
MGDSRCPS(Glas)   4 Jan
Cook, E. BChD qs   23 Feb
Jones, T. W. MSc BDS   6 Mar
Frick, T. BDS   2 Aug
King, J. M. BDS qs   11 Aug
Austin, J. F. BDS
MGDSRCPS(Glas)
qss   13 Sept

2001

Reith, M. J. BDS qss   10 Aug

2002

Richardson, M. H. MSc
BDS MGDSRCS(Eng)
qs   29 Jan

Squadron Leaders

1993

Sinclair, J. W. BDS   1 Dec

1995

Lloyd, M. V. BDS   20 Jan

1996

Byford, M. BDS
MFGDP(UK) qss   13 Jan
Macbeth, N. D.
BDS   25 Jan
Laird, L. M. BDS   23 Aug
Hurst, S. E. BDS   25 Aug
Neppalli, R. P. K. BDS
DGDPRCS   25 Aug
Doyle, S. B. BDS   1 Sept
Ilsley, J. D. BDS   1 Nov

1997

Thomas, S. R. BDS   6 Jan
Wynne, J. E. BDS   17 Jan
Towlerton, A. J.
BDS   23 May
Savage, A. BDS
MFGDP(UK)
MFDSRCS(Ed)   20 Sept
Foster, M. R. BDS
MGDSRCS(Eng)
DGDP(UK) qs   14 Dec

1998

Smith, R. M. BDS
MFGDP(UK)
MFDSRCS(Ed)   21 Apr
Ritchie, K. L. BDS   3 Dec

1999

Scott, L. A. BDS
qcc   14 June

2000

Jones, I. R. BDS   23 June

Squadron Leaders	Flight Lieutenants	Pilot Officers

Squadron Leaders

2000—contd

Gagnon, R. L. BDS
  MFGDP(UK)   27 June

2001

Ross, A. M. BDS
  MFGDP(UK)   6 Aug
Clare, M. D. BDS   8 Aug

Flight Lieutenants

1996

Clayton, D. R. BChD   8 Aug

1997

Butler, S. R. BChD   7 Aug
Robb, S. M. BMSc BDS   7 Aug
Agbanobi, K. E. BDS   7 Oct

1998

Galbraith, J. R. BDS   5 Aug
Abbott, P. J. BDS   6 Aug
Houvenaghel, W. L.
  BDS   6 Aug
Mitchell, S. A. BDS   6 Aug

1999

Coburn, D. G. BDS   28 Jan

2000

Kirman, S. A. BChD   3 Aug
Porter, N. P. BDS   3 Aug
Smith, A. E. BDS   3 Aug

2001

Friend, M. J. W. BMSc
  BDS   9 Aug

2002

Smith, R. E. BDS   6 Feb

Pilot Officers

2001

Buckley, F. P.   3 Sept
Kenney, G. R.   21 Sept
Kudanowska, I.   24 Oct

PRINCESS MARY'S ROYAL AIR FORCE NURSING SERVICE

PRINCESS MARY'S ROYAL AIR FORCE

NURSING SERVICE

AIR CHIEF COMMANDANT H.R.H. PRINCESS ALEXANDRA, The Hon. Lady Ogilvy, GCVO

All Officers of Princess Mary's Royal Air Force Nursing Service hold the qualification of
Registered General Nurse or Registered Mental Nurse

Group Captains

1998

Forward, Bernard John ARRC BA RNT CertEd qs Born 27/1/48 . . . . 1 July

2002

Reid, Rosalie Ann OBE ARRC QHNS RM DipHE Born 26/4/46 . . . . 1 Jan

Wing Commanders		Squadron Leaders			
				Hutton, D. J. BSc	10 July
				Onions, A. C.	20 Sept

Wing Commanders

1997

Chew, L. RRC qs — 1 Jan

1998

White, M. E. ARRC qs — 1 July

1999

Williams, W. B. RM qs — 1 Jan

2000

Gross, J. L. qs — 1 July
Wroe, B. CertEd qs — 1 July

2001

Callcott, S. T. RM qs — 1 July

2002

Beaumont, S. P. BA qs — 1 July
Warburton, A. M. — 1 July

Squadron Leaders

1987

Smith, J. A. RM qss — 22 July

1990

Massey, L. A. qs — 24 June

1991

Henderson, C. A. ARRC RM qss — 26 Dec

1994

Hill, D. M. W. MSc BSc FInstLM RMN qs — 17 Sept
Harper, P. J. — 3 Nov

1995

Cromie, S. E. MA CertFE RNT — 6 Apr
Baker, C. A. RM — 4 Oct

1996

Devenport-Ward, A. BSc RM DipN qss — 14 Jan
Jones, J. A. RM — 27 Jan
Barnes, M. qss — 8 Apr
Stewart, H. M. qs — 15 Apr
Gullidge, K. A. — 9 June
Ferguson, P. G. — 25 June
Roscoe, F. G. qss — 5 July

1997

Petter-Bowyer, D. A. RM — 21 Mar
Oakley, S. J. — 17 Nov

1998

Dickin, L. qss — 10 Jan
Durrant, Y. F. RM — 3 Mar
Ward, P. J. ARRC qs — 21 May

1999

Cushen, P. B. DipMgmt qsb qs — 9 Feb
Mackie, K. C. MSc BA — 21 May
Evans, A. W. BSc — 26 June
Hopper, T. M. — 31 Dec

2000

Tue, N. S. DipN qss — 18 Jan
Lockton, L. A. — 31 Jan
Priestley, M. J. MSc BSc — 5 Feb
Jones, D. C. — 6 Mar
Spragg, P. M. qcc — 15 Oct

2001

Smart, C. A. — 6 Feb
Ewart, A. P. G. — 16 Sept
Gardner, J. DipHE — 8 Oct

2002

Ball, S. J. RM — 6 Jan
Covill, L. M. — 13 Jan
Hymas, P. B. ARRC RM qcc — 8 Feb
Cuthbert, S. J. — 20 Feb
Griffiths, T. A. — 22 Feb
Ulke, D. — 2 Mar
Danby, A. P. — 3 Mar
Wallace, J. H. RM — 8 May
Raper, A. — 21 May

Flight Lieutenants

1994

Van Zwanenberg, G. qcc	9 June
Duffy, K. M. BSc	26 June
Doyle, S.	28 July
Davenport, J. RM	3 Aug
Toomer, S. F. RM	1 Sept
Edmondson, M. J.	18 Oct
Hardie, L. C.	8 Nov
Whiting, D.	14 Nov
Harrison, R. J.	15 Nov

1995

Lamb, D. W.	2 May
Rapson, K.	21 June
Parke, B. A.	7 Aug

1996

Hutchison, F. M.	22 Apr
Dyson, N. C.	27 July
Lester, A. J.	15 Oct
Roberts, A. E. BSc RM	22 Nov
Winslade, K. E. RM	8 Dec

1997

Quick, P. A. RSCN DipHE	4 Feb
Anderson, H. A. RM	27 May
Pascoe, S. W. BSc	27 May
Kiddey, V. K. RSCN RM	20 Aug
Phythian, S. M.	20 Aug
Rider, I. BSc RM	1 Sept
Swain, I. S. DipN	1 Sept
Parker, N.	8 Dec

1998

Mathison, E.	7 Jan
Bell, H. S. MSc	3 Feb
Richardson, L. Y. R. DipHE	14 Mar
Lewis, A.	26 May
Ricklesford, V. L.	12 July
McCann, D. C.	12 Sept
Ducker, S. J. BSc	11 Nov
Wadeson, Y.	15 Dec

1999

Salmon, A. C. RMN	14 Feb
Arroyo, G. H.	5 May
Pawlak, M.	24 May
Hall, J. P.	16 June
Pavitt, A. J.	24 June
Compton, N.	17 July
Peverall, S. RM	16 Nov
Allbones, N. L. DipHE	21 Nov
Hazzard, I.	24 Nov

2000

Van Carrapiett, D. M. B.	14 Jan
Lynn, S. B.	5 Mar
Grimmer, K. L.	9 Mar
Martyn, A. L.	23 Apr
Ryder, L. M.	9 June
Brown, J. S.	18 June
Tyler, S. J.	30 June
Bedford, S. T. BSc	22 July
Harris, M. J. BA	11 Sept
Dale, F. M. BSc RM	10 Oct
McKillop-Duffy, P. S. MSc	17 Dec

2001

Gibbs, H. L. DipN	23 Feb
Grady, E. L.	9 June
Colehouse, K. RSCN	17 Sept

2002

Martin, H. M. BSc	2 Jan
Nicol, A. W.	13 Jan

Flying Officers

1998

Marshall, J. M. BSc	7 Aug
Hart, D. A.	8 Sept
Dadds, C. M.	4 Oct
Thompson, C. J. BA	16 Dec

MEDICAL TECHNICIAN BRANCH

MEDICAL SECTION

Wing Commander		Squadron Leaders		Flight Lieutenants	
2001		**2000**		**1996**	
Farmer, T. P. MSc	1 Jan	Bain, R. MSc	4 June	Jones, R. J. BA MCSP	
				CertEd	1 June
		2001		Start, I. J.	10 June
				Beach, C. J.	27 Sept
		Dray, M. D.	1 Jan		
		Earp, M. T.	1 Jan	**1997**	
		Lawson, S. P. BSc			
		qs	11 May	Coleman, M. J. BSc	1 Aug
				Biggs, C. J.	27 Dec
				1998	
				Culpan, D. S. qcc	17 Aug
				2001	
				Castle, S. J.	22 July

Flying Officers

1998

Moyes, G. K.	26 Nov
Singleton, C. J.	23 Dec

MEDICAL TECHNICIAN BRANCH

(DENTAL SECTION)

Wing Commander	**Flight Lieutenants**	
1998	**1997**	
Stacey, J. qss 1 July	Mitchell, W. A. MSc	
	MCIPD	26 July
	1998	
	Tilling, E. J.	26 Nov
	1999	
	Harris, T. C.	14 Feb

MEDICAL SUPPORT BRANCH

Wing Commanders		Squadron Leaders		Flight Lieutenants	
1992		**1997**		**1992**	
Woods, T. L. qss	1 Jan	Cranfield, A. qs	1 Jan	Robinson, J. RMN qss	21 Jan
		Batley, R. J. qs	1 July		
1997				**1996**	
Lane, K. MBA DipMgmt		**1998**		Stezaker, M. BSc CBiol	
qs	1 Jan	Staniforth, C. A.		MIBiol	6 Oct
Rippon, D. qss	1 July	DipMgmt qs	1 Jan		
				1998	
1999		**1999**		Miranda, D. A. qss1	6 Oct
Allaway, R. J. BEd		Fleetwood, W. M. qs	1 Jan		
qss	1 Jan	Choppen, P. I. BSc		**1999**	
		CBiol MIBiol			
		DipMgmt qss2	1 July	Carlin, N. J. qs	27 Nov
2000		Smith, H. A. qs	1 July		
Cowan, A. MRIPH				**2000**	
MCMI DipMgmt		**2000**			
qs	1 Jan	Quinn, A. C. MHSM		Walker, M. J. qsb qss1	28 May
		DipMgmt qs	1 Jan	Cowell, J. A.	23 July
		Baird, W. P. MHSM qss	1 July		
2001				**2001**	
Burgess, P. MSc		**2001**			
DipMgmt qs	1 Jan	White, J. E. qsb qcc	1 Jan	Picken, S. A.	9 Jan
Hoyle, D. L. MSc				Hughes, A. J. qcc	27 May
MHSM qs	1 Jan				

Flying Officers

1994

Rutherford, I. R. E.	9 Feb

1996

Shephard, M. R.	11 Sept

1998

Ruffles, H. R. BSc	2 Oct
Dennis, J. BSc	30 Nov

1999

Ford, S. A. qsb qcc	20 Jan
Day, B. G. J.	22 July
Downes, C. qss	22 July
Rixon, F. BA	6 Aug
Rowley, C. W.	8 Oct
Fox, N. P. BSc	28 Nov

CIVIL CONSULTANTS

Mr J. P. Acheson MRCP FRCS FRCOphth
(Ophthalmology)

Dr B. A. Bannister MSc FRCP (Tropical Medicine &
Infectious Diseases)

Professor C. L. R. Bartlett MSc MB BS FRCPath
FRCP FFPHM (Communicable Disease Control)

Dr A. J. Boakes MSc MB BS FFARCS (Genito-
Urinary Medicine)

Mr A. E. Brown MB BS BDS FDSRCPS(Glas)
FDSRCS(Eng) FRCS(Edin) MRCS(Eng) LRCP
(Oral and Maxillo-Facial Surgery)

Mr P. D. Burge FRCS (Orthopaedic (Hand) Surgery)

Dr A. K. Clarke BSc MB BS FRCP (Rheumatology
and Rehabilitation)

Professor R. C. D. S. Coombes MD PhD FRCP
(Medical Oncology)

Mr C. B. Croft FRCS FRCS(Ed)(Laryngology)

Dr A. R. C. Cummin MA DM BM BCh MRCP
(Respitory Physiology)

Mr D. J. Dandy MD MChir FRCS (Knee Surgery)

Dr M. P. Deahl MA MB BS FRCPsych MPhil
(Psychiatry)

Mr M. A. Edgar MA MChir MB FRCS (Orthopaedic
Surgery)

Professor P. J. A. H. Foex DPhil MD MA FRCA
(Anaesthetics)

Professor G. L. French MB BS BSc MD FRCPath
FRCPA (Microbiology)

Mr P. Goldstraw FRCS(Eng) FRCS(Ed) (Thoracic
Surgery)

Professor E. C. Gordon-Smith MA MSc MB FRCP
FRCPath (Civil Consultant in Haematology)

Dr R. Gregory (Neurology)

Dr I. W. F. Hanham FCRP FRCR MA MB BChir
MRCP FFR DMRT (Radiotherapy)

Professor J. M. Harrington CBE BSc MSc MD
FRCP FFOM RCP (Epidemiology)

Dr G. R. V. Hughes MD FRCP (Rheumatology)

Mr D. H. A. Jones FRCS FRCSEd(Orth)(Paediatric
Orthopaedic Surgery)

Dr J. Keenan MA MB BChir FRCPath (Clinical
Chemistry)

Professor W. R. Lees FRCR FRACR(Hon)
(Radiology)

Professor A. O. Mansfield CBE ChM FRCS
(Vascular Surgery)

Dr E. B. MacDonald MB ChB FRCP(Glas) FRCP
FFOM DIH (Occupational Medicine)

Professor D. G. McDevitt DSc MD FRCP FFPM
FRSE (Experimental Medicine)

Dr C. M. Mckee MD MSc FRCP(UK) FFPHM (Public
Health Medicine)

Professor D. McLeod FRCS FRCOphth
(Ophthalmology (Retinal Surgery)

Dr A. T. Mitchell MB BS MRCP (Paediatrics)

Professor A. J. Newman Taylor OBE FRCP FFOM
FMedSci (Chest Diseases)

Mr M. Powell FRCS (Neurosurgery)

Mr D. W. Proops BSc FRCS (Otology)

Dr A. F. Rickards FRCP FACC FESC (Cardiology)

Dr J. W. Scadding BSc MB BS MD FRCP
(Neurology)

Mr D. S. Soutar MB ChB FRCS(Ed) FRCS(Glas)
ChM (Plastic Surgery)

Dr J. M. Thomas MS MRCP FRCS (Oncology)

Mr J. K. H. Webb MB BS FRCS (Spinal Trauma)

Professor P. D. Wheeler PhD MSc (Acoustic
Science)

Mr P. Worlock DM FRCS (Orthopaedic Trauma)

HONORARY CIVIL CONSULTANTS

Mr P. Banks BDS MB BS FDSRCS MRCS LRCP (Oral and Maxillofacial Surgery)

J. Barwood OBE MRCS LRCP DPH DIH FRAeS Group Captain (Retd) (Accident Investigation)

Professor R. W. Beard MD MB BChir FRCOG DObstRCOG (Obstetrics and Gynaecology)

Professor R. J. Berry RD Ost.J DPhil MD FRCP FRCR (HON FACR) FFOM (Radiobiology)

Professor R. S. Bluglass CBE MD FRCPsych FRCP DPM (Psychiatry)

Mr J. B. Booth FRCS MRAeS (Otology)

Professor W. Burns DSc ChB FRCP DRCOG (Acoustic Science)

Dr S. J. Carne CBE MB BS MRCS LRCP FRCGP DCH (General Practice)

Air Vice Marshal J. Ernsting CB OBE PhD MB BS BSc FRAeS MFOM MRCS FRCP RAF(Retd) (Aviation Medicine)

Dr M. R. Geake FRCP (Chest Diseases)

Dr F StC Golden OBE PhD MB BCh DAvMed (Survival Medicine)

Dr J. Harper MBE MB ChB FRCP(Edin) FRCPsych DPM (Psychiatry)

Dr J. C. Hasler OBE MD MA BS FRCGP DA DCM (General Practice)

Mr P. L. James FDS FRCS LRCP (Oral and Maxillo-Facial Surgery)

Dr R. C. Kocen TD FRCP (Neurology)

Professor D. Lowe MD FRCS FRCPath FIBiol (Histopathology)

T. F. Macrae OBE DSc PhD (Nutrition)

Dr W. R. MacRae MB ChB FRCA FFARCSI(Hon) FRCS(Ed) (Anaesthetics)

Mr M. A. Makey MS FRCS (Thoracic Surgery)

Professor J. R. E. Mills DDS FDS DOrthRCS (Orthodontics)

Air Vice Marshal P. J. O'Connor CB OBE MD BCh FRCP(Edin) FRCPsych DPM, RAF (Retd) (Neuropsychiatry)

Professor J. P. Payne MB ChB FFARCS DA (Anaesthetics)

Professor Sir Keith Peters FRS (Renal Medicine)

Professor I. Phillips MA MD FRCP FRCPath (Microbiology)

Mr A. H. N. Roberts MA BSc BM BCh FRCS (Plastic Surgery)

Mr M. D. Sanders FRCP FRCS FRCOPath (Ophthalmology)

Dr D. A. D. Slattery MBE FRCP FFOM (Occupational Medicine)

Dr W. Somerville CBE MD NUI MB BCh BAO FRCP (Cardiology)

Dr A. G. Stansfeld MA(Cantab) MB BChi FRCPath (Histopathology)

Professor Sir Eric Stroud BSc MB BCh FRCP DCH (Paediatrics)

Air Commodore P. D. Sutton MB BS FRCR DMRD RAF (Retd) (Radiology)

Mr K. Till MA MB BCh FRCS MRCS LRCP (Paediatric Neurosurgeon)

Mr J. E. A. Wickham MS MD BSc FRCS FRCP FRCR (Urology)

CHAPLAINS BRANCH

The Air Member for Personnel administers the Chaplains Branch on behalf of the Minister of Defence for the Armed Forces

The Chaplains belonging to the Church of England are under the control of the Chaplain-in-Chief

Chaplains belonging to Churches other than the Church of England are under the control of the respective Principal Chaplains

Chaplains are known and addressed by their eccleciastical titles and not by the rank titles equivalent to their relative status in the RAF (QR 73)

Chaplain-in-Chief with the relative rank of Air Vice-Marshal

2001

Church of England—
The Venerable Ronald David Hesketh QHC BA Born 16/6/47 . . . . 21 Sept

Principal Chaplains: with the relative rank of Group Captain

1999

Roman Catholic—
The Rev Mgr Thomas James Devany QHC VG Born 5/7/43 . . . . 13 Sept

2001

Church of Scotland—
Rev Peter Watson Mills QHC BD CPS qss Born 9/2/55 . . . . 31 May

Chaplains with the relative rank of Wing Commander

1988

Church of England—
Rev D. S. Mackenzie   21 Apr

1991

Church of England—
Rev T. R. Lee AKC FRSA df qss   20 Jan

1996

Church of England—
Rev C. W. Long BA BTh   6 June

Church of England—
Rev S. J. Ware QHC BA   6 June

1997

Church of England—
Rev. A. L. Willis BA   14 Aug

Church of England—
Rev I. F. Greenhalgh qss   13 May

Church of Scotland—
Rev D. Shaw LTh CPS   13 May

1999

Roman Catholic—
Rev J. A. Daly   21 Jan

Methodist—
Rev J. R. Russell   17 Mar

2000

Church of England—
Rev E. Core MTh   19 Jan

Church of England—
Rev C. W. K. Berry-Davies   3 Mar

Church of England—
Rev J. W. G. Hughes MBE   24 Sept

Church of England—
Rev M. F. Loveless   28 Sept

2001

Church of England—
Rev L. E. D. Clark MBE   15 Feb

Church of England—
Rev W. L. F. Mounsey   18 Apr

Church of England—
Rev L. E. Spicer MEd   1 Aug

Church of England—
Rev D. T. Osborn BD AKC   1 Nov

2002

Church of England—
Rev A. J. D. Gilbert BA qs   1 Jan

Church of Scotland—
G. T. Craig BD qss   3 Apr

Chaplains with the relative rank of Squadron Leader

1988

Church of England—
Rev N. P. Heron BA BTh   10 May

1989

Church of England—
Rev D. Wynne-Jones   31 Jan

Church of England—
Rev K. Maddy GRSM MA   6 Mar

Church of England—
Rev J. E. Coyne MA BA   21 Aug

1990

Church of England—
Rev M. J. Elliott MTh PGDipTh PGCE
    FRSA   15 Jan

Church of England—
Rev A. C. Gatrill BTh   15 Jan

Church of England—
Rev A. J. Davies MTh BA PGCE qss   21 May

Church of England—
Rev I. S. Ward BD qss   21 May

Methodist—
Rev R. J. Taylor   25 June

227

Chaplains with the relative rank of Squadron Leader

1990—contd

Roman Catholic—
Rev A. J. Wilson .... 27 Aug

1991

Church of England—
Rev N. B. P. Barry BA qss .... 25 Feb

Church of England—
Rev J. P. Chaffey BA qs .... 20 May

Presbyterian—
Rev D. A. Edgar .... 20 May

Roman Catholic—
Rev P. A. Owens qs .... 20 May

Church of England—
Rev A. D. Hewett BA .... 1 July

Church of England—
Rev A. B. McMullon BSc .... 1 July

Church of Scotland—
Rev A. J. Jolly qcc .... 9 Aug

Church of England—
Rev R. J. Pentland qss .... 26 Aug

1992

Church of England—
Rev J. K. Wilson .... 13 Jan

Church of England—
Rev C. E. Hewitt MA BA .... 24 Feb

Church of England—
Rev G. Williams BD .... 6 Mar

Methodist—
Rev R. B. Hardman qss1 .... 25 Aug

Church of England—
Rev A. J. Turner .... 25 Aug

1993

Church of England—
Rev A. D. Bissell .... 23 Aug

Roman Catholic—
Rev C. Webb .... 15 Nov

Church of England—
Rev J. W. K. Taylor MSSc BD BTh .... 7 Dec

1994

Church of England—
Rev S. P. Iredale BA qss .... 21 Feb

Church of England—
Rev G. S. Brown .... 2 Aug

Church of England—
Rev J. C. Hetherington .... 5 Sept

1997

Church of England—
Rev A. T. Coates .... 8 Aug

Church of England—
Rev I. A. Jones BA .... 8 Aug

1998

Church of England—
Rev J. M. Beach BA BSc .... 7 Aug

Roman Catholic—
Rev J. E. Caulfield BD qcc .... 7 Aug

Roman Catholic—
Rev M. W. Hodges MTh .... 7 Aug

Methodist—
Rev M. A. Olanrewaju MA .... 7 Aug

Church of England—
Rev P. A. Rennie BSc LTh .... 7 Aug

1999

Methodist—
Rev K. M. Hart .... 5 Feb

Church of England—
Rev T. Wright BSc .... 5 Feb

2000

Baptist—
Rev P. S. Edwards .... 5 Aug

Roman Catholic—
Rev R. T. J. Halshaw .... 5 Aug

Church of England—
Rev M. P. D. Kennard .... 5 Aug

Chaplains with the relative rank of Squadron Leader

2000—contd

Church of England—
Rev E. J. Rance MA   5 Aug

2001

Church of England—
Rev V. R. Dunstan-Meadows BTh   12 June

Chaplains with the relative rank of Flight Lieutenant

1996

Baptist—
Rev B. McNeil MA   3 Feb

Methodist—
Rev P. Mellor   25 May

Church of Ireland—
Rev G. E. Withers BSc BTh   25 May

Church of England—
Rev S. J. Radley BTh   2 July

Church of Scotland—
Rev C. N. Kellock MA BD   27 Sept

1997

Roman Catholic—
Rev C. H. Marsden   1 Feb

Roman Catholic—
Rev I. R. Boyle MA BD BSc   9 Aug

Methodist—
Rev P. Lee BSc   1 Sept

Church of Ireland—
Rev J. M. Wylie MTh BD BSc   30 Sept

1998

Church of England—
Rev N. P. A. Pnematicatos MA BA   1 Sept

2000

Church of England
Rev G. L. Collingwood MA BA   3 Nov

LEGAL BRANCH

Air Vice-Marshal

1997

Weeden, John LLB Born 21/6/49. . . . . (Solicitor) 1 July

Air Commodore

1998

Charles, Richard Anthony LLB Born 24/2/54 . . . . (Solicitor) 1 Jan

Group Captains

1998

Boothby, William Henry BA Born 18/9/51 . . . . (Solicitor) 1 Jan

2000

Irvine, Lindsay John MA DipLaw Born 5/11/59 . . . . (Barrister) 1 Jan
McGrigor, Alastair James Buchanan Born 27/11/53 . . . . (Solicitor) 1 Jan

2001

Harding, Geoffrey John LLB Born 28/2/58 . . . . (Solicitor) 1 Jan

Wing Commanders

1993

Burns, P. A.
BA   (Solicitor) 9 June

1994

Baker, T. T. J.
LLB   (Solicitor) 21 July

1995

Wood, C. N. W.
MA   (Barrister) 4 Jan
Ash, D. LLB (Solicitor) 3 Feb

1999

Connell, P. J.
BA   (Barrister) 2 July

2000

Kell, S. J. LLB
qab   (Barrister) 25 Aug

Squadron Leaders

1997

Rowlinson, S. P.
LLB   (Solicitor) 18 Aug

2000

Dunn, R. J. LLB
qs   (Solicitor) 8 Feb
Dureau, S. LLB
qcc   (Solicitor) 8 Feb
Foster, M. S. LLB qab
qcc   (Solicitor) 8 Feb
Leonard, I.
LLB   (Solicitor) 8 Feb

2001

Mardell, A.
LLB   (Solicitor) 6 Feb
Wood, T. J.
LLB   (Solicitor) 18 Feb
Donington, S. J.
LLB   (Solicitor) 22 Apr

2002

Cowley, A. M.
LLB   (Barrister) 5 Feb
Severs, N. J.
LLB   (Solicitor) 5 Feb
McKendrick, A. G.
LLB   (Solicitor) 19 Feb

Flight Lieutenants

1994

Ip, K. H. LLB (Barrister) 10 May

1998

Dempsey, D. A.
BA   (Solicitor) 16 May
Pattenden, M. S.
MA   (Barrister) 6 Aug

1999

Sanders, K. J.
LLB   (Solicitor) 5 Aug

2000

Billingham, T. D.
BA   (Solicitor) 3 Feb
Froggatt, V. H. S.
LLB   (Solicitor) 3 Feb
Robertson, J. D.
BA   (Solicitor) 3 Feb
Thomas, V. L.
LLB   (Barrister) 3 Feb
Bremner, K. D. LLB
qcc   (Solicitor) 5 Apr
Phelps, M.
MA   (Barrister) 8 Apr
Fitzhenry, D. M. J.
LLM   (Solicitor) 25 May
Quincey, T. N.
LLB   (Solicitor) 25 May
Sanger-Davies, M. A.
LLB   (Solicitor) 25 May

2001

Worsley, S. E.
LLB   (Solicitor) 1 Feb
McClelland, E. J.
BA   (Solicitor) 9 Aug

DIRECTORS OF MUSIC

Wing Commander	Squadron Leaders	Flight Lieutenant
1998	**1997**	**1994**
Wiffin, R. K. OBE BA 　FTCL LRAM 　ARCM　　　1 July	Stirling, S. L. MA BMus 　FTCL LRAM 　ARCM　　　15 Aug	Bain, G. J. BA MIL 　LRAM ARCM qss　　10 Oct
	2000	
	Compton, D. W. 　ARCM　　　1 Jan Stubbs, D. J. G. BA 　PGCE ARCM 　LGSM　　　29 Mar	

WARRANT OFFICERS

1983

France, H. J. AFM   10 Dec

1985

Berry, I. W.   4 Nov
Davies, D. E.   11 Nov
Cooper, R. G.   13 Nov

1986

Jones, K. L.   25 Feb
Hooper, R. C.   1 Apr
Martin, P. H. MBE   2 Apr
Gipson, P. S.   30 May
Sweeney, E. W. T.   2 June
Bradford, I. D. R. H.   1 Aug
Wells, P. A.   24 Nov
Vince, L. R.   15 Dec

1987

McGrath, S. C.   27 Jan
McCombie, S.   15 Apr
Patrick, A. K. MBE   27 Apr
Voisey, J. J.   18 May
Cutler, C. J.   1 June
Sweeney, P. MBE   1 June
Kavanagh, J. J.   17 June
Facey, D. W.   20 July
Blair, J. R.   3 Aug
Jarrel, P. A. MBE   3 Aug
Roffey, J. M. MBE   3 Aug
Coppell, D. J. A. BEM   10 Aug
Standley, J. F.   17 Aug
Kellas, J.   24 Aug
Marshall, T. C.   2 Sept
Parker, B. BEM   7 Oct
Hamilton-Wilks, B. P.   6 Nov
Blair, T. F. BEM   1 Dec

1988

Gray, R. C.   1 Mar
Day, E. C. MBE   11 Apr
Kirkbride, J. S.   2 May
Bailey, P. W.   9 May
Taylor, K. L.   9 May
Hughes, B. W.   23 May

Wass, M.   23 May
Males, D.   27 June
Hodgetts, R. D.   4 July
Penrose, B. L.   4 July
Powell, M.   4 July
Smith, N. P.   7 Aug
Shaw, R. G. MBE BEM   30 Aug
Ayres, P. C. R. MBE   8 Sept
Pashley, D. A.   28 Sept
Saker, G.   30 Sept
Francis, R. A.   21 Oct
Connell, O. BEM   24 Oct
Raw, M. G.   28 Oct
McHugh, R. MBE   9 Dec

1989

Hughes, S. MBE BEM   14 Feb
Aitken, J. O.   20 Feb
Wright, J. R. B. BEM   20 Feb
McGilligan, M.   28 Mar
Livesey, G. BEM   31 Mar
Kelly, P. J. MBE   3 Apr
Gormley, A.   27 Apr
Marcer, P.   8 May
Carnan, B. N.   22 May
Howard, J.   30 May
Gant, R. W.   19 June
Haveron, A. B. BEM   19 June
White, W. MBE   26 June
Gore, M. F.   3 July
Allcock, M. W.   10 July
Dixon, M. G.   10 July
Morgan, W. BEM   10 July
Lee, P. J.   17 July
Steadman, K.   27 July
Knowles, A.   30 July
Welsh, B. H.   31 July
Brennan, N. P.   7 Aug
Tappin, D. BEM   7 Aug
Kidd, R. D.   10 Aug
Curzon, P.   21 Aug
Hyde, J. F.   11 Sept
Hyde, R.   18 Sept
Fosh, G. E. BEM   2 Oct
Mullen, J. L.   6 Oct
Philp, G. H. G. C. BEM   9 Oct
Simons, T. C.   9 Oct
Leiper, E. A.   16 Oct
Davies, T. R. W.   18 Oct
Page, D. C.   6 Nov
Roberts, P.   6 Nov
Stewart, A. B. MBE   27 Nov

Collins, W.   2 Dec

1990

Hampson, A. J.   8 Jan
Martin, J.   8 Jan
Roberts, R. G.   8 Jan
Woods, K. W.   9 Jan
Chalmers, M. A.   29 Jan
Smith, J. A.   5 Feb
Smith, J. D.   16 Feb
Cain, B. BEM   26 Feb
Angus, E. B. BEM   5 Mar
Goodwin, A. R. P. BEM   5 Mar
Walley, I. J.   19 Mar
Fields, B. G.   26 Mar
Herd, I.   29 Mar
Blyth, R.   2 Apr
Truelove, A. S.   2 Apr
Dickinson, M. D.   4 Apr
May, J. H. MBE BEM   24 Apr
Bilner, C. J. BEM   29 Apr
Griggs, J.   9 May
Garfoot, B. R.   25 May
Crisp, J. A.   28 May
Anderson, C. C.   8 June
Norris, I. M. MBE   11 June
Gorman, J. W.   18 June
Salisbury, E. MBE BEM   16 July
Lee, P. V.   30 July
Woodley, B. W.   30 July
Norton, G.   5 Aug
Jordan, M. R.   20 Aug
Cheshire, A. J.   28 Aug
Vater, J. BEM   28 Aug
Wesley, D. A.   28 Aug
Dodd, D. J.   28 Sept
Tyler, P. A.   1 Oct
Ashwood, A. J.   4 Oct
Cowling, N. W. F.   10 Oct
Foulds, R. J.   17 Oct
Smooker, E. P.   22 Oct

1991

Peacock, A. M.   11 Jan
Dunphy, A. J. MBE   4 Feb
Shiells, A. D.   4 Mar
Pointon, D.   25 Mar
Nightingale, J. A. BEM   2 Apr
Jones, T. I.   3 Apr
Billingsley, J. L.   8 Apr

1991—contd

Stevens, J. H.	7 May
Ward, B. J.	13 May
Robertson, D.	17 June
Sparks, B. J.	17 June
Akers, P. A.	22 July
Smailes, M. J.	19 Aug
Gillett, P.	2 Sept
Taylor, M.	2 Sept
Price, I.	30 Sept
Wilson, R. B.	14 Oct
Graham, W. J. BEM	21 Oct
Crump, S. A.	4 Nov
Williams, W. E. R.	4 Nov

1992

Ingledew, V. E. MBE BEM	27 Apr
Luckhurst, A. R.	27 Apr
Mallison, J. G.	11 May
Molyneaux, R. C.	8 June
Low, W. R.	15 June
Curson, R. G.	20 July
Winspear, R. I.	27 July
Tyler, C. R.	2 Aug
Evans, G.	10 Aug
Jones, D.	10 Aug
McGill, B.	10 Aug
Tibble, C. G.	14 Sept
Jones, M. B.	25 Sept
McCune, T. BEM	5 Oct
Waterhouse, A. H.	5 Oct
Andrew, K. MBE BEM	23 Nov
Streek, M. A. MBE	30 Nov
Crossman, A. A. MBE	18 Dec

1993

O'Brien, D. J.	1 Mar
Sanderson, J. A.	5 Apr
Callaghan, A. J.	19 Apr
Andrews, N.	26 Apr
Mason, J. P.	1 June
Fleming, R. J.	7 June
Hurd, A. A. BEM	14 June
Hope, D. R.	21 June
Ayres, M. F. W.	28 June
Hannis, J.	28 June
Williams, R. J.	29 June
Lambert, S. W.	5 July
Dark, W. J.	12 July
Macrae, J. C. MBE	12 July
Duff, J.	19 July
Follett, S. K.	19 July
Milne, A. P. R.	26 July
Sowerby, P. J.	29 July

Wylie, J. S.	2 Aug
Kennedy, I.	16 Aug
Murray, D. G.	23 Aug
Sewell, C. P.	23 Aug
Edgeworth, J. R.	1 Sept
Scott, P. K.	20 Sept
Hoban, C.	4 Oct
Shipley, R.	25 Oct
Winters, I. S. MBE	1 Nov
Shepherdson, D.	8 Nov

1994

Wilcox, J. A.	17 Jan
McVey, F.	8 Feb
Harper, J. C.	21 Feb
Williams, K.	21 Feb
Kynaston, T. G.	28 Feb
Peirce, D.	28 Feb
Regan, D.	7 Mar
Downe, D. F.	22 Mar
Lloyd, R. C.	28 Mar
Forster, L. E.	5 Apr
Heaton, R. J.	5 Apr
Ramsdale, L. J.	25 Apr
Cardy, B. M. MBE	16 May
Nelson, J.	16 May
Hall, M. Mc L.	6 June
Champion, D. R.	13 June
Fell, G.	13 June
Stewart, J. B.	13 June
Bate, R. A.	4 July
Exton, N. P.	4 July
Magee, B. MBE	18 July
Fryer, K. P.	25 July
Rawle, A. P. MBE BEM	25 July
Hopkins, B.	15 Aug
Hunter, I. N.	12 Sept
Ruhle, C. J. K.	31 Oct
Ashman, W. L.	1 Nov
Hastie, J. P.	1 Nov
Walliman, C. G. M.	1 Nov
Pullen, C. R.	7 Nov
Davidson, J. H.	21 Nov
Kilner, I. F.	4 Dec
Feeney, P. J.	5 Dec
Wark, S.	12 Dec

1995

Fewings, P. A.	20 Feb
Meldrum, D. H. A. BEM	27 Feb
Beal, N. P.	21 Mar
Fox, T.	27 Mar
Stevenson, C. MBE	18 Apr
Woodbridge, F. D.	9 May
Kerr, A. McA. MBE	5 June
Jennings, M. D. MBE	12 June

Green, N. MBE	3 July
Hardinges, D. A.	3 July
Lord, B. D.	4 July
Harrison, R. A.	1 Aug
Kirkham, B. M.	1 Aug
O'Reilly, D. F.	1 Sept
Gascoigne, P. G.	4 Sept
Taylor, R.	4 Sept
Williams, L. F.	2 Oct
McMath, J. G. F. MBE BEM	23 Oct
Pollard, J. S.	6 Nov
Robertson, M.	20 Nov
Pettitt, D. J.	27 Nov
Hebert, C. J.	4 Dec
Horsburgh, J.	4 Dec
Mason, M. K.	4 Dec

1996

Hassall, B.	3 Jan
Sealy, K. A.	8 Jan
Battersby, P. G.	22 Jan
Martin, A. J.	25 Jan
Clarkson, D.	5 Feb
Hardy, D. P.	5 Feb
Norman, G. L. BEM	12 Feb
Yelland, D. J.	4 Mar
Ralph, R. R.	18 Mar
Smith, F. W. J. MBE BEM	31 Mar
Gilbert, P. C. BEM	7 Apr
Ramsay, W.	12 Apr
Lowry, W. S.	13 May
Anderton, N. H.	20 May
Harding, M. H. R.	20 May
Murray, A. BEM	20 May
Wells, M. J.	1 June
Brydon, J. W.	4 July
Howell, R. A.	8 July
Morris, I. S. MBE	15 July
Ogden, B.	15 July
Barnes, P.	29 July
Nicol, B.	5 Aug
Steen , G.	5 Aug
Burton, P. R.	12 Aug
Currie, W. R.	19 Aug
Hynam, R. A. MBE	19 Aug
Spicer, A. D.	19 Aug
Armitage, R.	27 Aug
Smaldon, C. R. E.	1 Sept
Payne, J. K. H.	2 Sept
Saul, A. W.	2 Sept
Logue, M. J.	9 Sept
Copsey, L. J.	16 Sept
Hodgett, P.	16 Sept
Nash, W. V.	16 Sept
Sheppard, A. B.	16 Sept

1996—contd		Burhouse, M. N. MBE	6 Aug	Straney, A. McC.	14 Sept
		Butt, M. A. MBE	11 Sept	Mair, K. A.	21 Sept
Granger, T. W.	23 Sept	Muir, J. M.	16 Sept	Lofting, P. J.	28 Sept
Muncey, R. D.	23 Sept	Smyth, J.	29 Sept	Winfield, D. J.	28 Sept
Hogg, R. J.	30 Sept	Ash, I. R.	6 Oct	Jenkinson, A. J.	5 Oct
Goldsmith, C. R.	7 Oct	Harmer, G. R.	27 Oct	Savage, D.	5 Oct
Jackson, P.	7 Oct	Harfield, G. D.	3 Nov	Robinson, J. V.	12 Oct
Restall, D. I.	7 Oct	Martin, I. D. M.	3 Nov	Hoyland, G.	26 Oct
Taylor, D. G.	14 Oct	McMahon, S. M.	3 Nov	Owen, K. R.	26 Oct
Cilia la Corte, F.	21 Oct	Dunlap, A. C.	17 Nov	West, N. J.	26 Oct
Day, D. W.	11 Nov	Austin, P. J.	24 Nov	Bolton, R.	2 Nov
Fraser, I. B.	11 Nov	Smith, W. K.	1 Dec	Boucher, D. S.	2 Nov
Hobbs, R. J.	11 Nov	Brompton, J. A.	8 Dec	Lawrence, P. A.	9 Nov
Shorthose, P. C.	11 Nov	Lovell, D. J.	8 Dec	Pimperton, W. K.	12 Nov
Stuart, R. M.	11 Nov	Wilson, D. C. BEM	8 Dec	MacKay, P. I.	16 Nov
Tarran, J. V.	2 Dec	MacDonald, N. Mc. K.	15 Dec	Banks, G. N.	30 Nov
Thorne, W. G.	2 Dec	Waite, C. A.	15 Dec	Dempsey, M. BEM	30 Nov
Bradfield, S. P.	9 Dec	Watkins, J. D.	22 Dec	Hurley, Y. G.	30 Nov
Blackman, C. A. R.	9 Dec			Sandilands, B. W.	30 Nov
Pepper, G. A.	9 Dec			Collins, E. J. BEM	14 Dec
Chopping, D. V.	16 Dec	**1998**			
Peace, M. J.	16 Dec				
Mepham, K. D.	30 Dec	Chapman, A. E. W.	5 Jan	**1999**	
		Ingram, M. J.	5 Jan		
		McCaffrey, J. P. M.	5 Jan	Jones, B. J. MBE	4 Jan
1997		Bishop, C.	21 Jan	Kindleysides, C. J.	4 Jan
		McTavish, J. C.	26 Jan	Latham-Warde, P.	4 Jan
Gwilliam. M. J.	6 Jan	Phillips, M. J.	2 Feb	Mylchreest, M. J. C.	4 Jan
Mahoney, B. R.	6 Jan	Kilby, S. A.	3 Feb	Tonks, D. A.	4 Jan
Rollings, G. M.	6 Jan	Murphy, S. J.	11 Feb	Thorpe, M. R.	5 Jan
Nuttall, G.	20 Jan	Ellis, D. G.	16 Feb	Murton, W. J.	1 Feb
Spencer, B. R.	27 Jan	Brown, S.	9 Mar	Waik, M. L.	1 Feb
Bennett, R. J. MBE	3 Feb	Harris, D. A.	9 Mar	Foran, B.	8 Feb
Farmer, W. G.	3 Feb	Thomas, G. J.	9 Mar	Jones, M. J. E.	15 Feb
Gilroy, F. A.	3 Feb	Fletcher, R. A.	16 Mar	Youens, S.	15 Feb
Morning, J. L. BEM	3 Feb	Hembry, G. H.	16 Mar	Bailey, D. J.	1 Mar
Loughlin, R. B.	10 Feb	Norrish, G. C.	30 Mar	Walters, A. C.	1 Mar
Claxton, R. M.	3 Mar	Symonds, C. L.	30 Mar	Wood, A.	1 Mar
Clayton, P.	3 Mar	Walton, K. D.	13 Apr	Lewin, A. D.	8 Mar
Gardner, A. H.	3 Mar	Smith, M. A.	15 Apr	Hoyland, G. R.	15 Mar
Rouget, D. J.	3 Mar	Piddington, M. J.	17 Apr	Jacobs, N. T.	15 Mar
Knight, J. G.	17 Mar	Carr, G.E.	27 Apr	Busby, C. J.	22 Mar
Vaughan, E. A.	26 Mar	Jackson, V.	27 Apr	Paterson, A. L. B.	22 Mar
Wolford, M. J.	31 Mar	McQuigg, C. W.	27 Apr	Evans, C. J.	29 Mar
Jaques, R. A.	2 Apr	Durrant, I.	1 May	Johnson, M. K.	1 Apr
Sperring, A. P.	2 Apr	Marsden T. G.	8 June	Heywood, G. J. MBE	6 Apr
Snowden, G. N.	7 Apr	Smith, K. M.	29 June	James, G. A.	6 Apr
Yeaman, E.	7 Apr	O'Donoghue, J.	6 July	Arling, J. M.	12 Apr
Main, A.	28 Apr	Kennedy, B.	22 July	Forder, M. C.	15 Apr
Payne, A. G.	5 May	Bell, R.	24 July	Goodstadt, E. A.	26 Apr
Stout, E. J.	6 May	Jackson, E. A.	30 July	Hewitt, M. S. MBE	26 Apr
Hutton, I. D.	9 June	Haynes, B. A.	10 Aug	Morse, S.	26 Apr
Birt, M. J.	7 July	Boswell, G. G.	24 Aug	Wier, P. R.	26 Apr
Harrhy, D. P. MBE	21 July	King, J. D. MBE	1 Sept	Watson, D.	4 May
Hunt, J. L.	28 July	Shaw, W. B.	1 Sept	Connell, B.	10 May
Myton, R.	28 July	Soo, G. C. BEM	2 Sept	Menzies, J.	17 May
Jones, P. MBE BEM	31 July	Brankin, D. G.	7 Sept	Nicholas, M.	24 May
Frizzell, G. H.	4 Aug	McDonald, J. H.	7 Sept	Marsden, D. BEM	1 June
Horseman, D. C.	4 Aug	Forry, A. P.	14 Sept	Farrow, S. R.	14 June
		Needham, K. J. MBE	14 Sept	Wood, D. I.	14 June

1999—contd		Pearson, R. P. MBE	4 Jan	Dwyer, M. J.	9 June
		Ryder, A. P.	4 Jan	Mallows, J. S.	19 June
Ibbs, B. V.	5 July	Scott, P. A.	4 Jan	Sparrow, W. J. D.	19 June
Mills, J. F.	5 July	Stephens, G. T.	4 Jan	Hilditch, S. H. E.	26 June
Telfer, T. C.	5 July	Moffat, R. W. BEM	17 Jan	Knight, M. C.	26 June
Lawson, R. J.	9 July	Perry, M. J.	24 Jan	Kelly, B. A.	1 July
Vicary, P. J. BEM	12 July	Tipping, A. A. J.	24 Jan	Biddle, M. J.	3 July
Bullock, L. G. A.	15 July	Hunter, R. D.	31 Jan	Regan, S. M.	10 July
Slater, S.	15 July	McBey, R. J. BEM	31 Jan	Hagendyk, P.	17 July
Gould, G.	19 July	Wintrip, C.	31 Jan	Jackson, N. D.	17 July
Bagwell, D. J.	31 July	Price, A. V.	10 Feb	Phillips, B. L.	17 July
Dickerson, C. J.	2 Aug	Stewart, G. H. J.	10 Feb	Whitehead, K.	17 July
Rivett, R. J.	3 Aug	Weeks, I. S.	14 Feb	Brown, S. B.	24 July
Campbell, G. S.	23 Aug	Hunt, A. S.	16 Feb	Morgan, A. A.	24 July
Johnson, G. R.	23 Aug	Lawman, M. J.	20 Feb	Kyle, R.	25 July
Lapham, D. J.	23 Aug	Kennedy, T.	21 Feb	Gordon, P. M.	27 July
Fulton, G. D.	27 Aug	Lane, G. C.	21 Feb	Parker, S. C. MBE	31 July
Smith, R. J.	31 Aug	Reeves, A. MBE	21 Feb	Barden, L. F.	1 Aug
Birch, E. N.	1 Sept	Taylor, A.	21 Feb	Funnell, R. J.	13 Aug
Polidano, P.	13 Sept	Horsley, B.	28 Feb	Finter, K.	14 Aug
Smith, G.	13 Sept	Moore, I.	28 Feb	Oldham, R. C.	14 Aug
Thomas, R. G.	13 Sept	Tyrer, A.	28 Feb	Thaneja, B. B. MBE	30 Aug
Eden, J. A.	4 Oct	Morris, W.	2 Mar	Bourke, M. P.	4 Sept
Hurt, P. J. MBE BEM	4 Oct	Alexander, G. A.	6 Mar	Bond, P. J.	11 Sept
Jones, B. J.	4 Oct	Hamilton, R. BEM	6 Mar	Creswell, S. M.	11 Sept
Leath, E. C.	4 Oct	Mintey, D. R.	6 Mar	Coombs, M. C.	18 Sept
Roberts, A. G.	4 Oct	Osborn, M. R. MBE	6 Mar	Pink, C.	18 Sept
Biddle, R. G. MBE	7 Oct	Waterall, B. D.	6 Mar	Beaumont, S. W.	25 Sept
Kitchen, D.	18 Oct	Adams, I. D. MBE	13 Mar	Poultney, D. W.	25 Sept
Parker, C.	18 Oct	Galloway, J. M.	13 Mar	Rodgers, M. J.	25 Sept
Blythe, I.	25 Oct	Hill, B. L.	13 Mar	Wickham, D.	25 Sept
McKee, R. M.	25 Oct	Wood, N. M. MBE	13 Mar	Flanagan, J.	2 Oct
Candlish, L. S.	1 Nov	Carrick, B. A.	14 Mar	Flanagan, J. H. G.	2 Oct
Montgomery, E. M.	1 Nov	Hillocks, M. R.	15 Mar	Hughes, I. G.	2 Oct
Morris, P. F.	1 Nov	Nicoll, A. R.	27 Mar	Cheshire, B. A.	9 Oct
Weir, G. A. M.	1 Nov	Plummer, K. S.	27 Mar	Hunter, J. K.	9 Oct
Williams, R.	1 Nov	Ward, S. J.	27 Mar	Bailey, M. A. MBE	16 Oct
Kane, M.	2 Nov	McSheffrey, D. A.	29 Mar	Vanstone, D. M.	16 Oct
Nicol, A. D.	8 Nov	Holden, P.	1 Apr	Cuthbert, G. H.	23 Oct
Howey, R.	15 Nov	Coll, P. MBE	3 Apr	Dunning, P. R.	23 Oct
Warren, P. J.	15 Nov	Flinn, B. G.	3 Apr	Mitchell, R. N. MBE	23 Oct
Woodhead, M. E. BEM	15 Nov	Mitchell, D. J.	3 Apr	Steade, S. J.	23 Oct
Knight, S. J.	22 Nov	Stabler, W. S. MBE	3 Apr	Geerah, J. A.	24 Oct
Read, D. S. G.	22 Nov	Gavin, R. J.	19 Apr	Bashford, D. R.	6 Nov
Walker, G.	22 Nov	Bowsher, P. S. MBE	26 Apr	Carr, D. T.	6 Nov
Howe, R. E.	29 Nov	Cherry, E.	2 May	Griffiths, L. C. MBE	6 Nov
Lorimer, J. N.	29 Nov	Hughes, G. S.	8 May	Lambley-Steel, H. P.	6 Nov
Toogood, J. E.	29 Nov	Torrance, W.	8 May	Zweig, M. C.	6 Nov
Carr, J. P.	1 Dec	Shanks, D. A. BEM	10 May	Newett, G. D.	13 Nov
Miller, M. G.	6 Dec	Pitt, T.	15 May	Gough, R. A.	17 Nov
Simpson, J. E.	6 Dec	Blakey, D. BEM	22 May	White, J. S.	20 Nov
Wilson, G. S. J.	6 Dec	Rowland, C. F.	22 May	Morrow, I. A.	23 Nov
Heenan, S. A.	13 Dec	Starkings, D. A.	22 May	Butcher, M. M.	27 Nov
		Stewart, W.	22 May	Duddridge, P. J. MBE	27 Nov
		Barbour, R.	29 May	Harvey, A. P.	27 Nov
2000		Crump, K. P.	30 May	Drakard, C. W.	4 Dec
		Shea, R. D.	31 May	Lynch, D. J.	4 Dec
Brincau, P.	4 Jan	McWilliams, K. R.	5 June	Meech, M. G.	4 Dec
Durrant, A. V. BEM	4 Jan	Street, N. R.	5 June	Belcher, J. G.	11 Dec
Kent, O. J. S.	4 Jan	Metcalf, S. G.	7 June	Foster, B. T.	11 Dec

2000—contd		Burke, K. M.	2 Apr
		Purkis, R. J. I.	2 Apr
Fox, M. J. B.	11 Dec	Meehan, A. B.	5 Apr
Mutch, P.	11 Dec	Edwards, M. C.	8 Apr
Ovenden, R. W.	11 Dec	Brittain, P. C.	16 Apr
Smith, I. C.	11 Dec	Hill, L. D.	16 Apr
Walmsley, P. R.	11 Dec	Cunningham, R. F.	17 Apr
Wiltshire, G. W.	18 Dec	Hutchinson, T. K.	17 Apr
		Jenner, B. F. MBE	30 Apr
		Tedder, E. D.	30 Apr
2001		Williams, T. L. D.	1 May
		Salisbury, A. L.	3 May
Hayes, M. W.	2 Jan	Leighton, W. MBE	8 May
O'Neill, P. J.	2 Jan	Ward, G. G.	8 May
Barrie, W.	3 Jan	Briggs, A. R.	14 May
Cooke, S. P.	3 Jan	Baggley, P.	14 May
Lindop, A. R.	3 Jan	Hazelwood, N. C.	4 June
Felton, K. J.	8 Jan	Parker, C. E.	7 June
Parsons, R. R.	8 Jan	Simkin, P. M.	11 June
Pead, R.	8 Jan	Williams, D. J.	11 June
Woolls, R. J.	8 Jan	Cavanagh, P.	25 June
Bolton, A.	15 Jan	Canham, B.	2 July
Colby, M.	15 Jan	Ingram, P. R.	2 July
Donald, A. B.	15 Jan	Robson, J.	2 July
Hayes, R.	15 Jan	Russell, R. L.	2 July
Lightbody, H. L.	15 Jan	Snelling, G. M. MBE	2 July
Moody, C. P.	15 Jan	Mayes, D. N. BEM	9 July
Reid, G. J.	15 Jan	Bishop, G. T. C.	16 July
Shaw, G. C.	15 Jan	Hunt, E. J.	16 July
Curtis, P.	22 Jan	Mackenzie, J. A.	16 July
Morgan, R.	22 Jan	Waters, R. H.	23 July
Smith, S. J.	22 Jan	Middleton, J. K.	30 July
Hooley, R.	25 Jan	Mallett, A. D.	1 Aug
Bramley, T. S.	29 Jan	Davies, P. H.	6 Aug
Smith, M. D.	29 Jan	Henton, A. W.	6 Aug
Cowie, H. G.	5 Feb	Jones, G. L.	6 Aug
Hearne, M. D.	12 Feb	Maskell, R. P.	6 Aug
Liddle, I. M.	12 Feb	Bee, E. H.	13 Aug
Dickinson, G.	26 Feb	Hodges, P. K.	13 Aug
Harrap, P.	26 Feb	McNeill, J. W.	13 Aug
Simpson, S. C.	26 Feb	Passmore, P. A.	13 Aug
Carpenter, G. C.	5 Mar	Hart, D. J.	14 Aug
Davies, R. W.	5 Mar	Duncan, G. K.	17 Aug
McAteer, C. M. MBE		Appleyard, K. R.	20 Aug
BEM	5 Mar	Leaper, J. W.	20 Aug
Pollitt, J. S.	5 Mar	McIntyre, P. J.	20 Aug
Scott, K. C.	5 Mar	Whittle, A. M.	20 Aug
Trapps, P.	5 Mar	Partridge, M.	27 Aug
Robinson, N. E.	12 Mar	Wilkins, A. P.	27 Aug
Drew, R. J.	19 Mar	Butler, C. C.	28 Aug
Glover, F. A. J.	19 Mar	Oakley, B. A. F.	29 Aug
Welton, J. S. MBE	19 Mar	Quigley, K. G.	30 Aug
Armstrong, W. C. G.	26 Mar	Weldon, C. J.	30 Aug
Hargreaves, R. W.	26 Mar	Altham, B. R.	3 Sept
Taylor, A. J.	26 Mar	Hamilton, I. H.	3 Sept
Vincent, R. S. BEM	26 Mar	Meadows, L. J.	3 Sept
Waller, M.	26 Mar	Croft, R. J. MBE	10 Sept
Watson, A.	26 Mar	Dick, G. R.	10 Sept
Coulthard, J. S.	29 Mar	Turner, M. A.	14 Sept
Goodhead, B. F.	31 Mar	Jackson, S. C.	17 Sept

McCowan, T.	17 Sept		
McKechnie, C. T.	17 Sept		
Sewell, C. L.	17 Sept		
Freestone, K. L.	24 Sept		
Westworth, K.	24 Sept		
Balzano, A.	1 Oct		
Bell, S. R.	1 Oct		
Crockett, D. T.	2 Oct		
Sammut, M. J.	5 Oct		
Anderson, D. G. R.	8 Oct		
Fuller, A. R.	8 Oct		
Vaughan, A. J.	8 Oct		
Cording, A E.	15 Oct		
Jarvis, S. W.	15 Oct		
Mohindra, A. K.	15 Oct		
Daykin, J. T.	22 Oct		
Emery, P. R. MBE	22 Oct		
Jones, I. E.	22 Oct		
McEwan, J. C.	22 Oct		
Roberts, M. J.	22 Oct		
Simpson, J. A.	28 Oct		
Cable. F. C.	29 Oct		
Goodenough, R. W.	29 Oct		
Grant, F. D.	29 Oct		
Howard, S.	29 Oct		
McAleavy, B.	29 Oct		
Russell, P. F. BEM	29 Oct		
Stewart, J. H.	29 Oct		
Davies, T. N. RVM	5 Nov		
Higgins, N. K.	5 Nov		
Malpass, D.	5 Nov		
Moran, J. E.	5 Nov		
Swainston, L.	5 Nov		
Evanson, S.	8 Nov		
Haskell, J.	8 Nov		
Wilkinson, I. C.	9 Nov		
Hanson, T. C.	12 Nov		
Street, D. M.	15 Nov		
Fortune, P.	16 Nov		
Ballinger, R. F.	19 Nov		
Dykes, A. M.	19 Nov		
Earl, S.	19 Nov		
Golding, P.	19 Nov		
Higgins, J. J.	19 Nov		
Hinkins, R. C.	19 Nov		
Roberts, D. M.	19 Nov		
Shimwell, R.	19 Nov		
Sterio, C. R.	19 Nov		
Graham, I. G.	20 Nov		
Bell, D.	26 Nov		
Bradshaw, P.	26 Nov		
Fraser, R.	26 Nov		
Gordon, J. A.	26 Nov		
Littlemore, K. J.	26 Nov		
Artley, S.	26 Nov		
Birkett, P.	3 Dec		
Brookman, G.	3 Dec		
Curtis, A. D.	3 Dec		
Forsythe, T. D.	3 Dec		
Hardy, K. N. BEM	3 Dec		

2001—contd

Holland, P. J.	3 Dec
Lowe, S.	3 Dec
Watson, S. T.	3 Dec
Wormald, E. A.	3 Dec
Wheable, P.	10 Dec
Wilcox, G.	10 Dec
Shephard, P. A.	10 Dec
Simmonds, K. P.	10 Dec
Brown, M. RVM	17 Dec
Dye, E. C. R.	17 Dec
Hughes, P. S. R.	17 Dec
Munro, D. S.	17 Dec
Currie, G.	21 Dec

2002

McKenzie, P. M.	3 Jan
O'Loughlin, C. M.	4 Jan
Arnold, M.	7 Jan
Barlow, W. M.	7 Jan
Norton, M. T.	7 Jan
Robinson, A. J.	7 Jan
Barnes, J A. R. MBE	14 Jan
Leivers, A. F.	14 Jan
Roberts, S.	14 Jan
O'Hara, F.	22 Jan
Harris, C. A.	28 Jan
Bell, R. F.	29 Jan
Perrin, L. R.	1 Feb
Balding, E. J.	4 Feb
Richards, N. D.	4 Feb
Mansell, A. B.	6 Feb
Leonard, D. A.	20 Feb
Harrison, T. D. A.	24 Feb
Stainer, R. H.	25 Feb
Salkeld, D. B.	1 Mar
Curry, D. MBE	4 Mar
Guppy, S. J. P.	4 Mar
Gillett, D. B. C.	8 Mar
Coulthard, D. H.	11 Mar
Kettle, B.	15 Mar
Martin, K. P.	25 Mar
Webb, N. R.	31 Mar
Edmondson, G. E.	1 Apr
Hufton, J. W.	1 Apr
McMenamin, P. G. M.	1 Apr
Aspinall, S. P.	2 Apr
Ash, K. BEM	3 Apr
Patterson, D. A. G.	7 Apr
Allardyce, D. G. P.	8 Apr
McKinnon, P. T.	8 Apr
Mottram, R. G.	8 Apr
Treviss, M. J.	8 Apr
Thorne, M. H. W.	12 Apr
Chappell, D. G.	14 Apr
Bufton, D. A.	15 Apr
Guest, M. R.	15 Apr

Knight, A. D.	15 Apr
Miles, C. C.	15 Apr
Williams, M. R.	15 Apr
McWilliam, D. G.	22 Apr
Johnson, S. P.	22 Apr
Kafel, P. R. BSc	29 Apr
Marshall, S. D.	29 Apr
Robinson, A.	30 Apr
Morris, J.	15 May
Bowden, R. J.	20 May
Milhench, P.	20 May
Topham, P. J.	20 May
Waldie, D. E.	27 May
Jones, D. D.	10 June
Bowen, C. G.	17 June
Chapman, P. H.	17 June
Conway, A. M.	17 June
Cowans, P. W. S.	17 June
Goslin, B. H.	17 June
MacGregor, G. B.	24 June
Seamarks, M. J.	26 June
Burgess, P. K.	27 June
Mitchell, W. C.	28 June
Hempstock, K. R.	1 July
Howard, M.	1 July

MASTER SIGNALLERS

1980

Luke, P.   10 Jan

1988

Rock, D.   1 Nov

1994

Gibney, J. C.   1 July

1997

Cook, M. D. A.   1 Jan

1998

Waterfield, W. E.   1 July

1999

Caldicott, D.   1 Jan
McDonald, S. R.   1 July

2000

Townsend, P. L.   1 July

2001

Nicolson, W. C.   1 July

MASTER ENGINEERS

1979

Hardy, H. R.   1 July

1980

Murrell, J. R. MBE   1 July

1981

Smith, D. J.   1 Jan

1982

Hall, R.   1 July

1984

Quick, K. J.   22 Aug
Skate, J. A.   16 Oct
Smith, C. A.   2 Nov

1986

Pace, K.   17 Jan
Crosland, J. D.   23 Feb
Hampson, G. R.   4 May

1987

Wishart, W. S. C.   24 Jan
Dodd, D. M.   1 July

1988

Nobbs, P. D.   1 Jan
Riley, N. J.   1 June
Sheldon, S. J.   29 July

1989

Mitchell, K.   1 Jan
Sutton, A.   14 June

Carter, R. A.   1 July

1990

Gregson, P.   1 July
Iddon, R. P.   1 July
Keable, M. J. cfs(e)   1 July
Nurse, K.   1 July

1991

Rockley, A. P. B.   1 July
Simpson, D. W.   1 July

1992

Paull, N. MBE   1 July

1993

Lee, T.   1 Jan
Hamill, M.   1 July

1994

Mohun, A. R.   1 Jan
Morris, J.   1 Jan
Pogue, T.   1 July

1995

Hall, C. I.   1 Jan

1997

Moxon, M. D.   1 Jan

1998

Allan, J. W.   1 July
Deepan, N. K.   1 July

1999

Ashman, A. P.   1 July
Brown, M. K.   1 July

2000

Gunter, N. J.	1 Jan
Bogg, C. L.	1 July
McConville, P. J.	1 July

2001

Chappell, P. G.	1 Jan
Kelly, I.	1 Jan
Hammond, S. C.	1 July
Moffatt, A. T.	1 July

2002

Land, J. D.	1 Jan
Nicholson, G.	1 July

MASTER AIR ELECTRONICS OPERATORS

1980

Pewton, A. V.	16 Jan
Clack, M. E.	18 Jan
Torrance, D. A.	1 July

1981

Abbott, P. L.	1 July
Hunt, B. I. S.	1 July

1983

Thompson, M. S.	1 Jan
Morrice, J. C.	21 Jan
Cornes, M. R.	5 July

1984

Flint, R. G.	7 Apr
Webb, R.	1 July
Scott, D.	6 July
Fielding, M. W.	1 Sept

1985

Knight, K. M.	1 Jan
McGregor, I. J.	29 July

1986

Cox, E. P. cfs(c)	1 Jan
Moore, S. P.	1 Jan
Davies, A. E.	24 Feb
Dewfall, A.	28 Mar
Lofts, D. A.	12 May
Amos, R.	30 May
Brown, C. M.	1 July
Muir, D.	1 July
Bush, J. A.	11 Dec

1987

Ward, S. J.	1 Jan
Holdway, P. MBE	18 Mar

Thompson, K. T.	27 July
Headland, M. J.	10 Aug
Nichols, B. G.	7 Oct
Brown, R. E.	23 Nov

1988

Hallett, D.	1 Jan
Silvester, E. A.	29 Mar
Woolfson, A. J. MBE	22 Apr
Reid, W.	8 Sept
Masson, A.	3 Nov

1989

Wade, W. H.	1 Jan
Wetherell, M. J.	1 Jan
Lawrence, R. A.	1 July
McCabe, A. J. M.	4 July

1990

Pratt, E. J.	16 May
Wilkinson, R. A.	1 July

1991

Dewar, A. J. M.	1 Jan
Nicholson, D. C.	1 Jan

1992

Bird, J.	1 July
Keracher, R. I.	1 July

1993

Dixon, D.	1 Jan
Hitchin, D. K.	1 Jan
Schiavone, A. P.	1 July

1994

Benton, N. J.	1 Jan
Curtis, A. J.	1 Jan
Paterson, J.	1 Jan
Bruce, D. W.	1 July
Clarke, A. J.	1 July
Forbes, W. B.	1 July

1995

Vongyer, G. G.	1 Jan
Berry, R. W.	1 July
Geary, S. G.	1 July
Haynes, R. B.	1 July

1996

Jeffrey, D. S.	1 Jan
Penlington, D. W. E.	1 Jan
Oates, S. T.	1 July

1997

Bayne, J. T.	1 Jan
Stansfield, D.	1 Jan
Hart, S. D.	1 July
Whitham, P. E.	1 July

1998

Hawksworth, I. R.	1 Jan
Bowyer, S. J.	1 July
Warren, P. L.	1 July

1999

Bayford, D. J. cfs(ae)	1 Jan
Randall, I. L.	1 Jan
Young, K. S.	1 Jan
Doane, S. L.	1 July
Hyams, P. D.	1 July
Yost, K. A.	1 July

2000

Canton, A.	1 Jan
Holt, P. A.	1 Jan
Mack, T. N.	1 Jan
Stalker, J. A.	17 Jan
Greenfield, R. K.	17 Apr
Heald, S. R.	17 Apr
Wallis, T. P.	17 Apr
Harrison, G. E.	1 July
Lister, M. R.	1 July
MacFarlane, I. W. cfs(c) cfs(h)	1 July
Tull, M. E.	1 July

2001

Burge, P. J.	1 Jan

Clarke, G. D.	1 Jan
Moncur, M. W. M.	1 Jan
Shirley, M. A.	1 Jan
Dodds, J. E.	1 July
Osgood, I. P.	1 July
Royce, K. P.	1 July
Taft, S. J.	1 July

2002

Batchelor, A. P.	1 Jan
Coffey, R. A.	1 Jan
Kennedy, J. R. A.	1 Jan
Tagima, M. S.	1 Jan
Andrews, M. J.	1 July
Cocker, D. J.	1 July
McChristie, C. I.	1 July
Street S. J.	1 July

MASTER AIR LOADMASTERS

1977

Pringle, N. cfs(c)	1 July
Unwin, C. MBE	1 July

1980

Felton, M. J.	1 Jan
Mursell, K. T.	22 Feb
Broome, I. M.	31 Mar
Evans, R. E.	1 July

1981

Collings, K.	1 Jan
Graham, R. S.	1 Jan
Maggs, C. M. MSc	1 Jan
Scott, A. R. cfs(c)	1 July
Glenton, C. I.	16 Sept
Connolly, B.	18 Nov

1982

Willis, C. W.	1 July
Samwell, T. J.	9 Nov
Armstrong, J. MBE MIPD cfs(c)	13 Dec

1983

Venn, B. F.	1 Jan
Allen, D.	23 Jan
Mills, R. A.	1 July
Clements, D.	1 Oct

1984

Rowe, S. A.	25 May
Payne, A. D.	1 July
Lowe, S.	6 July

1985

Cross, K. J.	8 Mar

1985—contd

McLeod, A.	6 May

1986

Porter, D. R.	6 Jan
Colley, P. C.	7 Mar
Cuthell, T. M.	28 Apr
Davies, G.	22 June
Maddison, M. J.	11 Sept
Jones, A. W.	31 Dec

1987

Bateson, G.	1 Jan
Birkin, B. M.	1 Jan
Lester, D. R.	1 Jan
McCullough, K. D.	1 Jan
Magee, T. M.	1 Jan
Wain, A. G.	1 Jan
Dowell, P. D.	1 July
Morrison, H. C.	1 July
Taylor, K. J.	28 Aug
Morris, C. M.	3 Sept
Laken, W. E. cfs(c)	30 Sept
Stanhope, I. W.	1 Nov
Gudgin, G. D.	26 Nov

1988

Bragg, R. J. AFM cfs(c)	1 Jan
Gosney, P.	1 Jan
Tucker, K. C. MBE cfs(c)	1 Jan
Guttridge, I.	1 Mar
Mellor, J. R. D. cfs(c)	1 July
Seward, G. N.	1 July
Thraves, P. T.	11 Nov
Milward, R. G.	30 Nov

1989

Mackenzie, G. T.	9 Feb
Lynch, S. C.	7 June
Jones, C. J.	1 July
Thompson, A. R. cfs(c)	1 July
Connell, P. R. C.	18 July
Roberts, G. W.	23 July

1990

Blake, P. K.	1 July

Turnbull, P. A. cfs(c)	1 July

1991

Watts, S. H.	1 Jan

1993

Ritson, A.	1 July

1994

Evans, D. J. cfs(c)	1 Jan
Hamilton, I. D.	1 Jan
Muir, J. D.	1 Jan
Aitken, D. S.	1 July

1995

Bottomley, M.	1 Jan
Gale, R. D.	1 Jan
Grogan, A. P.	1 Jan
Walmsley, D. A.	1 Jan
Dodsworth, V. G. S.	1 July
Franks, N.	1 July
Mahef, G. M.	1 July

1996

Maxwell, D. F. A. AFM	1 Jan
Tait, M. W. cfs(c) cfs(h)	1 Jan
Morgan, G. N.	1 July
Sampson, F. J.	1 July

1997

Bridge, M. V.	1 Jan
Pearson, B. G.	1 Jan
Prall, T. G. E.	1 Jan
Archard, P. W. MBE	1 July

1998

Bence, A. J.	1 Jan
Dearing, G. J.	1 Jan
Galloway, J. R.	1 Jan
McKay, W A.	1 Jan
Davies, G.	1 July
Docherty, T. G.	1 July
Hunter, B. H.	1 July

1999

Drake, P. M.	1 Jan
McCormick, J. W.	1 Jan
Neill, P. B.	1 Jan
Sheldon, J. R.	2 Feb
Cruttenden, P. F. cfs(c)	1 July

2000

Cooke, R. P.	1 Jan
Couchman, P. N.	1 Jan
McCabe, I.	1 Jan
Du Cros, A. P.	1 July
Epton, N. I. G.	1 July
Hollingworth, P. R.	1 July

2001

Mallam, G E.	1 Jan
Orr, J.	1 Jan
Shooter, T. G.	1 Jan
Colley, T. G.	1 July
Owers, J. D.	1 July

2002

Morgan G. T.	1 Jan
O'Leary, M.	1 Jan
Stevens, M.	1 Jan
Eversfield, J. H.	1 July
Lomgmuir, G. R.	1 July
Warren, T. A.	1 July

ROYAL AIR FORCE RESERVE

GENERAL DUTIES BRANCH

Wing Commanders

Warren, P. J. BEng
cfs qss   (P) 21 Nov

Ward, K. A. BSc cfs (P)   26 Oct

2000

Ware, A.   (P)   29 Apr
Horton, B. A.   (P)   1 Sept

2001

McCarthy, W. J.
qss   (AEO) 12 Feb

2001

Ternouth, M. L. cfs
qss   (N)   5 Mar
Day, P. OBE AFC   (P)   2 Apr
Williams. A. H. BSc
qs   (N)   7 July
Stanton, S.   (P)   1 Oct
Browne, W. N. DFC (N)   2 Oct

1990

Saunders, P. BSc   (N)   28 Feb
Weatherly, S. A. BA (P)   25 Mar
Gibson, I. S. BA   (P)   11 Apr
Rose, D. A. BSc   (P)   14 Nov

1991

Greig, D. A. BSc cfs (P)   15 Jan
Sumner-Lockwood,
G. BA   (P)   14 Feb
Madgwick, I. A.   (P)   15 Feb
Wright, I. BA cfs   (P)   25 Mar
Gallon, J. C. BEng (N)   6 May
Phillips, P. A. BSc (P)   6 May
Walker, A. R. BSc   (P)   6 May
Woods, R. M. BEng (P)   6 May
Abraham, D. L. BSc (P)   8 July
Spencer, J. J.   (P)   13 Aug
Williams, D. M. P. (P)   13 Aug
Paterson, N. A. BSc (P)   1 Oct
Everall, E. J. cfs   (P)   19 Dec

Squadron Leaders

Flight Lieutenants

1993

Mayer, W. L. M. AFC (P)   1 Oct

1995

Turgoose, R. BSc   (P)   4 Sept

1997

Jewiss. J. O.   (P)   1 Apr
Steen, B. A. MBE   (P)   6 Oct

1998

Williamson, M. C.
qss   (P)   13 July
Ilsley, C. W.   (P)   11 Dec

1999

Bagnall, R. A.   (AEO) 18 July
Horton, B. A. BA   (P)   31 Aug

2000

Robertson, I. M. psc (P)   26 Oct

1986

Seymour, M. A. BSc
tp   (P)   11 Mar
Hill, M. J. R. BSc   (N) 11 June

1987

Boyd, F. D. S. BSc (P)   16 Aug
Reynolds, G. R. BSc (N)   11 Nov

1988

Dairon, L. J. T. BSc (P)   3 Feb
Cooper, A. H. C. BSc (P) 29 Mar
Haigh, W. D. P. BSc
cfs   (P)   29 Mar
Siddall, P. J. BSc   (P)   29 Mar

1989

Gill, C. S. BSc   (P)   15 Jan
Wilson, R. D. BSc cfs (P)   15 Jan
Farrar, M. P. qss   (P)   17 Jan
Read, M. P.   (P)   17 Jan
Loftus, P. BEng   (P)   28 Feb
Shenton, P. J. BSc (P)   14 Mar
Devine, N. BA   (N)   26 Oct

1992

Slater, A. M. BSc   (P)   15 Jan
Spratt, C. J. BEng (P)   19 Feb
Aspden, S. M. BSc (N)   20 Feb
Hayter, D. P.   (P)   11 Mar
Lees, D. M. BSc   (P)   1 Apr
Hadlow, D. M. BSc (P)   1 Oct
Woolley, M. G.   (P)   23 Oct
Hamer, P. M.   (P)   4 Dec

1993

Vardy, M. J. BA   (P)   19 Feb
Leigh, C. J.   (P)   27 Feb
Pearcy-Caldwell,
J. L. D.   (P)   27 Feb
Whittaker, I. D. BCom
qwi   (P)   30 Mar
Ashton, S. E. BA   (P)   11 May
Faulkner, J. R. H. BSc (P) 11 May

Flight Lieutenants

1993—contd

Segal, A. P. BEng qwi	(P)	6 July
Shingles, J. S. BSc cfs qwi	(P)	17 Aug
Harris, M. R. cfs	(P)	25 Aug
Hurt, T. S. BSc	(P)	30 Sept

1994

Bonser, A. C. L.	(P)	22 Mar
Lear, M. J. cfs	(P)	2 May
Jhoolun, A. S. J. qss1	(P)	16 Aug
Hunter, N. E. MA BA	(P)	29 Sept

1995

Stinson, R. J.	(P)	21 Feb
Bielby, M. C.	(P)	28 Mar
Hillyer, K. S.	(P)	28 Mar
Price, M. C. L.	(P)	21 June
Hatton-Ward, J. qwi	(P)	21 Dec

1996

Holmes, R. qwi	(P)	2 Feb
Doidge, J. G. qwi	(P)	20 Dec

1997

Johnson, M. C.	(P)	24 Mar
Morley, P. R.	(P)	1 Apr
Bowen, A. J.	(P)	7 Apr
Edenbrow, R. A. O. BSc	(P)	7 Apr
Janiurek, J. D.	(P)	7 Apr
Mannings, E. J.	(P)	7 Apr
McDougall, D. J. DipEd	(P)	7 Apr
Woods, R. D.	(P)	7 Apr
Johnson, H. R. BSc	(P)	14 Apr
Pearce, A. G.	(P)	16 Apr
Kennedy, G. S.	(P)	28 Apr
Wiseman, R. A. BSc	(P)	6 May
Patterson, L. J. BSc	(P)	7 May
Danby, C. I.	(P)	12 May
Ford, M. A.	(P)	19 May
Clark, D. H.	(P)	28 May
Sproul, E. C.	(P)	26 Aug
Campbell, D. A.	(P)	2 Sept

Chew, C. P. BA BArch	(P)	8 Sept
Eeles, T. BA	(P)	15 Sept
Clements, R. E.	(P)	22 Sept
Shuster, R. C. AFC	(P)	27 Sept
Garton, A. C.	(P)	7 Oct
Hall, M. R. BA	(P)	18 Oct
Newman, R. A.	(P)	21 Oct
Taylor, G. T.	(P)	7 Nov
Logan, S. T. BSc	(P)	3 Dec
Mathieson, D.	(N)	20 Dec

1998

Clark, M. A.	(P)	5 Jan
Barnard, J. B. qss	(P)	2 June
Biglands, S. BSc cfs	(P)	23 July
Hewitt, P. A.	(P)	24 Aug
Ball, M. W. AFC jsdc cfs qwi qs	(P)	28 Sept
Carey, D. J. cfs	(P)	1 Nov
Guyatt, D. J. cfs qss	(P)	2 Nov
Hayes, L. J.	(ALM)	16 Nov

1999

Crouch, C. A.	(P)	11 Jan
Brooks, D. BSc	(P)	11 May
Williams, M. A.	(P)	2 July
Ray, P. R. MSc	(P)	6 July
Sollitt, A. G. MBE	(P)	27 July
Hitchcock, P. G.	(P)	6 Sept
Tomlinson, M. I.	(N)	27 Sept

2000

Carmichael, B. K. BSc	(P)	5 Jan
Sargent, R. H.	(P)	10 Jan
Wood, M. H. MBE	(P)	1 Feb
Griffiths, S. G. MBE MBA	(P)	1 Mar
Rowell, M. F.	(P)	10 Mar
Sayer, M. J.	(N)	13 Mar
Owen, P. S.	(P)	1 May
Fowler, S. M. qss	(N)	14 May
Saunders, M. G. jsdc cfs qs	(P)	11 June
Starling, M. C.	(P)	23 June
Underwood, S. C.	(P)	10 July
Murty, J. K. BSc	(P)	14 July
Williams, J. K.	(P)	17 July
Lawrence, M. J.	(P)	31 July
Mason, K. cfs	(P)	1 Aug
Wesley, C. J. asq snc qss	(N)	1 Aug

May, N.	(P)	22 Aug
Williams, D. A. AFC qwi(AD) qs	(P)	28 Aug
Hilliker, C. psc cfs	(P)	31 Aug
Yarrow, T. B. J. MBE psc qwi(AD)	(P)	11 Sept
King, C.	(P)	18 Sept
Stacey, A. J. AFC	(P)	22 Sept
Morris, B. S. OBE AFC	(P)	1 Oct
Holding, B. C. AFC	(P)	11 Oct
Boon, T. R.	(N)	15 Oct
Roe, M. cfs	(P)	16 Oct
Slatter, C. BSc(Eng)	(P)	19 Oct
Lakey, M. J. GM	(P)	1 Nov
Marriott, M. B. R.	(P)	1 Nov
Pilkington, M. G. qss	(AEO)	6 Nov
Sharp, D. J. AFC BSc cfs qss	(P)	23 Nov
Milne, D. F. BSc(Eng)	(P)	4 Dec

2001

Readfern, P. A. psc(m)	(P)	1 Jan
Brocklebank, R. A. DipEurHum cfs qss	(N)	3 Jan
Pring, R. M.	(AEO)	3 Jan
Wilson, J. S.	(P)	16 Jan
Beard, J. S. snc	(N)	29 Jan
Mawby, A. J. OBE BSc psc cfs	(P)	29 Jan
Elliott, H. J. qs	(P)	5 Feb
George, R. J. AMIEE	(N)	5 Feb
Butt, L. C. snc qs	(N)	7 Feb
Howlett, P. W.	(P)	20 Feb
Wylie, M. D.	(P)	1 Mar
Beresford, G. cfs	(P)	12 Mar
Jones, K. A. cfs* qss	(P)	26 Mar
Shankland, D. cfs	(P)	3 Apr
Fowler, D. qwi qss	(P)	23 Apr
Charlton, E. M. BSc cfs	(N)	26 Apr
Low, R. A. C. RGN jsdc qwi(T) qs	(N)	21 May
Gregory, R. D. cfs qss	(P)	9 June
Adams, P. S. G. MBE qwi qs	(P)	1 July
Whitehead, M. D. BTech qwi qss	(P)	1 July
Wholey, R. E. jsdc qwi qs	(P)	16 July
Garratt, W. H.	(P)	19 July
Mason, G. qwi qss	(P)	23 July
Prissick, M. CBE	(P)	11 Aug
Kirkhope, T. BSc psc cfs	(P)	4 Sept

Flight Lieutenants

2001—contd

Wood, D. M. (P) 10 Sept
Harper, I. F. MBE psc
asq (N) 11 Sept
Bolsover, D. R. (P) 17 Sept
Barker, C. M. I. MA
psc (P) 29 Oct
Boyle, T. L. OBE jsdc
qab qwi qs (P) 30 Oct
Castle, D. A. BSc (N) 18 Nov
Walters, R. J. BSc
asq qs (P) 18 Nov
Bird, J. C. cfs qss (P) 6 Dec
Legg, P. D. MA FCMI
MRAeS psc(n) qwi (P) 10 Dec
Partington, T. G.
BSc(Eng) (P) 10 Dec

2002

Lees, M. N. MA FRAeS
psc(j) (N) 14 Jan
Faulkner, P. M. cfs
qss (P) 21 Jan
Brooke, M. C. AFC psc
tp cfs (P) 26 Jan
Hamilton, D. A. BTech
qs (P) 1 Feb
Izatt, G. N. AIB (P) 26 Feb
Coleby, B. F. (AEO) 18 Mar
Buchanan, W. D. cfs (P) 25 Mar
Bucklow, S. P. (P) 25 Mar
Kirkpatrick, W. J. BA
jsdc qwi qs (P) 5 Apr
Eckersley, A. M. qwi
qss (P) 22 Apr
Nash, A. J. (N) 6 May
Murkin, S. D. AFC
psc (P) 12 May
Challis, P. BSc psc
cfs (P) 27 May
Gault, R. K. OBE jsdc
snc qs (N) 27 May

Flying Officer

2002

Cornes, A. B. (P) 7 Feb

OPERATIONS SUPPORT BRANCH

Group Captain

1998

Jones, D. J. (FLTOPS) 20 Jan

Wing Commanders

1986

McQueen, W. R. MBE
QVRM AE (FLTOPS) 23 Jan

1993

Grange, M. J. (FLTOPS) 1 Jan

1995

Green, R. J. C. (FLTOPS) 6 Mar
Gibb, R. W. (FLTOPS) 4 Dec

1996

Moses, H. H. (FLTOPS) 29 Jan
Campbell, A. D. K.
(FLTOPS) 10 June

1997

Vary, C. E. (FLTOPS) 3 Feb

1998

Milsom, R. J. OBE
jsdc awcc psc
cfs (FLTOPS) 10 Dec

1999

Squires, J. V. (FLTOPS) 1 July

2000

Stewart, H. (FLTOPS) 24 Aug
Cocksedge, M. P. rcds
osc(Fr) cfs (FLTOPS) 29 Aug

2001

Smith, G. P. psc
awcc (FLTOPS) 11 June

Squadron Leaders

1985

Philpott, J. H.
AE (FLTOPS) 15 Aug

1991

Dixon, R. S. (FLTOPS) 9 Dec

1993

Hall, B. T. F. AE (REGT) 1 Mar

1994

Hudson, C. P. M.
(FLTOPS) 16 May
Noyes, S. G. (FLTOPS) 30 Aug
Williams, R. G. C.
(FLTOPS) 10 Oct

1996

Campbell, C. H.(FLTOPS) 23 Sept
Goodman, P. J. (FLTOPS) 3 Oct

1997

Glasspool, I. D.(FLTOPS) 8 July
Coles, R. G. (FLTOPS) 9 July
Bray, D. B. (FLTOPS) 3 Dec

Squadron Leaders

1999

Byrne, M. S. (FLTOPS) 18 May
Horn, K. (FLTOPS) 11 Oct
Pickthall, C. R. (ATC) 11 Oct
Hussey, P. J. (FLTOPS) 1 Nov

2000

Chapman, N. (FLTOPS) 1 Feb
Skinner, K. E. (FLTOPS) 27 Mar
Wilkey, R. C. (FLTOPS)) 27 Mar
Dalley, K. P. (ATC) 3 May
Hinton, P. N. MBA
  MCMI qab
  qs (FLTOPS) 2 Sept
Ward, J. F. (FLTOPS) 1 Nov

2001

Jackson, M. R.
  qs (OPS SPT) 2 July
Lloyd, D. G.
  psc (FLTOPS) 4 Aug
Hill, D. snc qs (FLTOPS) 24 Sept
Andrews, A. W. MA
  PhD MSc BSc CPhys
  CChem MRSC
  MInstP MCIPD
  qss (FLTOPS) 4 Oct
Henry, B. L. MBE
  snc qs (FLTOPS) 23 Nov

2002

Webster, D. S.
  MBE (ATC) 1 Jan
Grove, A. D. W.
  qs (ATC) 17 Feb

Flight Lieutenants

1987

Guy, M. R. BSc (INT) 3 Oct

1990

Easton, S. T. BSc (ATC) 14 Mar

1991

Barnes, P. N.
  AE (FLTOPS) 1 Feb
Wallis, C. M. (ATC) 11 Apr
Hammond-Doutre,
  G. I. (FLTOPS) 14 Oct

1992

Adkin, M. E. (FLTOPS) 25 Sept
Hurst, I. P. (FLTOPS) 25 Sept

1993

Armstrong, A. E.
  AE (FLTOPS) 4 Feb
Norman, R. E. J.
  (FLTOPS) 3 Aug
West, D. J. (FLTOPS) 3 Aug
Burgess, C. BSc (FC) 1 Oct

1994

Donnelly, M. G. (ATC) 17 Jan
Scott, I. C. (FLTOPS) 27 Jan
Lloyd, T. E. L. (FLTOPS) 3 Feb
Maeer, K. W. (FLTOPS) 3 Feb
Steel, M. K. (FLTOPS) 3 Feb
Watson, J. R.
  AE (FLTOPS) 9 Feb
Jones, D. J. R. (FLTOPS) 9 Mar
Dunbar, L. (FC) 2 July
Bennett, A. BA (INT) 17 Aug

1995

Davies, R. W. (FLTOPS) 3 Apr
Dawson, K. J. BA (ATC) 10 May
Cholerton, M. P.
  BEng (REGT) 6 June
Bissett, W. C. BA
  PGCE (INT) 5 July
Cook, R. M. S.
  MBE (FLTOPS) 31 July
Hickton, K. N. BEng (FC) 14 Aug
McKay, K. R. BSc (ATC) 14 Aug
Gallon, J. D. (FLTOPS) 1 Sept

Matthews, I. D. (FLTOPS) 8 Sept

1996

Cowell, R. W. (ATC) 5 Feb
Kiggel, L. J. (ATC) 5 Feb
Howells, D. K. (FLTOPS) 7 Feb
Burdekin, P. A. (FLTOPS) 19 Feb
McFarland, C. A. (ATC) 28 Mar
Mason, I. M. (FLTOPS) 11 Apr
Brown, T. C. (FLTOPS) 13 May
Quick, M. C. (ATC) 14 Oct
Jones, J. N. (FLTOPS) 28 Oct
Wigglesworth, C. A.
  (ATC) 7 Nov

1997

Locke, G. H. (FLTOPS) 27 Jan
Baker, H. M. (FLTOPS) 1 Apr
Johnston, G. J.
  BEd (FLTOPS) 10 July
Young, A C. M. N.
  (FLTOPS) 18 Aug
Kent, K. J. BSc (ATC) 3 Nov
Hallowes, S. D. (ATC) 8 Nov
Broome, T. J. (FLTOPS) 24 Nov

1998

McKeown, J. D. P.
  (FLTOPS) 19 Jan
Cain, P. S. qcc (REGT) 29 Jan
Sumner, D. G. (ATC) 23 Feb
White, D. A. C. (ATC) 1 Mar
Tournay, R. N. A. J.
  (REGT) 1 Apr
Culmer, B. E. (ATC) 4 Apr
Baker, B. A. F. (ATC) 8 Apr
George, G. H. E. (ATC) 8 Apr
Toogood, W. R. qs (ATC) 2 May
Stewart, W. E. (INT) 15 May
Simpson, A. qss (ATC) 2 June
Young, M. J. MA BA
  MCIPD CertEd (ATC) 2 June
Randall, E. W. (ATC) 22 July
Robinson, B. (ATC) 22 July
Romeo, J. T. (ATC) 22 July
Stuart, K. (ATC) 22 July
Talbot, R. (ATC) 22 July
Vardy, D. P. (ATC) 22 July
Ward, J. (ATC) 22 July
Lakeland, C. (FLTOPS) 29 July
Mill P. D. (REGT) 18 Aug
Ashwell, R. J.
  BSc (FLTOPS) 24 Aug
Elliott, T. J. (FLTOPS) 24 Aug

Flight Lieutenants

1998—contd

Ward, M. J.	(ATC)	25 Aug
Priestley, D.	(FLTOPS)	23 Sept
Barradell, D. J.		
snc qss	(FLTOPS)	29 Sept
Clark, M.	(FLTOPS)	4 Dec

1999

Morris, P. L. qss	(ATC)	4 Jan
Reid, S. C.	(ATC)	18 Jan
Day, P. qss	(ATC)	30 Jan
Little, R.	(ATC)	30 Jan
Bailey, J. M.	(FC)	24 Mar
Green, M. A. BSc	(INT)	8 Apr
Taylor, N. J. L. BA	(FC)	8 Apr
Cawkwell, P. A. R.		
TD	(FLTOPS)	19 Apr
Merriman, J. L.	(ATC)	7 June
Bishop, J. M.	(FC)	13 July
Carpenter, F. J.	(FC)	25 Oct
Poole, A. N.	(ATC)	1 Nov
Sherratt, C. J. B.		
	(FLTOPS)	16 Nov

2000

Hare, J. A.	(ATC)	21 Feb
Nugent, S. G. qss	(ATC)	23 Feb
Bainbridge, A. C.	(ATC)	27 Mar
Douglas, C. D.	(ATC)	8 May
Walsh, J. P.	(ATC)	8 May
Chiddention, J. A.	(FC)	10 May
Weight, N.		
BSc	(FLTOPS)	15 May
Lovegrove, G. B.		
	(FLTOPS)	18 May
McGeough, P. J. R.	(ATC)	1 June
McKay, D. S.	(ATC)	5 June
Durban, S. J.	(ATC)	7 Aug
Dring, C. A. psc(j)	(ATC)	21 Aug
O'Brien, T. M.	(ATC)	11 Sept
Hardman, A. H.	(ATC)	14 Oct
Bloomfield, P. R.	(ATC)	1 Nov
Print, C. P. MSc		
BSc	(ATC)	1 Nov
Trice, J. M.		
BSc	(FLTOPS)	1 Nov

2001

Hall, N. A. BA	(ATC)	3 Jan

Barker, R. J. qss	(ATC)	22 Jan
Martin, E. H.	(REGT)	27 Feb
Harrison, I.	(FLTOPS)	1 Mar
Watts, R. J.	(FLTOPS)	1 Apr
Williamson, B. T.		
qs	(ATC)	30 Apr
Keenan, T.	(FLTOPS)	1 May
Sanderson, A. C.	(ATC)	8 May
Carlton, E. J.	(FLTOPS)	1 June
Steer, M. A.	(FLTOPS)	1 June
Marks, P. J. snc		
qss	(ATC)	16 July
Thurtle, I. C.	(FLTOPS)	1 Oct
Gibb, P. H. qs	(FC)	5 Nov

2002

Ruglys, M. P. PhD		
BSc	(FLTOPS)	2 Jan
Boden, R. A. qss	(ATC)	28 Jan
Laing, B.	(FLTOPS)	1 May
Thompson, S. M.		
	(FLTOPS)	1 May

Flying Officers

1992

Davis, A. S.	(ATC)	10 Nov

1994

Gerrard, C. P.	(ATC)	26 Sept
Ledger, A. J.	(ATC)	16 Dec

1995

Wallace, P. N. R.	(FC)	30 Jan

1996

Edmeston, M. C.	(ATC)	28 Jan

1997

Ansell, K. M. J.	(INT)	28 July

1998

Maclaren, A. F.	(INT)	28 Jan

1999

Boyle, P. A.	(FLTOPS)	26 Nov

Acting Pilot Officers

2000

Jackson, G.		
MSc	(FLTOPS)	9 Nov

2002

Bowden, A. J.	(FLTOPS)	27 Mar
Davies. O. D.		
BSc	(FLTOPS)	8 Apr
Tame, G. J.	(FLTOPS)	11 Apr
Lewis. K. H.		
BSc	(FLTOPS)	21 May

ENGINEER BRANCH

Wing Commander

1998

Maunder, M. J. qs   26 Oct

Squadron Leaders

1992

Swan, A. J.   13 July

1994

Carrington, D. J.   10 Oct

1997

McKenzie, I. BA CEng
  MIEE MRAes   6 Jan
Thorpe, G. S. E.   9 Dec

1998

Wood, R. B. qss   21 Aug
Flavell, D. M. qss   3 Dec

2000

Apps, R. M. qss   25 Sept

2001

Watson, C. R.   2 Apr
Horrocks, P. A. BSc
  CEng MIEE qs   2 Oct

Flight Lieutenants

1989

Morris, C. V. BSc   7 June

1992

Whitfield, M. M. MEng   18 Aug

1993

Darling, T. BEM   29 Mar
O'Dell, S. J. BEng   18 Apr
Davies, A. R. BEng   18 Aug
Barrett, C. L. BSc   30 Sept
Johnson, I. C. BEng   18 Dec

1994

Allinson, M. MEng   19 Feb
Collie, P. D. BSc   12 Nov

1995

Lamont, M. M. BA
  qss2   14 Aug
Broatch. D. M. BSc
  PGCE   29 Sept
Jayne, B. M. BEng   29 Sept

1996

Clancy, D. G. R. BA   15 Feb
German, A. D. BEng   11 Apr

1997

Goddard, A. MSc BSc   10 Oct

1998

Grace, R. qss   1 Nov

2001

MacDonald, G. B. qss   31 Aug

Flying Officer

2002

Densham, B. J.   7 Apr

SUPPLY BRANCH

Wing Commander

2000

Taylor, P. C. OBE BA	1 Jan

Squadron Leaders

1997

Lamonte, E. S. M.	2 Apr

1998

Ayers, C. R.	5 Jan

2000

Martin, S. E. MILT	6 May
Willmot, P. S.	1 July

2001

Evans, D. J.	13 Aug
Kingwill, P. M. qs	14 Sept

Flight Lieutenants

1991

Cook, N. M.	25 Mar

1993

Chatterton, S. A.	8 May
Potter, C. BSc	1 Oct
Robertson, C. S. A. BSc	24 Dec

1994

McGrath, L. J.	15 May

1995

Coote, A. H. BA	16 Feb

1996

Stamp, S.	9 May

1998

Fletcher, H. S. BA	9 Apr

2001

Mason, J. qs	1 May

Flying Officer

1993

Freear, D. J.	28 Sept

ADMINISTRATIVE BRANCH

Group Captain

1999

Dickson, A. OBE QVRM AE FRSA FCMI (Sec)	1 Oct

Wing Commanders

1999

Allport, M. K. MBE (Sec)	31 Aug

2001

Nicholson, M. J. qss	(Sec)	24 Jan
Bentley, D. E. qs	(Sec)	7 May

Squadron Leaders

1994

Edmunds, D. J.	(Sec)	17 Jan

1996

Morgan, M. L.	(Sec)	2 Jan
Whelan, J. B. D.	(Sec)	15 Apr
Bacon, T. J. OBE	(Sec)	3 June

1997

Wilson, W. J.	(Sec)	1 Oct

1998

Pell, K. L. BA CertEd	(Sec)	1 July
Russell, R. M. BA	(Sec)	1 Aug

Squadron Leaders

1999

Barkway, R. J.	(Sec)	1 Jan
Bell, J. J.	(Sec)	1 Jan
Hack, K. S.	(Sec)	1 Jan
Jessiman, W.	(Sec)	1 Jan
Lawrance, I.	(Sec)	1 Jan
McCulloch, T.	(Sec)	1 Jan
Stanton, R. H. MVO		
MRAeS MRIN	(Sec)	1 Jan
Pudney, K. W.	(Sec)	4 Jan
Johnson, W. A. BSc	(Sec)	5 Mar
Sturgeon, B.	(Sec)	1 Apr
Davey, J. M.	(Sec)	6 Apr
Livingston, R. J.	(Sec)	7 June
Peterson, S. J. BSc	(Sec)	1 July
Jones, C. A.	(Sec)	25 Oct
Taylor, M. F. H.	(Sec)	1 Nov
Pittson, K. T.	(Sec)	15 Nov
O'Donnell, R. E.		
BSc(Econ) AIB		
qss	(Sec)	22 Nov

2001

Carr, M. C. qss	(Sec)	19 Mar
Anderson, L. E. qs	(Sec)	20 May
Dean, G. M. LLB		
psc	(Sec)	11 June
Morgan, C. R.	(Sec)	17 Sept
Mitchell, R. A. snc	(Sec)	2 Nov

Flight Lieutenants

1989

Spanner, H. M. BSc	(Trg)	30 May

1990

Heyes, W. J. BEd	(Trg)	7 July
Hayllor, P. A. BSc	(Trg)	30 Oct

1991

Guthrie, M. E. G. BEng		
adp	(Trg)	19 Aug

1992

Astley-Jones, J. G. MSc		
BSc	(Trg)	25 Mar

1993

Carder, T. C. BSc	(Sec)	1 Apr
Campbell, G. J.		
BSc	(Trg)	12 May

1994

Gilley, R. M. BSc	(Trg)	30 Mar
Thompson, Y. BA	(Sec)	30 Sept

1995

Swanson, F. C. M.		
BSc	(Sec)	10 May
Cheesbrough, D.	(Sec)	25 Oct
Corrie, N. C. BA	(Sec)	10 Nov
Rose, S. M.	(Sec)	11 Nov

1996

Mackmurdie, R. L.	(Sec)	9 May
Davis, W. MBE	(Sec)	1 July
Hadley, S. MA	(Sec)	29 Sept

1997

Read, P. J. BSc	(Sec)	15 Jan
Ginnever, J. D.	(Sec)	28 Sept

1998

Hansell, C. L.	(Sec)	1 Mar
Lovett, Z. K. qss1	(Sec)	7 May
Ploutarchou, L. M.	(Sec)	7 Nov

1999

Kitson, B. BA	(ProvSy)	6 Apr
Mitchell, G. M.	(Sec)	4 Aug

2000

Dhese, I. R. qs	(Trg)	25 Sept

2001

Seaward, P. V. A. DMS		
MRIN MCMI qss	(Sec)	15 Oct

Flying Officers

1993

Hardy, D. N.	(ProvSy)	17 Aug
McNea, P.	(Sec)	28 Sept

1994

Rawnsley, L. M.		
BSc	(Sec)	14 Feb
Bruce, T. J.	(Sec)	7 Nov

MEDICAL BRANCH

Squadron Leaders

1993

Burling, P. M. MB ChB   30 Nov

1995

Bartlett, D. W. MB
  ChB   25 Feb
Jones, J. W. M. BSc MB
  ChB   1 Aug

1996

Rowland, P. O. MD
  FRCS   15 Mar
Barr, E. J. MB ChB   1 Aug
Dyer, M. F. MB ChB   1 Aug
Fox, E. V. MB BS   1 Aug
Kennish, N. P. MB BCh
  MRCGP   1 Aug

1997

Burton, T. BSc MB BS
  MRCGP DCH
  DiplMC   1 Aug
Cotton, S. J. MB ChB   1 Aug
Forde, S. C. O. MB ChB
  FRCA DA(UK)   1 Aug
Fox, G. C. MB BS
  MRCPsych   1 Aug
Gregory, K. L. MB
  ChB   1 Aug
Brunskill, J. M. E. MB
  BS   5 Aug
Flores, M. MB BS MS
  MCh   5 Aug

1998

Pickering, P. M. MA BSc
  MB BChir MRCGP
  DRCOG   1 Feb
Stammers, J. B. MB   28 June
Hastle, J. A. BM BS   1 Aug
Sareen, S. D. MB BCh   1 Aug

Durrani, A. K. MB BS
  FRCS   1 Dec

1999

Craig, J. P. MB ChB   1 Feb
Sheehan, J. P. A. MB
  BCh   6 Mar
Smith, M. B. MB BS   3 Aug

2000

Sparks, S. E. MB ChB   1 Aug
Flewers, G. M. BM   2 Aug
Jackson, C. E. MB ChB   10 Aug

Flight Lieutenants

1992

Howell, J. R. MB BS   1 Aug

1994

Ambler, L. C. MB BS   1 Aug

1996

Cartwright, A. J. MB
  ChB   7 Aug

DENTAL BRANCH

Squadron Leaders

1993

Andrews, N. A. G.
  BDS   20 Feb

1995

Cooper, D. J. BDS   4 Feb

1996

Pratt, A. C. BDS   5 Feb

1997

Savage, A. BDS
  DGDP(UK)   17 Sept

Flight Lieutenants

1993

Belcher, K. A. BDS   9 Dec
King, M. L.   8 Aug

PRINCESS MARY'S ROYAL AIR FORCE NURSING SERVICE

All Officers of Princess Mary's Royal Air Force Nursing
Service hold the qualification of Registered General
Nurse and/or Registered Mental Nurse

Flight Lieutenants

English, M. E.	3 Sept
Rimmer, V. A. RM	27 Sept

1986

Wingham, A. E.	10 June

1996

Hold, C. K. BSc	15 Jan

1989

Bray, L. M. RM	17 July

1997

Hill, M. K.	28 Apr
Stratford-Fanning, P. J.	10 Oct

1990

Pardoe, A. L. RM	1 June

1999

O'Brien, J. M.	17 Mar

1991

Merritt, J. C. RM	13 Jan
Morris, C. RM	1 July

1992

Cox, A. J.	25 July
Preece, A. D. RSCN	27 Nov

1993

Gormley, S. RM	1 May
Smith, K. A.	7 June
Philpott, N. F. M. BA	28 June
Pierpoint, V. J. RSCN	7 July

1994

Hecht, D. A. RSCN	28 July
Tilley, L. H. A.	19 Nov

1995

Taylor, S. E. BNurs	7 July
Hughes, D. A. RM	15 Aug

MEDICAL SUPPORT BRANCH

Wing Commander

1998

Fares, D. B. MInstAM
MHSM MCMI   1 May

Squadron Leader

1999

Williams, K.   25 Aug

Flying Officer

2000

Kennan, N. P. LLB   6 Aug

LEGAL BRANCH

Flight Lieutenant

1996

Moore, N. J.
LLB   (Barrister)   8 Aug

CLASS "CC"

Group Captains

1993

Gambold, W. G.   25 Oct

1994

Kiggell, P. S. OBE   6 Apr

1997

Cross, W. M. N. OBE   26 May
Hakin, L. OBE   10 July

1998

Ford, J. A. F. FCMI   25 May

1999

Wight-Boycott, A. B.
OBE   20 Apr

2001

Remlinger, M. J. psc   16 May

Wing Commanders

1988

Herd, H. D. OBE   24 Nov

1991

Woods, G.   22 Apr

1993

Canning, P. F. A.   31 Aug

Wing Commanders

1995

Kermeen, R. W.	2 Oct

1996

Stephens, M. A.	1 Apr
Thorley, M. A. MRAeS	1 Apr
Wright, W. W. BA BA DipEd	1 Apr
MacLachlan, A. J. C. CEng MRAeS	20 Sept

1997

Jones, M. J. OBE MCMI	3 Mar
Carter, P. R.	1 Sept

1999

Eveleigh, M. OBE MCMI	20 Jan

2000

Joose, C. A.	4 Jan
Wynn, D. I. MBE CertEd	1 May
Ward, A. W. MBE BSc	23 May
Kennedy, B. J. O. qs	14 Apr
Johnson, B. W. aws asq snc qss	21 June
Ashcroft, G. A. ssc qs	26 Sept

2001

Middleton, J. BA jsdc qwi(AD) qs	30 July

Squadron Leaders

1985

Tisbury, J. A. MBE MCMI qss	1 July
Moorhouse, M. G. BSc	2 Sept

Miller, R. W. A. cfs(g)*	4 Oct

1987

McEwan, A. R.	4 Sept

1990

Foley, T.	10 Dec

1992

Dinmore, G. W.	1 Sept
Davies, W. G.	30 Oct
Douglass, M. P.	23 Nov

1993

Johnson, D. L. MCIPD MCMI	4 Mar
Grant, T. cfs(g)*	1 June
McCluskey, R. AFC DPhysEd pji qs	6 Sept
Butler, V. P. L.	1 Oct
Booth, R. E.	21 Oct

1994

Roberts, R. E.	14 Feb
Taylor, R.	5 Apr

1995

Abbott, R. J.	6 Mar
Maddocks, B. J.	18 Apr
Dole, T. F.	8 May
Foster, J. E.	19 June
Hastings, A.	4 July
Fairhead, I. F. BSc(Eng)	17 July
Grand-Scrutton, J.	4 Sept
Griffiths, A.	16 Oct

1996

Bruce, A. J.	8 Jan
Bird, P. R.	15 Feb
Lang, B.	8 Mar
Nadin, J. L.	1 July
Wright, R. C.	19 Aug
Lunt, J. D. BA	24 Sept
Locke, M. A. MCMI	16 Oct
Cobb, J. W. MBE	11 Nov

Carr, E. MILT MCIPD	18 Nov
Broom, B. A.	27 Nov

1997

Shorter, B.	27 Jan
Chalkley, K. B. MBE	3 Mar
Spence, B. G. BA IEng MIIE	21 Apr
Low, I. N.	9 June
Hathaway, J. H. T.	11 Sept
Collins, R. M. MCMI	6 Oct
Massey, R. G. MCMI	11 Dec

1998

Duguid, M. D. MCMI	5 Jan
Margiotta, G. L.	2 Feb
Campbell, R. S.	7 Feb
Moore, G. J. T.	17 Mar
Jones, R. N. IEng MIIE semc qs	21 Aug
Hill, B. H.	9 Nov
Phillips, G. T. BSc qs	25 Nov
Rowe, D. H. W.	1 Dec
Giles, W. J.	2 Dec
Sandeman, C. A. qss	7 Dec

1999

Reed, K. B.	1 Jan
Yates, R.	25 Oct
Edgell, J. A.	19 Nov

2000

Davies, R.	1 Feb
Vine, D. C.	1 Feb
Forster, R. A. A. BA MILT MCMI	28 Feb
Yarram, M. F. BSc qs	1 June
Britton, P. D. MILT qs	23 Oct

2001

Gilchrist, J. I. qs	2 Jan
Phillips, A. J. qss	3 Jan
Berry, R. D. qss	24 Apr
Rodgers, P. J. MBE psc qs	1 Oct

Squadron Leaders

2002

McKendrick, D. I.	12 Apr
Webb, E. A. H. DMS FISM MInstAM MCIPD MCMI	12 Apr

Flight Lieutenants

1975

Tapson, B. cfs(g)*	3 Jan

1978

Throssell, M. G. cfs(g)*	5 Apr

1982

Ward, T. J. cfs(g)*	6 Aug

1987

Hood, L. S. cfs(g)*	13 Aug

1989

Cliff, M. E.	1 Sept

1990

Pleasant, D. M.	12 Mar
Mason, A. D. cfs(g)*	12 Sept
Young, G. A. cfs(g)*	19 Oct

1991

Vernon, J.	7 Jan
Rigby, C. M. R.	16 Sept
Parrini, A. L.	4 Nov

1993

Hermolle, M. A.	19 Aug

1994

Anderson, J. D.	5 Apr

1995

Samme, R. J. cfs(g)*	1 June
James, J. R. BA	3 Aug
Wood, M. J.	31 Aug
Miller, R. E. BA PGCE FRGS	25 Sept
Watkins, M.	13 Nov
Coker, J. D.	4 Dec

1996

Webber, G. R. cfs(g)*	9 Jan
McCran, J. B.	19 Feb
Morris, D. G.	22 July
Shephard, R. G.	2 Sept
Pelcot, A. F.	7 Oct
Fahey, J. B.	28 Oct

1997

Hamon, S.	18 Apr
Inman, P. G.	6 June
Flaherty, S. D.	8 Dec

1998

Heys, P. J. IEng FIIE qs	30 Oct
Fearn, M. H. qss	8 Dec
Mutch, P. MSc BEd qss	8 Dec

1999

Bargewell, T. A. IEng MIIE	4 Mar
Quick, D. M.	6 Apr
Simpson, D. A. MBE	13 Apr
Johnson, M. A. qss	12 Aug
Anderson, G. G. MHCIMA	8 Sept

2000

Southwould, B. W. BA snc qss	1 Aug
Williams, M. cfs(g)	9 Aug
Valentine, M. C. qs	24 Sept
Wardlaw, K.	16 Oct

Monie, G. K. cfs(g)	9 Nov

2001

McKenna, M. J. MBE snc qs i*	26 Aug
Pointon, P. W.	14 Sept
West, J. S. BEd qss	30 Oct

Flying Officer

2000

Dolphin, M. G. cfs(g)	6 Mar

WARRANT OFFICERS

1989

Lamb, C.   27 May

1998

Copeland, E.   1 May
Sumpter, V. G.   9 Nov

1999

Marjoram, R. A.   1 Apr

2000

George, I. H.   5 Jan
Daniels, R. A.   1 Oct

2001

Walton, D. M.   21 Dec

MASTER ENGINEERS

MASTER AIR LOAD- MASTER

1999

Hatton, K. C.	3 Nov
Hoffman, P. P.	3 Nov
Lock, G. D.	3 Nov
McGrath, J. J.	3 Nov

1999

Pountney, R. J.	2 Aug

2002

Buckley, R. F.	21 May

2000

Brundell, M. E.	1 Feb
Doyle, D. J.	1 Feb
Hollingsworth, K.	1 Feb
Wilson, M. J.	1 Feb

ROYAL AUXILIARY AIR FORCE

Air Commodore-in-Chief .... H.M. THE QUEEN

Honorary Inspector-General of the Royal Auxiliary Air Force
Air Vice-Marshal B. H. Newton, CB OBE FCMI
Inspector—Group Captain R. G. Kemp, QVRM AE ADC FRIN
Honorary Air Commodores

HRH The Duke of Gloucester, GVCO No 501 (County of Gloucester) Squadron RAuxAF

Sir Richard George, KT No 504 (County of Nottingham) Squadron RAuxAF

HM The Queen, No 603 (City of Edinburgh) Squadron RAuxAF

Air Vice-Marshal B. H. Newton, CB OBE FCMI No 606 (Chiltern) Squadron RAuxAF

The Viscount of Arbuthnott, KT CBE DSC No 612 (County of Aberdeen) Squadron RAuxAF

Air Vice-Marshal T. P. White, CB CEng FIEE No 2503 (County of Lincoln) Squadron RAuxAF Regiment

Sir Michael Oswald, KCVO DSc MA No 2620 (County of Norfolk) Squadron RAuxAF

Air Vice-Marshal G. A. Chesworth, CB OBE DFC No 2622 (Highland) Squadron RAuxAF Regiment

Colonel E. Bolitho, No 2625 (County of Cornwall) Squadron RAuxAF Regiment

Mr M. V. Gauntlett, Bt DL No 4624 (County of Oxford) Movements Squadron RAuxAF

Air Chief Marshal Sir William Wratten, GBE CB AFC CCMI FRAeS RAF (Retd) No 4626 (County of Wiltshire) Aeromedical Evacuation Squadron RAuxAF

Mr A. Dickson, OBE AE** FRSA FRAeS FCMI No 7644 (VR) Public Relations Squadron RAuxAF

Air Chief Marshal Sir Michael Knight, KCB AFC DLitt BA FRAeS No 7630 (VR) Intelligence Squadron RAuxAF

GENERAL DUTIES BRANCH

Squadron Leader

1998

Harper, H. R.	(N)	1 Nov

Flight Lieutenants

1991

Graham, K. P. BSc	(P)	4 Nov

1994

Chandler, H. T.	(P)	21 Nov

1996

Jordan, R. J. B. BSc	(P)	30 Aug
Roberts, H. D. BSc(Eng)	(P)	30 Aug
Ford, J. A. BSc	(P)	1 Oct

1997

Lawrenson, A. J. BA	(P)	25 Feb
White, M. J. H. BSc	(P)	5 Mar
Baatz, A. P.	(N)	30 May
Finch, G. P.	(P)	1 July
Kingsford, P. G. BSc	(P)	5 July
McLea, C. D.	(P)	3 Oct
Offord, R. J. BCom qwi qs	(P)	16 Nov
Lewis, D. H.	(N)	8 Dec
Coulson, D. L.	(N)	17 Dec

1998

Marshall, R. A.	(P)	23 Feb
Brown, G. P.	(N)	27 Feb
Neill, A. BSc cfs qs	(P)	28 Apr
Jones, P. D.	(P)	8 May
Nichol, C. R.	(P)	14 May
Manser, R. C. H. qss	(P)	3 June
Airey, N. D.	(P)	6 July
Duncan, G. qss	(P)	1 Sept
Berresford, C. S.	(P)	11 Nov

1999

Speight, W. MBE	(ENG)	10 Mar
Spreckley, G. C.	(N)	11 Mar
Woodman, P. M.	(ENG)	24 Mar
Robson, J.	(P)	2 July
Creighton, W. H.	(ALM)	1 Aug
Todd, J. S.	(P)	8 Nov

2000

Pickard, A. C. BA	(P)	16 May
Hulme, L. M.	(N)	30 June
Clarke, S. M. BEng cfs	(P)	28 June
Young, G. L.	(P)	18 Sept
Cook, C. J.	(N)	22 Nov
Ims, M. K. qwi	(P)	1 Dec

2001

McLuskie, I. R. OBE MSc psc cfs	(P)	12 Feb
Weston, P. J. qss	(P)	11 Apr
Brown, A. D. qwi(AD) qss	(P)	4 June
Heaton, M. R. BSc qss	(N)	11 Sept
Earl, J. cfs qss1	(P)	27 Sept
Hardy, N. J.	(P)	8 Nov
Williams, C. C. qhti	(P)	28 Nov
Norton, J. R. cfs	(N)	3 Dec

OPERATIONS SUPPORT BRANCH

Group Captain

2001

Kemp, R. G. QVRM AE
ADC FRIN (FLTOPS) 1 July

Wing Commanders

1996

Partridge, E. F. OBE AE
BEd (FLTOPS) 21 Apr

1997

Hyde, C. B. (REGT) 2 June
Colver, R. J. OBE
jsdc awcc snc
qs (FLTOPS) 4 Dec

2000

Kohn, E. F. BSc
FCMI (FLTOPS) 21 Aug

Squadron Leaders

1987

Blanche, J. B. QVRM AE
MSc BSc DIC (INT) 1 Feb

1988

Dawson, S. AE
MRIN (FLTOPS) 16 Sept

1990

Carr, F. R. (REGT) 1 Mar

1992

Dulson, P. P.
AE (FLTOPS) 1 May

1993

Hodgson, P. AE
MA (INT) 1 July
O'Shaughnessy,
K. M. P. AE (FLTOPS) 1 Oct

1995

Roberts, S. G. AE
BA (INT) 3 Mar

1996

Culpitt, J. V. (INT) 1 Feb
Pattenden, S. M. (INT) 1 Oct
Beaton, A. J. (FLTOPS) 22 Nov

1997

White, D. J. (FLTOPS) 29 Jan
Ridge, M. C. FCMI
MILT (INT) 1 Apr
Bunkell, G. W. QVRM
AE FCII (REGT) 1 Sept
Plumridge, D. L.
AIB (INT) 1 Oct

1998

Wallbank, D. J. (INT) 1 Feb
Crudgington, S.
AE (FLTOPS) 1 July
Bratton, E. G. R.
AE (REGT) 17 Sept
Adamson, G. D. W.
MBE TD AE
MA (REGT) 1 Oct

1999

Byrne, J. D. AE
MA (INT) 1 Feb
Lynn, T. DMS FCMI
MRIN (FLTOPS) 1 June
Ahearn, A. S. AE (INT) 1 July

2001

Alldritt, D. P. G.
qss (REGT) 1 Feb
Angus, P. J. M. MBE BA
jsdc qs (FLTOPS) 26 July
Greenfield, C. W.
BEng (INT) 18 Aug
Whiteley, H. E. LLB (INT) 18 Aug
Redgrave, M. S. J. (INT) 1 Sept

2002

Nicoll, R. F. (INT) 4 Feb

Flight Lieutenants

1985

Wright, W. F. AE BSc
  BArch RIBA (FLTOPS) 1 Sept

1986

Gray, N. M. BSc (INT) 3 Jan
Horn, J. A. BSc (INT) 12 Jan

1987

Colhoun, D. N. T.
  (FLTOPS) 18 May
Reid, J. C. BA (INT) 18 May
Tingle, D. AE
  DipElEng (INT) 7 Nov

1988

van Geene, R. G.
  (FLT OPS) 29 Mar
Tooze, R. J. W. AE
  IEng (FLTOPS) 3 May
Shields, D. (INT) 16 Dec

1989

Tomlinson, P. F.
  BEd (INT) 5 Feb

1990

Purdy, R. B. MA MITI
  qss i (FLTOPS) 6 Nov

1991

Shaw, R. J. AE
  RIBA (INT) 1 Jan
Everitt, A. J. (FLTOPS) 22 Aug

1992

Creed, N. R. E. AE (INT) 1 Aug
Drew, J. L. BSc
  MCIPD (INT) 1 Aug

1993

Chappell, J. I. BSc (INT) 1 Jan
Hellyer, R. J. (FLTOPS) 27 July

1994

Langston-Jones, P. G.
  (REGT) 7 Feb
Weekes, N. C. F. MA
  psc(m) (INT) 5 May
Gardner, M. J. MBA
  BSc (REGT) 22 June
Eves, D. G. E. D. (INT) 2 Aug
Beynon, G. G. (FLTOPS) 18 Oct
Lovegrove, G. B.
  (FLTOPS) 1 Nov

1995

Bruster, A. G. (FLTOPS) 25 Jan
Collins, K. (FLTOPS) 27 Jan
Lyall, G. AE BA (INT) 1 May
Morrison, D. (INT) 1 May
Murray, B. A. BA (INT) 1 May
Verril, M. (FLTOPS) 29 Nov

1996

Woodhead, S. J. M.
  BSc (FLTOPS) 21 Jan
Davies, J. C. (INT) 1 Feb
Burgess, S. F.
  BSc (FLTOPS) 1 May
Launder, W. A.
  AE (REGT) 1 May
Bradshaw, P. N.
  MSc (INT) 26 May
Shaw, G. (INT) 1 June
Zervoudakis, A.
  BA (INT) 1 June
Slingsby, E. T.
  BEng (FLTOPS) 26 June
Greenhalgh, S. B.
  (FLTOPS) 25 Sept
Nichol, D. A.
  BA (FLTOPS) 9 Oct

1997

Anning J. E. (INT) 1 Jan
Turnbull, J. G. (FLTOPS) 21 Jan
Reeves, A. C. (INT) 11 Mar
Talton, S. J. S. (INT) 1 Apr
Abram, E. A. (INT) 28 Apr

Bayne, P. BSc (FLTOPS) 4 May
Whichelo-Page, E. A.
  (INT) 3 June
Partridge, S. J. (INT) 16 June
Stenson, R. BA (FC) 19 Nov

1998

Gilbert P. N. qtm (INT) 12 Jan
Newman, R. D.
  (FLTOPS) 29 Jan
Chattaway, A. M.
  BA (REGT) 2 Mar
Austin, P. D. (INT) 1 May
Wilson, A. D.
  BA BSc (FLTOPS) 1 May
Johnston, D. D. (REGT) 27 May
Burke, H. R. (FLTOPS) 3 July
Fraser, J. (FLTOPS) 6 Aug
Parlour, R. S. MA (INT) 10 Aug
Onley, M. J. BSc (INT) 12 Aug
Rousseau, N. A. B. (INT) 19 Aug
Donlon, C. J. BEng (INT) 2 Sept
Phillips, I. BSc qtm
  qss (INT) 27 Sept
Preece, M. L. (INT) 7 Oct
Rogers, J. S. (REGT) 13 Nov
Reynolds, S. G. (REGT) 9 Dec

1999

Leach, K. L. BA (FLTOPS) 6 Jan
Owen, C. M. (INT) 1 Feb
De Maine, M. J. MPhil
  BSc (INT) 12 Apr
Bliss, N. A. (REGT) 14 Apr
Farrant, W. F. (INT) 1 May
Crisp, R. J. (FLTOPS) 16 May
Metcalfe, J. W. (REGT) 19 Aug
Avery, J. W. L. S. (INT) 20 Sept
Vincent, H. A. (FLTOPS) 1 Oct
Parker, J. E. BA
  PGCE (INT) 2 Oct

2000

Kerley, M. L. A. (ATC) 2 Mar
Cason, L. M. (REGT) 28 June
Fines, G. J. (REGT) 1 July
Moir, A. G. C. BSc (INT) 6 Aug
Bull, R. M. qss (ATC) 1 Sept
Taylor, P. A. (REGT) 7 Nov

2001

Dunwell, R. E. (REGT) 1 Jan

Flight Lieutenants

2001—contd

Waite. I. P.	(INT)	5 Jan
Du Pre, G. M.	(INT)	24 Jan
Trotman, A. J.	(FLTOPS)	31 Mar
Chegwidden, P.	(REGT)	1 Apr
Foster, M. BA	(REGT)	1 Apr
Fox, S. BA	(INT)	1 May
Kyffin, R. G. M.		
BA qs	(REGT)	6 June
McCormick, D. G.		
BSc qss	(FLTOPS)	19 June
Jeavons, R. A.	(INT)	26 June
Crayford, K. A. J.	(INT)	1 July
Lindsay, G. J. BA		
PGCE	(REGT)	27 Sept
Rodgers, J. D.	(REGT)	29 Oct
Cowe, R. I.	(FLTOPS)	4 Nov
Leach, P. W.		
BSc	(FLTOPS)	7 Nov
Walker, A. F. BSc snc		
qs	(FLTOPS)	6 Dec
Cochrane, J. qss	(INT)	17 Dec

2002

Spry-Leverton, H. H.		
	(FLTOPS)	1 Feb
Harrison, B. P. BA	(INT)	14 Feb
Moore, M. A. S.	(INT)	16 Feb
Claesens, A. P.	(INT)	1 Mar
Leyshon, T. J. R.	(INT)	25 May

Flying Officers

1992

Nokes, S. M.	(INT)	2 Apr
Pike, S. BA	(INT)	25 Nov

1993

Oliphant, L. J.	(INT)	21 Jan

1994

Smith, T. F. MA BA	(INT)	18 Nov

1995

Austin, T. N.	(INT)	19 Jan
Muntus, S. J.	(FLTOPS)	17 Mar
Comfort, S. B. RM	(INT)	2 July
Morcom, B. W. AE	(INT)	2 Sept

1996

Roche, J. A.	(INT)	25 Mar
Cavie, G. R.	(INT)	1 July
Skidmore, T. R.	(INT)	18 July
McDonald-Webb, R. N.		
	(INT)	16 Aug

1997

Bagley, J. V.	(INT)	1 June
Jones, J. A.	(INT)	10 Dec

1998

Thompson, S. P.		
BA	(INT)	13 Apr
Ince, N. D. BA	(INT)	12 June
Patel, R. C.	(INT)	12 June
Featherstone, R. A. J.		
	(INT)	4 Sept
Berry, S. L.	(INT)	12 Oct
Bowles, C. M.	(REGT)	1 Dec
Cowling, J. T.	(FLTOPS)	16 Dec

1999

Padgett. L.	(INT)	11 June
Paton, R. A.	(REGT)	13 Oct
Coulson, S. G.	(INT)	12 Nov

2000

Parker, A. G. BSc	(INT)	9 Feb
Flory, M. J. BSc	(INT)	10 Feb
Hanson, S. C.	(INT)	4 Mar
Williams, D. M.	(REGT)	24 May
Duddy, S. J.	(FLTOPS)	11 Aug
Moss, A.	(FLTOPS)	12 Aug
Easton, D. M.	(INT)	16 Nov
Hough, S. J.	(REGT)	11 Dec

2001

Grimshaw, M. D.	(INT)	19 Jan
Chalcraft, J. D.	(REGT)	25 Feb

Gilham, D. J.	(FLTOPS)	4 Mar
Fenwick, T. J. BSc		
BA	(INT)	1 Apr
Arderne, L. E.	(INT)	27 May
Morgan, M. J. LLB	(INT)	27 May
Gardiner, C. D. MSc		
BSc	(INT)	23 June
Weeks, R. L. BA	(INT)	23 June
Harrison, K. L. MSc	(INT)	12 Oct
Hughes, C. M. LLB	(INT)	12 Oct
Lane, G. A.	(FLTOPS)	13 Oct

Pilot Officers

1997

Walters, T. J. MA		
BA	(INT)	21 Nov

1999

Carolan-Cullion, J.		
	(FLTOPS)	8 June

2001

Melia, I. C. BA	(INT)	12 Jan
Dixon, R. J.	(FLTOPS)	20 Apr
Walters, S.	(INT)	20 Apr

Acting Pilot Officers

1998

Kingston, D. BSc (INT) 2 Feb

2000

Ham, I. A. J. (REGT) 8 May
Langtree, C. R.
  BSc (REGT) 20 July
Peterken, P. J. L. (INT) 25 July

2001

Mitchell, G. P. (REGT) 26 Sept
Hepburne-Scott, H. W.
  PhD BSc (FLTOPS) 13 Dec

2002

Flood, G. (REGT) 22 Mar

ENGINEER BRANCH

Squadron Leaders

2001

McAnally, A. D. BSc
  CEng MIMechE 1 Feb

2002

Waller, C. J. N. IEng FIIE
  AMRAeS 14 May

Flight Lieutenant

2001

Mackie, W. S. MSc BSc
  BEng CEng MIIE
  MIEE qss1 30 May

SUPPLY (MOVEMENTS) BRANCH

Wing Commander

1994

Dixon, R. OBE MCIPS
MInstPet MCMI aws
psc im 16 May

Squadron Leaders

1995

Symonds, M. L. AE 20 Oct

1996

Gingell, A. S. BSc 27 Nov

1998

Mallon, M. G. 15 Feb

2001

Williams, R. B. BSc
  MCIPD MCMI 26 Nov

Flight Lieutenants

1993

Dover, M. R. AE 1 Jan

1996

Anderson, C. G. BEd 22 Feb

ADMINISTRATIVE BRANCH

Flight Lieutenants

1997

Saddington, J. P.   1 Jan

2000

Burch, P. F. R.   27 June

2001

Miller, J. qcc   1 Oct

Flying Officers

1996

Smith, H. J.   3 Sept

1997

Morgan, D. L.   14 May

1999

Stephens, J. C.   6 Nov

2000

Fennell, A. J. BA   23 Jan

Acting Pilot Officer

2001

Vickers, G.   1 Nov

Squadron Leaders

1993

Merrick, V. E.   (Sec)   28 July

1995

Mitcham, D. T. AE (Sec)   9 Aug

1997

Forde, W. L. T.
MCMI   (Sec)   11 June

1998

Cunningham, G. C. (Sec)   1 May
Dargan, S.   (Sec)   1 Nov

1999

Difford, H. AE MA
BA   (Sec)   1 Sept

2000

Cairns, M. J.   (Sec)   1 Aug

2001

Waite, B.   (Sec)   1 Feb
Battey, F. J. BA qss   (Trg)   1 Oct

Flight Lieutenants

1987

Storey, C. B. BSc   (Sec)   23 Nov

1991

Morgan, I. D. AE MB
ChB MRCGP   (Sec)   4 Sept

1992

Norman, D.   (Sec)   17 Jan
Johnston, P. T. MBE
MIL qs i   (Sec)   22 Nov

1994

Seaword, R. W.   (Sec)   25 Feb
Lynch, J. R.   (Sec)   12 Apr
Taffinder, S. J. S.   (Sec)   17 July

1995

Masson, D. G. AE
MA   (Sec)   17 Jan
Power, C. S.   (Sec)   25 Sept
Corbett, A. J.   (Sec)   6 Nov

1997

Willis, R. J. BA   (Sec)   29 Jan
Moult, C. J. AE   (Sec)   1 Apr
Chitty, D. A. MA   (Sec)   12 Apr
McNulty, K. BA   (Sec)   1 Aug
Shrubsole, S. C.   (Sec)   1 Aug

1998

Hearn, P. J. MBE MCMI
qs   (Sec)   1 Jan
Fovargue, A. J. BSc snc
qss   (Sec)   12 July
Williams, K. L. D. (Sec)   14 Dec

1999

Burton, J. M.   (Sec)   29 Mar
Gilligan, J. A. P.   (Sec)   10 June

Flight Lieutenants

1999—contd

Mitchell, G. MIL (Sec) 18 Nov

2000

Radcliffe, N. J. R. (Sec) 11 Apr
Sawers, L. (Sec) 1 May

2001

Buckley, D. AMBCS (Sec) 12 Feb
Streeter, S. M. BSc (Sec) 1 Nov

2002

Leach, J. W. P. PhD MSc
   BSc FRGS (Sec) 1 Mar
Earle, P. J. BSc (Sec) 1 Apr

Flying Officers

1991

de Banzie, S. E. BA
   MIL (Sec) 21 June

1994

Dorey, P. M. (Sec) 25 Feb

1997

Bishop, L. (Sec) 7 Mar

1999

Dalboozi, F. BA (Sec) 12 Sept

2001

Sherburn, M. P.
   BA (Sec) 12 Jan
Donaghue, K. J. (Sec) 1 May

Cooper, J. P. (Sec) 19 July

2002

Bennett, D. E. BA (Sec) 24 Jan

Pilot Officers

1998

Muchowski, A. J. (Sec) 30 Nov

1999

Dillon, D. A. BA (Sec) 11 June
Tebbit, J. K. (Sec) 23 Aug

2001

Eklund, J. D. BL (Sec) 12 Oct

Acting Pilot Officers

2000

Leader, H. S. (Sec) 30 Oct

2001

McDill, S. A. BA (Sec) 30 Apr
Smyth, P. R. BA (Sec) 7 Nov
Darling, P. G. BEng (Sec) 17 Nov
Blakey, T. N. (Sec) 26 Nov

2002

Shepherd, J. (Sec) 9 Jan
Morris, J. N. (ProvSy) 19 Apr
Murtagh, M. BA (Sec) 30 Apr
Jolly, S. (Sec) 1 May

MEDICAL BRANCH

Wing Commanders

1992

Grant, H. S. MB ChB
   MFOM MRAeS
   DRCOG DAvMed 27 July

1997

Curnow, J. BMedSci
   BM BS 1 Sept
Almond, M. K.
   BMedSci BM BS
   MRCP 28 Nov

Squadron Leaders

1986

Pote, J. BSc MB BS
   MRCGP 22 June
Lee, C. P. MSc BSc MB
   ChB DRCOG DPH
   DTM&H 10 Nov

1991

Martin, T. E. BSc MB BS
   MRCGP MRCS LRCP
   DRCOG MRAeS 11 June
Elcock, S. M. MB BCh
   MRCGP DRCOG
   DA 29 Oct

1995

Hannaford, P. F. MB
   ChB MRCGP DRCOG
   DCH DAvMed 26 Jan

1996

Pugsley, W. B. BA MB
   BS FRCS 19 Mar

Squadron Leaders

1996—contd

Barlow, P. BSc MB ChB FRCS	26 Mar
Sowden, G. R. MB BS MRCS LRCP FCA	30 Mar
Day, T. K. MChir MB MRCP	10 June
Adeboye K. O. A. BSc MB BS	25 June
Shirley, P. J. MB ChB FRCA DA DiplMC	2 Aug

1997

Stewart, A. V. G. MB ChB FRCA DA	2 July

1998

Douglas, A. F.	13 Feb
Casey, W. F. MA MB ChB FRCA	10 May

1999

Mathew, P.	7 Sept

2000

Acton, K. J. BSc MB BS	2 Aug

Flight Lieutenant

1999

Miller, K. A. MB BS	10 Feb

PRINCESS MARY'S ROYAL AIR FORCE NURSING SERVICE

Wing Commander

2001

Kyte, D. I.	6 Dec

Squadron Leaders

1994

Orzel, M. N. F. RSCN	1 Aug

1999

Warncken, B. C. ARRC RMN	1 Apr

2000

Haggo, S. J. MBE	18 Aug

Flight Lieutenants

1993

Baranski, P. B. RM	1 Sept

1995

Charters, S. E.	18 Feb

1996

Horton, H. J.	18 June
Bond, E. F.	12 Sept

1997

Pitts, J.	5 Aug

MEDICAL SUPPORT BRANCH

Flight Lieutenants

1997—contd

Lawton, L. H.   29 Nov

1999

Finlinson, D.   29 Sept

2000

Martin, J. E.   30 Oct

Squadron Leaders

1988

Walker, S. MBE AE
  RNT   3 May

1996

Hird, J. C. M.   1 Oct

1999

Walden-Hughes, P. P.   1 Mar
Moodie, A. M. AE RGN
  RM   13 Sept

2000

Edwards, N. H.   24 Apr

Flight Lieutenants

2001

Irwin, M. J.   18 Mar

2002

Borgman, P. S. BSc   19 Jan

Flying Officer

1997

Mathieson, C. A. C. AE   2 May

WARRANT OFFICERS

1984

Copeland, C. J. AE   15 July

1989

Jeffrey, D. G. AE   22 Feb

1990

Kutassy, R.   18 Mar

1993

Brown, G. A.   3 Oct
Cross, W. A. M.   9 Nov

1994

Grace, E. J.   1 May
McQueen, D. C. MBE
  AE   1 June
Pickett, A. R. MBE   21 Sept
Ramshaw, G. P.   29 Oct
Mackie, A. D. J. MBE   1 Dec

1995

Coupe, S.   1 Sept

1996

Mapp, D. W.   1 Jan
Thorington, F. G. MBE   28 Feb
Shipsides, M. G.   21 Oct
Kingshott, C.   29 Oct

1997

Bailey, A.   11 Dec

1998

Griffiths, J. P.   10 Jan
Harris, P. A.   1 Oct
Hiscoke, D. L.   1 Oct

McKay, M. J.   1 Oct
Timms, K. G.   1 Oct
Haxton, J. A. AE*   1 Nov
Simpson, H. G.   1 Nov

1999

Loosemore, A. R.   3 Sept
Hiscocks, K. G.   18 Nov
Smith, S. P.   4 Dec

2000

Wrightson, S. A.   2 Feb

MASTER ENGINEERS		MASTER AIR ELECTRONICS OPERATORS		MASTER AIR LOAD-MASTERS	
1999					
Jones, R. L. M.	2 June	**1997**		**1997**	
Hessing, N. J.	9 Sept	Simpson, N. W. W.	2 Apr	Owen, A.	1 Jan
				Armour, B. G.	30 May
		1998		Freeman, T. P.	30 Aug
		Richards, J.	21 Aug	**1999**	
		Harwood, J. S.	19 Nov	Purvis, G. L.	25 Mar
		1999		**2001**	
		Whittaker, E.	13 Jan	Lowther, J. F.	2 Oct
				2002	
				Glass, B.	1 Jan

ROYAL AIR FORCE VOLUNTEER RESERVE
(Training Branch)

Flying Officers

1961

Smith, G. MBE MCMI	6 Aug

1963

Blunn, K.	30 June
Beeley, G. R. LLB	9 Aug
Higgins, B. T. MBE	16 Dec

1964

Scott, P. G. BSc	9 July

1965

Lemm, D. H. W.	29 Apr
Hearn-Grinham, M. C. V.	14 Sept
Gilbert, M. J. BA	6 Nov

1966

Goddard, J. S. cfs(g)	12 Feb
House, B. N. M. cfs(g)	11 June

1967

Gillett, F. R.	26 Jan
Wallace, P. R.	10 Apr
Green, R. W.	4 May
Selwyn-Yates, I. M. P.	15 Sept

1968

Grierson, S. W. MA	8 Jan
Sollars, A. J. MA	12 July
Bartram, I.	19 Nov

1969

Alleyn, W. G.	27 Jan
Moor, R. G. BSc	29 Mar
Arnold, R. W. MBE	6 Apr
Stedman, K. B. cfs(g)	4 May
Allen, T. J. BA	26 June
McCarroll, P. J.	30 June
Murray, A. V. M. MA	14 Sept
Young, K. A.	14 Sept
Strickland, C. S. P.	29 Nov
Todd, I. F. OBE	29 Nov

1970

Fawkes, R. E. MCMI MInstAM	27 June
Emmerson, B.	16 July
Sims, A. W. BSc	16 Aug
North, StJ. D. B.	5 Sept
Shepperd, K. H.	10 Sept
Pomeroy, D. E. BSc	28 Oct

1971

Brackenborough, K.	1 Mar
Starling, R. H.	23 Apr
Jones, I. D. L. MBE BSc cfs(g)	25 June
Richards, D. J. OBE	25 June
Ramsden, G.	10 July
Speed, D. R. MBE	10 July
Sutton, M. J. F. C.	1 Aug
Gallup, S. BSc	23 Oct
Price, B. V.	5 Dec

1972

Bacon, C. J. BA MCIPS	29 Jan
Brown, R. W.	4 Mar
Sturman, H.	30 Apr
Wiggins, A.	30 Apr
Harrison, D. L.	30 June
Endean, B. W.	1 July
Shepherd, P. W. BSc CEng MIMechE cfs(g)	3 July

Singleton, J. E. DPhysEd	3 Aug
Mott, B. G.	4 Oct
Murphy, B.	14 Oct
Kerr, I. S.	15 Oct
Curry, J.	1 Dec
Hayler, P. BA	7 Dec
Yarrow, P. N. S.	16 Dec

1973

Mobey, R.	3 Feb
Harris, J. C.	15 Feb
Vass, R. I.	6 Apr
Arnold, I. D.	21 Apr
Gilmour, C. R.	7 May
Bowen, D. I.	27 May
Broadwith, B. E. BSc	2 June
Bullock, J.	8 June
Johns, T. J. OBE	7 July
Hotston, P. R.	14 July
Arnott, R. H. C.	30 Sept
Lyall, G. BA	22 Nov
Wallis, P. S. BA	10 Dec
Doust, R. J. C.	13 Dec

1974

Lloyd, D. M.	4 Jan
Scott, R. J. I.	4 Jan
Beaumont, R. A.	14 Jan
Young, M. cfs(g)	14 Jan
Talbot, K.	27 Jan
Connolly, T. E.	14 Feb
Campbell, G.	15 Feb
Williams, F. S.	1 Mar
Gray, T. D.	20 Mar
Walsh, R. H.	28 Mar
Quartly, A. F. BSc	29 Mar
Colebrook, M. C.	1 May
Olver, J. N.	12 May
Smith, K. R. J.	18 May
Flood, C. J. MA	26 May
Whitestone, A. E. N. BA	7 July
Walton, J. N.	4 Aug
Protheroe, L.	10 Aug
Greer, A. T. BSc	18 Aug
Hearle, E. M.	20 Aug

Flying Officers

1974—contd

Gridley, M. J.	4 Sept
Pertwee, M. N.	9 Sept
Broom, B. N.	4 Oct
Rawlings, D. G.	4 Oct
Coldwell, R. A.	11 Oct
Lewis, C. A.	11 Oct
Quarman, B. cfs(g)	8 Nov
Thomson, D. cfs(g)	20 Nov
Vaughan, M. D.	5 Dec
Beech, R. C.	20 Dec

1975

Mustard, A.	22 Jan
Wilson, G. A.	2 Feb
Cousins, C. MA	28 Feb
Lewis, R. BSc	10 Mar
Parker, D. E.	12 Apr
Hodges, P. BSc	1 July
Clement, J.	9 July
Sheehan, D. W. MBE	11 July
Clavell, A. R. FCA MCMI	29 Aug
Irlam, J. C. BSc	1 Sept
Senft, S. W.	29 Sept
Barker, A. A.	12 Nov
Howarth, B.	29 Nov
Spence, J. R.	29 Nov
Rooney, W.	18 Dec
Wilson, F. K. BA	29 Dec

1976

Middleton, D. J.	30 Jan
Reed, P. H.	1 Feb
Anthony, D. R.	20 Feb
Morrell, C. J.	20 Mar
Wise, P. G. BSc	9 July
Mockeridge, P. MCMI cfs(g)	25 July
Wills Pope, B. W.	1 Aug
Sandford, G. S.	5 Aug
Carter, E. J. BSc	20 Sept
Briant, D. R. H.	25 Sept
Biggs, C. J.	9 Oct
Wilkie, R. M.	10 Oct
Lines, B.	16 Oct
Ball, B. J. W. GTCL	29 Oct
McCleave, M. J. MBE cfs(g)	4 Nov
Nicholson, J. ACA	17 Nov
Abbott, J.	20 Nov
Smith, A. A.	5 Dec

Stockill, S.	16 Dec

1977

Thomas, A.	22 Jan
Oram, B. K.	5 Feb
Cook, A. BSc	20 Feb
Mans, K. D. R.	5 Apr
Albone, M. S. C.	29 Apr
Osborne, A. J.	5 May
Liquorish, N. J.	1 Oct
Wilby, P. D.	8 Oct
Gallagher, K.	29 Oct
Wilson, R. L.	29 Nov
Webster, M. S.	11 Dec

1978

Miller, C. A.	29 Jan
Lowe, B. C.	8 Feb
Mosses, J. P.	16 Feb
Place, J. K.	23 Feb
Windo, A. R.	26 Feb
North, M. J.	26 Mar
Woolliscroft, R. E. cfs(g)	5 Apr
Edwards, G.	10 Apr
Horsley, T. J. cfs(g)	1 May
Richards, F. R.	3 May
Lutton, P. F. BA	4 May
Watson, C. L.	7 June
Martin, D.	23 June
Cope, C. S.	4 July
Kirkland, F. B.	20 July
Fairington, R. W.	21 July
Morvan, G.	28 July
McCrae, D. C.	9 Aug
Davies, K.	26 Aug
Beecroft, A. J.	11 Oct
Wells, D. J.	11 Oct
Begent, T. A.	15 Nov
Piper, G. R. BSc	5 Dec
Dimond, J. cfs(g)*	6 Dec
Pardoe, D. J. D.	6 Dec

1979

Blaikie, A. R.	7 Feb
Peasgood, D. J.	7 Feb
Lyttle, T.	9 Feb
Hammond, I.	23 Feb
Moss, R.	2 Mar
Molnar, B. R. cfs(g)	7 Mar
Warrender, B. R. MA	15 Mar
Tancell, P. cfs(g)	31 Mar
Parry, J. K. BSc	11 Apr
Kirby, R. J.	19 Apr

Mills, S. M.	15 June
Nichols, J. P.	22 June
Bower, P. E. L.	14 Sept
Lawrence, T. MA	23 Sept
Richards, P. J.	4 Oct
Sheehan, A. V.	11 Oct
Edwards, B. R. cfs(g)	23 Nov
Hucker, S. J.	30 Nov
Hackett, R. PhD	1 Dec
Bussetil, S. G.	22 Dec

1980

Kinnon, D. McF.	7 Feb
Paterson, R. A.	7 Feb
Catterall, R.	6 Mar
Shilladay, S. BA	6 Mar
Goldsworthy, R. cfs(g)	7 Mar
Cartwright, B. cfs(g)	8 Mar
Upham, P.	21 Mar
Clark, D. A.	22 Mar
Harris, A. R. cfs(g)*	6 Apr
Flower, H.	25 Apr
Massey, P.	25 Apr
Molloy, S.	25 Apr
Thrussell, P. C. S.	25 Apr
Davison, I. F.	27 Apr
Walker, J. A. BSc	19 June
Chalmers, I. MacD.	26 June
Apiafi, H.	27 June
Ledamun, R.	29 June
Fradley, D.	23 July
Geddes, R.	2 Aug
Keel, J. S.	4 Aug
Hills, E. R.	25 Aug
Cutting, D. J. BA	12 Sept
Wilkinson, T. S.	14 Sept
Symons, M. T.	20 Sept
Docking, P. W.	4 Oct
Osborne, R.	16 Oct
Austin, A. L. BA	18 Oct
Colvin, D. P.	7 Nov
Raynor, G.	8 Nov
Whitters, P. D. cfs(g)	15 Nov

1981

Percival, D. cfs(g)	29 Jan
MacKay, D. J.	19 Feb
Swan, B.	19 Feb
Price, D.	28 Feb
Clemerson, G. C. BSc	4 Mar
Chart, D. I. J.	7 Mar
Vinnicombe, W. J.	8 Mar
Byng, E. F.	14 Mar
Kern, S. J. MA	29 Mar
Toon, T. H.	17 May
Challoner, E. IEng MIIE	4 June

Flying Officers

1981—contd

Jackson, B. K.	5 June
McClenagham, P. S. BEd	5 June
Jackson, T. A.	20 June
Doughty, A.	26 June
Priest, P. T.	11 July
Seazell, P. G.	19 July
Matthews, G. R.	22 July
Gunter, N. J.	26 July
Turnbull, W. E.	26 July
Kelly, I.	30 July
Wallace, I.	8 Aug
Walker, R. L. H. BSc	12 Aug
Christmas, K.	13 Aug
Richards, S. J.	13 Aug
Nicholls, P. T.	22 Aug
Wake, G. R.	24 Aug
Harrison, S. D.	1 Oct
Elliott, A. G.	3 Oct
Wood, S. MCIT MILT	17 Oct
Acland, C. A.	23 Oct
Beardwood, P. N.	29 Oct
Miller, R. R. BTech MBCS	31 Oct
McCall, J. M.	12 Nov
Brennan, P. M. BSc	14 Nov
Aldred, J. BSc	26 Nov
Woolcock, D. H. cfs(g)	30 Nov
Mayes, G. J.	12 Dec
Ralph, P. S.	17 Dec
Woods, S. J. BSc	17 Dec
Walker, P.	21 Dec

1982

Broomfield, I. K.	14 Jan
Ellis, B. I.	14 Jan
Bowers, J. W.	30 Jan
Doubell, P. T.	30 Jan
Hugo, R. L.	30 Jan
Thirkell, C.	31 Jan
Adamson, C. J.	8 Feb
Curtis, A. J.	27 Feb
Poloczek, J. A.	7 Mar
Barton-Greenwood, G. C.	10 Mar
Thompson, A. G. F.	10 Mar
Metcalfe, J. W.	20 Mar
Bowles, G. J.	1 Apr
Fisher, C. J.	10 Apr
Buehner-Coldrey, M. J. M.	30 Apr
Atherton, H. S. J.	2 May
Watts, P. A. cfs(g)	2 May
Greenslade, A. L. J.	8 May
Pitts, G. K.	9 May

Faulkner, C. R. BSc	20 May
Warren, J. S. BSc	22 May
Dunn, D. J.	16 June
Lyons, P. C. cfs(g)	16 June
Taylor, W. L.	16 June
Armstrong, A. P.	17 June
Milne, T. A.	17 June
Charnock, G.	11 July
Melmore, A. C.	11 July
Kaye, M. P. BA	9 Aug
Brickley, C. J. A.	22 Aug
Nicholls, S.	26 Aug
Chapman, G. W. LLM MCMI	29 Aug
Simpson, A. J. BSc	29 Aug
Guy, S. D.	12 Sept
Semple, N. DipEE	20 Sept
Thompson, A. P. BSc	24 Sept
Biddles, D.	26 Sept
Bennett, G. E. D. BA	7 Oct
Little, G. I. BSc	7 Oct
Bailey-Woods, G. MRAeS	9 Oct
Bennett, A. R. T.	9 Oct
Dicks, C. P.	9 Oct
Lewis, M. A.	9 Oct
McKeown, B. J.	11 Oct
Coffer, P.	28 Oct
Gibson, T. H. G.	28 Oct
Mehmet, K.	28 Oct
Swierczek, A. F. I. AIB	29 Oct
Evans, M. R. BSc	3 Nov
Chapman, J. W.	13 Nov
Walter, T. D. BA	14 Nov
Burton, P. J.	17 Nov
Melican, J. J. BA	21 Nov
Abbey, S. M. BA	26 Nov
Baker, M.	28 Nov
Jelfs, R. G. BEd	28 Nov
Measures, P. J.	8 Dec
Passfield, A.	8 Dec
Page, J. R.	17 Dec
Willman, W. T. BA MCMI	19 Dec

1983

Harris, D. L.	6 Jan
Wilson, R. J.	6 Jan
Hill, T. J. BSc	14 Jan
Cox, D. C.	26 Jan
Day, C. M.	27 Jan
Goodier, R. L.	2 Feb
Barbour, E. C.	24 Feb
Mitchell, J. A.	24 Feb
Borwick, J. P.	11 Mar
Shelbourn, P. J.	27 Mar
Freehold, D. R. cfs(g)	31 Mar
Sweetman, R. C.	31 Mar

Clark, M.	8 May
Archibald, D.	13 May
Finch, D. J.	13 May
Wood, D.	13 May
Bethell, A. H.	20 May
Pettitt, B. W.	9 July
Routledge, P. W.	9 July
Stroud, J.	9 July
Forrester, A. BTech	10 July
Scott, P. R. BPharm MPS	10 July
Behenna, R. N.	17 July
Lee, R. E.	17 July
Sherry, S. T.	17 July
Miller, D. C. BSc	4 Aug
Rushton, F. A. StJ.	4 Aug
Coats, B.	12 Aug
Easson, S. RGN RMN DN cfs(g)	1 Sept
Miller, D. K.	15 Sept
Timothy, R. C.	17 Sept
Steele, R. M. G. BSc	25 Sept
Taylor, A. T. H. BSc MCMI	5 Oct
Brown, D.	14 Oct
Munro, B.	19 Oct
Robinson, C.	29 Oct
Southwell, G. W. PhD MSc BSc	29 Oct
Smith, G. J.	30 Oct
Birkett, B.	12 Nov
Lewis, M. A.	12 Nov
Reywer, G.	12 Nov
Bohanna, P. J.	27 Nov
Twemlow, W. J. BA	27 Nov
Thynne, D.	15 Dec

1984

Harrison, M. D.	6 Jan
Mathews, M. G. BA	6 Jan
Seaton, I. G.	6 Jan
Carter, M. A.	4 Feb
Sergeant, P. S. BEd	4 Feb
Slaney, P. J.	4 Feb
Kalamatianos, C. M. BA	12 Feb
Ensor, S. J.	19 Feb
Eaton, M. A.	2 Mar
Williams, S. MBE	2 Mar
Baker, N. W.	11 Mar
Horn, J. A.	11 Mar
Ulrich, M. P. ACA	11 Mar
Hartley, J. R. L. BSc	26 Mar
Smith, P. J.	26 Mar
Staniszewski, C. S.	26 Mar
Marshall, I. P.	30 Mar
Huntley, A. D.	1 Apr
McNamara, H. M.	10 Apr
Ferguson, C. G.	16 Apr

Flying Officers

1984—contd

Wood, A. J.	16 Apr
Colbourne, D. J.	12 May
Davies, K.	12 May
Perriam, D. A.	12 May
Thompson, M. L.	12 May
Blundell-Pound, G. BSc MCIT MILT	20 May
Gill, G. BA cfs(g)	20 May
Westgate, P. R.	20 May
Collins, P. W.	11 June
Ely, D. E. MCMI	29 June
Parker, G. G.	29 June
Parker, K. B. M.	29 June
Hoy, P. J. MCMI	6 Aug
Hughes, D. M.	6 Aug
Mistry, K. K. G.	8 Aug
L'astrange, J. P.	25 Aug
Dent, M. A.	1 Sept
Gordon, J.	1 Sept
Neilson-Hansen, S. A. cfs(g)	7 Sept
Trueman, R.	13 Sept
Lane, P. S. BSc	14 Sept
Redmore, R. J.	17 Sept
Powell, P. J.	22 Sept
Greenow, J. W.	30 Sept
Brady, G.	4 Oct
Harper, M. E.	4 Oct
Lee, R. E. BA	4 Oct
Bennet, M. G. DFC	16 Oct
Churnside, T. W.	3 Nov
Wilson, M. J.	3 Nov
Flynn, C. P.	11 Nov
Moffat, J. C.	11 Nov
Linehan, M.	22 Nov
Callow, B.	6 Dec
Clark, A. E. C.	6 Dec
Jenkins, G. A.	8 Dec
Suddards, D. G.	8 Dec
Willacy, B. F.	21 Dec
Fry, J. M. BSc	22 Dec

1985

Parsons, J.	3 Jan
McLauchlan, W. W.	27 Jan
Nicholls, D. T.	27 Jan
Breward, R. W. MSc	1 Feb
Meath, P.	1 Feb
Silver, S. E.	7 Feb
Sucksmith, P. S.	15 Feb
Sutton, A. J.	14 Mar
Broadbridge, I. J. D.	21 Mar
Jones, P. M.	21 Mar

Haswell, M. R. BSc MIEE	25 Mar
Streule, C. R. BSc	25 Mar
Courtney, R. B. MSc BTech	29 Mar
Heath, J. G. RMN	29 Mar
Jones, G. D. R. PhD BSc	14 Apr
Penn, A. D.	22 Apr
Muskett, N. P.	28 Apr
Smith, D. BSc MB ChB	30 Apr
Fitzpatrick, B. J.	5 May
Gould, R. G.	11 May
Holloway, G.	11 May
Hullott, S.	11 May
Padgham, A. J.	22 May
Oliver, A. D. cfs(g)	24 May
Anderson, P. B.	30 June
Bate, K. M.	30 June
Houston, T. W.	30 June
McNeill, C. T.	30 June
Milford, C.	30 June
Moore, K. S.	30 June
Parker, E. R.	28 July
Smith, J. I.	28 July
MacKay, D. J.	12 Aug
Taylor, R. S.	6 Sept
Beardsley, C. L.	19 Sept
Steggles, T. P.	19 Sept
Foster, H.	21 Sept
Allison, K. D. BA	5 Oct
Stansfield, J. D.	7 Oct
Cheeseman, G. C.	19 Oct
Standish, J. L. IPFA	20 Oct
Bratt, L. BSc	26 Oct
Ving, I. C.	2 Nov
Dudek, M.	9 Nov
Fitch, G. R.	9 Nov
Barnes, C. R.	24 Nov
Strunwick, A.	24 Nov
Coleman, P. A. BSc	25 Nov
Dooley, S. F.	29 Nov
Hawke, T. R.	29 Nov
Taylor, W. A. cfs(g)	6 Dec
Naeem, S. M.	16 Dec
Tuff, V. G.	16 Dec

1986

Cartwright, A. C.	3 Jan
Dimond, W. B.	3 Jan
Grix, A. D. H.	3 Jan
Lloyd, S.	3 Jan
Sheppard, P. W. V.	5 Jan
Gillespie, D.	9 Jan
Hodges, C. J. M. BA	17 Jan
Bishop, I. L. BSc	23 Jan
Ancell, T.	27 Jan
Bristow, J. C.	27 Jan
Barber, S.	1 Feb

Davey, P. R.	1 Feb
Duffin, J. E.	1 Feb
Kirczey, A. M.	1 Feb
Ward, R. J.	16 Feb
Dignan, J. C. MCMI	19 Feb
Newman, T. P.	3 Mar
Wiper, K. J. cfs(g)	7 Mar
Wright, G.	7 Mar
Plant, J.	13 Mar
Morris, R. A. F.	19 Mar
Holt, A. BA JP	22 Mar
Boyd, A.D. BEd	2 Apr
Mitchell, R. T. MBE	10 Apr
Levick, P.	16 Apr
Rundle, C. B.	16 Apr
Truberg, P. A.	16 Apr
Hawkes, G. R.	11 May
Kelsey, G.	15 May
Bovingdon, A. D.	21 May
Scott, P. J.	21 May
Sterland, R. J. MBE	11 June
Smith, R. C.	23 June
Rowland, D.	26 June
Goodier, R. E.	5 July
Higgins, D. T.	5 July
Saunders, M. J. cfs(g)	5 July
Watkins, D. V.	10 July
Gardner, T. P.	25 July
Stanley, D. S.	5 Aug
Gillott, C.	13 Aug
Gregory, T. W.	13 Aug
Foster, R. W.	28 Aug
Cox, B. R.	14 Sept
Latimer, J. S.	16 Sept
Armitage, J. P. BSc	1 Oct
Thomas, B. C.	1 Oct
Hipperson, A. J.	11 Oct
Bosworth, D. PhD BSc	24 Oct
Lark, M. A.	24 Oct
Dickinson, N. C.	15 Nov
Eccles, R. S. FCMA	15 Nov
Skinner, D. S.	15 Nov
Vance, W. G.	15 Nov
Carter, D. E.	17 Nov
Iliffe-Rolfe, G. D.	18 Nov
Flower, P. C. MBE	3 Dec
Mullan, I. J. cfs(g)	3 Dec
Singer, J. C.	3 Dec
Roberts, T. G. BA	10 Dec
Morgan, D. J.	14 Dec
Yates, G. J.	14 Dec
Penwarden, R. J.	16 Dec
Wood, M. R. O.	20 Dec

1987

Barrett, M. E.	9 Jan
Gibson, G. V. BSc	17 Jan
Kemp, R. A.	21 Jan

Flying Officers

1987—contd

French, B. S.	24 Jan
Shingler, F. J. MA	31 Jan
Anderton, K. R. OBE	11 Feb
Byrne, M. P.	22 Feb
Cubitt, P. A.	22 Feb
Griffiths, D.	22 Feb
Yeomans, M. J. M.	22 Feb
Nash, M. A.	8 Mar
Goodayle, R. C.	25 Mar
Suchorzewski, D. G.	25 Mar
Wellings, H. J.	25 Mar
Blance, L. H. BEd	28 Mar
Loynton, J. C. MA BEd	28 Mar
Thomas, J. E.	28 Apr
Ridge, J. P. MA	1 May
Ledster, C. cfs(g)	2 May
Manfield, R. F. W.	8 May
Boyce, D. R.	13 May
Pritchard, K.	20 May
Riley, M. W.	3 June
Wickwar, P. J. cfs(g)	3 June
Shepherdson, K. A.	9 June
Dart, N. MA BEd	1 July
Davies, H. B.	1 July
Harris, R. W. BSc	1 July
Hollington, R. V.	1 July
Hoyle, R. F.	1 July
Jukes, R. W.	1 July
Parsons, P.	1 July
Sutton, B. J. N.	1 July
Gregor, G. R.	30 July
Hornsey, L. BSc	30 July
Keane, L.	30 July
Smale, J. A. BEd	30 July
Souter, T. W.	30 July
Hambly, C. J.	6 Aug
Hudson, I. M.	14 Aug
Mihailovic, D.	14 Aug
Davies, A. J.	5 Sept
Hedley, R. L. BSc CEng MIMechE cfs(g)	5 Sept
Moran, J. P. BA	13 Sept
New, S. P.	19 Sept
Stacey, C.	23 Sept
Pomeroy, C. A.	28 Sept
Williamson, J. W.	30 Sept
Ross, H. S.	20 Oct
Blakey, M. P.	21 Oct
Lee, F.	21 Oct
Tunnah, J. E.	3 Nov
Goggin, J. F.	5 Nov
Gurney, R. F.	5 Nov
McLennan, J. D.	5 Nov
Bradfield, M. A. H. BA	7 Nov
Eaton, J. G.	18 Nov

Hincks, P. S.	2 Dec
Swallow, R. J.	13 Dec
Howard, D.	17 Dec
Penn, B. W. BSc	18 Dec

1988

Roberts, R.	7 Jan
Penn, C. M.	23 Jan
Sewell, R. G.	23 Jan
Merriman, D. A. P. MA BA	2 Feb
Barton, N.	4 Feb
Kelly, L. D. BSc	14 Feb
Morse, J. E.	14 Feb
Ronaldson, D. D.	14 Feb
Walkley, J. R.	14 Feb
Yee, R.	18 Feb
Weir, D. C. J.	20 Feb
Winton, N. O.	21 Feb
Adams, P.	10 Mar
Horsley, D. C.	20 Mar
Kerr, R. J. BSc CEng MIEE	20 Mar
Flynn, A. J.	11 Apr
Soughton, K. J.	11 Apr
Crew, D. R.	16 Apr
Woods, S. A. BSc	30 Apr
Ford, P.	1 May
Totten, P. A.	19 May
Barnes, P. D.	6 June
Hector, H. M.	6 June
Stock, M. B.	23 June
Timmins, D. AIB	30 July
Turner, D.	30 July
Vincent, J. N.	30 July
Richardson, P. J. BSc	14 Aug
Page, A. M. BA	15 Aug
Hutton, C. R. BSc CEng MIEE JP	18 Aug
Unthank, R.	2 Sept
Beech, J. A.	8 Sept
Parker, M. C.	8 Sept
Hamilton, A.	17 Sept
Ward, I. M.	17 Sept
Gant, D. McK. MA	23 Sept
Shaddick, D. W. C.	23 Sept
Tippell, R. J. BA MCMI	27 Sept
Rowan, P. R. BSc	30 Sept
Smith, R. L. cfs(g)	30 Sept
Lovett, M. S.	1 Oct
Warner, D. L. BSc	2 Oct
McNaught, R.	6 Oct
Paish, C. M. BA	11 Oct
Fox, A. BSc	22 Oct
Thubron, B. F.	27 Oct
Boden, C. G. BSc	30 Oct
Butler, A. G.	6 Nov

Green, M. H. MEd MRAeS cfs(g)	25 Nov
Sinclair, S. B. M.	25 Nov
Webb, A. W. cfs(g)	4 Dec
Wratten, A. J. BTech	4 Dec
Joynson, D. BEd	11 Dec
Godden, J. R.	15 Dec
Wort, G. L. P.	15 Dec
Beaney, V. R.	18 Dec

1989

Carr, S. J.	2 Jan
Smith, A. L.	6 Jan
Westacott, E. BA	6 Jan
Williams, R. S.	12 Jan
Breedon, R. LLB	2 Feb
Jones, P. E. C.	6 Feb
Reid, N. J. W.	9 Feb
Keen, G.	19 Feb
Withers, N. R. cfs(g)	20 Feb
Cochran, A. N. MSc BSc CEng MIEE	28 Feb
Waller, A. J.	2 Mar
Butterley, J. D.	22 Mar
Britton, K. M. MSc BA	31 Mar
Browne, R. A.	31 Mar
Gale, C. A. F.	31 Mar
Guy, R. M.	31 Mar
Brown, J. A.	27 Apr
Dunnett, S. K.	27 Apr
Smith, W. H.	5 May
Cotton, E. M. cfs(g)	7 May
Bickerdike, H. J.	29 May
Jones, J. E. M. BA	29 May
Whittenbury, W. P.	29 May
Jordan, A. P.	11 June
Stroh, J.	18 June
Button, D. MCMI	25 June
Winks, C. W. BSc	25 June
Broughton, B. W.	10 July
Dodd, M. S.	10 July
Howard, B. M. RGN	10 July
Mitchell, P. V.	10 July
Cyster, C. D.	11 July
Evans, A. M.	13 July
Haygarth, P. W. J.	28 July
Hollyer, P. A.	28 July
Jefferies, N.	28 July
Grover, J. D.	11 Aug
Lawrence, J. M.	13 Aug
Burford, D. P.	19 Aug
Down, F. C. BSc	18 Sept
Maggs, C. K.	18 Sept
Owen, J. E.	18 Sept
Bass, M.	28 Sept
Ellison, C. R. cfs(g)	28 Sept
Stephenson, B.	28 Sept
Evans, D. K.	19 Oct

Flying Officers

1989—contd

Delaney, G. T. cfs(g)	20 Oct
Parfitt, A. P.	20 Oct
Revell, I. L.	20 Oct
Talbot, A. J.	20 Oct
Weston, P. T.	20 Oct
Winder, D.	22 Oct
Laycock, J. BA	2 Nov
Kay, E.	9 Nov
Stanton, T. M.	9 Nov
Watson, N. A.	9 Nov
Emmins, D. J.	12 Nov
White, R.	12 Nov
Crawley, E. J.	13 Nov
Hildersley, C.	13 Nov
Langfield, P. A.	13 Nov
Holden, R. E.	16 Nov
Ephgrave, P. J.	18 Nov
Knight, Sir Michael KCB AFC BA DLitt FRAeS	19 Nov
Simpson, A. C.	26 Nov
Spokes, A. J.	1 Dec
Davies, K.	10 Dec
Seymour, V. R.	15 Dec
Evans, S. E. BA	18 Dec
Hodges, T. A. ACII	20 Dec

1990

Franklin, S. J. W.	12 Jan
Guy, B. J.	12 Jan
Lundy, R. P.	21 Jan
Tisley, B. P. F. cfs(g)	24 Jan
Bage, K. M. BSc	26 Jan
Robetts, W. C. R. MEd BA	2 Feb
Single, G. J.	4 Feb
Griffith, E. D. cfs(g)	5 Feb
Cooke, I.	19 Feb
Davies, L. S.	19 Feb
Dixon, P.	19 Feb
Edwards, D. G.	19 Feb
Hardwick, S. J.	19 Feb
Peers, J. K.	19 Feb
Young, B.	19 Feb
Grapes, N. P. P.	26 Feb
Bowyer, R. E. cfs(g)	1 Mar
Hair, J. L.	3 Mar
McAtamney, E. J.	3 Mar
Walker, D. J.	3 Mar
Adgar, B.	8 Mar
Dean, J. D. E. BSc	20 Mar
Lockwood, N. C.	8 Apr
Ridgway, E.	8 Apr

Sewell, M. A.	8 Apr
Tunstall, R.	18 Apr
Love, M. A.	28 Apr
Shimmons, R. W.	9 May
Baldwin, T. M. A. BSc MIBiol PGCE	11 May
Kerr, R. W.	11 May
Naismith, I. E.	11 May
Waller, S. E.	11 May
Mayes, D. C.	24 May
Shakespeare, M. N.	24 May
Brookbank, C. K.	26 May
Wright, A. S.	26 May
Roy, T. D.	27 May
Day, P. J. J.	9 June
Bell, S. G. cfs(g)	27 June
Gillespie, A. J. cfs(g)	27 June
Lawrance, A. D.	30 June
Pollard, J. E.	30 June
Welborne, R. G. BA	30 June
Reynolds, G. W.	4 July
Bulley, B. BSc	13 July
Rutledge, G. A. BA	14 July
Forster, J. B.	26 July
Gallagher, M.	31 July
Anderson, J. M.	2 Aug
Bracey, K. W.	2 Aug
Hansen, D. cfs(g)	2 Aug
Hynes, A. C. LLB	2 Aug
Morrell, S.E.	2 Aug
Parker, N. E.	2 Aug
Patterson, G. D.	2 Aug
Poulton, M. J.	2 Aug
Scott, J. G.	2 Aug
Webb, D. J.	2 Aug
Wright, M. R. BSc	2 Aug
Kerr, A. T.	2 Sept
Shepherd, S. V.	2 Sept
Stevens, E.	2 Sept
Brittain, A. J.	4 Sept
Edmonds, R. S. P.	4 Sept
Robinson, A. H.	5 Sept
Gould, H.	9 Sept
Hackshall, S. E.	9 Sept
Stancombe, K. M. BSc PGCE	12 Sept
Baker, A. J.	14 Sept
Griffin, A. C.	14 Sept
Pavitt, R. G.	14 Sept
Kent, B. L. CertEd	16 Sept
Tebbs, R. C. cfs(g)	20 Sept
Carr, J. M.	27 Sept
Ireland, D. E.	27 Sept
Roe, C. P.	27 Sept
White, M.	27 Sept
Blacklock, C. N. BA CertEd	30 Sept
Boland, W.	30 Sept
Hoskins, M. J.	4 Oct
Mead, S. M.	4 Oct

Swatridge, J. C.	6 Oct
Bartlett, A. J.	13 Oct
Palmer, P. J.	13 Oct
Bell, C. G.	24 Oct
Brown, A. J.	28 Oct
Sweeney, M.	31 Oct
Brad, W. G. M.	1 Nov
Martin, I. J.	2 Nov
Anderson, I. F.	15 Nov
Meredith, C.	15 Nov
Pinching, S. J. cfs(g)	21 Nov
Barwick, R. L.	27 Nov
Lamb, A. R. MIBiol	5 Dec
Rogers, F. C.	5 Dec
Wood, C. P.	5 Dec
Wood, J. A. cfs(g)	5 Dec
Pratt, B. R. D.	9 Dec
Ogden, P. J.	14 Dec
Blake, N. cfs(g)	22 Dec
East, C. A.	22 Dec
Hitchen, J. B.	22 Dec
Sullivan, R. J.	22 Dec

1991

Cook, B. J.	17 Jan
Bruguier, G. P.	6 Feb
Loxton, J. V.	9 Feb
Keable, J.	10 Feb
Bass, S.	28 Feb
Gracey, M. H. BA	28 Feb
Jenkins, D. P. BA PGCE	28 Feb
Stubbs, M. K.	28 Feb
Cliffe, A. J. cfs(g)	14 Mar
Scanlon, N. F. J.	14 Mar
Thomas, B. A.	14 Mar
Bryan, A. S.	22 Mar
Davies, J.	25 Mar
Kocbusz, G.	7 Apr
Anderson, S. D.	11 Apr
Gilvary, R. B.	12 Apr
Anderson, J. S.	15 Apr
Howlett, M. A.	19 Apr
Johnson, K. R.	19 Apr
Stonestreet, C. J.	19 Apr
Tolley, P. J.	19 Apr
Sutherland, D. F. cfs(g)	28 Apr
Delafield, J.	13 May
Kelly, A. J.	17 May
Kidby, M. J.	17 May
Truman, W. E.	17 May
White, D. A. C. BSc	19 May
King, A.	25 May
Moss, D. W.	25 May
Welbourne, R. J.	25 May
Smithson, P. J.	26 May
Alexander, B. A.	13 June
Thorrington, B. W. G.	13 June
Livingston, R. C.	21 June

Flying Officers

1991—contd

Buckland, S.	22 June
Flitcroft, S. E.	28 June
Adams, J. E.	2 July
Brown, A. K. BSc	2 July
Atkinson, S. P.	4 July
King, T. R.	4 July
Rattle, R.	4 July
Boustead, S.	20 July
Walshaw, R. N. BA PGCE ARCO	20 July
Wilcock, N. BTech	20 July
Lees, A. cfs(g)	26 July
Blunt, G. J.	28 July
Clift, A. D.	2 Aug
Reis, F.	2 Aug
Elms, D. J.	11 Aug
Combe, A. G.	14 Aug
Miller, A. A. BA	14 Aug
Haller, D.	19 Aug
Hall, D.	25 Aug
Hill, D. A.	25 Aug
Hooton, G. A.	25 Aug
Hill, R.	29 Aug
Neate, M. W. J.	4 Sept
Endean, J. P.	5 Sept
Hatch, M. L.	11 Sept
Eke, M. J.	14 Sept
Henson, D. R. cfs(g)	14 Sept
Williams, T. J. W.	14 Sept
Turner, Y. A.	18 Sept
Taylor, R. D. DPhysEd	29 Sept
Henderson, D. J. PhD BSc PGCE	2 Oct
Hutchinson, S. A.	11 Oct
Mayoh, S. A.	11 Oct
Goddard, C. M.	16 Oct
Howes, R. W.	23 Oct
Pidgeon, P. R.	23 Oct
White, A. J.	23 Oct
Biddles, D.	26 Oct
Goring, P. D.	26 Oct
Jeremiah, L.	26 Oct
Palmer, D. J.	26 Oct
Tucker, K. D.	3 Nov
Wilson, K. R.	13 Nov
Cambra, J. M.	16 Nov
Jones, D. A.	16 Nov
Hallam, J. W. R.	30 Nov
Hunt, J. L.	30 Nov
Kearns, G.	30 Nov
Robinson, D. A.	30 Nov
Rogers, G. L.	30 Nov
Swinge, P. D.	30 Nov
Downs, T.	11 Dec
Vernon, M. BSc PGCE	12 Dec

Atkins, A. M.	20 Dec
Goodger, G.	20 Dec

1992

Burrows, G. W.	8 Jan
Davison, E. D.	8 Jan
Hamilton, M. R.	8 Jan
Monro, I. W.	8 Jan
Potter, S.	8 Jan
Smith, J. H.	8 Jan
Stanton, P.	8 Jan
Brett, M. I.	13 Jan
Mitchell, A.	22 Jan
Johnson, S.	23 Jan
Mead, A. B.	24 Jan
Medhurst, P. W.	30 Jan
Halliday, J. W.	5 Feb
Hobbs, D. G.	7 Feb
Arnold, W. J. W. BA PGCE	15 Feb
Haggo, S. J. MBE	15 Feb
Lee, J. F.	15 Feb
Teague, W. W. L.	15 Feb
Middleton, K. J. BEng	20 Feb
Miskimmin, M. D.	26 Feb
Chivers, G. C. R.	27 Feb
Jones, J.	27 Feb
Roberts, P. G.	2 Mar
Retallick, R. N.	12 Mar
Woolven, A. J.	12 Mar
Hale, D. I.	20 Mar
Whitehead P. F.	23 Mar
McNeill, S. D.	28 Mar
Porter, E. A.	28 Mar
French, D.	2 Apr
Spring, D. R.	2 Apr
Cleeter, A. G.	4 Apr
Mathie, A. R. C.	4 Apr
Nutland, C. F.	4 Apr
Ford, C. A.	10 Apr
Evans, A. L. BSc	22 Apr
Newton, C. J.	1 May
Copsey, C.	14 May
Robertson, A. BSc	14 May
Teggin, C. M. BA	17 May
Clarke, G. A. BA	19 May
Creveul, I. C. BA	21 May
Adam, S. D.	30 May
Alburey, D.	4 June
Donnelly, D. P.	4 June
Swann, G. B. G.	4 June
Costin, G. A.	11 June
Gardner, J.	20 June
Crandon, D.	4 July
Hill, K. M.	4 July
Walton, E.	4 July
Starling, P. G.	16 July
Taylor, G.	16 July

Wiggins, D. A.	16 July
Wiggins, S. J.	16 July
Worsnop, A. M.	16 July
Irving, D. J.	23 July
Whitehead, V. G. MCMI	23 July
Pyett, G. W.	24 July
Smith, N. G.	24 July
McKay, A. FCMI	3 Aug
Fox, B. J.	9 Aug
Walker, C. BA cfs(g)	17 Aug
Brooks, A. R.	20 Aug
Hortop, D. BA	20 Aug
Carnegie, D. N.	24 Aug
Lee, G.	24 Aug
Godfrey, P. A.	6 Sept
Drury, C.	10 Sept
Jones, D. A. G.	10 Sept
Stone, S. A.	10 Sept
Wells, P. A.	10 Sept
Westlake, R. G.	11 Sept
Kensett, C. J. cfs(g)	12 Sept
Bagshaw, M. J.	19 Sept
Brunt, G. H.	19 Sept
Winrow, N.	19 Sept
Chandler, H. T.	22 Sept
Duff, M.	25 Sept
Reditt, J. L.	25 Sept
Gilbert, B. R.	4 Oct
Grant, D. I.	4 Oct
Hawke, C. D.	8 Oct
Spencer, C. J.	8 Oct
Toth, V. M.	8 Oct
Huyton, D. G.	11 Oct
Smith, A. L. BEd FSERT	11 Oct
Robson, J. D.	16 Oct
Hacksall, D.	17 Oct
Humphreys, N. A.	17 Oct
Law, D. W.	17 Oct
Caffyn, B.	25 Oct
Morrison, S. W.	30 Oct
Southwell, R.	1 Nov
Stone, J. B.	5 Nov
Stone, P.	5 Nov
Turner, S. J.	5 Nov
Cambra, A.	12 Nov
Kilminster, W. B.	12 Nov
Hughes, G. W. A.	22 Nov
Pepper, I. K.	22 Nov
Podger, S.	22 Nov
Jones, N. R.	30 Nov
Metherell, M. J. BA	1 Dec
Grant, M. J. MA PGCE	5 Dec
Gill, J. L.	10 Dec
Smith, M. J.	10 Dec
Douglass, I. J. BSc PGCE	13 Dec
Tanner, H. S. T.	14 Dec
Cunningham, A. M.	17 Dec
Danson, C. A.	17 Dec
Johnson, R. G.	17 Dec

Flying Officers

1992—contd

Southwell, D. L.	28 Dec

1993

Feltham, C.	7 Jan
Willey, R. E. cfs(g)	7 Jan
Anderson, A.	14 Jan
Hetterley, E. C.	22 Jan
Clarke, H. PhD BSc	28 Jan
Clapp, G. D.	29 Jan
Forward, A. J. cfs(g)	29 Jan
Birch, F. J.	8 Feb
Rees, D. W. BSc	8 Feb
Tomlinson, J.	11 Feb
Houghman, D. M.	18 Feb
Artt, M. H. BA PGCE	19 Feb
Owen, D.	28 Feb
Child, R. PhD BSc PGCE	7 Mar
Weatherston, S. A.	8 Mar
Blackford, P. K.	11 Mar
Browell, A.	11 Mar
Entwistle, G. S.	11 Mar
Gilbey, S. L.	11 Mar
Hayes, G. P. cfs(g)	11 Mar
Bennett, P. J.	15 Mar
Wilson, R. C.	28 Mar
Robinson, C. I.	1 Apr
Willison, D. J. BSc	7 Apr
Marr, J. D.	8 Apr
Brabner, J. R. cfs(g)	14 Apr
Hatton, C. I.	19 Apr
Bolt, C.	23 Apr
Graddon, L. B. BA CertEd	25 Apr
Parkin, M. J. CertEd	25 Apr
Toon, S. M.	25 Apr
Griffiths, R.	29 Apr
Pallister, D. H.	29 Apr
Jago, T. M.	7 May
Castle, M. E.	30 May
North, G. W. cfs(g)	30 May
Thomas, E. A.	30 May
Hewitt, R. S.	3 June
Atkins, P. M.	12 June
Kamper, R.	12 June
Moyes, T. E. cfs(g)	25 June
Sansom, T. D. BEng	25 June
Parkes, G. F. H. BSc PGCE	26 June
Conway, G. E.	2 July
Smith, P. R.	2 July
Barnes, M. J. FISM MRIN cfs(g)	5 July
Reyes, E. J. BTh	5 July

Burnett, W. M.	9 July
Chapman, P. J.	9 July
Sutcliffe, K.	9 July
Gregory, R. J. BSc	16 July
Whitelaw, D. J. BA	18 July
Holman, B. C. L.	19 July
Parsons, J. D. F.	22 July
Cameron, W.	23 July
Craghill, W. M.	30 July
Watt, N. R.	30 July
Robson, A. A.	5 Aug
Dale, J. N.	7 Aug
Rose, J. S. cfs(g)	7 Aug
Smart, R. W.	9 Aug
Martin, J. F. S.	11 Aug
Gale, P. S.	13 Aug
Lemmon, L. J.	13 Aug
Fincher, D.	16 Aug
Musgrove, D. J.	19 Aug
Henley, P. S.	26 Aug
Cunningham, A.	2 Sept
Gillett, R. A.	2 Sept
Thomas, F. E.	4 Sept
Frowe, N. J. BA	9 Sept
Anderson, P.	11 Sept
Czarnecki, P. E.	11 Sept
Lovett, A. W.	11 Sept
Byatt, M. J. BEd	12 Sept
Robertson, A. R. BSc	12 Sept
Chaplin, R. E.	17 Sept
Fallon, J. F.	17 Sept
Leigh, J. M. BEd	17 Sept
Lloyd, J. R. BA	17 Sept
McCutcheon, M.	23 Sept
Easson, I. M. RGN RMN	4 Oct
Short, G.	4 Oct
Yorston, I. S.	5 Oct
Taylor, I. A. cfs(g)	15 Oct
Doughty, P. D.	22 Oct
Gore, S. A.	22 Oct
Horncastle, S.	30 Oct
Newman, T. C. M. MA	31 Oct
Hutchinson, L. D.	6 Nov
McNaught, J. A. B. MA	6 Nov
Wheeler, D. J. BSc	6 Nov
Mussett, P. G.	7 Nov
Simms, V. A. M.	7 Nov
Burke, M.	11 Nov
Gridley, S. A.	11 Nov
Alexander, J. A. BA	14 Nov
Meehan, L. B.	14 Nov
Palmer, P. M.	14 Nov
Morgan, L. I.	19 Nov
Davies, R. M.	21 Nov
Sumbler, K. S. BA	21 Nov
Nisbett, B.	12 Dec

1994

Bibby, A. J.	6 Jan
Bullock, S.	6 Jan
Gilbert, P.	6 Jan
Mair, D. T.	6 Jan
Melville, F. S.	10 Jan
Stanley, C. D. W.	13 Jan
Tinson, P. J.	17 Jan
Lundy, A.	21 Jan
Maclean, A. G.	23 Jan
Grantham-Hill, M. R. BSc	24 Jan
Oram, M. C. BEng	28 Jan
Freeman, D. J.	5 Feb
Husbands, D. J. T.	5 Feb
Jones, G. F. MA	5 Feb
Lowe, G.	5 Feb
McGowan, A. P. BSc PGCE	5 Feb
Parker-Moore, D. J.	5 Feb
Tooke, M. B.	5 Feb
Hill, R. R. J.	7 Feb
McClune, J. M. BA	11 Feb
Irvine, M.	14 Feb
Lyle, R. cfs(g)	14 Feb
Lambert, C. R. BSc	17 Feb
Rolfe, D. G.	20 Feb
Saunders, W. L.	27 Feb
Butt, V. R.	3 Mar
Dalby, W. J.	3 Mar
Parker, R. C.	3 Mar
Riley, P.	3 Mar
Robinson, I.	3 Mar
Robinson, S. A.	3 Mar
Cremen, M. F.	10 Mar
Crichton, A. T.	10 Mar
Utting, A. D. AMIIE	10 Mar
Bidgood, S. J. BSc	20 Mar
Fox, K. A.	20 Mar
Gray, R. W.	20 Mar
Mayhew, G. A.	20 Mar
McFarlane, W. L.	20 Mar
Rennison, J. P.	20 Mar
Upton, N. J.	23 Mar
Beaumont, S. C. BSc	24 Mar
Lightowler, N. J,	24 Mar
Thomas, G. R. S.	24 Mar
Rushen, P. C.	31 Mar
Wilson, N. J.	31 Mar
Woodman, G. PhD MSc BSc	31 Mar
Gamlin, D.G. CertEd	6 Apr
Mellish, P. W. BA	7 Apr
Mollard, D. R. G.	7 Apr
Young, A. I.	7 Apr
Griffiths, J. A.	11 Apr
Diskett, D. J.	22 Apr
Dolan, K. P.	22 Apr
Fordham, A. G. cfs(g)	22 Apr

Flying Officers

1994—contd

Whalvin, H. J. J. N.	27 Apr
Heslin, M.	5 May
Naylor, P.	5 May
Ritson, M.	5 May
Staincliffe, A. W.	5 May
Steel, J. M.	5 May
Buckley, J. C.	13 May
Lines, M. J.	13 May
McColgan, P. E. BA	13 May
McCormick, R.	13 May
Rogers, A. J. E.	13 May
Rogers, G. R. D.	13 May
Anwar, N.	14 May
Cairns, R. J. BA	18 May
Testro, B. J.	19 May
Williamson, M. A.	26 May
Woods, R. M. BSc	26 May
Sutherland, D.	1 June
Taylor, I.	4 June
Tipping, P. W.	4 June
Blair, G. A.	7 June
Hutchings, C. D.	9 June
Allam, C. M.	15 June
Grinstead, M. G. P. R.	18 June
Sheehan, T. D.	18 June
Crewe, I. L.	29 June
Brain, T.	30 June
Human, A. R. D.	30 June
Stuart, B. G.	30 June
Griffiths, M. E.	1 July
Eccles, P. J.	3 July
Davies, H. M.	6 July
Fish, L. A.	6 July
Hickie, K. M.	6 July
Gilbert, J. M.	13 July
Sneider, A. J. BA	13 July
Longhurst, S. E.	17 July
Montgomery, N.	17 July
Temple, D. R.	17 July
Miller, R.	20 July
Hamlen, W. W.	28 July
Parfrey, C. J.	28 July
Lee-McCloud, C. P.	13 Aug
Knight, O. J. A.	17 Aug
Roberts, A. P.	18 Aug
Lovering, M. L. BA	23 Aug
Pallett, B. J.	28 Aug
Long, D. BSc	6 Sept
Thum, M. J.	9 Sept
Jardine, A.	10 Sept
McCammont, L. E. W.	10 Sept
Wadsworth, M. E.	20 Sept
Hake, A. A. S.	21 Sept
Fenner, J. M. BSc PGCE	23 Sept
Rood, P.	23 Sept

Eckersley, M. A.	25 Sept
Fitzpatrick, I. A.	25 Sept
Goacher, M.	25 Sept
Adair, C. R.	27 Sept
Lee, B.	28 Sept
Stanley, T. J.	28 Sept
Stobbie, J. A.	28 Sept
Whittaker, S. M.	28 Sept
Burns, J. C. S. BA PGCE	30 Sept
Westley, P. J.	8 Oct
Bayliss, J. R. N.	20 Oct
Thomson-Clark, C. L.	20 Oct
Tziros, N. A. L. B.	21 Oct
Butterworth, R. BSc	22 Oct
Terrett, A. L.	25 Oct
Turner, P. D. C.	25 Oct
Burchett, K. J.	28 Oct
Loft, N. L.	28 Oct
Basnett, L.	2 Nov
Oldham, W. P.	2 Nov
Oakley, N. W.	4 Nov
Baxter, D. S.	12 Nov
Lansley, A. P. BEd	12 Nov
MacLeod, J. A.	12 Nov
Stubbs, P. N. MA	12 Nov
Bradley, L. Y.	19 Nov
Davies, G.	19 Nov
Dixon, S. A. E. MA BD	19 Nov
Parks, T.	19 Nov
Thompson, E. J.	23 Nov
Trevena, M. J.	1 Dec
Woods, I. R.	1 Dec
Collins, P. W.	7 Dec
Caulfield, G. A. BA	15 Dec
Maycock, S.	15 Dec
McAdam, N. W. E. MA	15 Dec
Turley, R. C.	15 Dec

1995

Tegg, B. A.	9 Jan
Davies, R. RGN	11 Jan
Lewry, G. J.	11 Jan
Macleod, S. L.	11 Jan
Smith, M. J. cfs(g)	11 Jan
Tickell, R.	11 Jan
Woods, T. E.	11 Jan
Dacre, J. P.	13 Jan
Harris, S. J.	14 Jan
Boothroyd, J. M.	25 Jan
Iles, S. D.	25 Jan
Ruskin, D. J. BA PGCE	28 Jan
Hynett, M. T.	29 Jan
Hullis, S. BA	4 Feb
Parker, J. E. BA PGCE	10 Feb
Warman, J. L.	15 Feb
Clark, N. S.	18 Feb
Flower, J.	18 Feb
Norton, P. D.	18 Feb

O'Connell, B. C.	18 Feb
Westwood, E. A.	18 Feb
Wohlgemuth, J. F.	18 Feb
Haley, J. G.	22 Feb
Smyth, F. D. MA	22 Feb
White, J. E.	24 Feb
Perry, P. J.	27 Feb
Quinn, J. J.	27 Feb
Hakes, M. D. BEd CertEd	4 Mar
Bennett, J. K.	8 Mar
Brown, K. A.	8 Mar
Hibberd, J. P.	8 Mar
Tanner, R. J.	8 Mar
Thompson, S. T.	8 Mar
Grant, S. J.	15 Mar
Cobbold, D. J.	17 Mar
O'Neill, G. L. BA PGCE	17 Mar
Wilkinson, M.	17 Mar
Wood, S. W.	17 Mar
Flower, L. E.	18 Mar
Tapsell, A.	20 Mar
Nickson, A. J.	24 Mar
Vasey, D. C. cfs(g)	24 Mar
Maddox, J. P. MA	29 Mar
Metcalfe, M.	1 Apr
Hiley, P.	2 Apr
Strand, A. M. cfs(g)	2 Apr
Joslin, I. E. BSc	7 Apr
Bremner, G. A.	10 Apr
Flitcroft, S. K.	11 Apr
Hoe, W. J. BSc	26 Apr
Ward, M. C. J. BSc	26 Apr
Brant, T. D.	29 Apr
Buscombe, C. B. cfs(g)	29 Apr
Woodbury, M. J.	29 Apr
Connolly, M. T.	6 May
Hinchliffe, D. A. R.	6 May
Pike, G. J. S.	6 May
Price, R. A. cfs(g)	6 May
Bellamy, M. G. FCA	14 May
Cottrell, S. E. BEd	14 May
Daniel, B. L.	14 May
Henderson, G. P.	14 May
Smith, I. P.	14 May
Stanley, M. T.	14 May
O'Shaughnessy, S. E.	19 May
Chart, P. L.	27 May
Greenow, K. F.	27 May
Hall, A. J.	27 May
Simmons, D. C.	27 May
Keech, R. A.	7 June
Kidley, M. F.	7 June
Levett, M. J.	7 June
Botten, L. D.	10 June
Dewhurst, R. M.	10 June
Fusedale, J. S.	16 June
Mathieson, P.	22 June
Ryan, J. L.	22 June
Vincent, R. A.	22 June

Flying Officers

1995—contd

White, C. M.	22 June
Dunkley, D. I.	25 June
Willis, T. C.	25 June
Ash, T. A. BA PGCE	5 July
Billingham, N. J.	5 July
Maitland, P.	5 July
McCarthy, M.	5 July
Jones, L. S.	7 July
Logan, A.	7 July
Coe, D. F.	17 July
Hibbert, C. J. MSc BA	18 July
Clift, S. A.	19 July
Gilham, J. K.	19 July
Lawton, S. M. cfs(g)	19 July
Parsons, J. J.	19 July
Pearce S. J.	19 July
Saunders, D.	19 July
Smith, A. P.	21 July
Fox, A. C.	23 July
Evans, S. E.	5 Aug
Hunt, W. G.	15 Aug
Noble, J. P. BSc	15 Aug
Ashpole, C. E.	16 Aug
Christmas, K. H.	16 Aug
Dempsey, P. D. cfs(g)	16 Aug
Donaldson, L. S.	16 Aug
Tindall, N. M.	16 Aug
Woodcock, P.	16 Aug
O'Dell, V. E.	26 Aug
Stevens, K. R.	26 Aug
Wootton, S.	26 Aug
Mellors, W. C.	24 Aug
Taylor, G. E.	24 Aug
Downie, J. C. P.	27 Aug
Duncan, P. A. BSc	27 Aug
Canning, T.	6 Sept
Scott, J. BSc	6 Sept
Tarttelin, R. B.	6 Sept
Donovan, K. B.	9 Sept
Russell, M. J.	9 Sept
Hawkins, P. W. BSc	12 Sept
Coalfield, I. P.	14 Sept
Meacock, A. P.	14 Sept
Taylor, S. V.	14 Sept
Barnfather, C. R.	23 Sept
Steele, J. R.	23 Sept
Rankin, L.	24 Sept
Battram, J. M.	30 Sept
Skillman, J. J.	30 Sept
Tandy, G. F.	30 Sept
McMillan, A. B.	4 Oct
Hollings, J. I.	6 Oct
Elliott, G. L. BSc	13 Oct
Mumford, C. M.	13 Oct

Oram, R. M. D. BA ARCM DipTh	13 Oct
Yates, C. E. BSc	14 Oct
Donald, G. D.	27 Oct
Downie, L.	27 Oct
Benham, D. A.	2 Nov
Bennett, K. D. BA	2 Nov
Capon, G. J. C.	2 Nov
Milner, M. J.	2 Nov
Graham, D. H.	11 Nov
Andersen, K. L.	15 Nov
Austing, D. R.	15 Nov
Hassanali, A. cfs(g)	15 Nov
Patel, R. K.	15 Nov
Rogers, D. J. P.	18 Nov
Mottram, J. M.	23 Nov
O'Connor, F. P.	25 Nov
Cairns, S.	6 Dec
Coutts, S. BSc	6 Dec
Catcheside, S. J.	10 Dec
Dodman, L. M.	10 Dec
Growcott, J. A. BSc PGCE	10 Dec
McKee, J. V.	10 Dec
Smith, A. J. BSc	10 Dec
Smith, V. J.	10 Dec
Twin, J. F.	10 Dec
Elvins, L. J.	20 Dec
Southern, L. W.	20 Dec
Thorn, T. G. AFC FRAeS	29 Dec

1996

Loftus, P. BEng	4 Jan
Brennan, G. J. P.	6 Jan
Atherton, V. A.	10 Jan
Smith, C. F. BSc	10 Jan
Wilson, B. B.	10 Jan
Braddon, R.	12 Jan
Searl, P. D.	12 Jan
Watson, D. A.	12 Jan
McMullan, T. A. BSc PGCE	13 Jan
Vincent, P. J.	16 Jan
Bell, J.	18 Jan
Fairhurst, D. T.	18 Jan
Everett, A. M.	21 Jan
Walker, M. J. BSc PGCE	21 Jan
Sawyer, M. G. BSc MIBiol	25 Jan
Davies, D. L.	27 Jan
Pearson, T. A.	27 Jan
Prigmore, G. T.	27 Jan
Duke, C. M.	31 Jan
Felton, P. H.	2 Feb
Haywood, C. C.	2 Feb
Henry, M. W.	2 Feb
Hickin, J. V.	2 Feb
Hutchings, A. W.	2 Feb

Lee, P. A. cfs(g)	2 Feb
Phillips, B. E.	2 Feb
Reed, E. C.	2 Feb
Smith, A. M.	2 Feb
Willows, S. L.	2 Feb
Blain, R. T.	10 Feb
Rolfe, M. J.	10 Feb
Grimshire, L. K. BEd cfs(g)	15 Feb
Hillier, M. A. T.	15 Feb
Kelso, C. W.	16 Feb
Noyce, R. A.	16 Feb
Perera, T. E.	16 Feb
Camwell, A.	22 Feb
Schofield, N. C.	25 Feb
Pearson, I. D. BA	1 Mar
Bartley, D.	9 Mar
D'Anna, G. W. S. MSc BSc	9 Mar
Walker, R. C. S.	9 Mar
Loftus, K. B.	11 Mar
Steed, A.	11 Mar
Tait, I. A.	11 Mar
Lowery, M. D.	15 Mar
Achilles, L. E. A.	21 Mar
Mellor, A. D.	21 Mar
Newton, M. E.	21 Mar
Nicholson, J. D. PhD BSc	21 Mar
Butcher, A. J.	24 Mar
Gough, C. F.	24 Mar
Murphy, S. D.	24 Mar
Rose, I. K.	24 Mar
Flynn, J. A.	29 Mar
Jenkins, D. J.	29 Mar
Webb, J. F.	29 Mar
Butler, C.	11 Apr
Plane, R. P.	11 Apr
Malling, S. H. BEd	23 Apr
Reed, G. M.	26 Apr
Tilson, N.	26 Apr
Callister, J. W. BA	30 Apr
Baldwin, J.	9 May
Montgomery, D. W. MA	9 May
Thomson-Clark, P.	9 May
Dickie, A. D. BSc	11 May
Hogben, R. J. J.	25 May
Powell, V. E.	25 May
Browne, W. F.	31 May
Stretton, A. I.	31 May
Tilton, D. R. BSc	31 May
Cross, R.	2 June
Freeman, P. R.	2 June
MacDonald, J. P. BSc cfs(g)	2 June
Drew, R. W. F.	7 June
Mackenzie, P. J.	7 June
Rickerby, C. D.	7 June
Rodger, G. N.	7 June
Webb, R. G.	7 June

Flying Officers

1996—contd

Higgins, K. M.	13 June
Head, L.	14 June
Marsh, C. J.	14 June
Abubakar, A. B. PhD MSc BSc	16 June
Brittain, M.	22 June
Elliott, J. L.	27 June
Pickersgill, A. J. BSc	27 June
Agate, J. J.	30 June
Evans, R. M.	30 June
Prigmore, V. J.	30 June
Hawkins, D. J.	2 July
Morton, E. M.	6 July
Steven, R.	6 July
Duffey, M. G.	10 July
Robinson, C. E.	11 July
Leggott, S. P. BSc	15 July
Mott, J. F.	15 July
Bevan, K. J.	20 July
Dodd, P. J. BEng	20 July
Millar, J. D.	20 July
Stones, M. D. BEng	20 July
Cleeter, N. Y.	25 July
Balshaw, H. S. BA	31 July
Bonneywell, J. E. BSc PGCE	3 Aug
Stanbury, P. W. BWng PGCE	3 Aug
Todd, A. D. BA MPhil	8 Aug
Green, K. J.	9 Aug
Kirby, O. J. A.	9 Aug
Stewart, M. J.	12 Aug
Borthwick, J. H.	23 Aug
Edney, M. R.	23 Aug
Thomson, G.	23 Aug
Wall, D.	23 Aug
Barnes, J. A.	1 Sept
Graham, A.	1 Sept
Hannent, P. A.	1 Sept
Mottershead, J. C.	1 Sept
Archibald, S. J.	7 Sept
Harrison, S. J.	7 Sept
Martin. K. H. D. BA	7 Sept
Fielder, C. BSc	13 Sept
Forrester, J. PhD BSc	13 Sept
Gill, S.	13 Sept
Hickie, L. RGN RMN	13 Sept
Bates, D. L.	20 Sept
Baynes, T. M. J.	20 Sept
Bissell, K. D.	20 Sept
Walters, K.	20 Sept
King, N. J. BSc PGCE	27 Sept
Martin, H. S.	27 Sept
Humphrey, R.	1 Oct
Woodland, R. K. BSc	1 Oct

Timms, S. J.	2 Oct
Davies, P. J. cfs(g)	3 Oct
Dow, S. M. MA PhD	3 Oct
Thomas, D.	3 Oct
Haskell, G. BSc	5 Oct
Cooper, S. R.	6 Oct
Harpur, K. M. T. cfs(g)	6 Oct
Slack, R. A.	6 Oct
King, B. W.	7 Oct
Warren, L. C.	7 Oct
Egerton, C. J.	11 Oct
Stear, Sir Micheal KCB CBE MA	11 Oct
Allen, N. J.	21 Oct
Munro, I. R.	21 Oct
Rennison, S. RGN RMN	22 Oct
Hendry, R. S.	25 Oct
Brown, J. A.	31 Oct
Green, M.	31 Oct
Smith, D. P. cfs(g)*	31 Oct
Cox, J. M.	4 Nov
Le Worthy, D. A.	5 Nov
Rishman, G. BSc	14 Nov
Glover, A. M.	16 Nov
Murray, H. D.	22 Nov
Wainwright, G. J.	22 Nov
Clayson, T. P. S.	24 Nov
Judge, C. P. B.	24 Nov
Lane, D.	24 Nov
Whitehead, M. S.	24 Nov
Smith, A. L.	25 Nov
Booth, S. J.	30 Nov
Harper, S.	30 Nov
Davies, A. R.	3 Dec
Abbott, M. I.	5 Dec
Brackett, L. A.	13 Dec
Laidler, P.	13 Dec
McElroy, G. F.	13 Dec
Renshaw, I.	13 Dec
Stephenson, T. cfs(g)	13 Dec
Sullivan, D. B. BA	13 Dec
Corteen, J. B.	20 Dec
Hallowes, R. A. D.	20 Dec
Bostock, S. N. MSc FCMI	24 Dec

1997

Burdess, S. BEng CEng FRAeS	2 Jan
Cox, R. I.	9 Jan
Addison, G. BSc PGCE	11 Jan
Faulkner, M. A.	11 Jan
Bodger, M. A. BEng	17 Jan
Breward, C. J. W. BA	17 Jan
Ellen, G. P.	17 Jan
Ward, P. D.	17 Jan
Brooke, A. J. BA PGCE	19 Jan
Balson, J. D.	25 Jan

Butchers, M. J.	6 Feb
Horsley, N. J. BA	6 Feb
Pettengell, N. C.	6 Feb
Stannard, I. N. BA	6 Feb
Donne, R. H. S. MA PGCE	10 Feb
Chandler, N. J.	15 Feb
Mamoany, T. J.	15 Feb
Sawyer, M. A. G.	15 Feb
Turley, K. E.	15 Feb
Gough, B.	18 Feb
Legatt, C. P.	26 Feb
Astin, D. A.	27 Feb
Bain, C. A. BEng cfs(g)	27 Feb
Hill, D. L. BSc	27 Feb
Jones, K. W.	28 Feb
Jones, M. A.	28 Feb
Mawson, S. J. BTech	3 Mar
Singer, M. J.	3 Mar
Hale, D. H. cfs(g)	7 Mar
Hicks, C. J. cfs(g)	7 Mar
Watson, M. cfs(g)	7 Mar
Pursehouse, A. J.	13 Mar
Rogers, R. M. cfs(g)	13 Mar
Bulgin, J. P.	14 Mar
Gilchrist, K.G.	14 Mar
Hurrell, A. J. BA	14 Mar
Patel, H. S.	14 Mar
Davidson, M. D. MA	18 Mar
Wetherall, M.	23 Mar
Cooper, A. C. BA PGCE	24 Mar
Colman, D. J.	28 Mar
Hutchins, D. J.	28 Mar
Kerr, E. R.	28 Mar
Laird, S. P.	28 Mar
Mustafa. S.	28 Mar
Southern, L. A.	28 Mar
Baxby, D. R.	30 Mar
King, H. R. cfs(g)	30 Mar
Williams, C. G.	30 Mar
Adams, G. BA	12 Apr
Best, J. T.	12 Apr
Boulton, P.	12 Apr
Dunlop, C. A.	12 Apr
Marriott, G. A. BTech	12 Apr
Morris, J. N.	12 Apr
Niven, S. O.	12 Apr
Park, D. MSc	12 Apr
Surry, D. D. BSc	12 Apr
Tatar, P. N.	12 Apr
Tidman, J. E.	12 Apr
Collins, M. S.	24 Apr
Curtis, T.	24 Apr
Harrison, S. D.	24 Apr
Riach, C. J.	30 Apr
Arthur, L. O.	2 May
Bell, J. M.	2 May
Dale, N. T.	2 May
Michel, R. G. BA	2 May
Parry, C.	2 May

Flying Officers

1997—contd

Simmons, C. J.	2 May
Stamp, G. D.	2 May
Thompson, W. C.	2 May
Warman, A. D.	2 May
Spinks, J. C.	3 May
Fay, J. C. BA	7 May
Wright, S. L.	10 May
Saunderson, K.	15 May
Stapleton, K. R.	15 May
Stokoe, A. M.	17 May
Austin, Sir Roger KCB AFC FRAeS	22 May
Derbyshire-Reeves, M. C.	24 May
Flitton, D. C.	24 May
Goodacre, R. G.	24 May
Hannaford, P. F.	24 May
Hooper, C. P.	24 May
Banks, T. J.	25 May
Beswick, G. T. W.	25 May
King, A. C.	1 June
Perring, I. D.	1 June
Miller, H. A. BSc	4 June
Young, A. J.	4 June
Hourican, D. M.	8 June
Screen, D. A.	8 June
Smith, R. G.	9 June
Gerrish, H.	10 June
Colbron, S. L.	15 June
Jancis, A. BSc PGCE	24 June
Warburton, R. G.	24 June
Brady, J. P. BA	3 July
Cockrill, M. J. MBE	9 July
Falle, P. R.	9 July
Barlow, P.	17 July
Blackwell, T. W.	17 July
Brown, D. W.	17 July
Carlisle, A.	17 July
Dunn, R. A.	17 July
Dunn, S. S.	17 July
Graham, S. P.	17 July
Jarvis, I.	17 July
Morgan, A. D.	17 July
Sinfield, A. J.	17 July
Stilgoe, G. P. BSc	17 July
Swatridge, E. L.	17 July
Webb, J. F.	17 July
Lambert, S.	21 July
Morten, J. A.	21 July
Williams, J. T. BA	21 July
Gerrish, D. J.	27 July
Alford, A. M.	28 July
Exton, D. V.	28 July
Geddes, S. J.	28 July
Lovell, P. M.	28 July

Barker, D. BSc	30 July
Joyce, T. J.	6 Aug
Cantwell, P. J. BSc	14 Aug
Ackerley, D. J.	15 Aug
Betts, J. D. BEng	15 Aug
Dudgeon, P.	15 Aug
Jackson, N.	15 Aug
Lewis, N. M.	15 Aug
Stamp, M. R.	15 Aug
Hawthorne, M. E. BSc	24 Aug
Priestly, R. M. BSc	24 Aug
Henderson, J.	25 Aug
Kay, R.	25 Aug
Seabrook, R. J.	5 Sept
Cork, S. J.	6 Sept
Davies, A. M.	6 Sept
Ridge, J. G.	6 Sept
Thompson Ambrose, W. I.	6 SeptW
Bewley, J. W.	12 Sept
Golding, S. T.	12 Sept
Martin, J. W. cfs(g)	12 Sept
Perkins, A. D.	17 Sept
Gardiner, C. D.	19 Sept
McQueen, S. E.	19 Sept
Molloy, M. P.	19 Sept
Jones, J. T. D.	20 Sept
Dabell, S. W. BSc	26 Sept
Melrose, W.	26 Sept
Axon, P. J. W.	29 Sept
Pudney, K. W.	29 Sept
Ratinon, J. G. A.	29 Sept
Tyler, F. M.	29 Sept
Beesley, M. J.	6 Oct
Fraser, I. E.	6 Oct
Haworth, D. BSc	6 Oct
Ireland, D. P. BEng PGCE	6 Oct
Jones, A. D.	6 Oct
Nolan, A. D. BSc	6 Oct
Slater, A. D.	6 Oct
Smith, F. M. BSc	6 Oct
Freeney, D.	10 Oct
Hall, M. I.	10 Oct
Hodge, R. J. W. BSc	13 Oct
Coombes, G. R.	17 Oct
Evans, J. R.	17 Oct
Gregory, K.	17 Oct
Kilby, D. J.	17 Oct
Roberts, P. M.	17 Oct
Baker, R.	23 Oct
Mitchell, C. BA	23 Oct
Sibley, J. BEd	23 Oct
Walker, D. K. BTech	24 Oct
Edwards, P. J.	29 Oct
Dean, R. J.	31 Oct
Gaywood, R. C.	31 Oct
Keenan, A.	31 Oct
Rankin, D. M.	31 Oct
Aala, R. MA ACA	20 Nov

Banks, N. K. M.	20 Nov
Brown, D. BA	20 Nov
Ireland, C. BA PGCE	20 Nov
Rogers, N. S.	20 Nov
Turner, R. R.	20 Nov
Plane, K. L.	21 Nov
Cooper, A. H. C. BSc	27 Nov
Laycock, P. M. BSc	2 Dec
Hawkins, D. G. PhD BSc	3 Dec
Bagnall, R. D. A.	4 Dec
Denton, D. J.	4 Dec
Taylor, C. L. BA	7 Dec
Cowell, A. C.	7 Dec
Davison, M. G.	7 Dec
King, A. P.	7 Dec
Milligan, D. R.	7 Dec
Partridge, J. M. BSc	7 Dec
Thomas, J. N. cfs(g)	7 Dec
Young, J. S.	7 Dec
Coram-Wright, N. H. MA	8 Dec
Grace, M. J. BSc PGCE	8 Dec
Penny, S. D. BA BSc MBCS MIEE MRAeS	8 Dec
Bone, K. L.	19 Dec
Pym, J. D.	19 Dec
Abdy, M. J.	20 Dec
Kocbusz, M. D.	20 Dec

1998

Manktelow, J. A.	4 Jan
Johnson, A. G.	10 Jan
Martin, P. M.	10 Jan
Gant, I. S.	12 Jan
Wilson, E. R. BSc	14 Jan
Bell, M. F.	17 Jan
Crane, N. M.	17 Jan
Bailey, A. J.	25 Jan
Galley, P. T. PhD BSc	25 Jan
Kuschirow, D. K.	25 Jan
Kay, M.	26 Jan
Masters, D. A.	26 Jan
Schenk, K. S. R.	28 Jan
Fry, R.	31 Jan
Rees, D. E.	31 Jan
Kirsopp, G. N. J.	2 Feb
Smith, I.	2 Feb
Chipman, P. D. PhD BSc PGCE	5 Feb
Hindley, K. L. BA	9 Feb
Jones, E. G. BSc MB ChB	10 Feb
Bennett, M. J.	12 Feb
MacDonald, B.	12 Feb
Lamb, S. G. MA PGCE	16 Feb
Gee, M. J.	19 Feb
Hall, M. J.	19 Feb
Higginson, S. J. cfs(g)	19 Feb

Flying Officers

1998—contd

Salt, G. T. BEng	19 Feb
Davies, D. I.	21 Feb
McLachlan, S. C. J.	21 Feb
Moore, M. J.	21 Feb
McCotter, B. W.	27 Feb
Green, P. D.	2 Mar
Fox, C. J.	12 Mar
Quinn, M. S.	13 Mar
Thompson, G. BEd	13 Mar
Treutlein, J.	13 Mar
Xavier, F. Y.	13 Mar
Hudson, J.	20 Mar
O'Brien, P. S.	20 Mar
Shepherd, D. J. BSc	20 Mar
Gunstone, J. P.	25 Mar
Impey, M. J.	25 Mar
Pace, S.	25 Mar
Routledge, S.	27 Mar
Lawton, S. R.	29 Mar
Organ, A.	29 Mar
Gadd, S. I.	7 Apr
Riley, S. C.	8 Apr
Belshaw, A. M. T.	15 Apr
Madge, A. D.	15 Apr
Carter, R. S. BEd	17 Apr
Siddall, P. J. BSc	17 Apr
Forward, W. J.	19 Apr
Perkins, C.	19 Apr
Cowan, J. A. BA	23 Apr
Angelosanto, A. BSc PGCE	30 Apr
Jarvis, K. W.	5 May
Parsons, M. G. cfs(g)	5 May
Head, D. P.	9 May
Purkiss, A.	9 May
Terry, S. J. BA	9 May
Robinson, S. M. BEng	14 May
Davidson, G.	23 May
Noble, K. G. BSc(Eng)	29 May
Baker, E. A. BA	31 May
Flint, R. S. B.	31 May
Howard, D. F.	31 May
Hudson, A. C.	31 May
Laird, J. E.	31 May
Marshall, S. W.	31 May
Milne, A. C.	31 May
Parkes, S. M.	31 May
Pocock, J. R.	31 May
Pollock, J. M.	31 May
Ross, A. I.	31 May
Sie, E. R. H. B. PhD BSc	31 May
Elliott, M. A.	2 June
Brown, R. C.	5 June
Shepherd, D. M.	5 June
Rennie, A. E. W. BSc	7 June

Smith, D. E.	7 June
Anderson, D. I.	10 June
Johnson, H. M.	10 June
Bain, J. B.	18 June
Crumpton, D. L.	18 June
Fisher, T.	18 June
Lobban, A.	18 June
McTeir, J.	18 June
Bull, M. M.	4 July
Edwards, R. T. MInstAM	4 July
Herniman, M. C. J.	4 July
Marriott, G. E.	4 July
Saunders, P.	4 July
Weston, N. S.	4 July
Allan, J.	8 July
Duplock, S. J.	8 July
Turner, K. P.	8 July
Balmford, S. J.	9 July
Bass, C. R. BA	9 July
Taylor, M. A.	9 July
Morris, K. R. BSc PGCE	12 July
Kinnear, N. R. MA	16 July
Connolly, G. M.	19 July
Holmes, J. G.	19 July
Piccavey, S. K. E.	19 July
Holmes, A. T.	22 July
Hall, J. E. BA	6 Aug
Heckel, P. A. cfs(g)	6 Aug
Walker, M. A.	6 Aug
Webb, C. J. P.	8 Aug
Turoczy, S.	10 Aug
Cemm, N. A. BSc	21 Aug
Stone, C. A.	21 Aug
Stubbs, C. M.	21 Aug
Burrett, T. J.	28 Aug
Porter, S. A.	28 Aug
Jenkins, L. C.	11 Sept
Bragg, D.	13 Sept
Poole, C. J.	13 Sept
Cheetham, G. E.	17 Sept
Blythe, R. T. C.	19 Sept
Bailey, S. M.	24 Sept
Burnham, K. A. BSc	24 Sept
MacMillan, L. D. BSc	24 Sept
Eyre, P. S.	7 Oct
Nowlan, K. A.	7 Oct
Palmer, R. F.	7 Oct
Smith, M.	7 Oct
Arnold, R. J.	11 Oct
Capron-Tee, J. A.	11 Oct
Deadman, I. A. BA	11 Oct
Watson, L. B.	11 Oct
Little, S. P.	14 Oct
Barre, G. R.	15 Oct
Foster, C. T.	15 Oct
Laurence, P. E.	15 Oct
Manning, D. A.	15 Oct
Shearer, L. E.	15 Oct
Whalvin, J. C.	15 Oct

Simmonds-Short, P. R.	20 Oct
Ashton, B.	22 Oct
Abbott, S. J.	6 Nov
Pickup, G. R.	6 Nov
Taylor, S. R.	6 Nov
Colverson, A.	11 Nov
Woods, A. J.	11 Nov
Drew, A. A. BSc PGCE	16 Nov
Henderson, N. T.	25 Nov
Bell, M. J.	27 Nov
Brennan, K. L.	27 Nov
Cottier, K. J. S. BSc	27 Nov
Dawson, A.	27 Nov
Howlett, S. A.	27 Nov
MacDonald, J. A.	27 Nov
Reed, S. J.	27 Nov
Shaw, T. L. BA	27 Nov
Mundill, R. R. PhD MA PGCE DipEd	30 Nov
Hayward, J. L.	3 Dec
Muller, J. V.	3 Dec
White, A. J. BSc PGCE	3 Dec
O'Brien, R. P. CB OBE BA FRAeS	4 Dec
Hemsil, K. I.	5 Dec
Ross, I. S. PhD BSc	5 Dec
Ruscoe, R. M. cfs(g)	5 Dec
Edey, N. J. MSc BSc PGCE	8 Dec
Walters, A. M. cfs(g)	8 Dec
Chandler, N. A.	9 Dec
Lillywhite, G. J.	9 Dec
Burton, S. B.	12 Dec
Derrick, L. M. H.	12 Dec
Gay, S. J. BSc	12 Dec
Powell, K. D. BSc PGCE	12 Dec
Baines, N.	17 Dec
Cooper, S. L.	17 Dec
Smith, S. M.	17 Dec
Fray, H. A.	19 Dec
Howarth, S.	19 Dec
Price, J.	19 Dec
Thomas, J. S.	19 Dec
Tyson, N. K.	19 Dec

1999

Thompson, D. MSc BSc PGCE	1 Jan
Bailey, J.	6 Jan
Blease, M.	6 Jan
Furley, S. J.	6 Jan
Hood, B.	7 Jan
Campbell, R. I.	10 Jan
Pitts, A.	10 Jan
Looker, P. G.	12 Jan
Roche, T. J. MA	12 Jan
Courtnadge, S. E.	14 Jan

Flying Officers

1999—contd

Coombes, S. R. A. BSc	20 Jan
Giess, N. P.	21 Jan
Leese, J. BA	21 Jan
Collins, S.	24 Jan
Haynes, C.	24 Jan
Day, P. W. AFC	25 Jan
Deere, G. W.	27 Jan
Kenchington, N.	27 Jan
Pendlebury, S. R.	27 Jan
Bennett, N. A. D.	3 Feb
Coyne, C. P.	3 Feb
King, K. A.	3 Feb
Brewer, E.	6 Feb
Hammond, G. G.	6 Feb
Elder, R. D. CBE FRAeS	8 Feb
Gardner, J. A. BA PGCE	11 Feb
Conley, C. R.	18 Feb
Faulkner, S. C.	18 Feb
Hayton, P.	19 Feb
Taylor, A. B. BSc	19 Feb
Johnson, N. I.	20 Feb
MacFadyen. I. D. CB OBE FRAeS	20 Feb
Davey, J. R. BA PGCE	25 Feb
Bennett, D. J.	26 Feb
Forrest, C. C.	26 Feb
Bartlett, J. D.	4 Mar
Pocock, M. D.	4 Mar
Walker, S.	4 Mar
Bullingham, M. C.	7 Mar
Carroll, I. H.	7 Mar
Cheesman, D. A. J. BSc	13 Mar
Curran, I. J.	13 Mar
Leworthy, S. L.	13 Mar
Lynch, C. BA	13 Mar
Todd, D.	13 Mar
Willies, A. M.	13 Mar
Yaku, L.	13 Mar
Langley, A. M.	15 Mar
Oliver, P. R.	23 Mar
Houlihan, M. S. BSc	24 Mar
Appleby, R. C.	2 Apr
Smith, B. A.	2 Apr
Thorpe, J. W. AFC FRAeS	11 Apr
Armstrong, C. J.	14 Apr
Bellamy, C. H.	14 Apr
Gallop, M. P.	14 Apr
Pearce, H. G.	14 Apr
Hart, D. J. BD	16 Apr
Close-Ash, W. P.	28 Apr
MacIntosh, F. I.	28 Apr
Smith, B. D.	28 Apr
Ovel, W. E.	29 Apr
Plummer, K. G. BSc	29 Apr

Wright, D. M.	2 May
Balchin, A. W.	7 May
Garrod-Bell, G. M.	7 May
Jenkins, K. F.	7 May
Moore, D. A. S.	7 May
Colley, P.	12 May
Williamson, M. A.	12 May
Reeves, M. J.	19 May
Farr, J. E.	20 May
Hughes, P. M. cfs(g)	20 May
Lawson, P. S.	20 May
Brady, N. H.	21 May
Eade, F. R. PhD	22 May
Parry, D. H.	23 May
Baxby, S. J.	29 May
Burgess, L. A.	29 May
Smith, P. J.	29 May
Turner, P. L.	29 May
Allen, L. I.	4 June
Anthony, G.	4 June
Brooksbank, R. E.	4 June
Bromley, G. L.	4 June
Lemmon, D. S.	4 June
Adams, S. L. BSc	6 June
Morris, A.	6 June
Hastings, S. W.	8 June
Wilson, N.	9 June
Wilson, P.	9 June
Driscoll, K. J. S.	11 June
Mayfield, P. S. BA PGCE	11 June
Shenton, P. J. BSc	11 June
Wood, R.	11 June
Ayre, A. M.	16 June
Mason, A. C.	16 June
Scudder, D. R. M.	16 June
Clark, J. E.	20 June
Belham, P. W.	28 June
Rogers, N. C. BSc	28 June
Taylor, B. T.	28 June
Moore, R. A.	30 June
Withersby, E. D.	30 June
Gilhooly, D. BA DipEd	9 July
Taylor, G. D.	9 July
Cepelak, A.	10 July
Mortimer, D. F.	10 July
Pearce, G. M.	10 July
Durkin, C. B. J. BSc	14 July
Sharrard-Williams, E. L. BEd	14 July
Hick, S.	17 July
Reece, D. J.	17 July
Williams, J. D. BSc	17 July
Fulbrook, I. S.	21 July
Partington, J. E.	21 July
Prentice, K. J. BA BSc	21 July
Pursehouse, M. C.	21 July
May, J. A. G. CB CBE	23 July
Pace, D. A.	27 July
Booth, L. A.	31 July

Berry, I. C.	4 Aug
Divver, J. A.	4 Aug
Hunt, R. A. J.	4 Aug
Stobbie, L. C.	4 Aug
Macher, D.	5 Aug
Swierczek, J.	5 Aug
Thirlwall, C. OBE AFC BA	5 Aug
Terry, Sir Colin KBE CB CEng FRAeS FRSA FILT FCGI	7 Aug
Davenport, L. F.	12 Aug
MacMillan, D. F.	18 Aug
Oldham, C. M.	18 Aug
Prescott-Morrin, H. J. BSc PGCE	18 Aug
Magill, B. F.	24 Aug
Dalling, R. cfs(g)*	1 Sept
Dewhurst, L. M.	1 Sept
Carrington, J. F.	2 Sept
Collins, M. J.	2 Sept
Darwin, K. A.	5 Sept
French, M. J.	5 Sept
Head, G. M. M. BA IEng MIEIE	5 Sept
Burwell, C. C. N. MBE	9 Sept
Kelly, A. B. BSc CPhys CEng MInstP	9 Sept
Perrins, M. A. BA BEd	9 Sept
Towse, J. L.	9 Sept
Byford, J. E. BSc PGCE	10 Sept
McGuire, J. A.	10 Sept
Summers, P.	13 Sept
Urbanowicz, T. J.	13 Sept
Marrett, P. J. BA PGCE	15 Sept
Cooper, N. L.	18 Sept
Dalrymple, I. V. J.	18 Sept
Davies, A. S.	18 Sept
Davies, J. T.	18 Sept
Forster, D. MA	18 Sept
Hall, V. E. L.	18 Sept
Malik, S. BEng	18 Sept
Roberts, P. F.	18 Sept
Smith, D. P.	18 Sept
Quarmby, C. A. MA PGCE	19 Sept
Ravenhall, S. R. MPhil BA	19 Sept
Ripley, J. K. PhD BSc	19 Sept
Elder, L. N.	26 Sept
Kuperus, S.	26 Sept
Vardon, A. J. BEd FRSA	26 Sept
Fryett, B. W.	1 Oct
Smith, J. A. BA	3 Oct
Eastment, R. M. OBE MRAeS	11 Oct
Jefferson, B.	11 Oct
Bone, P. J.	13 Oct
Britton, P. J.	13 Oct
Crane, M. A. J.	13 Oct

Flying Officers

1999—contd

Edwards, J. O. LTCL	13 Oct
Field, J. DPhysEd	13 Oct
Hockin, M. J. BEng cfs(g)	13 Oct
Smart, M. Z. BEd	13 Oct
Allen, G. D.	15 Oct
Gibson, D. J.	15 Oct
Nadin, R. T. BEng cfs(g)	15 Oct
Hinchcliffe, N. B. CertEd	21 Oct
Jelley, D. G. cfs(g)	21 Oct
Evans, B. J. BSc(Eng)	23 Oct
Smith, T. D. BA PGCE	23 Oct
Dunn, R. J.	6 Nov
Holman, M. R.	9 Nov
Cole, P. A.	11 Nov
Gordon, J. A. BSc	11 Nov
Gunner, P. A.	11 Nov
Knell, G. C.	11 Nov
Millyard, P. A.	11 Nov
Tucker, J. M. BSc	11 Nov
Jenkins, S. R.	18 Nov
Mimpress, P. J.	18 Nov
Moreton, D. K.	18 Nov
Fotheringham, J. T.	19 Nov
Norris, S. T.	19 Nov
Arbuthnott, B. cfs(g)	22 Nov
Berry-Robinson, J. A. S.	24 Nov
Machin, J. A.	24 Nov
Rosewarn, P. J.	24 Nov
Stedman, L. S.	24 Nov
Brewster, R. A. BSc	25 Nov
Holdsworth, B. J. BA	25 Nov
Brayford, M. A.	27 Nov
Harbar, D. J.	30 Nov
Andrews, R. P.	1 Dec
Briggs, A. D. PhD BSc	1 Dec
Yates, F. L.	1 Dec
Costain, J. P. BA	2 Dec
Power, C. P.	5 Dec
Nettleton, P. J. BSc	7 Dec
Cornell, G. W.	11 Dec
Pass, A. C.	12 Dec
Jennings, R. D.	15 Dec
O'Brien, P. A. F.	15 Dec
Smith, B. A.	15 Dec

2000

Sachedina, K. A. BSc	1 Jan
Doveton, L. J.	5 Jan
Fisher, H. J.	5 Jan
Howell, R.	5 Jan
Lee, A. G. C. Y.	5 Jan
Lester, M. S.	5 Jan
Machin, J. G.	5 Jan
Melia, C. P. cfs(g)	5 Jan
Walker, R. A.	5 Jan
Still, B. J.	6 Jan
Cullen, D. J.	7 Jan
Fenlon-Smith, P. A.	7 Jan
Smith, S. C. BSc	7 Jan
Crawford, J. A. BSc	11 Jan
Andrews, G. H. L.	12 Jan
Cornish, P. M.	12 Jan
Hamilton, P. D. BMet	14 Jan
Armitstead, A. R.	16 Jan
MacQuarrie, J. B.	16 Jan
McDonnell, G. T. MSc	16 Jan
Ramage, C. A.	16 Jan
Whittaker, C. G. E. BSc	18 Jan
Gould, R. H. CBE MA BSc FRAeS	22 Jan
Pinckston, P. K.	24 Jan
Ford, J. A. F. FCMI	25 Jan
Cave, S.	26 Jan
Longmuir, M. C. BA PGCE	26 Jan
Mann, J. CertEd	26 Jan
Monk, F. S. BA PGCE	26 Jan
O'Connor, P.	26 Jan
Rogers, G. T.	26 Jan
Cook, S. M.	27 Jan
Crebbin, C. B. BEng	27 Jan
Hardy, D.	27 Jan
Hawksfield, D.	27 Jan
John, J. K.	27 Jan
Morrisey, S. M.	27 Jan
Peacock-Edwards, R. S. CBE AFC FRAeS FCMI	27 Jan
Sumner, A. J.	27 Jan
Woodburn, B. W.	27 Jan
Brooks-Johnson, A. J.	28 Jan
Penberthy, M. P.	28 Jan
Young, S-D.	28 Jan
Hogan, J. F.	3 Feb
Brekke, J. K.	6 Feb
Evans, A.	6 Feb
Rigby, S. I.	8 Feb
Cope, J.	9 Feb
Last, G. A. BA PGCE	9 Feb
James, M. D.	16 Feb
Pears, J. S. BA MIIM	16 Feb
Sault, D. A.	16 Feb
Collier, D.	19 Feb
Gilmour, K.	25 Feb
Leith, D. McK. cfs(g)	25 Feb
Shields, H.	25 Feb
Walmsley, D. MIFireE	25 Feb
Bradshaw, R.	26 Feb
Izzard, T. C. BSc	26 Feb
Wilson, C. S.	26 Feb
Jones, J. M. BEng	29 Feb

Beal, S.	12 Mar
Erasmuson, H. J.	12 Mar
Fleming, M. E.	12 Mar
Gillies, S.	12 Mar
Horton, J. M. BEng	12 Mar
Hutchinson, C. A.	12 Mar
King, J. BSc(Econ)	14 Mar
Stables, A. J. CBE FRAeS	17 Mar
Morris, D. W.	18 Mar
Bardoe, S. J.	19 Mar
Corfield, A. G.	19 Mar
Marshallsay, P. J. BEd	19 Mar
Rigsby, A. E. cfs(g)	19 Mar
Robertson, L.	31 Mar
Vernon, P. I.	31 Mar
Sheldon, T.	5 Apr
Davis, A. McB. OBE	12 Apr
Ellis, W.	20 Apr
Glennon, A. M.	20 Apr
Pimm, J. A. cfs(g)	20 Apr
Sadler, D. A.	20 Apr
Herd, G. D.	21 Apr
Prestage, S. D.	21 Apr
Austin, L. BA PGCE	22 Apr
Clark, A. R. D.	22 Apr
Mixture, D. BEng	22 Apr
Skinner, A. J.	22 Apr
Wellsteed, M. A.	22 Apr
Ayre, J.	23 Apr
Di Domenico, A. J. MSc BEng	23 Apr
Leach, W. T. BSc	23 Apr
Richards, M.	23 Apr
Sewart, P. R. BSc	23 Apr
Freeman, S. R.	29 Apr
Kidd, N. S.	29 Apr
Long, D. P.	29 Apr
Milton, P. BEd	29 Apr
Patel, Y. BSc PGCE	5 May
Wood, C. S. MSc BSc PGCE	5 May
Barnard, J. B.	6 May
Weight, C. D.	8 May
Hookham, K. P.	14 May
Dicks, M. A. BA	18 May
Thornell, P. J.	18 May
Mitchell, W. M.	27 May
Elliot, L. J.	29 May
Matten, P. A.	29 May
Vernon, M. N.	29 May
Moon, N. Y.	3 June
Powell-Jones, H. D.	3 June
Sheerin, C. E. BA	3 June
Campbell, A. A.	10 June
Vint, R. J.	10 June
Walker, S. M.	10 June
Baines, J. L.	11 June
Crockford, P. D.	11 June
Roberts, P. BA DipEd	12 June

Flying Officers

2000—contd

Head, K. L.	13 June
Crosby, R. E. BSc PGCE	15 June
Coleman, T.	17 June
Thomson, J. C.	17 June
Luxton, P. A. BEng	18 June
Bartlett, P. L.	24 June
Bisby, M.	24 June
Butt, D. J.	24 June
Child, E. A.	24 June
Drew, N. J. BA PGCE	24 June
Kent, P.	24 June
Rose, P. A.	24 June
Smith, D. S. BSc BEng MIFireE	24 June
Williams, K.	24 June
Armeanu, Z. K.	25 June
Cook, K. M.	25 June
Flynn, C.	1 July
Cooper, J. T. BA	3 July
Clements, P. M.	6 July
Gardner, J. W.	6 July
Kanas, T. G. BDS	6 July
Onions, M. J.	6 July
Twose, P. M.	6 July
Murray, A. BSc PGCE	10 July
Braddy, J. P.	13 July
Callaghan, S. E.	13 July
Murray, M.	13 July
Nicholas, S. B.	13 July
Parker, R. L.	13 July
Russell, I. E.	13 July
Turner, S.	13 July
Chick, S. D. BSc	20 July
Hunnisett, S. P.	26 July
Thomas, P. M. BA DipEd	26 July
Willshire, D. J.	30 July
Moore, B. T.	4 Aug
Barker, A. M. BSc	9 Aug
White, F. C.	10 Aug
Blanchard, L. S.	17 Aug
McNeill, A. B.	17 Aug
Kerr, A. D. BSc PGCE	22 Aug
Anderson, V.	24 Aug
Cowan, J. M.	24 Aug
Sneider, C. B.	24 Aug
Young, S. J.	24 Aug
Lowndes, P. S.	27 Aug
Middlemiss, J. J.	1 Sept
Ambrose, A. B.	2 Sept
Biddles, L. E.	2 Sept
Horton, N. K.	2 Sept
Hunter, D. C.	2 Sept
Ledson, T. D. MSc BA	2 Sept

Howarth, G. W. L. BTech PGCE	4 Sept
McAvoy, G. B. MBE MA BA	6 Sept
Budd, D. G.	8 Sept
Edmondson, P.	8 Sept
Frost, R. E. P.	8 Sept
Gardner, S.	8 Sept
Hartley, K. L.	8 Sept
Sales, K.	8 Sept
Daw, D. I.	17 Sept
Ford, R. W.	17 Sept
Nunnerley, L. A.	17 Sept
Ward, C. A. BSc	17 Sept
Cromie, L. D.	21 Sept
Malcolm, G. R.	21 Sept
Price, D. G.	21 Sept
Allen, P. R. BA PGCE	22 Sept
Cheesman, P. J.	22 Sept
Lang, R. I. W.	22 Sept
Mills, J. R.	22 Sept
Nicoll, D. C.	22 Sept
Rae, S. A.	22 Sept
Tanner, J. M.	22 Sept
Ashby, A. P.	23 Sept
Wright, J. D. BSc PGCE	26 Sept
Tebay, H. P. MA PGCE	2 Oct
Blatchford, L. M.	7 Oct
Bush, E. K. D. BA PGCE	12 Oct
Davies, R. BA PGCE	12 Oct
McMorran, M. I. BSc PGCE	12 Oct
Smith, A. BSc	12 Oct
Reid, J. A.	13 Oct
Griffiths, J. E. BA PGCE	16 Oct
Hatch, P. F. BSc	19 Oct
Kinvig, J. P. MEng	19 Oct
Turgoose, R. BSc	19 Oct
Waplington, L. M.	19 Oct
Childs, A. P.	21 Oct
Grant, L. J.	21 Oct
Kerr, J. A.	21 Oct
Scott, T. R.	21 Oct
Hogan, R. A.	28 Oct
Taylor, J. S.	28 Oct
Hadfield, N. A. MA	6 Nov
Bailey, N. E. BSc PGCE	6 Nov
Holman, A. N. MA	6 Nov
Marlow, P. M. BSc PGCE	6 Nov
Leach, S. C. BSc	8 Nov
Cullen, S. M. MA DPhil MLitt	11 Nov
Barr, K. E.	12 Nov
Laidler, P. D. BSc	12 Nov
Murfin, A. S. BSc cfs(g)	12 Nov
Richardson, C. M.	12 Nov
Higgins, L. M.	13 Nov
Hill, D. W.	13 Nov

Gregory, R. J. MBBS MRCP LRCP DRCOS	22 Nov
Anderson, J. E. BSc	23 Nov
Campbell, G.	23 Nov
Curtis, J. P.	23 Nov
Harvey, J. R. A.	23 Nov
Jones, S. M.	23 Nov
Moss, S. cfs(g)	23 Nov
Nelson, J. H. BA cfs(g)	23 Nov
Collantine, M. G. BSc	27 Nov
Gill, B. G.	27 Nov
Ashworth, C. D. I. BA	30 Nov
Hesketh-Roberts, R. D.	30 Nov
Miller, R. G. S.	30 Nov
Pache, A. E. BA	30 Nov
Ratcliffe, D. C. BSc	30 Nov
Swift, S. BA	30 Nov
Boyle, R. C. BSc	1 Dec
Bunting, R. W.	1 Dec
Chinnery, E. J.	1 Dec
Howard-Carter, M. S.	1 Dec
Ibbitson, C. S.	1 Dec
Lenard, D. M.	1 Dec
MacAuley, R. J. S. MA BA PGCE	1 Dec
Noyce, H. A. BA PGCE	1 Dec
Rousseau, D. R.	1 Dec
Whiten, M.	1 Dec
Forey, D. M.	2 Dec
Kent, J. D.	2 Dec
Kirkby, R. I. BA PGCE	2 Dec
Pickering, C. M. BSc cfs(g)	2 Dec
Bernard, J. K.	4 Dec
Melhado, S. J.	4 Dec
Ramage, D.	4 Dec
Therwell, P.	4 Dec
Regan, G. D.	6 Dec
Bannister, P. S.	7 Dec
Fox, G. A. BSc	7 Dec
Harrison, M. A.	7 Dec
Kimberley, M.	7 Dec
Telfer, G. A.	7 Dec
Allsop, K. C.	8 Dec
Dwyer, D. A. BA PGCE	8 Dec
Maxwell, D. J.	8 Dec
Withnall, D. J.	8 Dec
Walcuch, J. M. A.	9 Dec
Dewey, H. J.	14 Dec
Lees, L. M.	14 Dec
Nuttall, K. L.	14 Dec
Stringer, P.	14 Dec
Weddle, D. G.	14 Dec
Ratcliffe, A. J.	18 Dec
Stephenson, A. F.	18 Dec
Berryman, D. G.	22 Dec
Reed, K. I.	22 Dec
Doble, L. A. OBE FRAeS	29 Dec

Flying Officers

2001

Dennis, N. C. H.	3 Jan
Knight, D.	4 Jan
Llewellyn, A. J.	4 Jan
Doyle, F. T. McA. TD	5 Jan
Craven, I. W.	19 Jan
Franks, J. E.	25 Jan
Hawley, P. J.	25 Jan
Kidd, A.	25 Jan
Strongman, M. A.	25 Jan
Davies, B. J. BA	26 Jan
Freeburn, M. L.	26 Jan
Newcombe, P. J.	26 Jan
Stafford, R. P. BSc PGCE	27 Jan
Stanyer, R. J. BSc BEd	27 Jan
Barratt, S. Y.	29 Jan
English, G. J.	29 Jan
Firth, D.	2 Feb
Guzy, S. J.	2 Feb
Logan, A.	2 Feb
Travis, J. E. L. BSc	2 Feb
Davis, B. T. DPhysEd	4 Feb
Coppell, S. MA	11 Feb
Creber, E. J. BSc PGCE	11 Feb
Martin, S. F. BSc PGCE	11 Feb
Johnson, S. P.	16 Feb
Lambert, M. S.	16 Feb
Wild, C.	16 Feb
Eve, J. S.	21 Feb
Francey, M. D. MBA BSc	23 Feb
Nutten, D. D.	25 Feb
Whitford, P. T.	26 Feb
Warren, P. J. BEng	28 Feb
March, A. BSc	5 Mar
Brown, A. R. BSc	8 Mar
Guest, J. A. TD BA	8 Mar
Jupe, G. V. BA	8 Mar
Scully, N. M. BA	8 Mar
Wilding, J. A. BSc	8 Mar
France, S. J. cfs(g)	10 Mar
Worthington, A. E. BA PGCE	13 Mar
Sparkes, K. L. BSc PGCE	14 Mar
Fawkes, R. L.	15 Mar
MacCarron, D. F.	15 Mar
Riley, S. D.	15 Mar
Green, D. L. MBA	16 Mar
Ibell, A. J.	16 Mar
Knight, P. R.	16 Mar
Maunder, S. G.	16 Mar
Ritchie, L.	16 Mar
Shardlow, C. H.	16 Mar
Charters, S. BEng BEd	17 Mar

Bannister, A. S. BSc CertEd	19 Mar
Barrett, J. L.	19 Mar
Humphries, A. J.	19 Mar
Skew, M. E. BEd CertEd	19 Mar
Wright, F. K.	19 Mar
Douglas, A. R. BSc PGCE	22 Mar
Norriss, Sir Peter KBE CB AFC MA FRAeS	23 Mar
Roberts, N. O.	23 Mar
Russell, A. W.	24 Mar
Shaw, R. J.	24 Mar
Warren, L. A.	24 Mar
Cromie, D. S.	25 Mar
Faskin, E. J.	26 Mar
Twose, J. D. BEd	26 Mar
Williamson, C. G.	29 Mar
Beaty, A. M. BSc CertEd	30 Mar
Bingham, P.	31 Mar
Franks, G. G.	31 Mar
Jones, J. A.	31 Mar
Thompson, P.	31 Mar
Ayling, S. J.	5 Apr
Calvert, D. A.	5 Apr
Gulam, M.	5 Apr
Hodgson, J.	5 Apr
Manville, S.	9 Apr
Naylor, J.	14 Apr
Williams, S. D.	14 Apr
Chadwick, P. J. AFC BSc FCMI MRAeS	25 Apr
Clark, T. A.	27 Apr
Carter, D. P. BNurs	27 Apr
Cusack, K.	27 Apr
Hedley, R. K. MSc PGCE	28 Apr
Waller, L. BSc PGCE	28 Apr
Dudgeon, L. P.	29 Apr
Campbell, D.	1 May
Jewiss, J. O. MRAeS	1 May
Earley, P.	5 May
Gulliver, S. J. D. BSc PGCE	14 May
Hayton, M. C.	17 May
McElhinney, R. P.	17 May
McLoughlin, K. G.	17 May
Pollock, C. L.	17 May
Wood, M. A.	17 May
Herbert, N. F.	19 May
Thompson, W. M.	19 May
Weatherall, J. H.	19 May
Massey, J. J.	22 May
Coates, S. P. BEng MIMechE	24 May
Jenkins, S. A. MEng	24 May
McCluney, J. G.	1 June
Millikin, P. M. MBE	1 June
Morris, J. E. P. MA PGCE	1 June
Allsopp, H. J.	2 June

Fallows, J.	2 June
Pickersgill, N. K.	2 June
Wilby, J. M. BA PCGE	2 June
Krausz, A. D.	7 June
McIlroy, D. C. MSc MCIPD	7 June
Barton, D. S.	8 June
Bromley, R. H. BSc AMIEE	8 June
Campion, A. P.	8 June
Harrison, A. J.	8 June
Murad, K. W. A.	8 June
Smith, J. BEd	8 June
Reardon, P. T. BA	11 June
Seeley, S. D.	11 June
Sharman, A. M. BSc(Eng) FRAeS cfs(g)	11 June
Thomson, J.	13 June
Abbott, C. M.	15 June
Smith, C. W.	15 June
Shawyer, A. J.	22 June
Smith, R. E.	22 June
Stevenson, D. L.	22 June
Nurbhai, H. T.	23 June
Cameron, A.	25 June
Kingswood, C. J.	25 June
Lowe, J. F. C.	25 June
Mingham, P. L. BSc PCGE	25 June
Brown, J. B.	26 June
Willson, T. C.	28 June
Stosiek, D. J. BSc CPhys MInstP	29 June
Lamond, M. J. BSc	30 June
McAloney, J. V. MSSCh MBChA	30 June
Murray, D. L. MPharm	30 June
Jones, R. R.	1 July
Heir, J. S. BSc PGCE	2 July
Adcock, B.	9 July
Locke, L. J.	12 July
Lane, S. A. BSc PGCE	15 July
Rattle, S. A.	15 July
Stone, N. J.	15 July
Tanzi, D. A. A. BSc	15 July
Cormack, J. J.	20 July
Donaldson, L. J.	20 July
Johnston, A.	20 July
Leslie, D. T.	20 July
Markham, A. P. BA	20 July
Westerberg, R. A. P.	20 July
Jones, B. E.	27 July
Stewart, N. R.	30 July
Banks, B. D. BEd	1 Aug
Pagliano, J. S.	2 Aug
Reach, C. BSc	2 Aug
Richarads, S. J.	2 Aug
Sermon, N. A.	2 Aug
Wheeler, D. J. BSc	3 Aug

Flying Officers

2001—contd

Geoghegan, M.	6 Aug
Day, S. T.	10 Aug
MacDonald, F. M. MSc BSc PGCE	11 Aug
Baxter, R.	16 Aug
Collie, A. J.	21 Aug
Grant, J.	23 Aug
Major, K. A.	23 Aug
Sullivan, M. BA	23 Aug
McGrath, J. G. BSc	28 Aug
Phillips, M. T.	29 Aug
Alexander, D. S.	6 Sept
Middleditch, S. N.	6 Sept
Allkins, E. D. H.	7 Sept
O'Connell, A.	8 Sept
Ling, O. M.	9 Sept
Martin, J. A. BSc	10 Sept
Corbett, S. A.	13 Sept
Ap Sion, G. BA PGCE	15 Sept
Baker, J. V. BSc PGCE	15 Sept
Jackson, D. J. BA PGCE	17 Sept
Carter, C. A. BSc	23 Sept
Madeira, N. C.	24 Sept
Roberts, D. G.	24 Sept
Blake, R. J.	28 Sept
Mott, V. E. M.	28 Sept
Raynor, D. H. MA MLitt PGCE	28 Sept
Smith, T.	28 Sept
Wilson, H. M.	28 Sept
Askam, M. J.	4 Oct
Inder-Gray, T. W.	4 Oct
Prismall, L. A.	4 Oct
Seale, G. BSc DipEd	4 Oct
Morris, S. T. BSc	5 Oct
O'Flanagan, D. F.	6 Oct
Turley, T. C. C.	6 Oct
Lawson, G. C.	9 Oct
Allen, D. P.	13 Oct
Rumley, A. K. BA BSc PGCE	13 Oct
Silver, K. L.	13 Oct
Singh, V.	13 Oct
Madge, P. BA PGCE	15 Oct
Clardige-Jones. C. J.	17 Oct
Cope, M. P.	17 Oct
Coram, M. J.	17 Oct
Hughes, C. J. M.	17 Oct
Jordan, J. M.	17 Oct
O'Shaughnessy, L. M.	17 Oct
Routledge, S.	17 Oct
Rushbrooke, J. BSc	17 Oct
Lightfoot, R. MSc PGCE	19 Oct
Oswald, C. G. BSc PGCE	19 Oct

Thompson, D. N.	26 Oct
Turner, M.	26 Oct
Watson, M.	26 Oct
Harvey, R.	27 Oct
Jessop, L. M. BSc	1 Nov
John, D. A. R.	1 Nov
Thorpe, I. F. BEd CertEd	1 Nov
Owen, A. A.	3 Nov
Stockbridge, M. J.	3 Nov
Towns, P. T. W.	3 Nov
Leadbetter, S. M. MA PGCE	10 Nov
Rance, C. A.	10 Nov
Woan, S. J.	10 Nov
Adams, R. B.	11 Nov
Selfridge, E. S.	11 Nov
Young, J. W.	11 Nov
Sherring, I. D.	12 Nov
Buddery, C. A. MEng	15 Nov
Hulland, M.	15 Nov
Irwin, P.	15 Nov
Smith, B. I.	15 Nov
Carter, A. L. MA BA PGCE	18 Nov
Colby, C. J. BSc PGCE	18 Nov
Eyre, P. D. M. C. BSc CertEd	18 Nov
Fairweather, M. M. MA PGCE	18 Nov
Roberts, P. A. BSc	20 Nov
Ball, M. G. DFC	22 Nov
Bidston, P. M.	23 Nov
Taylor-Heard, S. A. BSc	26 Nov
Panton, M. E.	28 Nov
Ketteringham, S. J.	30 Nov
Murray, S. A. BA	30 Nov
Woods, T. J.	4 Dec
Featherstone, N. BSc PGCE	6 Dec
Bradford, N. S.	7 Dec
Cartwright, P. D. BEng	7 Dec
Coates, S. P.	7 Dec
Haywood, M. J.	7 Dec
Smith, A. W.	7 Dec
Brember, C. L. BSc	10 Dec
Johnstone, M.	10 Dec
Kempster, M. J. BSc	10 Dec
Killingback, M. B.	13 Dec
Scott, P. J.	13 Dec
Morgan, D. E.	15 Dec
Morgan, E. L. K.	15 Dec
Emberson, M.	16 Dec
Main, A. S. MSc	16 Dec
Godden, M. J.	17 Dec
Green, J. B. BSc PGCE	19 Dec
Hodgson, S. BEng	20 Dec
Marshall, C. L.	20 Dec
Simpson, M. T. BEng	20 Dec
Taylor, P.	20 Dec
Bagnall, N. R.	22 Dec

Goddard, J. P. M. BSc cfs(g)	22 Dec
Howarth, C. L.	22 Dec
Purchase, W. MBE	22 Dec

2002

Betts, R. T. BEd	5 Jan
Morrison, T.	5 Jan
Stewart, D.	5 Jan
Boycott, D. W.	14 Jan
Micklewright, S. A. BA	14 Jan
Sharma, R.	14 Jan
Berrow, J. J. BA PGCE	17 Jan
Humphrey, R. L. BA PGCE	17 Jan
Savine, A.	18 Jan
Steele, R. C.	18 Jan
Scragg, J. R. B. BA	19 Jan
Falconer, M. D. BEng	20 Jan
Henderson, J. McL.	20 Jan
Hodgson, N. J.	20 Jan
Tune, S. E.	20 Jan
Williams, S. J.	20 Jan
Wright, F. C.	20 Jan
Pattenden, G. E. P. LLB	21 Jan
Ray, D. A.	23 Jan
Annis, M. L.	24 Jan
De Santis, D. S. BA	24 Jan
Gibson, G.	24 Jan
Hughes, K.	24 Jan
Shaw, P. R.	24 Jan
Small, J. E.	24 Jan
White, M. T.	24 Jan
Hutchinson, I. G.	27 Jan
Dixon, P. S.	29 Jan
Goodgame, S. J. BEng CEng MIChemE	1 Feb
Hilditch, M. C. G.	2 Feb
Hobson, A. P.	2 Feb
Powe, I. D.	2 Feb
Swann, A.	2 Feb
Cawdron, D. A. BA PGCE	3 Feb
Herod, J. R. MBE	8 Feb
Sinclair, D. MA PGCE	9 Feb
Barron, B.	14 Feb
Barson, E. K. MSc BSc PGCE	14 Feb
Leaney, C.	14 Feb
McGregor, I. J.	14 Feb
O'Farrell, R. J. BA PGCE	14 Feb
Story, G. D.	14 Feb
Bullard, G. E.	17 Feb
Measures, C. BSc	17 Feb
Travers, M.	17 Feb
Alderman, L. G. BSc	18 Feb
Davies, G. J.	21 Feb
Gordon, M. J. BSc	23 Feb

Flying Officers

2002—contd

Watson, G. M.	23 Feb
Wilson, C. E. BA	23 Feb
McLackland, I.	25 Feb
Pell, L. J.	25 Feb
Williams, T. G. BSc MRAeS	25 Feb
Stevens, W. J.	2 Mar
Campion, E. M.	6 Mar
Foster, N. A.	6 Mar
Quine, I. J.	6 Mar
Smith, B. P.	6 Mar
Smith, D. J.	6 Mar
Tate, P. S. G.	6 Mar
Brockbank, J. M. BA	10 Mar
Wilkinson, P.	10 Mar
Howlett, P. D.	13 Mar
Robinson, I. P.	13 Mar
Spry, C. M. PhD MPhil BA	13 Mar
Stevens, R. M.	13 Mar
Young, J. BSc PGCE	13 Mar
Woodward, I. D.	14 Mar
Jones, P. J. R. BSc PGCE	16 Mar
Jones, R. J.	16 Mar
Morison, I. P. T. BA CertEd	18 Mar
Asher, L. E. BSc	21 Mar
Broadhurst, J. E.	22 Mar
Button, K. A. BA	22 Mar
Dibb, E.	22 Mar
Fisher, G. S.	24 Mar
Howard, C.	24 Mar
Millar, K. BSc	26 Mar
Padgett, K. BSc PGCE	27 Mar
Steele, H. J. V. T.	27 Mar
Farr, D. A. S. BA PGCE	29 Mar
Piper, L. M.	29 Mar
Adcock, C. B. BA	2 Apr
Sully, J. F. MRAeS	2 Apr
Blenkiron, S. BA CertEd	3 Apr
Thomas, A. P. W.	5 Apr
Moyle, G. R.	6 Apr
Boyd, K. A.	7 Apr
Davidson, B. J.	7 Apr
Flynn, B.	7 Apr
Marsh, S.	7 Apr
McCallum, H. A.	7 Apr
Ross-Bell, S.	7 Apr
Baker, J. M.	12 Apr
Davies, S.	12 Apr
Delamar, K. BA	12 Apr
Morgan, D.	14 Apr
Murray, B. J.	14 Apr
Woodward, G. D.	14 Apr

Bowler, A. P. BSc(Econ)	17 Apr
Groves, C. M.	19 Apr
Alletson, S. L.	23 Apr
Betts, R. J. BA	26 Apr
Neesom, J. K.	26 Apr

Pilot Officers

1990

Hunter, L. M.	27 Feb
Rotherham, D. J. BEd	20 Mar

1991

McLintock, C. M. BSc	25 June
Cameron, J.	2 July
Cooper, P. R. BEng	2 July
Alexander, A. J.	9 Dec
Cheetham, M. K.	9 Dec
Coates, N. D.	10 Dec
Davies, M. R.	10 Dec
Bird, I. N.	12 Dec

1992

Marshall, G. P. B.	9 June
Brennan, M. I.	18 Aug
Child, J. J.	18 Aug
Davies, P. A.	18 Aug
Hart, D. L.	28 Aug
Elliot, S. D.	19 Nov

1993

Moore, E.	24 Mar
Garwood, R. MCMI	5 July
Langdon, N. G.	19 July
Wilkes, C. A. BA PGCE	6 Oct
Redican, S. N.	4 Dec
Leech, E. J.	10 Dec
Moy, A. J.	10 Dec
Van Rhyn, S. J.	10 Dec
Bentley, K. LTCL	12 Dec
Seward, C. M.	12 Dec
Paul, C.	16 Dec
Nash, D. J.	18 Dec

1994

Symonds, D. C. BA	19 Oct

1995

Peat, C. I. BSc	25 Apr
Hayward, P. J.	6 Oct

1996

Riding, P. M.	1 Sept
Flux, M. J.	15 Oct
Finck, P. H.	6 Nov

1997

Le Worthy, S. L.	13 Mar

1998

Thorne, N. E.	11 June
Anson, N. A. BEd	11 Nov

1999

Adams, C. D.	4 Jan
Brown, A. E. BEd	27 Jan
Bingham, P.	31 Mar
Phillips, C. J.	2 June
Roberts, J. A.	22 June
Kempton, M. I.	23 June
Reddy, R. A.	2 July
Ephgrave, V. J.	20 July
Hadfield, J. M.	20 July
Dobney, R. G.	2 Aug
Metcalfe, I. A.	2 Aug
Fuller, I.	28 Sept
Nicholls, J. C. PhD BSc	13 Oct
Short, G. M.	17 Oct
Bradding, M. E.	27 Oct
Kelly, G. M.	27 Oct
Lane, S. J.	10 Nov
Holmes, C. J.	26 Nov
Aucott, C.	7 Dec
Devereux, I. B. BEd	13 Dec
Lightfoot, C. A. BSc cfs(g)	22 Dec

2000

McKenna, S-J. BEng PGCE	17 Jan
Wallis, M. BA	17 Jan
Pottle, N. J. BSc	28 Jan
Parmentier, A. J. A. BA PGCE	1 Feb

Pilot Officers

2000—contd

Ellis, R. J.	9 Feb
Nesbit, A. J. BEd	14 Feb
Flux, S. J.	17 Feb
Worth, N. D.	17 Feb
Scott, W.	21 Feb
Holness, M. P.	10 Mar
Clarke, A. BSc cfs(g)	13 Mar
Newman, J. D. BA	5 Apr
Johnson, N. R.	6 Apr
Ashlee, M.	19 Apr
Price, R. M.	19 Apr
Richards, B.	2 May
Hall, E. R. BSc PGCE	8 May
Castle, N. J.	12 May
Coles, P. J.	12 May
Munns, A.	12 May
Robinson, J.	12 May
Alloway, A. G.	17 May
Adam, L.	19 May
Cawley, M. B.	19 May
Cowley, S.	19 May
Needham, C. C.	19 May
Smith, D. cfs(g)	19 May
Coates, C. A. J.	21 May
McWilliams, R. J. BSc PGCE	21 May
Steinitz, F. M. BA CertEd	21 May
Winslade, K. J.	21 May
Crombie, J. cfs(g)	24 May
Kazi, J. H. BA PGCE	29 May
Marriott, M. S.	29 May
Anderson, E. J. BSc	12 June
Ballantyne, M. L. BSc	12 June
Capstick, S.	12 June
Hatton, T. J. BA PGCE	12 June
Slaven, E. A. M.	12 June
Weston, P. D.	12 June
Williams, M. D.	12 June
Baggett, S. A.	13 June
Evans, R. A.	13 June
Rayner, S. T. A.	13 June
Bertram, R. H.	14 June
Mustafa, M. I.	14 June
Mennell, J. P. BSc	14 June
Whiteley, S.	14 June
Holford, D. W. BSc PGCE	16 June
Lovering, D. P. BSc PGCE	16 June
Alden-Fenn, N. C.	19 June
Elwell, G. J.	20 June
Peake, K. L.	20 June
Marley, C. BSc PGCE	22 June
Simmons, D. P. BEd	22 June

Smith, H. S. PhD MA BA	22 June
Allan, W. J. BSc	3 July
Brown, J. B. K.	3 July
Coletta, N. S.	3 July
Colman, S. R.	3 July
Forristal, A. L. J. BA	3 July
Mitchell, E. W. LLB	3 July
Ridley, C. N. R.	3 July
Simpson, A. T. C.	3 July
Josephs, M. cfs(g)	6 July
Knight, P. D.	6 July
MacDonald, A. C. G. BA	6 July
Andrews, S. P.	6 July
Jenkins, I. C.	10 July
Sheard, C. M.	10 July
Smith, L. A.	10 July
Snelson, S. T.	10 July
Venus, J. M.	10 July
Dymond, H. J.	17 July
Gunn, R. S.	17 July
Kett, C.	17 July
Mortimore, P. J.	17 July
Smith, S. J.	17 July
Aspinall, J. C.	26 July
Billington, K.	26 July
Francis, D. R. A.	26 July
Hall, T. J. R.	26 July
Hebblethwaite, J.	26 July
Leadbetter, G. J.	26 July
Bush, R. J.	1 Aug
Gardner, M. J.	2 Aug
Noye-Allen, J.	2 Aug
Parry, I. J.	2 Aug
Antrobus, S. J.	8 Aug
Jones, E. L.	8 Aug
Smith, M. J.	8 Aug
Noble, J. D. BSc	14 Aug
Dorritt, H. J.	15 Aug
Podger, K. D.	15 Aug
Porter, A. T.	15 Aug
Paton, R.	22 Aug
Nicholls, T. W.	4 Sept
Wood, M. J.	4 Sept
Cove, F. L. BSc PGCE	6 Sept
Barnett, N. P.	8 Sept
Coxey, P. S. BSc BEng	8 Sept
Rushworth, D. MA BA PGCE	8 Sept
Farr, A. E.	18 Sept
Hudson, K. R.	18 Sept
Lilley, J. S. BSc	18 Sept
McKinnon, E. G.	18 Sept
Nicholls, G. L.	18 Sept
Quigley, J. C. W.	18 Sept
Inderwick, D. R. L. MA BA	19 Sept
Logan, E. J. BA	19 Sept
Burns, R.	20 Sept
Tunesi of Liongam, J. J.	20 Sept

Ford, W. A.	22 Sept
Kiely, P. D.	22 Sept
Robinson, S. L.	22 Sept
McNally, W. E. BSc PGCE	28 Sept
Patel, D. K. BSc PGCE	28 Sept
Adams, W. V.	6 Oct
Griffiths, D. W.	6 Oct
Weston, S. K.	6 Oct
Ladwa, M. J.	9 Oct
MacDonald, E. C.	9 Oct
Small, D. R. BSc	9 Oct
Smith, A. C. P.	9 Oct
Feist, M. G.	13 Oct
Lewis, S. M.	13 Oct
Fedrick, L. R.	23 Oct
Parker, K. E.	23 Oct
Davies, L. R. BA	30 Oct
Miles-Carew, M. L.	30 Oct
Slater, M. K. BSc	30 Oct
Anderson, L. C.	1 Nov
Holder, K. MA PGCE	1 Nov
Furnival, L. A. BA PGCE	2 Nov
Donothey, R.	14 Nov
Farman, R. W.	14 Nov
Shiel. E. A.	14 Nov
Amodeo, F. P. L. F. BA PGCE	15 Nov
Hammersley, A. P. BSc PGCE	15 Nov
Hampson, L. A.	15 Nov
McLean. M. C. BSc PGCE	15 Nov
Parker, R. S.	15 Nov
Stones, S. MA BA PGCE	15 Nov
Andrew, P. C. R. BEng PGCE	22 Nov
Sage, E. P. BA PGCE	12 Dec
Laird, P. L. BSc PGCE	14 Dec
Rose, C. M. BA CertEd	14 Dec
Bradley, S.	18 Dec
Cooper, S. D.	18 Dec
Hogg, J. BSc	18 Dec
McAdam, B. A. BEng	18 Dec
Patrick, E. M.	18 Dec
Whittaker, I. J. A.	18 Dec
Lloyd, T. M.	20 Dec
Marwood, P. R. BSc	20 Dec
Stott, J. W.	20 Dec
Braid, D. cfs(g)	21 Dec
Title, C. J.	21 Dec
Yeates, S. P.	21 Dec

2001

Kocijancic, S.	10 Jan
Burrell, J. MA PGCE	12 Jan
Martlew, T.	12 Jan

288

Pilot Officers

2001—contd

Mathew, C. T. BEd	12 Jan
Clark, H. D. BSc PGCE	15 Jan
Harte, E. S. BSc PGCE	15 Jan
Benson, D. BSc PGCE	22 Jan
Briggs, S. M.	22 Jan
Gillard, S. J.	22 Jan
Liversedge, K. J. MA PGCE	22 Jan
Terry, P. A.	22 Jan
Tracey, C. F.	22 Jan
Whitmarsh, M. R.	22 Jan
McLaughlin, A. M.	24 Jan
Price, J. S.	24 Jan
Corbett, C. L.	26 Jan
Bravin, T. D.	29 Jan
Carney, M. D. BSc	29 Jan
Wright, A. D.	29 Jan
Condy, M. H. BSc	1 Feb
Ferguson, J. A.	1 Feb
Atkins, S. M.	5 Feb
McCrossan, R. L. H. BA	5 Feb
McVean, D. L.	5 Feb
Mickiewicz, J. BSc PGCE	5 Feb
Nicholls, V. E. BA	5 Feb
Lambert, C. L. BA	13 Feb
Moss, A. J. PGCE	13 Feb
O'Neill, B. P.	13 Feb
Gregory, C. J.	20 Feb
Lyall, B.	20 Feb
Mullan, T. P. BSc PGCE	20 Feb
Wardle, C. B. BSc	20 Feb
Hendry, J. M. C.	21 Feb
Huckstep, T. J.	21 Feb
Henderson, J. W.	2 Mar
Sutherland, A. J.	2 Mar
Butler, J. J. MSc BEng cfs(g)	5 Mar
Lynas, J. cfs(g)	5 Mar
Massey, J. A. BEng	5 Mar
Pearson, S. M. BEng	5 Mar
Ellis, J. M. D.	8 Mar
King, M. A.	8 Mar
Lawes, L. A. cfs(g)	8 Mar
Reed, P. J.	8 Mar
Knott, B. R.	13 Mar
Ashdowne, R. K. BA	19 Mar
Callaghan, Y.	19 Mar
Cathrow, P. D.	19 Mar
Humble-Smith, E. J.	19 Mar
Pinkstone, I. R. BSc	19 Mar
Morgan, A. J.	21 Mar
Newman, M. S.	26 Mar
Rance, T. I.	4 Apr
Shave, A. J.	4 Apr

Westman, M. S. MBA BA PGCE	4 Apr
White, D. J.	4 Apr
Vousden, J. C.	4 Apr
Brinkley, B. R.	9 Apr
Coxey, T. V.	9 Apr
Crebbin, C.	9 Apr
Hemes, E. D.	9 Apr
Kirby, C. J.	9 Apr
Ball, K. L.	20 Apr
Beckett, B.	20 Apr
Drew, J-A.	20 Apr
Jeffery, N.	20 Apr
Webb, D. M. BSc	20 Apr
Conibeer, S. A.	25 Apr
Penny, S. C.	25 Apr
Logan, J. J. MA CertEd	27 Apr
Roberts, C. E.	27 Apr
Akyildiz, D. BA PGCE	2 May
Leah, L. BA PGCE	2 May
Riddle, D. E. MA PGCE	2 May
Davies, T. C.	3 May
Binks, P. BA PGCE	8 May
Duncan, L.	8 May
Lawday, K.	8 May
Booth, C. S.	11 May
Evans, D. J.	11 May
Gordon, K. S.	11 May
Ingram, R. D. BSc	11 May
Pinfold, N. E.	11 May
Battye, N. D.	14 May
Bower, M. J. W. BSc	14 May
Button, G. J. LLB	14 May
Fisher, D. T. C.	14 May
Gray, P. E. BSc	14 May
Mehta, R.	14 May
Ridings, D. J. BSc PGCE	14 May
Vile, L. J.	14 May
Berridge, R. P. BEd	15 May
Horsted, D. J. CertEd	16 May
Orbell, M. H. BA PGCE	16 May
Cooper, N. K. PhD BSc AKC PGCE	22 May
Cullen, P. A. MSc	22 May
Crane, K. L. BA	23 May
Fullard, J. BEng	23 May
Gammons, C. J. BA PGCE	23 May
Oakes, A. C.	23 May
Turnbull, P. E. MSc BA PGCE	23 May
Bagnall, M. A. BSc	24 May
Glattback, L. P.	24 May
Barnett, A. J. BSc	30 May
Jones, G. A.	30 May
Stanley, M. A. MA PGCE	7 June
Sherlock, C. C.	10 June
Godsland, M.	11 June

Hodder, S. D. G. BSc	11 June
Bothamley, D. J.	14 June
Bramwell, I. D.	14 June
Brittain, C. L.	14 June
Hedges, G. M.	14 June
Nichols, V. K.	14 June
Demers, M.	25 June
Demers, T. G.	25 June
Griffiths. P. M.	25 June
Kempton, N.	25 June
Pratt, I. G.	25 June
Sheldon, R. G. R.	25 June
Slater, N. J. BA	25 June
Williams, N. B.	25 June
Gale, J. A. BEng PGCE	26 June
McLeod, A. J.	26 June
Milne, S. J.	26 June
Rainforth V. A. M. BSc PGCE	26 June
Harris, S. P. MA MSc MSc PGCE	28 June
Prichard, P. M. R. BSc	28 June
Thomas, K. A. BSc	28 June
Bell, T. H. BSc PGCE	9 July
Brackston, A. M.	9 July
Brown, D.	9 July
Callender, J. E.	9 July
Fowler, K.	9 July
Hewson, A. P.	9 July
Morris, A. L.	9 July
Peake, J. M. BA PGCE	9 July
Thomas, L. J.	9 July
Delvallee, M. PGCE	11 July
Bunn. K, BA	12 July
Lane, K. A.	12 July
Ridley, A.	12 July
Bilson, S. M.	16 July
Crowley, A. P.	16 July
Evans, E. V. BTech	16 July
Henry, M. R.	16 July
Horsfield, S. G.	16 July
Johnston, S. M.	16 July
Rushton, A. J.	16 July
Allison, S. A. PhD BSc	18 July
Gadd, C.	18 July
Llewellyn, C. A. BA	18 July
Turner, M. J. MSc	18 July
Grove, D. A. PGCE BA	23 July
Kingman, T. G.	23 July
Maple, M.	23 July
Stanway, M. R.	23 July
Aird, R. C.	30 July
Dobson, A. J.	30 July
Driscoll, M.	30 July
Hamnett, H. J.	30 July
Roberts, S. J.	30 July
Smales, T.	30 July
Wilkie, S. E.	30 July
Saw, C. A.	31 July
Campbell, D. W.	13 Aug

289

Pilot Officers

2001—contd

Falls, G. C.	13 Aug
Ford, H. P. BSc	13 Aug
Hanna, C. A.	13 Aug
Hay, E. R.	13 Aug
Llewellyn, F. J. BA	19 Aug
Burton, S. L.	21 Aug
Dartnell, R. J.	21 Aug
Oliver, J. E.	21 Aug
Burgess, S. J.	23 Aug
Bell, D. A.	31 Aug
Disbrey, A. K.	31 Aug
Flynn, J. M.	31 Aug
Little, M. C.	31 Aug
Plagmann, R. K.	31 Aug
Roberts, J. A. BEng	31 Aug
Robinson, B.	3 Sept
Wright, R. C. BA PGCE	3 Sept
Barnard, A. J.	4 Sept
Moakes, B. D. S.	4 Sept
Hunt, D. D.	7 Sept
Hunn, S. A. DPhil BA	20 Sept
Price, S. A. MA	24 Sept
Edwards, S. E. A. BA PGCE	25 Sept
Bell, S.	26 Sept
Bright, J. R. H. BSc	26 Sept
Teague, M. W.	26 Sept
Humble, A. V. PhD BSc PGCE	28 Sept
Broderick, T. M. BSc	1 Oct
Halman, G. D. BEng	1 Oct
Larkin, D.	1 Oct
Thomas, H. L.	1 Oct
Blackburn, M. J. BSc PGCE	5 Oct
Goodey, D. L.	5 Oct
Tekell, N. A. BSc PGCE	5 Oct
Forey, H.	8 Oct
Friend, J. C. BSc PGCE	8 Oct
Smith, T. A. BEng PGCE	8 Oct
Taylor, D.	11 Oct
Tempest, L. M.	11 Oct
Cottrell, P.	15 Oct
Dawson, M. L.	15 Oct
Garner, P. C.	15 Oct
Lees, N. M.	15 Oct
Spain, M. P. MSc BSc CEng MIEE	15 Oct
Wilkins, R. O.	15 Oct
Da Cunha, F. A.	25 Oct
Lynch, J. P.	25 Oct
Price, G. E.	25 Oct
Spiller, A. J. MEng	30 Oct
Toomey, D. BEd	30 Oct
Bryce, A. M.	31 Oct

King, S. J.	1 Nov
Dunkley, P. K. BEng MRAeS	5 Nov
Ingram, R. S. BEd	5 Nov
Thackery, G. D.	5 Nov
Carrington, P. C.	12 Nov
Chapman, R. G. BSc	12 Nov
Fry, B. D.	12 Nov
Harrison, A. R.	12 Nov
McShane, J. D.	12 Nov
Turner, A. R.	12 Nov
Butler, E. L.	16 Nov
Kidd, L. S. BEng	16 Nov
Coady, P. B.	19 Nov
Grant, J. C.	19 Nov
Robertson, J. A.	19 Nov
Prescott, S. L. MSc BSc	20 Nov
Day, N. A.	4 Dec
Loveday, T. Q.	4 Dec
Wood, L. J.	4 Dec
Boakes, L. J. BSc PGCE	6 Dec
Bemand, M. J.	6 Dec
Crossman, I. M. BA PGCE	6 Dec
Corfield, P. D.	14 Dec
Hanson, X. J.	14 Dec
Mead, N. I. E.	14 Dec
Buxton, C. A.	18 Dec
Emms, A. A.	18 Dec
Johnson, S. A.	18 Dec
Mabb, S. T. W.	18 Dec
Morris, M. M.	18 Dec
Ovenden, N. A.	18 Dec
Parker, C. J.	18 Dec
Costin, A. M.	19 Dec

2002

Mollan, A. M. J.	11 Jan
Bromley, A. J. L.	21 Jan
Davies, S. A.	21 Jan
Green, A. M.	21 Jan
Gullam, H.	21 Jan
Masters, M. E.	21 Jan
Moore, S. V.	21 Jan
Ward, C. BSc	21 Jan
Welsh, P. J.	21 Jan
Wilman, T. H.	21 Jan
Edwards, M. S. BA	24 Jan
Harper, A. E.	24 Jan
Hillier, R. W. BSc	24 Jan
Faro Wood, C. M. DMS CertEd	28 Jan
Foster, S. J. LLB	28 Jan
Lumley, G. CertEd	28 Jan
Sinclair, S. R. E. BSc PGCE	28 Jan
Walker, R. J. E. MEng	28 Jan
Coleman, C. R.	29 Jan

Fowler, G.	29 Jan
Moore, R. L.	5 Feb
Overy, K. A. BA PGCE	5 Feb
Radford, J. C.	5 Feb
Turner, G. M. BSc PGCE	5 Feb
Barker, P. E.	11 Feb
Horobin, C. S. BSc	11 Feb
Long, A.	11 Feb
Thomas, P. G.	11 Feb
Clark, H. J. M. MEng	12 Feb
Ingham, P. A.	12 Feb
Ladwa, S. P. BA	12 Feb
Fitzpatrick, C. M.	18 Feb
McAloney, E. M.	18 Feb
Wilson, M. E.	18 Feb
Ferguson-Dalling, L.	20 Feb
Lumsden, B. W. BEng	20 Feb
Beedie, S. A.	25 Feb
Harrison, R. J.	25 Feb
Morse, G. J. BEd	25 Feb
Toulouse, M. G.	25 Feb
Wheatley, J. L. BEng AMIEE	25 Feb
Bee, S. M. BA PGCE	28 Feb
Bradshaw, A. R.	4 Mar
Burge, J. M. M. BSc	4 Mar
Dalton, O. M. S.	4 Mar
Powell, J. B.	8 Mar
Arrowsmith, S. P.	11 Mar
Cowley, N. E.	11 Mar
Boughen, M. J.	14 Mar
Debbage-Philp, G.	14 Mar
Harris, P. M. IEng	14 Mar
Lincoln, R. J.	14 Mar
Bolderow, S. BA	18 Mar
Carter, J. B.	18 Mar
Sarsfield, C.	18 Mar
Tomkins, D. C. BSc PGCE	18 Mar
Ahsan, F. Z.	19 Mar
Garside, V. L.	19 Mar
McFarland, C. L.	19 Mar
Pinder, R. J. BSc	19 Mar
Foy, N.	20 May
Averill, I. J.	27 Mar
Brazier, K. D. BEng	27 Mar
Leadbeater, C.	9 Apr
Morgan, R. BSc	9 Apr
Disbury, S. D. BSc	11 Apr
Gallagher, P. BSc	11 Apr
Crowle, C. D. W.	15 Apr
Adamson, E. P. LLB	16 Apr
Cunliffe, G.	16 Apr
Elliott, E.	16 Apr
Everett, G. F.	22 Apr
Titchen, J. W. BA PGCE	22 Apr
Twining, R. F.	22 Apr
Hoskin, P. R. PhD BSc	24 Apr
Moseley, D. J.	25 Apr

Pilot Officers

2002—contd

Crofts, V. P. P. MPhil BA LLM CertEd	26 Apr
Ryan, C. E.	26 Apr
Bowcutt, C. M.	29 Apr
Butt, C. J. G.	29 Apr
Cohen, S. N.	29 Apr
Gillard, M. K. W. BSc PGCE	29 Apr
Tolley, S. M.	29 Apr

BATTLE HONOURS—RAF SQUADRONS

(**BOLD** PRINT INDICATES HONOURS ACTUALLY EMBLAZONED ON THE EXISTING STANDARD)

1 SQUADRON RAF

1st STANDARD PRESENTED 24 APRIL 1953 BY AVM SIR CHARLES LONGCROFT.
2nd STANDARD PRESENTED 27 JUNE 1983 BY MRAF SIR DERMOT BOYLE.

HONOURS WITH THE RIGHT TO EMBLAZONMENT

WESTERN FRONT, 1915–1918 YPRES, 1915 NEUVE CHAPPELLE LOOS **SOMME, 1916** ARRAS YPRES, 1917 LYS AMIENS SOMME, 1918 HINDENBERG LINE **INDEPENDENT FORCE & GERMANY, 1918** **FRANCE & LOW COUNTRIES, 1939–1940 BATTLE OF BRITAIN, 1940** CHANNEL & NORTH SEA, 1941–1945 HOME DEFENCE, 1940–1945 **FORTRESS EUROPE, 1941–44** ARNHEM NORMANDY, 1944 **FRANCE & GERMANY, 1944–1945** BISCAY, 1944–1945 RHINE **SOUTH ATLANTIC, 1982**

HONOURS WITHOUT THE RIGHT TO EMBLAZONMENT

KURDISTAN, 1922–1925 IRAQ, 1923–1925

2 SQUADRON RAF

1st STANDARD PRESENTED 31 OCTOBER 1953 BY ACM SIR ROBERT M FOSTER.
2nd STANDARD PRESENTED 30 MAY 1984 BY ACM SIR ALASDAIR STEEDMAN.

HONOURS WITH THE RIGHT TO EMBLAZONMENT

WESTERN FRONT, 1914–1918 MONS **NEUVE CHAPPELLE YPRES, 1915** LOOS **SOMME, 1916** ARRAS SOMME, 1918 LYS **FRANCE & LOW COUNTRIES, 1939–1940 DUNKIRK** FORTRESS EUROPE, 1942–1944 FRANCE & GERMANY, 1944–1945 **NORMANDY, 1944 ARNHEM** WALCHEREN RHINE **GULF, 1991**

3 SQUADRON RAF

1st STANDARD PRESENTED 11 DECEMBER 1953 BY ACM SIR PHILIP JOUBERT de la FERTE.
2nd STANDARD PRESENTED 3 JUNE 1983 BY AM SIR PATRICK B HINE.

HONOURS WITH THE RIGHT TO EMBLAZONMENT

WESTERN FRONT, 1914–1918 MONS NEUVE CHAPELLE LOOS SOMME, 1916 CAMBRAI, 1917 **SOMME, 1918** HINDENBERG LINE **FRANCE & LOW COUNTRIES, 1940 BATTLE OF BRITAIN, 1940** HOME DEFENCE, 1940–1945 DIEPPE FORTRESS EUROPE, 1942–1944 CHANNEL AND NORTH SEA, 1941–1945 **NORMANDY, 1944 ARNHEM** RHINE **FRANCE & GERMANY, 1944–1945**

4 SQUADRON RAF

1st STANDARD PRESENTED 20 NOVEMBER 1953 BY MRAF SIR JOHN SLESSOR.
2nd STANDARD PRESENTED 6 JULY 1984 BY AM SIR PATRICK B HINE.

HONOURS WITH THE RIGHT TO EMBLAZONMENT

WESTERN FRONT, 1914–1918 MONS NEUVE CHAPPELLE SOMME, 1916 **YPRES, 1917** LYS SOMME, 1918
FRANCE & LOW COUNTRIES, 1939–1940 FORTRESS EUROPE, 1942–1944 **FRANCE & GERMANY, 1944–1945**
NORMANDY, 1944 ARNHEM RHINE

5 SQUADRON RAF

1st STANDARD PRESENTED 24 APRIL 1954 BY ACM SIR LESLIE N HOLLINGHURST.
2nd STANDARD PRESENTED 11 AUGUST 1983 BY AVM G A WHITE.

HONOURS WITH THE RIGHT TO EMBLAZONMENT

WESTERN FRONT, 1914–1918 MONS NEUVE CHAPPELLE **YPRES, 1915 LOOS ARRAS** SOMME, 1918 **AMIENS**
HINDENBERG LINE **ARAKAN, 1942–1944** MANIPUR, 1944 **BURMA, 1944–1945**

HONOURS WITHOUT THE RIGHT TO EMBLAZONMENT

WAZIRISTAN, 1920–1925 MOHMAND, 1927 NORTH WEST FRONTIER, 1930–1931
NORTH WEST FRONTIER, 1935–1939

6 SQUADRON RAF

1st STANDARD PRESENTED 31 JANUARY 1954 BY AM SIR CLAUDE B R PELLY.
2nd STANDARD PRESENTED 31 OCTOBER 1980 BY ACM SIR KEITH WILLIAMSON.

HONOURS WITH THE RIGHT TO EMBLAZONMENT

WESTERN FRONT, 1914–1918 NEUVE CHAPPELLE YPRES, 1915 LOOS **SOMME, 1916** YPRES, 1917 AMIENS
HINDENBURG LINE EGYPT & LIBYA, 1940–1943 EL ALAMEIN **EL HAMMA ITALY, 1944–1945**
SOUTH EAST EUROPE, 1944–1945 GULF, 1991

HONOURS WITHOUT THE RIGHT TO EMBLAZONMENT

IRAQ, 1919–1920 KURDISTAN, 1922–1924 PALESTINE, 1936–1939

7 SQUADRON RAF

1st STANDARD PRESENTED 9 OCTOBER 1953 BY MRAF SIR JOHN SALMOND.
2nd STANDARD PRESENTED 8 JUNE 1978 BY HRH PRINCESS ALICE DUCHESS OF GLOUCESTER.

HONOURS WITH THE RIGHT TO EMBLAZONMENT

WESTERN FRONT, 1915–1918 YPRES, 1915 LOOS **SOMME, 1916** YPRES, 1917 **FORTRESS EUROPE, 1941–1944**
BISCAY PORTS, 1941–1944 RUHR, 1942–1945 GERMAN PORTS, 1942–1945 **BERLIN, 1943–1945**
FRANCE & GERMANY, 1944-1945 NORMANDY, 1944 RHINE GULF, 1991

8 SQUADRON RAF

1st STANDARD PRESENTED 9 APRIL 1954 BY SIR TOM HICKINBOTHAM.
2nd STANDARD PRESENTED 25 FEBRUARY 1967 BY HIS EXCELLENCY SIR RICHARD TURNBALL.
3rd STANDARD PRESENTED 28 MAY 1992 BY HRH THE DUKE OF GLOUCESTER.

HONOURS WITH THE RIGHT TO EMBLAZONMENT

WESTERN FRONT, 1915–1918 **LOOS** **SOMME, 1916** **ARRAS** **CAMBRAI, 1917** SOMME, 1918 AMIENS
HINDENBURG LINE **EAST AFRICA, 1940-1941 EASTERN WATERS, 1942–1945 BURMA, 1945**

HONOURS WITHOUT THE RIGHT TO EMBLAZONMENT

KURDISTAN, 1922–1924 ADEN, 1928 ADEN, 1934

9 SQUADRON RAF

1st STANDARD PRESENTED 9 OCTOBER 1956 BY ACM SIR HUGH LLOYD.
2nd STANDARD PRESENTED 23 MAY 1984 BY ACM SIR DAVID CRAIG.

HONOURS WITH THE RIGHT TO EMBLAZONMENT

WESTERN FRONT, 1915–1918 **SOMME, 1916** **YPRES, 1917** AMIENS HINDENBURG LINE
CHANNEL & NORTH SEA, 1939–1945 BALTIC, 1939–1945 FRANCE & LOW COUNTRIES, 1940 NORWAY, 1940
GERMAN PORTS, 1940–1945 **FORTRESS EUROPE, 1940–1944** **BERLIN, 1941–1945** BISCAY PORTS, 1940–1945
RUHR, 1941–1945 FRANCE & GERMANY, 1944–1945 **TIRPITZ** **THE DAMS** RHINE **GULF, 1991**

10 SQUADRON RAF

1st STANDARD PRESENTED 21 OCTOBER 1958 BY HRH THE PRINCESS MARGARET.
2nd STANDARD PRESENTED 30 SEPTEMBER 1988 BY RT HON MARGARET THATCHER.

HONOURS WITH THE RIGHT TO EMBLAZONMENT

WESTERN FRONT, 1915–1918 LOOS SOMME, 1916 **ARRAS** **SOMME, 1918** **INVASION PORTS, 1940**
CHANNEL & NORTH SEA, 1940–1945 NORWAY, 1940 **FORTRESS EUROPE, 1940–1944** BISCAY PORTS, 1940–1945
RUHR, 1940–1945 GERMAN PORTS, 1940-1945 **NORMANDY, 1944** **BERLIN, 1940–1945**
FRANCE & GERMANY, 1944-1945 RHINE

HONOURS WITHOUT THE RIGHT TO EMBLAZONMENT

GULF, 1991

11 SQUADRON RAF

1st STANDARD PRESENTED 28 AUGUST 1954 BY AM SIR OWEN JONES.
2nd STANDARD PRESENTED 17 AUGUST 1984 BY AVM P S COLLINS.

HONOURS WITH THE RIGHT TO EMBLAZONMENT

WESTERN FRONT, 1915–1918 **LOOS** SOMME, 1916 ARRAS **CAMBRAI, 1917** **SOMME, 1918** AMIENS
HINDENBURG LINE EAST AFRICA, 1940 **EGYPT & LIBYA, 1940–1942** GREECE, 1941 SYRIA, 1941
CEYLON, APRIL 1942 **ARAKAN, 1943–1944 NORTH BURMA, 1943–1944** MANIPUR, 1944 **BURMA, 1944–1945**

HONOURS WITHOUT THE RIGHT TO EMBLAZONMENT

NORTH WEST FRONTIER, 1930–1931 NORTH WEST FRONTIER, 1935–1939

12 SQUADRON RAF

1st STANDARD PRESENTED 23 JUNE 1954 BY MRAF THE LORD NEWALL.
2nd STANDARD PRESENTED 21 FEBRUARY 1975 BY AM SIR NIGEL MAYNARD.

HONOURS WITH THE RIGHT TO EMBLAZONMENT

WESTERN FRONT, 1915–1918 **LOOS** SOMME, 1916 ARRAS **CAMBRAI, 1917 SOMME, 1918** HINDENBURG LINE
FRANCE & LOW COUNTRIES, 1939–1940 **MEUSE BRIDGES** FORTRESS EUROPE, 1940–1944
GERMAN PORTS, 1941–1945 BISCAY PORTS, 1940–1945 **BERLIN, 1941–1945** **RUHR, 1941–1945**
FRANCE & GERMANY, 1944–1945 **RHINE GULF 1991;**

13 SQUADRON RAF

1st STANDARD PRESENTED 3 MAY 1957 BY FM SIR JOHN HARDING.
2nd STANDARD PRESENTED 12 FEBRUARY 1993 BY HRH THE DUKE OF KENT.

HONOURS WITH THE RIGHT TO EMBLAZONMENT

WESTERN FRONT, 1915–1918 SOMME, 1916 **ARRAS CAMBRAI, 1917 SOMME, 1918** HINDENBURG LINE
FRANCE & LOW COUNTRIES, 1939–1940 DIEPPE NORTH AFRICA, 1942–1943 MEDITERRANEAN, 1943
ITALY, 1944–1945 GUSTAV LINE GOTHIC LINE **GULF, 1991**

14 SQUADRON RAF

1st STANDARD PRESENTED 21 AUGUST 1954 BY AVM T C TRAILL.
2nd STANDARD PRESENTED 26 NOVEMBER 1982 BY ACM SIR KEITH WILLIAMSON.

HONOURS WITH THE RIGHT TO EMBLAZONMENT

EGYPT, 1915–1917 ARABIA, 1916–1917 PALESTINE, 1917–1918 GAZA MEGIDDO **EAST AFRICA, 1940–1941**
EGYPT & LIBYA, 1941–1942 MEDITERRANEAN, 1941–1943 SICILY, 1943 ATLANTIC, 1945 GULF, 1991

HONOURS WITHOUT THE RIGHT TO EMBLAZONMENT

TRANSJORDAN, 1924 PALESTINE,1936–1939

18 SQUADRON RAF

1st STANDARD PRESENTED 14 JUNE 1962 BY HRH THE PRINCESS MARGARET.
2nd STANDARD PRESENTED 3 FEBRUARY 1989 BY ACM SIR PETER HARDING.

HONOURS WITH THE RIGHT TO EMBLAZONMENT

WESTERN FRONT, 1915–1918 SOMME, 1916 **SOMME, 1918** LYS **HINDENBURG LINE**
FRANCE & LOW COUNTRIES, 1940 **INVASION PORTS, 1940** FORTRESS EUROPE, 1940–1942
CHANNEL & NORTH SEA, 1940–1941 GERMAN PORTS, 1940–1941 **MALTA, 1941–1942** EGYPT & LIBYA, 1942
NORTH AFRICA, 1942–1943 MEDITERRANEAN, 1943 SICILY, 1943 SALERNO SOUTH EAST EUROPE, 1943–1944
ITALY, 1943–1945 GOTHIC LINE **SOUTH ATLANTIC, 1982 GULF, 1991**

22 SQUADRON RAF

1st STANDARD PRESENTED 20 OCTOBER 1960 BY AM SIR RALPH SORLEY.
2nd STANDARD PRESENTED 15 MARCH 1978 BY ACM SIR DAVID EVANS.

HONOURS WITH THE RIGHT TO EMBLAZONMENT

WESTERN FRONT, 1916–1918 **SOMME, 1916** **YPRES, 1917** CAMBRAI, 1917 SOMME, 1918 LYS AMIENS
HINDENBURG LINE **CHANNEL & NORTH SEA, 1939–1941** FRANCE & LOW COUNTRIES, 1940
INVASION PORTS, 1940 BISCAY PORTS, 1940–1941 **MEDITERRANEAN, 1942** **EASTERN WATERS, 1942–1945**
BURMA, 1944–1945

23 SQUADRON RAF

1st STANDARD PRESENTED 28 JUNE 1957 BY MRAF SIR JOHN SLESSOR.
2nd STANDARD PRESENTED 2 FEBRUARY 1987 BY AM SIR ANTHONY SKINGSLEY.

HONOURS WITH THE RIGHT TO EMBLAZONMENT

HOME DEFENCE, 1916 WESTERN FRONT, 1916–1918 SOMME, 1916 ARRAS **YPRES, 1917** **SOMME, 1918**
CHANNEL & NORTH SEA, 1939–1940 FORTRESS EUROPE, 1940-1944 **NORTH AFRICA, 1943** SICILY, 1943
ITALY, 1943–1944 **ANZIO & NETTUNO** **FRANCE & GERMANY, 1944–1945** RUHR, 1944–1945

24 SQUADRON RAF

1st STANDARD PRESENTED 4 MARCH 1954 BY AM SIR CHARLES E N GUEST.
2nd STANDARD PRESENTED 15 SEPTEMBER 1981 BY HRH THE PRINCESS ANNE.

HONOURS WITH THE RIGHT TO EMBLAZONMENT

WESTERN FRONT, 1916–1918 **SOMME, 1916** SOMME, 1918 **AMIENS** **HINDENBURG LINE**
FRANCE & LOW COUNTRIES, 1939–1940 **MALTA, 1942** **NORTH AFRICA, 1942–1943** ITALY, 1943–1944
BURMA, 1944–1945

HONOURS WITHOUT THE RIGHT TO EMBLAZONMENT

GULF, 1991

25 SQUADRON RAF

1st STANDARD PRESENTED 21 JUNE 1954 BY AM SIR DERMOT BOYLE.
2nd STANDARD PRESENTED 15 MAY 1984 BY ACM SIR THOMAS KENNEDY.

HONOURS WITH THE RIGHT TO EMBLAZONMENT

HOME DEFENCE, 1916 **WESTERN FRONT, 1916–1918** SOMME, 1916 ARRAS **YPRES, 1917** **CAMBRAI, 1917**
SOMME, 1918 LYS HINDENBURG LINE CHANNEL & NORTH SEA, 1939–1941 **BATTLE OF BRITAIN, 1940**
FORTRESS EUROPE, 1943–1944 HOME DEFENCE, 1940–1945 **FRANCE & GERMANY, 1944–1945**

27 SQUADRON RAF

1st STANDARD PRESENTED 7 JANUARY 1955 BY AVM A E BORTON.
2nd STANDARD PRESENTED 22 JUNE 1979 BY ACM SIR DAVID EVANS.

HONOURS WITH THE RIGHT TO EMBLAZONMENT

WESTERN FRONT, 1916–1918 SOMME, 1916 ARRAS **YPRES, 1917 CAMBRAI, 1917** SOMME, 1918 LYS AMIENS
HINDENBURG LINE **MALAYA, 1941–1942 ARAKAN, 1942–1944 NORTH BURMA, 1944 BURMA, 1944–1945**
GULF, 1991

HONOURS WITHOUT THE RIGHT TO EMBLAZONMENT

MAHSUD, 1920 WAZIRISTAN, 1920–1925 MOHMAND, 1927
NORTH WEST FRONTIER, 1930–1931 MOHMAND, 1933
NORTH WEST FRONTIER, 1935–1939

28 SQUADRON RAF

1st STANDARD PRESENTED 16 MARCH 1955 BY AM F J FRESSANGES.
2nd STANDARD PRESENTED 29 JUNE 1977 BY HE SIR MURRAY MACLEHOSE.

HONOURS WITH THE RIGHT TO EMBLAZONMENT

ITALIAN FRONT & ADRIATIC, 1917–1918 PIAVE VITTORIO VENETO BURMA, 1942 ARAKAN, 1943–1944
MANIPUR, 1944 BURMA, 1944–1945

HONOURS WITHOUT THE RIGHT TO EMBLAZONMENT

WAZIRISTAN, 1921–1925 NORTH WEST FRONTIER, 1939

30 SQUADRON RAF

1st STANDARD PRESENTED 1 JULY 1954 BY ACM SIR JAMES M ROBB.
2nd STANDARD PRESENTED 18 MAY 1978 BY HRH THE PRINCESS ANNE.

HONOURS WITH THE RIGHT TO EMBLAZONMENT

EGYPT, 1915 MESOPOTAMIA, 1915–1918 EGYPT & LIBYA, 1940–1942 GREECE, 1940–1941
MEDITERRANEAN, 1940–1941 CEYLON APRIL, 1942 ARAKAN, 1944 BURMA, 1944–1945

HONOURS WITHOUT THE RIGHT TO EMBLAZONMENT

IRAQ, 1919-1920 NORTH WEST PERSIA, 1920 KURDISTAN, 1922–1924 IRAQ, 1923–1925 IRAQ, 1928–1929
KURDISTAN, 1930–1931 NORTHERN KURDISTAN, 1932 GULF, 1991

31 SQUADRON RAF

1st STANDARD PRESENTED 13 SEPTEMBER 1956 BY ACM SIR ALEC CORYTON.
2nd STANDARD PRESENTED 14 NOVEMBER 1986 BY AM SIR LESLIE MAVOR.

HONOURS WITH THE RIGHT TO EMBLAZONMENT

NORTH WEST FRONTIER, 1916–1918   IRAQ, 1941   SYRIA, 1941   **EGYPT & LIBYA, 1941–1942   BURMA, 1941–1942
NORTH BURMA, 1943–1944   ARAKAN, 1943–1944   MANIPUR, 1944   BURMA, 1944–1945**   GULF, 1991

HONOURS WITHOUT THE RIGHT TO EMBLAZONMENT

AFGHANISTAN, 1919   MAHSUD, 1919–1920   WAZIRISTAN,1919–1925   NORTH WEST FRONTIER, 1939

32 (THE ROYAL) SQUADRON RAF

1st STANDARD PRESENTED 6 JUNE 1957 BY ACM SIR JAMES M ROBB.
2nd STANDARD PRESENTED 6 JUNE 1987 BY ACM SIR MICHAEL KNIGHT.

HONOURS WITH THE RIGHT TO EMBLAZONMENT

WESTERN FRONT, 1916–1918   **SOMME, 1916–1918**   ARRAS   **YPRES, 1917**   **AMIENS
FRANCE & LOW COUNTRIES, 1939–1940   BATTLE OF BRITAIN, 1940**   HOME DEFENCE, 1940–1942   **DIEPPE
NORTH AFRICA, 1942–1943**   ITALY, 1943   **SOUTH EAST EUROPE, 1944–1945**

HONOURS WITHOUT THE RIGHT TO EMBLAZONMENT

GULF, 1991

33 SQUADRON RAF

1st STANDARD PRESENTED 24 APRIL 1958 BY ACM SIR PHILIP JOUBERT de la FERTE.
2nd STANDARD PRESENTED 19 MAY 1988 BY ACM SIR DENIS SMALLWOOD.

HONOURS WITH THE RIGHT TO EMBLAZONMENT

**HOME DEFENCE, 1916–1918   EGYPT & LIBYA, 1940–1943   GREECE, 1941   EL ALAMEIN
FRANCE & GERMANY, 1944–1945   NORMANDY, 1944   WALCHEREN   RHINE   GULF, 1991**

HONOURS WITHOUT THE RIGHT TO EMBLAZONMENT

PALESTINE, 1936–1939

39(1 PRU) SQUADRON RAF

1st STANDARD PRESENTED 26 JUNE 1954 BY AM SIR CLAUDE B R PELLY.
2nd STANDARD PRESENTED 25 SEPTEMBER 1981 BY ACM SIR KEITH WILLIAMSON.

HONOURS WITH THE RIGHT TO EMBLAZONMENT

**HOME DEFENCE, 1916–1918   EAST AFRICA, 1940   EGYPT & LIBYA, 1940–1943   GREECE, 1941
MEDITERRANEAN, 1941–1943   MALTA, 1942   NORTH AFRICA, 1942–1943   SOUTH EAST EUROPE, 1944–45**

HONOURS WITHOUT THE RIGHT TO EMBLAZONMENT

NORTH WEST FRONTIER, 1930–1931   MOHMAND, 1933   NORTH WEST FRONTIER, 1935–1939

41 SQUADRON RAF

1st STANDARD PRESENTED 14 JULY 1957 BY AM SIR THEODORE MCEVOY.
2nd STANDARD PRESENTED 5 DECEMBER 1985 BY ACM SIR PETER HARDING.

HONOURS WITH THE RIGHT TO EMBLAZONMENT

WESTERN FRONT, 1916–1918 **SOMME, 1916** ARRAS **CAMBRAI, 1917** SOMME, 1918 LYS **AMIENS**
BATTLE OF BRITAIN, 1940 HOME DEFENCE, 1940–1944 **FORTRESS EUROPE, 1940–1944** **DIEPPE**
FRANCE & GERMANY, 1944–1945 ARNHEM WALCHEREN GULF, 1991

43 SQUADRON RAF

1st STANDARD PRESENTED 4 JUNE 1957 BY HM QUEEN ELIZABETH II.
2nd STANDARD PRESENTED 26 MAY 1988 BY HM QUEEN ELIZABETH II.

HONOURS WITH THE RIGHT TO EMBLAZONMENT

WESTERN FRONT, 1917–1918 ARRAS **YPRES, 1917** CAMBRAI, 1917 **SOMME, 1918** LYS AMIENS **DUNKIRK**
BATTLE OF BRITAIN, 1940 HOME DEFENCE, 1940–1942 FORTRESS EUROPE, 1942 DIEPPE
NORTH AFRICA, 1942–1943 SICILY, 1943 SALERNO ITALY, 1943–1945 **ANZIO & NETTUNO** GUSTAV LINE
FRANCE & GERMANY, 1944

HONOURS WITHOUT THE RIGHT TO EMBLAZONMENT

GULF, 1991

47 SQUADRON RAF

1st STANDARD PRESENTED 25 MARCH 1955 BY MRAF SIR JOHN SLESSOR.
2nd STANDARD PRESENTED 3 MAY 1984 BY HRH THE PRINCESS ANNE.

HONOURS WITH THE RIGHT TO ENBLAZONMENT

MACEDONIA, 1916–1918 **EAST AFRICA, 1940–1941** **EGYPT & LIBYA, 1942** **MEDITERRANEAN, 1942–1943**
BURMA, 1945

HONOURS WITHOUT THE RIGHT TO EMBLAZONMENT

SOUTH ATLANTIC, 1982 GULF, 1991

51 SQUADRON RAF

1st STANDARD PRESENTED 9 JULY 1968 BY ACM SIR WALLACE KYLE.
2nd STANDARD PRESENTED 11 NOVEMBER 1999 BY HRH THE DUKE OF GLOUCESTER.

HONOURS WITH THE RIGHT TO EMBLAZONMENT

HOME DEFENCE, 1916–1918 CHANNEL & NORTH SEA, 1940–1943 **NORWAY, 1940**
FRANCE & LOW COUNTRIES, 1940 **RUHR, 1940–1945** **FORTRESS EUROPE, 1940–1944** GERMAN PORTS, 1940–1945
INVASION PORTS, 1940 BISCAY PORTS, 1940–1944 BERLIN, 1940–1944 **BALTIC, 1940–1944** BISCAY, 1942
ITALY, 1943 **FRANCE & GERMANY, 1944–1945** NORMANDY, 1944 WALCHEREN RHINE

HONOURS WITHOUT THE RIGHT TO EMBLAZONMENT

SOUTH ATLANTIC, 1982 GULF, 1991

54 SQUADRON RAF

1st STANDARD PRESENTED 24 MAY 1963 BY MAJOR K K HORN RFC.
2nd STANDARD PRESENTED 21 JANUARY 1988 BY ACM SIR PETER HARDING.

HONOURS WITH THE RIGHT TO EMBLAZONMENT

WESTERN FRONT, 1916–1918 **ARRAS YPRES, 1917 CAMBRAI, 1917 AMIENS** HOME DEFENCE, 1940–1945 FRANCE & LOW COUNTRIES, 1940 **DUNKIRK BATTLE OF BRITAIN, 1940 FORTRESS EUROPE, 1941 EASTERN WATERS, 1943–1945** GULF, 1991

70 SQUADRON RAF

1st STANDARD PRESENTED 16 JULY 1955 BY AVM SIR HAZELTON NICHOLL.
2nd STANDARD PRESENTED 3 MAY 1984 BY HRH THE PRINCESS ANNE.

HONOURS WITH THE RIGHT TO EMBLAZONMENT

WESTERN FRONT, 1916–1918 SOMME, 1916 ARRAS **YPRES, 1917** SOMME, 1918 MEDITERRANEAN, 1940–1943 **EGYPT & LIBYA, 1940–1943** GREECE, 1940–1941 SYRIA, 1941 **IRAQ, 1941** EL ALAMEIN **NORTH AFRICA, 1942–1943** EL HAMMA SICILY, 1943 **ITALY, 1943–1945** SALERNO ANZIO & NETTUNO GUSTAV LINE GOTHIC LINE **SOUTH EAST EUROPE, 1944–1945**

HONOURS WITHOUT THE RIGHT TO EMBLAZONMENT

KURDISTAN, 1922–1924 IRAQ, 1928–1929 KURDISTAN, 1930–1931 NORTHERN KURDISTAN, 1932 NORTH WEST FRONTIER, 1937 SOUTH ATLANTIC, 1982 GULF, 1991

78 SQUADRON RAF

STANDARD PRESENTED 11 FEBRUARY 1965 BY Lt Gen SIR CHARLES HARINGTON.

HONOURS WITH THE RIGHT TO EMBLAZONMENT

HOME DEFENCE, 1916–1918 FORTRESS EUROPE, 1940–1944 RUHR, 1940–1945 INVASION PORTS, 1940 BISCAY PORTS, 1940–1943 **BERLIN, 1940–1944 CHANNEL & NORTH SEA, 1942–1945 NORMANDY, 1944** WALCHEREN **FRANCE & GERMANY, 1944–1945 RHINE**

84 SQUADRON RAF

1st STANDARD PRESENTED 5 JANUARY 1956 BY ACM SIR FRANCIS FOGARTY.
2nd STANDARD PRESENTED 23 OCTOBER 1980 BY AM SIR KEITH WILLIAMSON.
3rd STANDARD PRESENTED 8 NOVEMBER 2001 BY AVM T. W. RIMMER.

HONOURS WITH THE RIGHT TO EMBLAZONMENT

WESTERN FRONT, 1917–1918 CAMBRAI, 1917 **SOMME, 1918** AMIENS **HINDENBURG LINE EGYPT & LIBYA, 1940–1942 GREECE, 1940–1941 IRAQ, 1941** HABBANIYA SYRIA, 1941 **MALAYA, 1942 NORTH BURMA, 1944** MANIPUR, 1944

HONOURS WITHOUT THE RIGHT TO EMBLAZONMENT

IRAQ, 1920 IRAQ, 1923–1925 IRAQ, 1928–1929

99 SQUADRON RAF

STANDARD PRESENTED 27 SEPTEMBER 1957 BY ACM SIR RONALD IVELAW-CHAPMAN.

HONOURS WITH THE RIGHT TO EMBLAZONMENT

WESTERN FRONT, 1917–1918 INDEPENDENT FORCE & GERMAY, 1918 GERMAN PORTS, 1940–1941 **BALTIC, 1940–1941 FRANCE & LOW COUNTRIES, 1940 FORTRESS EUROPE, 1940–1942 RUHR, 1940–1942 BERLIN, 1940–1942** BISCAY PORTS, 1940 **ARAKAN, 1942–1944 BURMA, 1944–1945** MANIPUR, 1944 **EASTERN WATERS, 1945**

HONOURS WITHOUT THE RIGHT TO EMBLAZONMENT

MAHSUD, 1919–1920 WAZIRISTAN, 1919–1920

100 SQUADRON RAF

1st STANDARD PRESENTED 21 OCTOBER 1955 BY AM SIR GEORGE MILLS.
2nd STANDARD PRESENTED 14 DECEMBER 1984 BY MRAF SIR MICHAEL BEETHAM.

HONOURS WITH THE RIGHT TO EMBLAZONMENT

WESTERN FRONT, 1917–1918 **YPRES, 1917 SOMME, 1918 INDEPENDENT FORCE & GERMANY, 1918 MALAYA, 1941–1942 FORTRESS EUROPE, 1943–1944** BISCAY PORTS, 1943–1945 **RUHR, 1943–1945 BERLIN, 1943–1945** GERMAN PORTS, 1943–1945 BALTIC, 1943–1945 FRANCE & GERMANY, 1944–1945 **NORMANDY, 1944** WALCHEREN

101 SQUADRON RAF

1st STANDARD PRESENTED 14 JUNE 1962 BY HRH THE PRINCESS MARGARET.
2nd STANDARD PRESENTED 24 JUNE 1988 BY ACM SIR PETER HARDING.

HONOURS WITH THE RIGHT TO EMBLAZONMENT

WESTERN FRONT, 1917–1918 YPRES, 1917 SOMME, 1918 LYS HINDENBURG LINE **FORTRESS EUROPE, 1940–1944 INVASION PORTS, 1940 RUHR, 1940–1945 BERLIN, 1941** CHANNEL & NORTH SEA, 1941–1944 BISCAY PORTS, 1941–1944 GERMAN PORTS, 1941–1944 BALTIC, 1942–1945 BERLIN, 1943–1944 FRANCE & GERMANY, 1944–1945 **NORMANDY, 1944** WALCHEREN

HONOURS WITHOUT THE RIGHT TO EMBLAZONMENT

SOUTH ATLANTIC, 1982 GULF, 1991

111 SQUADRON RAF

1st STANDARD PRESENTED 30 APRIL 1957 BY ACM SIR HARRY BROADHURST.
2nd STANDARD PRESENTED 2 AUGUST 1987 BY ACM SIR PATRICK HINE.

HONOURS WITH THE RIGHT TO EMBLAZONMENT

PALESTINE, 1917–1918 MEGIDDO **HOME DEFENCE, 1940–1942** FRANCE & LOW COUNTRIES, 1940 **DUNKIRK BATTLE OF BRITAIN, 1940 FORTRESS EUROPE, 1941–1942** DIEPPE **NORTH AFRICA, 1942–1943** SICILY, 1943 **ITALY, 1943–1945** SALERNO ANZIO & NETTUNO GUSTAV LINE **FRANCE & GERMANY, 1944**

120 SQUADRON RAF

1st STANDARD PRESENTED 14 AUGUST 1961 BY HM QUEEN ELIZABETH II.
2nd STANDARD PRESENTED 26 MAY 1988 BY HRH THE DUKE OF EDINBURGH.

HONOURS WITH THE RIGHT TO ENBLAZONMENT

ATLANTIC, 1941–1945   BISCAY, 1941–1944   ARCTIC, 1942–1944   CHANNEL & NORTH ATLANTIC, 1941–1944

HONOURS WITHOUT THE RIGHT TO EMBLAZONMENT

SOUTH ATLANTIC, 1982   GULF, 1991

201 SQUADRON RAF

1st STANDARD PRESENTED 16 DECEMBER 1955 BY AVM G W TUTTLE.
2nd STANDARD PRESENTED 9 NOVEMBER 1984 BY HRH THE DUKE OF EDINBURGH.

HONOURS WITH THE RIGHT TO EMBLAZONMENT

WESTERN FRONT, 1915–1918   ARRAS   YPRES, 1917   SOMME, 1918   AMIENS   HINDENBURG LINE
CHANNEL & NORTH SEA, 1939–1945   NORWAY, 1940   ATLANTIC, 1941–1945   BISMARCK   BISCAY, 1941–1945
NORMANDY, 1944

HONOURS WITHOUT THE RIGHT TO EMBLAZONMENT

SOUTH ATLANTIC, 1982   GULF, 1991

202 SQUADRON RAF

1st STANDARD PRESENTED 6 SEPTEMBER 1957 BY ACM SIR DOUGLAS EVILL.
2nd STANDARD PRESENTED 16 JUNE 1987 BY ACM SIR PETER TERRY.

HONOURS WITH THE RIGHT TO EMBLAZONMENT

**WESTERN FRONT, 1916–1918   ATLANTIC, 1939–1945   MEDITERRANEAN, 1940–1943   NORTH AFRICA, 1942–1943
BISCAY, 1942–1944**

206 SQUADRON RAF

1st STANDARD PRESENTED ON 28 JULY 1966 BY HRH THE PRINCESS MARGARET.
2nd STANDARD PRESENTED 21 MAY 1992 BY HRH THE DUKE OF EDINBURGH.

HONOURS WITH THE RIGHT TO EMBLAZONMENT

WESTERN FRONT, 1916–1918   ARRAS, 1917   LYS   **CHANNEL & NORTH SEA, 1939–1945   ATLANTIC 1939, 1941–1945
DUNKIRK**   INVASION PORTS, 1940   **FORTRESS EUROPE, 1940, 1942**   GERMAN PORTS, 1940, 1942
BISCAY, 1941, 1943–1944   BISMARCK   BALTIC, 1945

HONOURS WITHOUT THE RIGHT TO EMBLAZONMENT

SOUTH ATLANTIC, 1982   GULF, 1991

216 SQUADRON RAF

1st STANDARD PRESENTED ON 24 MAY 1957 BY ACM SIR DONALD HARDMAN.
2nd STANDARD PRESENTED ON 24 JUNE 1988 BY ACM SIR PETER HARDING.

HONOURS WITH THE RIGHT TO EMBLAZONMENT

INDEPENDENT FORCE & GERMANY, 1917–1918   GREECE, 1940–1941   EGYPT & LIBYA, 1940–1942   SYRIA, 1941
EL ALAMEIN   EL HAMMA   NORTH AFRICA, 1943   MEDITERRANEAN, 1943   MANIPUR, 1944   NORTH BURMA, 1944
SOUTH EAST EUROPE, 1944–1945

HONOURS WITHOUT THE RIGHT TO EMBLAZONMENT

GULF, 1991

230 SQUADRON RAF

1st STANDARD PRESENTED ON 26 OCTOBER 1962 BY HRH THE DUKE OF GLOUCESTER.
2nd STANDARD PRESENTED ON 27 OCTOBER 1992 BY HRH THE DUKE OF GLOUCESTER.

HONOURS WITH THE RIGHT TO EMBLAZONMENT

HOME WATERS, 1918   MEDITERRANEAN, 1940–1943   EGYPT & LIBYA, 1940–1943   GREECE, 1940–1941
MALTA, 1940–1942   EASTERN WATERS, 1943–1945   NORTH BURMA, 1944   BURMA, 1945   GULF, 1991

617 SQUADRON RAF

1st STANDARD PRESENTED ON 14 MAY 1959 BY HM QUEEN ELIZABETH II.
2nd STANDARD PRESENTED ON 13 JANUARY 1988 BY HM QUEEN ELIZABETH THE QUEEN MOTHER.

HONOURS WITH THE RIGHT TO EMBLAZONMENT

FORTRESS EUROPE, 1943–1944   THE DAMS   BISCAY PORTS, 1944   FRANCE & GERMANY, 1944–1945
NORMANDY, 1944   TIRPITZ   CHANNEL & NORTH SEA, 1944–1945   GERMAN PORTS, 1945   GULF, 1991

RAF RESERVE SQUADRONS

15 (RESERVE) SQUADRON RAF

1st STANDARD PRESENTED ON 3 MAY 1961 BY HRH PRINCESS MARINA, DUCHESS OF KENT.
2nd STANDARD PRESENTED ON 8 MAY 1981 BY SQN LDR P J S BOGGIS.

HONOURS WITH THE RIGHT TO EMBLAZONMENT

WESTERN FRONT, 1915–1918   SOMME, 1916   ARRAS   CAMBRAI, 1917   SOMME, 1918   HINDENBURG LINE
FRANCE & LOW COUNTRIES, 1939–1940   MEUSE   BRIDGES   DUNKIRK   INVASION PORTS, 1940
FORTRESS EUROPE, 1941–1944   RUHR, 1941–1945   BERLIN, 1941–1945   BISCAY PORTS, 1941–1945
FRANCE & GERMANY, 1944–1945   NORMANDY, 1944   GULF, 1991

16 (RESERVE) SQUADRON RAF

1st STANDARD PRESENTED ON 6 APRIL 1956 BY HRH PRINCESS MARINA, DUCHESS OF KENT.
2nd STANDARD PRESENTED ON 12 JULY 1985 BY AVM D PARRY-EVANS.

HONOURS WITH THE RIGHT TO EMBLAZONMENT

WESTERN FRONT, 1915–1918   NEUVE CHAPPELLE   LOOS   **SOMME, 1916**   **ARRAS**   **YPRES, 1917**
FRANCE & LOW COUNTRIES, 1940   **DUNKIRK**   **FORTRESS EUROPE, 1943–1944**   FRANCE & GERMANY, 1944
NORMANDY, 1944   ARNHEM   RUHR, 1944–1945   GULF, 1991

19 (RESERVE) SQUADRON RAF

1st STANDARD PRESENTED ON 6 APRIL 1956 BY ACM SIR DONALD HARDMAN.
2nd STANDARD PRESENTED ON 19 JANUARY 1988 BY AM SIR ANTHONY SKINGSLEY.

HONOURS WITH THE RIGHT TO EMBLAZONMENT

WESTERN FRONT, 1916–1918   SOMME, 1916   ARRAS   **YPRES, 1917**   SOMME, 1918   LYS   AMIENS
HINDENBURG LINE   **DUNKIRK**   HOME DEFENCE, 1940–1942   **BATTLE OF BRITAIN, 1940**
CHANNEL & NORTH SEA, 1941–1942   **FORTRESS EUROPE, 1942–1944**   DIEPPE   **NORMANDY, 1944   ARNHEM**
FRANCE & GERMANY, 1944–1945

20 (RESERVE) SQUADRON RAF

1st STANDARD PRESENTED ON 13 JULY 1954 BY HRH THE PRINCESS MARGARET.
2nd STANDARD PRESENTED ON 26 NOVEMBER 1982 BY ACM SIR KEITH WILLIAMSON.

HONOURS WITH THE RIGHT TO EMBLAZONMENT

WESTERN FRONT, 1916–1918   **SOMME, 1916   ARRAS   YPRES, 1917   SOMME, 1918**   LYS   HINDENBURG LINE
NORTH BURMA, 1943–1944   ARAKAN, 1943–1944   MANIPUR, 1944   BURMA, 1944–1945   GULF, 1991

HONOURS WITHOUT THE RIGHT TO EMBLAZONMENT

MAHSUD, 1919–1920   WAZIRISTAN, 1919–1925   MOHMAND, 1927   NORTH WEST FRONTIER, 1930–1931
MOHMAND, 1933   NORTH WEST FRONTIER, 1935–1939

42 (RESERVE) SQUADRON RAF

STANDARD PRESENTED ON 14 JULY 1966 BY HM QUEEN ELIZABETH II.

HONOURS WITH THE RIGHT TO EMBLAZONMENT

WESTERN FRONT, 1916–1918   ITALIAN FRONT & ADRIATIC, 1917–1918   SOMME, 1916   ARRAS, 1917   YPRES, 1917
LYS   **CHANNEL & NORTH SEA, 1939–1942**   BISCAY, 1940   BALTIC, 1941   FORTRESS EUROPE, 1941
PACIFIC, 1943–1945   **EASTERN WATERS, 1943   ARAKAN, 1943–1944   MANIPUR, 1944**   BURMA, 1944–1945

HONOURS WITHOUT THE RIGHT TO EMBLAZONMENT

SOUTH ATLANTIC, 1982   GULF, 1991

45 (RESERVE) SQUADRON RAF

1st STANDARD PRESENTED 9 FEBRUARY 1955 BY AM F J FRESSANGES.
2nd STANDARD PRESENTED 4 OCTOBER 1994 BY ACM SIR ANDREW WILSON.

HONOURS WITH THE RIGHT TO EMBLAZONMENT

WESTERN FRONT, 1916–1917   SOMME, 1916   YPRES, 1917   **ITALIAN FRONT & ADRIATIC, 1917–1918**   PIAVE
INDEPENDENT FORCE & GERMANY, 1918   **EGYPT & LIBYA, 1940–1942**   **EAST AFRICA, 1940**   SYRIA,1941
BURMA, 1942   **ARAKAN, 1943–1944**   **BURMA, 1944–1945**

HONOURS WITHOUT THE RIGHT TO EMBLAZONMENT

KURDISTAN, 1922–1924   IRAQ, 1923–1925

55 (RESERVE) SQUADRON RAF

1st STANDARD PRESENTED 20 JULY 1962 BY HRH PRINCESS MARINA, DUCHESS OF KENT.

HONOURS WITH THE RIGHT TO EMBLAZONMENT

WESTERN FRONT, 1917–1918   ARRAS   **YPRES, 1917**   **INDEPENDENT FORCE & GERMANY, 1918**
EGYPT & LIBYA, 1940–1943   **EL ALAMEIN**   **EL HAMMA**   NORTH AFRICA, 1943   SICILY, 1943   SALERNO
ITALY, 1943–1945   GUSTAV LINE   **GOTHIC LINE**

HONOURS WITHOUT THE RIGHT TO EMBLAZONMENT

IRAQ, 1920   KURDISTAN, 1922–1924   IRAQ, 1928–1929   KURDISTAN, 1930–1931   NORTHERN KURDISTAN, 1932
SOUTH ATLANTIC, 1982   GULF, 1991

56 (RESERVE) SQUADRON RAF

1st STANDARD PRESENTED 27 APRIL 1956 BY HRH PRINCESS MARINA, DUCHESS OF KENT.
2nd STANDARD PRESENTED ON 23 OCTOBER 1986 BY ACM SIR JOHN ROGERS.

HONOURS WITH THE RIGHT TO EMBLAZONMENT

WESTERN FRONT, 1917–1918   ARRAS   **YPRES, 1917**   CAMBRAI, 1917   **SOMME, 1918**   AMIENS   HINDENBURG LINE
FRANCE & LOW COUNTRIES, 1940   **DUNKIRK**   **BATTLE OF BRITAIN, 1940**   FORTRESS EUROPE, 1942–1944   DIEPPE
FRANCE & GERMANY, 1944–1945   **NORMANDY, 1944**   HOME DEFENCE, 1942–1945   **ARNHEM**

60 (RESERVE) SQUADRON RAF

1st STANDARD PRESENTED 6 MAY 1955 BY ACM SIR JOHN BAKER.
2nd STANDARD PRESENTED 18 MAY 1984 BY ACM SIR DAVID LEE.

HONOURS WITH THE RIGHT TO EMBLAZONMENT

WESTERN FRONT, 1916-1918   **SOMME, 1916**   ARRAS   SOMME, 1918   **HINDENBURG LINE**   **BURMA, 1941–1942**
MALAYA, 1941–1942   **ARAKAN, 1942–1944**   NORTH BURMA, 1944   **MANIPUR, 1944**   **BURMA, 1944–1945**

HONOURS WITHOUT THE RIGHT TO EMBLAZONMENT

WAZIRISTAN, 1920–1925   MOHMAND, 1927   NORTH WEST FRONTIER, 1930–1931   MOHMAND, 1933
NORTH WEST FRONTIER, 1935–1939

203 (RESERVE) SQUADRON RAF

STANDARD PRESENTED 6 JUNE 1963 BY HRH THE PRINCESS MARGARET.

HONOURS WITH THE RIGHT TO EMBLAZONMENT

WESTERN FRONT, 1914–1918 INDEPENDENT FORCE & GERMANY, 1914–1918 AEGEAN, 1915 HELLES **ANZAC** SUVLA **ARRAS** LYS **SOMME, 1918** HINDENBURG LINE EAST AFRICA, 1940–1941 **MEDITERRANEAN, 1941–1943 IRAQ, 1941** HABBANIYA SYRIA, 1941 EGYPT & LIBYA, 1941–1942 NORTH AFRICA, 1943 SICILY, 1943 EASTERN WATERS, 1944–1945 **BURMA, 1945**

208 (RESERVE) SQUADRON RAF

1st STANDARD PRESENTED 18 NOVEMBER 1955 BY AVM SIR GEOFFREY BROMET.
2nd STANDARD PRESENTED 1 JUNE 1984 BY SIR HUMPHREY EDWARDES-JONES.

HONOURS WITH THE RIGHT TO EMBLAZONMENT

WESTERN FRONT, 1916–1918 ARRAS YPRES, 1917 LYS **SOMME, 1918 EGYPT & LIBYA, 1940–1942 GREECE, 1941** IRAQ, 1941 SYRIA, 1941 **EL ALAMEIN ITALY, 1944–1945** GUSTAV LINE GOTHIC LINE **GULF, 1991**

ROYAL AIR FORCE REGIMENT SQUADRONS

1 SQUADRON RAF REGIMENT

1st STANDARD PRESENTED 8 APRIL 1959 BY AM SIR HUGH CONSTANTINE.
2nd STANDARD PRESENTED 3 NOVEMBER 1988 BY AM SIR HUGH SKINGSLEY.

HONOURS WITH THE RIGHT TO EMBLAZONMENT

IRAQ, 1941 HABBANIYA EGYPT & LIBYA, 1941–1943 GULF, 1991

HONOURS WITHOUT THE RIGHT TO EMBLAZONMENT

KURDISTAN, 1922–1923 KURDISTAN, 1930–1931 PALESTINE, 1936

2 SQUADRON RAF REGIMENT

1st STANDARD PRESENTED 25 NOVEMBER 1959 BY ACM SIR HUBERT PATCH.
2nd STANDARD PRESENTED 5 JUNE 1989 BY ACM SIR PATRICK HINE.

HONOURS WITH THE RIGHT TO EMBLAZONMENT

EGYPT & LIBYA, 1940–1943 IRAQ, 1941 SYRIA, 1941 EL ALAMEIN NORTH AFRICA, 1943

HONOURS WITHOUT THE RIGHT TO EMBLAZONMENT

TRANSJORDAN, 1924 PALESTINE, 1936–1939

3 SQUADRON RAF REGIMENT

STANDARD PRESENTED 15 JUNE 1996 BY HRH THE DUKE OF YORK.

HONOURS WITH THE RIGHT TO EMBLAZONMENT

FRANCE & GERMANY, 1944–45

HONOURS WITHOUT THE RIGHT TO EMBLAZONMENT

IRAQ, 1923–1925

15 SQUADRON RAF REGIMENT

STANDARD PRESENTED 10 OCTOBER 1975 BY ACM SIR ANDREW HUMPHREY.

16 SQUADRON RAF REGIMENT

STANDARD PRESENTED 26 MAY 1977 BY AM SIR MICHAEL BEETHAM.

26 SQUADRON RAF REGIMENT

STANDARD PRESENTED ON 28 NOVEMBER 1979 BY AM SIR PETER TERRY.

HONOURS WITHOUT THE RIGHT TO EMBLAZONMENT

GULF, 1991

27 SQUADRON RAF REGIMENT

STANDARD PRESENTED ON 4 JUNE 1980 BY ACM SIR DAVID EVANS.

34 SQUADRON RAF REGIMENT

1st STANDARD PRESENTED ON 4 OCTOBER 1979 BY ACM SIR DAVID EVANS.
2nd STANDARD PRESENTED ON 20 MAY 1999 BY ACM SIR PETER SQUIRE.

HONOURS WITHOUT THE RIGHT TO EMBLAZONMENT

GULF, 1991

37 SQUADRON RAF REGIMENT

STANDARD PRESENTED ON 26 NOVEMBER 1980 BY AM SIR PETER TERRY.

51 SQUADRON RAF REGIMENT

STANDARD PRESENTED ON 22 DECEMBER 1977 BY AM P D G TERRY.

HONOURS WITH THE RIGHT TO EMBLAZONMENT

FRANCE & GERMANY, 1944–1945

HONOURS WITHOUT THE RIGHT TO EMBLAZONMENT

GULF, 1991

THE QUEEN'S COLOUR SQUADRON OF THE RAF—63 SQUADRON RAF REGIMENT

STANDARD PRESENTED ON 27 MAY 1976 BY HRH THE PRINCESS ANNE.

HONOURS WITH THE RIGHT TO EMBLAZONMENT

ITALY, 1943–1944   FRANCE & GERMANY, 1945   SOUTH ATLANTIC, 1982

QUEEN'S COLOURS TO THE ROYAL AIR FORCE

RAF COLLEGE CRANWELL

1st COLOUR PRESENTED ON 6 JULY 1948 BY HM KING GEORGE VI.
2nd COLOUR PRESENTED ON 25 JULY 1960 BY HM QUEEN ELIZABETH II.
3rd COLOUR PRESENTED ON 30 MAY 1975 BY HM QUEEN ELIZABETH II.
4th COLOUR PRESENTED ON 27 JULY 1989 BY HM QUEEN ELIZABETH II.
5th COLOUR PRESENTED ON 24 JULY 2001 BY HRH THE PRINCE OF WALES.

RAF IN THE UNITED KINGDOM

1st COLOUR PRESENTED ON 26 MAY 1951 BY HRH THE PRINCESS ELIZABETH.
2nd COLOUR PRESENTED ON 3 JULY 1964 BY HM QUEEN ELIZABETH II.
3rd COLOUR PRESENTED ON 29 JULY 1977 BY HM QUEEN ELIZABETH II.
4th COLOUR PRESENTED ON 1 APRIL 1993 BY HM QUEEN ELIZABETH II.

No 1 SCHOOL OF TECHNICAL TRAINING

1st COLOUR PRESENTED ON 25 JULY 1952 BY HM QUEEN ELIZABETH II.
2nd COLOUR PRESENTED ON 6 APRIL 1968 BY HRH THE PRINCESS MARGARET.
3rd COLOUR PRESENTED ON 25 SEPTEMBER 1990 BY HRH THE DUKE OF KENT.

ROYAL AIR FORCE REGIMENT

1st COLOUR PRESENTED ON 17 MARCH 1953 BY HM QUEEN ELIZABETH II.
2nd COLOUR PRESENTED ON 16 JUNE 1967 BY HM QUEEN ELIZABETH II.
3rd COLOUR PRESENTED ON 30 OCTOBER 1992 BY HM QUEEN ELIZABETH II.

NEAR EAST AIR FORCE
(TITLE CHANGED FROM MIDDLE EAST AIR FORCE ON 11 APRIL 1961)

COLOUR PRESENTED ON 14 OCTOBER 1960 BY HRH THE DUKE OF GLOUCESTER.

FAR EAST AIR FORCE

COLOUR PRESENTED ON 13 JANUARY 1961 BY THE EARL OF SELKIRK.

CENTRAL FLYING SCHOOL

1st COLOUR PRESENTED ON 26 JUNE 1969 BY HM QUEEN ELIZABETH II.
2nd COLOUR PRESENTED ON 4 JUNE 1992 BY HM QUEEN ELIZABETH THE QUEEN MOTHER.

ROYAL AIR FORCE GERMANY

COLOUR PRESENTED ON 16 SEPTEMBER 1970 BY HRH THE PRINCESS ANNE.

ROYAL AUXILIARY AIR FORCE
(Known as Sovereign's Colour)

COLOUR PRESENTED ON 12 JUNE 1989 BY HM QUEEN ELIZABETH II.

ROYAL AIR FORCE HALTON

COLOUR PRESENTED ON 31 OCTOBER 1997 BY HM QUEEN ELIZABETH II.

IMPORTANT NOTES CONCERNING RAF BATTLE HONOURS

The Battle Honours to which Royal Air Force Squadrons are entitled, and the conditions under which they are awarded are set out in AP 3327, originally published in 1957.

The Battle Honours Committee was first convened in 1947 to consider Honours for World War 1, World War 2 and the Inter War Years, however since the Army did not then award honours for battles between the wars the RAF fell in step and considered just World War 1 and World War 2. These recommendations were approved by the Air Council in AC 58 (47) of Nov 47.

The Standard will be awarded by order of the Monarch in every case, to Operational Squadrons qualifying in one of the following two respects:

1. By completion of 25 years of existence in the RAF, the Royal Flying Corps or the Royal Naval Air Service. This includes Squadrons with continuous or non-continuous service.

2. By having earned the Monarch's appreciation of specially outstanding operations.

Battle Honours awarded for operations during the First and Second World Wars, up to maximum of 8 in number, may be displayed on Squadron Standards. If a Squadron has been awarded more than 8, the Squadron Commander is to select those which are to be displayed. Battle Honours for operations during the period between the two wars were awarded to Squadrons but may not be emblazoned on Standards. Battle Honours awarded for operations occurring after the Second World War have been awarded both with and without the right to emblazonment. Only those Battle Honours with the Sovereign's permission to emblazon may be displayed but subject to a maximum of 15.

It was also agreed that only flying squadrons were entitled to receive a Squadron Standard, however in January 1952 Standards were to be awarded to RAF Regiment and Royal Auxiliary Air Force Squadrons.

The first Squadron to receive its Standard was No 1 Squadron and the first Regiment Squadron to receive its Standard was No 2 Armoured Car Company RAF Regiment.

Since 1945, 3 Battle Honours have been granted namely, "Korea 1950–1953", "South Atlantic 1982" and "Gulf 1991". However, no right to emblazonment was granted in the case of "Korea 1950–53", and the three Squadrons awarded their Battle Honours in 1987 have been disbanded in the intervening years. In the case of "South Atlantic 1982" 3 precedents were created;

a. For the first time, authority was given to emblazon an honour awarded outside the time frame of the 2 World Wars.

b. The right to emblazon was accorded to 3 Squadrons only (Numbers 1 and 18 Squadrons and Number 63 Squadron RAF Regiment) rather than being extended to all the Squadrons which were granted the Battle Honour, thus creating a two-tier Battle Honours system. The review of post-war operations conducted in 1987 considered that a distinction should be drawn between the award of the Battle Honours and the right of emblazonment. It was decided that the latter should be the ultimate accolade and be reserved to those Squadrons which were in direct confrontation with the enemy and had demonstrated gallantry and spirit under fire.

For seniority purposes an RAF Regiment Squadron is entitled to claim its service as an armoured car squadron.

WILKINSON SWORD OF PEACE

1999—RAF Kinloss
2000—RAF Lyneham

WILKINSON BATTLE OF BRITAIN SWORD

1998/2000—No Award
2000/02—No Award

THE ROYAL AIR FORCES ESCAPING SOCIETY TROPHY

2000—No 8 Squadron
2001—No 22 Squadron

QUEEN'S MEDAL FOR CHAMPION SHOTS OF THE AIR FORCE

2001—Sergeant J. T. Prictor
2002—Chief Technician J. T. Prictor

JOLLIFFE TROPHY

2000—RAF Marham
2001—RAF Leuchars

THE ARTHUR BARRATT MEMORIAL PRIZE

1999—51 Squadron RAF Waddington
2000—33 Squadron, RAF Benson

THE "L. G. GROVES" MEMORIAL PRIZES & AWARDS

Air Safety Prize
Joint Winners
1999—The Emergency & Aeronautical Information Flight at the London Air Traffic Control Centre (Military)
Distress & Diversion Cell at the Scottish Air Traffic Control Centre (Military)
2000—Flight Lieutenant S. M. Bartlett

Meteorology
1999—Dr M. MacVean
2000—Dr P. Cox

Meteorological Observation Award
1999—Squadron Leader J. H. Ayres
2000—Mr S. Nightingale

Ground Safety Award
1999—No award
2000—No award

ADRIAN RAY MEMORIAL AWARD FOR RAF ENGINEERING

1999—Sergeant M. J. Wainwright
2000—Not Awarded

"HYDE-THOMSON" MEMORIAL PRIZE

General Duties Officer Award
2000—Flying Officer D. S. King
2001—Not Awarded

Engineering Officer Award
2000—Flying Lieutenant R. Hutcheon, BEng
2001—Flying Officer K. R. Cranswick, MSc

"GORDON SHEPHARD" MEMORIAL PRIZE ESSAY

2001—Flight Lieutenant C. A. White, BA
2002—Flight Lieutenant C. A. White, BA

ROYAL AIR FORCE COMMAND TROPHIES

(listed in Command order of precedence)

HEADQUARTERS STRIKE COMMAND

GEORGE STAINFORTH TROPHY

2000—RAF Cottesmore
2001—RAF Waddington

SMALLWOOD ELECTRONIC WARFARE TROPHY

2000—No Award
2001—Training Test and Assessment Flight RAF Spadeadam

YELLOWGATE TROPHY

2001—No Award
2002—No Award

ABERPORTH TROPHY

2000—No Award
2001—No Award

DACRE TROPHY

1997/To Date—No Award
2001—111 Squadron

INGPEN TROPHY

1999/2000—No Award
2000/2001—No Award

SEED TROPHY

1996/97—No 5 Squadron
1997/To Date—No Award

SMALL STATIONS TROPHY

2001—Not Awarded
2002—Not Awarded

AIRD WHYTE TROPHY

2001—No 120 Squadron
2002—No 42(R) Squadron

FINCASTLE TROPHY

2001—Royal Air Force
2002—Not Yet Awarded

INTER SQUADRON PHOTOGRAPHIC TROPHY

2000—No 201 Squadron
2001—Not Yet Awarded

HARRIS TROPHY

2000—Not Awarded
2001—Not Yet Awarded

NAIRN TROPHY

2000—Not Contested
2001—Not Contested

SKYFAME TROPHY

2000—Nimrod Flight Trials Crew
2001—ARCC (Aeronautical Rescue Co-ordination Centre)

PLESSEY TROPHY

2000—Not Awarded
2001—Not Yet Awarded

HQ STC OPS SPT (ATC)

RAYTHEON FALONER TROPHY

2000—Brize Norton
2001—Cranwell

THE VOSPER THORNEYCROFT ATC TROPHY

2000—Flight Lieutenant N. Hope
2001—Corporal T. A. Perrett

HEADQUARTERS ROYAL AIR FORCE PERSONNEL & TRAINING COMMAND

DISTINGUISHED PASSES IN FLYING TRAINING

2001—Flight Lieutenant S. E. Bailey, BEng
Flight Lieutenant N. Mathew, BSc
Flight Lieutenant J. M. Howard, BEng
Flight Lieutenant N. C. Whitehead, MEng
2002—Flying Officer N. S. Thomas, BEng
Sergeant T. A. Elwood, MA

HEADQUARTERS ELEMENTARY FLYING TRAINING

HACK TROPHY

2000—Universities of Glasgow and Strathclyde Air Squadron
2001—East Midlands Universities Air Squadron

THE COOPER TROPHY

2000—Not awarded
2001—Not Contested

DE HAVILLAND TROPHY

2000—Not awarded
2001—Not Contested

REID TROPHY

2000—Not Awarded
2001—Not Contested

SCONE TROPHY

1999—Aberdeen, Dundee and St Andrews UAS
2001—Not Contested

ROYAL AIR FORCE REGIMENT

LLOYDS CUP (ROYAL AIR FORCE REGIMENT SKILL AT ARMS)

2000—37 Squadron RAF Regiment
2001—3 Squadron RAF Regiment

HIGGINSON TROPHY (EXCEPTIONAL PROFESSIONAL ACHIEVEMENT)

1999—2 Squadron RAF Regiment
2000—37 Squadron RAF Regiment

ARTHUR BARNARD TROPHY

1999—Not Awarded
2000—Not Awarded

ROBERTS LEADERSHIP TROPHY FOR THE RAF REGIMENT

1999—Flight Lieutenant G. J. Powell
2000—Flight Lieutenant B. W. Moss

RAF REGIMENT ESSAY COMPETITION

1999—Flight Lieutenant R. J. Cargill
2000—Flight Lieutenant J. C. Harris, BSc

THE RAF REGIMENT OFFICERS DINNER CLUB PRIZE AND KAPUSCINSKI SWORD

(Top Student on the Junior Regiment Officer's Course)

2000—Course 1—Flying Officer A. J. Field
2001—Course 2—Flying Officer J. G. Smith, BSc

THE VAUX TROPHY

(Student on the Junior Regiment Officer's Course displaying the greatest development of leadership qualities)

2000—Course 1—Flying Officer P. T. Hamilton, BA
2001—Course 2—Flying Officer J. J. Lynham, BA

ROYAL AIR FORCE MEDICAL SERVICES

"RICHARD FOX LINTON" MEMORIAL PRIZE

1999—Wing Commander R. S. J. Matthews, BSc MB BS MRCGP
2000—Group Captain A. J. Batchelor, CBE BSc MB BS FRCP FRAeS DRCOG DAvMed

THE LADY CADE MEDAL

1999—Wing Commander H. Kilbey, BSc MB BS
2000—Wing Commander D. P. Gradwell, PhD BSc MB ChB FRAeS DAvMed

THE SIR ANDREW HUMPHREY MEMORIAL MEDAL

2000—Wing Commander N. M. McGuire, BMedSci BM BS
2001—Squadron Leader G. W. Davies, MB BS MRCP(IREL)

LEAN MEMORIAL AWARD

2000—Group Captain R. G. Shepherd, BDS FDSRCPS LDSRCS MCMI
2001—Squadron Leader J. D. Ilsley, BDS

STEWART MEMORIAL PRIZE

2001—Squadron Leader M. J. A. Trudgill, MB BCh DAvMed DiplMC MRAeS
2002—Surgeon Commander M. R. Groom, MB ChB MRCGP MRAeS DipAvMed AFOM RN

THE SIR HAROLD WHITTINGHAM MEMORIAL PRIZE

2000—Group Captain B. T. Keatings, MMedSci MB ChB MFOM DAvMed
2001—Wing Commander A. D. Green, MB BS MRCPath DTM&H

ROYAL AIR FORCE MUSIC SERVICES
Competition Winners

THE TRINITY COLLEGE LONDON PRIZE

2001—Sergeant D. Richards
2002—Chief Technician D. Richards

THE ROSEHILL BOWL

2001—Sergeant P. Kenward
2002—Junior Technician N. Brizland, BMus

THE YAMAHA KEMBLE SOLOIST AWARD

2001—Junior Technician N. Hurrell
2002—Junior Technician C. McCrorie, BMus

THE STUDIO MUSIC AWARD

2001—Corporal P. Wayman
2002—Corporal E. Sellers, LRSM

BOOSEY AND HAWKES TROPHY

2001—Corporal P. Wayman
2002—Corporal E. Sellers, LRSM

WORSHIPFUL COMPANY OF MUSICIANS' SILVER MEDAL

2000—Not Awarded
2001—Sergeant D. Richards

THE SIR FELIX CASSEL SILVER MEDAL

2000—Junior Technician N. Hobson, BMus
2001—Junior Technician N. Hurrell, BA LGSM

THE SIR FELIX CASSEL BRONZE MEDAL

2000—Junior Technician M. Van-Emmerik, ATCL
2001—Junior Technician T. Hobson

SUPPLY BRANCH

THE GILL SWORD AWARD

2000—Flight Lieutenant P. Dorsett
2001—Flight Lieutenant J. F. A. Eastham

ADMINISTRATIVE (SECRETARIAL BRANCH)

ROYAL AIR FORCE HALTON

Secretarial Cup Winners

2001—Flying Officer S. J. Austin
Flying Officer T. A. Cooper, LLB
Flying Officer S. R. Parker
Flying Officer S. L. Carvell
2002—Flight Lieutenant C. Bell, BA

THE WORSHIPFUL COMPANY OF CHARTERED SECRETARIES AND ADMINISTRATORS' PRIZES

2001—Flying Officer E. L. Marshall
Senior Aircraftwoman R. Nice
2002—Flying Officer S. R. Parker
Leading Aircraftwoman R. A. L. Hewlett

ADMINISTRATIVE (CATERING BRANCH)

THE HEREFORD TROPHY

1999/2000—Flying Officer M. C. Cornell
2001—Not Awarded

R AUX AF TROPHIES & AWARDS

ROBINS TROPHY

1999/2000—No 7010 (VR) Photographic Interpretation
Squadron RAuxAF, RAF Waddington
2001/2002—No 606 (Chiltern) Squadron RAuxAF,
RAF Benson

STRICKLAND TROPHY

2001—No 2622 (Highland) Squadron RAuxAF Regiment
RAF Lossiemouth
2002—No 2620 (County of Norfolk) Squadron RAuxAF,
RAF Marham

INSPECTOR'S CUP

2000—No 2620 (County of Norfolk) Squadron RAuxAF,
RAF Marham
2001—No 612 (County of Aberdeen) Squadron RAuxAF,
RAF Leuchars

ROYAL MILITARY COLLEGE OF SCIENCE

COMMANDANTS PRIZE

1999—Acting Pilot Officer S. J. Oliver, BSc
2000—Captain W. D. J. Wilson, R Signals

ROYAL AIR FORCE HISTORICAL SOCIETY

"THE TWO AIR FORCES" AWARD

1999—Squadron Leader A. W. Riches, MA
2000—Squadron Leader C. H. Goss, MA MILT

The Awards Shown on this page are made at the Royal Air Force College, Cranwell

DEPARTMENT OF INITIAL OFFICER TRAINING

QUEEN'S MEDAL AND R. S. MAY MEMORIAL PRIZE

2000—Flying Officer C. K. Gill
2001—To be Notified

WILKINSON SWORD OF HONOUR AND R. S. MAY MEMORIAL PRIZE

2000—Flying Officer K. M. Brennan, BSc
2001—Flying Officer M. B. Wheildon

PRINCE BANDAR TROPHY AND PRIZE

2000—Flying Officer D. Grassby, BSc
2001—Flight Lieutenant C. Bell, BA

SWORD OF MERIT

2000—Pilot Officer N. J. Paton, BSc
Pilot Officer L. V. Robinson, BSc
Pilot Officer M. E. W. Pert
Pilot Officer K. M. Brennan, BSc
Flying Officer N. K. Thorpe
Flying Officer A. J. Field
2001—Student Officer A. D. R. Watts, BSc
Student Officer N. R. Heasman, BA
Student Officer J. S. Clayton, MEng
Officer Cadet M. B. Wheildon
Officer Cadet C. J. Butterfield
Officer Cadet S. A. Geary

HENNESSY TROPHY AND PHILIP SASSOON MEMORIAL PRIZE

2000—Flying Officer M. F. McLean, BEng
Flying Officer I. M. Bews, MEng
Flying Officer C. K. Gill
Flying Officer R. M. Northway
Flying Officer J. A. Walker
Acting Pilot Officer J. A. Roberts
2001—Student Officer H. L. Melville, BSc
Student Officer E. E. Rickards, MA
Officer Cadet K. A. Moran
Student Officer M. J. Bryson, BMus
Officer Cadet M. L. Reed
Student Officer L. J. Lockyer, MSc

THE BRITISH AEROSPACE TROPHY

2000—Flying Officer K. A. Stewart, MEng
Flying Officer A. L. Pearson, BSc
Pilot Officer R. J. Winchester, LLB
Pilot Officer F. Rixon, BA
Pilot Officer R. P. Pike, BSc PGCE
Pilot Officer A. J. Dickson, MSc BSc
2001—Student Officer J. D. Heeps, MSc BA
Student Officer K. M. J. Hall, LLB
Student Officer M. I. Crockford, BSc
Student Officer C. A. Mullineux, BSc
Officer Cadet M. L. Reed
Officer Cadet N. D. Ingram

OVERSEAS STUDENT'S PRIZE

2000—Second Lieutenant S. Aidahnie, UAE
Second Lieutenant M. Al Khalifa, BDF
Flying Officer A. Audu, BSc NAF
Officer Cadet A. I. M. Al Balchi, RAFO
2001—Officer Cadet S. A. Al Shihi, RAFO
Officer Cadet K. A. Salleh, BEng RBAF
Officer Cadet M. Y. Yusainey, RBAF

316

DEPARTMENT OF SPECIALIST GROUND TRAINING

WHITTLE PRIZE

2000—Squadron Leader A. J. Kimber, MSc
2001—Flight Lieutenant J. L. W. Browning, MSc BEng

THE SIR THOMAS SHIRLEY MEMORIAL CUP AND MINERVA SOCIETY PRIZE

2000—Flying Officer G. G. Sweatman
2001—Flying Officer I. Allen, BSc

HALAHAN PRIZE

2000—Flight Lieutenant R. Hutcheon, BEng
2001—Flying Officer J. R. Stephens

HERBERT SMITH MEMORIAL TROPHY

2000—Flight Lieutenant N. Bates, BEng RAAF
2001—Flight Lieutenant A. M. Shipp, MSc BEng

SUPPLY PRIZE

2000—Flying Officer H. M. Gledhill, BSocSc
2001—Flying Officer H. Millar

WORSHIPFUL COMPANY OF ENGINEERS' PRIZE

2000—Flying Officer S. W. Edmondson
2001—Flight Lieutenant L. R. Vickers, BSc

STUART BOULTON MEMORIAL PRIZE

2000—Flight Lieutenant J. E. Dodwell, BEng
2001—Flying Officer J. B. Morrison

BECKWITH TROPHY AND PRIZE

2000—Flying Officer R. J. E. Hart
2001—Flying Officer A. J. Main

ROYAL NEW ZEALAND AIR FORCE PRIZES

2000—Flight Lieutenant J. Attwood
Flying Officer S. Chapman
2001—Flight Lieutenant W. Rudge
Flight Lieutenant P. J. Searle

COLLEGE AWARDS
LOWE-HOLMES TROPHY

2000—Squadron Leader J. C. Bauer, MA BA
2001—Not Awarded

AIR WARFARE CENTRE CRANWELL

ANDREW HUMPHREY MEMORIAL GOLD MEDAL

2001—Flight Lieutenant N. J. Stringer, BEng
2002—Lieutenant Commander M. F. Ware, BSc BAvn RAN

ARIES TROPHY

2001—Flight Lieutenant N. J. Stringer, BEng
2002—Lieutenant Commander M. F. Ware, BSc BAvn RAN

BRABYN TROPHY

(Awarded annually to the winner of the individual
Aerobatics Competition for Hawk instructors from Royal
Air Force Personnel and Training Command)

2001—Not Awarded
2002—Not Awarded

WRIGHT JUBILEE TROPHY

(Awarded annually to the overall winner of the Aerobatics
Competition for instructors from Royal Air Force Personnel
and Training Command)

2001—Captain A. Wade—Joint Elementary Flying Training
School
2002—Flight Lieutenant S. Simpson, MA—No 1 Flying
Training School

BRITISH AEROSPACE BULLDOG TROPHY

(Awarded annually to the winner of the Aerobatics
Competition for Bulldog instructors from Royal Air Force
Personnel and Training Command)

2001—Not Awarded
2002—Not Awarded

SPITFIRE TROPHY

(Awarded annually to the winner of the individual
Aerobatics Comptition for instructors from Royal Air Force
Personnel and Training Command) Tucano

2001—Not Awarded
2002—Not Awarded

OBITUARY

ACTIVE LIST

Officers and Warrant Officers
whose deaths have been reported since September 2001

Rank and Name	Date of Death	Rank and Name	Date of Death
Squadron Leaders		**RAFVR(T)**	
J. C. Page, BA MCIPS...	8.1.02		
F. P. Smith	2.12.01	*Flying Officers*	
		A. C. Gildea	15.1.02
Flight Lieutenants		K. B. Latton	19.10.01
E. A. Bond, BSc	28.11.01		
J. A. Peterson, MSci	22.5.02	*Pilot Officer*	
S. G. Rooke	25.1.02	R. W. Streeton...	18.7.02
Flying Officer			
L. J. Lockyer, MSc	14.8.02		

LIST OF RETIRED OFFICERS OF
THE ROYAL AIR FORCE

Officers who have retired since 1 August 2002

ADAMS D. N. BSc FRAeS. Born 28/4/46. Commd 22/9/65. A Cdre 1/1/97. Retd GD 11/12/01.
ADDISON J. M. Born 15/12/63. Commd 8/5/86. Flt Lt 9/6/90. Retd GD 15/12/01.
AKEHURST R. Born 14/12/61. Commd 11/6/81. Sqn Ldr 1/1/97. Retd GD 1/8/01.
ALDER I. T. Born 29/7/46. Commd 23/9/82. Sqn Ldr 1/7/98. Retd SUP 29/7/01.
ALDRIDGE M. R. MBA MCMI. Born 3/12/57. Commd 1/7/82. Sqn Ldr 1/7/90. Retd ENG 1/7/01.
ALFANDARY C. M. BA. Born 20/4/49. Commd 16/2/86. Flt Lt 16/2/84. Retd ADMIN 16/2/02.
ALLAN K. T. BDS. Born 28/1/61. Commd 1/9/85. Wg Cdr 4/3/98. Retd DEL 1/9/01.
ALLEN J. M. Born 28/12/47. Commd 22/9/88. Flt Lt 22/9/90. Retd SUP 1/8/01.
ALLTON M. C. BSc. Born 23/8/62. Commd 11/12/83. Sqn Ldr 1/7/97. Retd GD 1/2/02.
ALTON J. S. Born 16/7/50. Commd 6/4/72. Wg Cdr 1/7/91. Retd ENG 29/4/02.
ANDREWS A. W. PhD MA MSc BSc CPhys CChem MRSC MInstP MCIPD. Born 30/10/46.
    Commd 18/8/85. Sqn Ldr 1/7/90. Retd ADMIN 3/10/01.
ARATHOON W. J. Born 30/12/61. Commd 5/12/81. Sqn Ldr 1/1/98. Retd GD 1/7/01.
ARCHER G. M. BSc. Born 24/5/64. Commd 23/9/83. Sqn Ldr 1/1/95. Retd GD 24/5/02.
ARDLEY J. C. Born 11/5/47. Commd 3/12/70. Sqn Ldr 1/7/93. Retd GD 11/5/02.
ARMSTRONG M. H. BA. Born 17/7/46. Commd 11/1/79. Wg Cdr 1/7/00. Retd ENG 17/7/01.
ARNOLD L. E. BA MCIPD. Born 1/3/63. Commd 1/4/85. Sqn Ldr 1/7/96. Retd ADMIN 29/8/01.
ARNOLD S. Born 24/5/64. Commd 15/3/84. Flt Lt 16/12/89. Retd SUP 25/5/02.
ARNOT T. M. K. OBE. Born 7/1/47. Commd 19/8/71. Gp Capt 1/7/96. Retd ADMIN 7/1/02.
ASHMAN R. J. L. BA. Born 21/7/56. Commd 4/6/87. Flt Lt 4/6/89. Retd ENG 4/6/01.
ASTILL M. C. BSc. Born 1/5/63. Commd 13/9/81. Sqn Ldr 1/1/99. Retd GD 1/1/02.
AUDET D. W. BSc. Born 29/1/63. Commd 8/5/88. Flt Lt 8/11/90. Retd GD 5/12/01.
AYERS J. H. Born 9/3/44. Commd 16/8/68. Sqn Ldr 1/7/93. Retd GD 9/6/01.
AYTON C. H. Born 30/3/58. Commd 18/10/79. Flt Lt 18/4/85. Retd GD 7/4/02.

BACON L. D. MA MSc BSc CEng MRAeS DIC. Born 11/7/62. Commd 31/8/80. Wg Cdr 1/1/99.
    Retd ENG 1/1/02.
BAKER S. A. BEng. Born 4/9/63. Commd 31/7/91. Flt Lt 15/7/94. Retd ENG 4/9/01.
BALLANTYNE A. C. Born 13/8/62. Commd 4/10/85. Flt Lt 4/4/91. Retd GD 5/8/01.
BANKS C. P. Born 4/11/61. Commd 28/7/93. Flt Lt 28/7/95. Retd OPS SPT 28/7/01.
BARKER C. M. I. MA. Born 7/4/54. Commd 22/5/75. Wg Cdr 1/1/96. Retd GD 29/9/01.
BARNES D. N. Born 2/8/46. Commd 23/3/66. Sqn Ldr 1/7/78. Retd ADMIN 15/10/01.
BARNES F. O. Born 1/12/42. Commd 6/7/62. Flt Lt 6/1/68. Retd GD 15/4/02.
BARROW S. Born 30/11/62. Commd 11/10/84. Sqn Ldr 1/7/95. Retd OPS SPT 30/6/01.
BATE B. G. Born 12/2/49. Commd 14/12/72. Gp Capt 1/1/95. Retd ENG 6/5/02.
BATEMAN R. I. MSc BA MCIT MILT MRAeS. Born 8/8/54. Commd 2/9/73. Gp Capt 1/7/98.
    Retd SUP 1/1/02.
BATHGATE P. BEng. Born 13/4/64. Commd 1/8/86. Sqn Ldr 1/1/99. Retd ENG 13/4/02.
BATTLEY S. P. Born 27/12/49. Commd 22/7/71. Wg Cdr 1/7/96. Retd ADMIN 8/12/01.
BAXTER K. Born 7/7/63. Commd 19/12/91. Flt Lt 19/12/93. Retd OPS SPT 7/7/01.
BAYLISS D. Born 17/8/62. Commd 5/5/88. Flt Lt 5/5/90. Retd GD 2/4/02.
BELL N. G. Born 16/4/44. Commd 12/7/63. Wg Cdr 16/4/02. Retd GD 16/4/02.
BENSON D. R. OBE. Born 11/11/46. Commd 3/7/65. Gp Capt 1/7/97. Retd SUP 11/11/01.
BERRY I. F. Born 20/12/62. Commd 5/1/86. Sqn Ldr 1/7/98. Retd ENG 1/3/02.
BEST R. E. AFC. Born 18/7/45. Commd 21/3/69. Wg Cdr 1/7/89. Retd GD 18/7/01.
BETTERIDGE P. A. MA MBA DipMgmt. Born 28/11/59. Commd 13/8/82. Wg Cdr 1/7/99.
    Retd ADMIN 1/8/01.

BIRKBECK P. C. L. BSc. Born 12/1/49. Commd 24/9/67. Sqn Ldr 1/1/89. Retd OPS SPT 30/9/01.
BLACKFORD P. A. Born 9/7/48. Commd 17/2/67. Gp Capt 1/1/97. Retd GD 31/5/02.
BLAKE R. G. Born 18/11/46. Commd 23/3/67. Wg Cdr 1/1/90. Retd GD 18/11/01.
BLOCK K. J. Born 8/5/50. Commd 2/11/88. Flt Lt 2/11/92. Retd ENG 1/8/01.
BOLSOVER D. R. Born 9/10/53. Commd 22/5/75. Wg Cdr 1/1/96. Retd GD 17/8/01.
BOOKHAM R. P. BA. Born 24/4/48. Commd 20/7/78. Sqn Ldr 1/7/86. Retd ENG 23/4/02.
BOTTOMLEY J. C. BSc. Born 22/1/64. Commd 18/8/85. Sqn Ldr 1/1/98. Retd GD 22/4/02.
BOWRON C. F. Born 25/9/48. Commd 29/3/68. Flt Lt 29/9/73. Retd GD 27/4/02.
BOYLAND P. S. AFC BSc. Born 12/5/61. Commd 26/9/82. Sqn Ldr 1/1/96. Retd GD 17/1/02.
BOYLE T. L. OBE. Born 21/9/50. Commd 24/1/74. Gp Capt 1/7/00. Retd GD 30/9/01.
BRANAGH N. OBE BEd. Born 8/11/46. Commd 12/12/71. Sqn Ldr 1/1/85. Retd ADMIN 1/1/88.
    Re-entered 2/5/89. Wg Cdr 1/1/93. Retd ADMIN 8/11/01.
BRANDON V. G. Born 8/8/61. Commd 8/11/90. Flt Lt 8/11/92. Retd ENG 26/1/02.
BRENNAN P. S. MA BA PGCE MCIPD MCMI. Born 14/3/50. Commd 2/8/90. Sqn Ldr 1/7/99.
    Retd ADMIN 7/7/01.
BREWER N. C. Born 19/4/49. Commd 23/6/67. Gp Capt 1/7/99. Retd OPS SPT 1/7/01.
BRIGHT R. M. Born 22/4/47. Commd 26/5/67. Sqn Ldr 1/7/84. Retd ENG 1/11/01.
BRITTON G. S. Born 30/12/46. Commd 27/1/67. Wg Cdr 1/1/88. Retd SUP 30/12/01.
BROADLEY S. M. Born 21/7/63. Commd 16/2/89. Flt Lt 10/2/93. Retd ADMIN 21/7/01.
BROWN M. W. Born 30/9/47. Commd 18/9/66. Wg Cdr 1/1/98. Retd GD 8/7/01.
BROWN R. B. Born 9/11/46. Commd 11/5/86. Flt Lt 11/5/92. Retd ADMIN 11/5/02.
BROWNE W. N. DFC. Born 20/8/47. Commd 15/9/67. Sqn Ldr 1/1/91. Retd GD 1/10/01.
BRUMPTON R. BA FRAeS. Born 4/1/47. Commd 21/4/67. A Cdre 1/7/97. Retd ENG 4/1/02.
BUCHANAN I. K. Born 15/5/57. Commd 13/12/79. Wg Cdr 1/1/98. Retd ADMIN 13/8/01.
BUCHANAN W. D. Born 20/2/47. Commd 25/2/66. Sqn Ldr 1/7/94. Retd GD 20/2/02.
BUCK C. W. D. MA. Born 13/7/46. Commd 16/1/72. Sqn Ldr 1/1/83. Retd ENG 13/7/01.
BUCKLER J. L. Born 22/7/46. Commd 18/8/67. Gp Capt 1/1/95. Retd GD 22/7/01.
BUFTON T. MSc BSc CEng FCMI MIEE DIC. Born 26/11/46. Commd 26/5/67. Gp Capt 1/1/97.
    Retd ENG 26/11/01.
BULL K. A. Born 24/5/47. Commd 25/11/68. Wg Cdr 1/1/90. Retd GD 11/4/02.
BULL K. M. Born 20/7/46. Commd 2/2/84. Sqn Ldr 1/1/94. Retd ADMIN 20/7/01.
BULLEN A. Born 7/7/54. Commd 23/4/87. Sqn Ldr 1/1/88. Retd ENG 10/6/01.
BUSK D. G. Born 18/1/45. Commd 13/3/80. Flt Lt 13/3/83. Retd GD 1/8/01.

CADDICK D. J. MBE MA MLitt BA FCIPD FCMI MInstD. Born 29/5/61. Commd 16/9/79.
    Sqn Ldr 1/1/91. Retd OPS SPT 23/7/01.
CALDER J. ACMA. Born 26/10/55. Commd 8/6/84. Wg Cdr 1/1/01. Retd ADMIN 27/2/02.
CALLOW A. R. Born 10/12/63. Commd 29/7/83. Sqn Ldr 1/1/98. Retd OPS SPT 10/12/01.
CAMPBELL A. BSc. Born 18/09/49. Commd 24/9/72. Gp Capt 1/1/96. Retd GD 31/5/02.
CAMPBELL D. C. Born 25/4/62. Commd 4/7/85. Sqn Ldr 1/1/97. Retd GD 17/6/01.
CAMPBELL P. E. IEng. Born 27/9/50. Commd 19/6/88. Flt Lt 19/6/88. Retd ENG 2/10/01.
CARDWELL M. A. BSc. Born 28/5/46. Commd 14/4/85. Flt Lt 14/10/81. Retd ADMIN 28/5/02.
CARTER C. A. BSc. Born 22/8/63. Commd 14/10/84. Flt Lt 14/4/87. Retd GD 22/9/01.
CASEY J. P. Born 5/2/60. Commd 3/7/80. Sqn Ldr 1/7/93. Retd OPS SPT 1/5/02.
CASTLE D. A. BSc. Born 14/7/55. Commd 2/9/73. Wg Cdr 1/1/97. Retd GD 19/10/01.
CHALMERS N. F. BSc. Born 3/1/63. Commd 18/8/85. Sqn Ldr 1/1/95. Retd ADMIN 18/8/01.
CHAMBERLAIN S. J. MSc BEng CEng MIMechE. Born 4/2/56. Commd 1/9/74. Sqn Ldr 1/1/88.
    Retd ENG 11/9/01.
CHAMBERS C. M. Born 12/2/47. Commd 1/3/68. A Cdre 1/1/95. Retd GD 6/4/02.
CHAMBERS M. G. MBE. Born 27/5/47. Commd 26/4/84. Sqn Ldr 1/1/99. Retd OPS SPT 1/9/01.
CHAPMAN C. R. BEng. Born 16/4/64. Commd 2/8/89. Flt Lt 15/7/92. Retd ENG 16/4/02.
CHINNECK M. R. S. MSc BSc. Born 21/2/51. Commd 26/2/71. Wg Cdr 1/7/99.
    Retd ENG 2/4/02.

CHURCHILL I. M. BSc. Born 1/9/63. Commd 2/9/84. Flt Lt 2/3/87. Retd GD 1/9/01.
CLARK D. J. Born 20/2/64. Commd 23/9/82. Sqn Ldr 1/7/97. Retd OPS SPT 20/2/02.
CLARK G. BSc. Born 16/2/62. Commd 29/9/85. Sqn Ldr 1/7/95. Retd GD 5/6/01.
CLARK L. J. BEd. Born 17/11/52. Commd 12/8/79. Sqn Ldr 1/1/90. Retd ADMIN 12/8/01.
CLARKE D. J. Born 23/7/63. Commd 4/5/84. Flt Lt 15/9/93. Retd OPS SPT 23/7/01.
CLARKE G. H. Born 11/5/47. Commd 21/7/65. Gp Capt 1/1/97. Retd GD 15/7/01.
COCKMAN P. R. Born 7/10/55. Commd 13/6/74. Sqn Ldr 1/1/87. Retd GD 1/8/01.
CONNOLLY B. T. BSc. Born 18/12/59. Commd 31/7/83. Sqn Ldr 1/1/96. Retd GD 31/12/01.
CONNOLLY D. M. MB BS MRCGP MRAeS DAvMed. Born 7/2/59. Commd 21/7/85.
    Wg Cdr 2/3/97. Retd MED 21/7/01.
CONNOLLY E. MSc BTech CEng MIEE. Born 14/3/50. Commd 11/8/74. Sqn Ldr 1/1/87.
    Retd ENG 18/11/01.
CONNOLLY J. AFC FRAeS. Born 5/2/52. Commd 4/2/71. A Cdre 1/1/98. Retd GD 28/8/01.
COOP G. A. MRAeS. Born 13/10/46. Commd 11/8/67. W Cdr 1/7/88. Retd GD 13/10/01.
COOPER I. R. Born 10/6/49. Commd 5/9/69. Gp Capt 1/7/97. Retd ADMIN 9/10/01.
COPE A. W. MBE AFC FRAeS. Born 13/2/47. Commd 1/3/68. Gp Capt 1/1/97. Retd GD 13/2/02.
CORDERY C. BEd FCIPD. Born 20/9/52. Commd 3/5/81. Wg Cdr 1/1/93. Retd ADMIN 6/8/01.
COULTER E. G. MSc CEng MIEE. Born 23/5/47. Commd 12/2/76. Wg Cdr 1/7/94.
    Retd ENG 23/5/02.
COWE R. I. Born 12/6/51. Commd 9/11/89. Flt Lt 9/11/91. Retd GD 30/6/01.
CRANE D. MDA BSc CEng MIEE. Born 13/4/63. Commd 2/9/84. Sqn Ldr 1/7/94. Retd ENG 1/8/01.
CROMBIE D. J. C. MBE. Born 15/11/42. Commd 28/4/65. Sqn Ldr 1/7/84. Retd GD 15/11/01.
CRYER N. C. Born 8/4/68. Commd 28/7/88. Flt Lt 28/1/95. Retd OPS SPT 1/10/01.
CUNNINGHAM D. J. MBE. Born 15/5/53. Commd 12/12/83. Sqn Ldr 1/7/98.
    Retd OPS SPT 1/7/01.
CUNNINGHAM S. BSc. Born 15/11/60. Commd 27/8/87. Flt Lt 18/7/91. Retd ENG 15/11/01.
CURRIE R. I. MSc BSc CEng MRAeS. Born 26/11/63. Commd 14/10/82. Sqn Ldr 1/1/95.
    Retd ENG 26/11/01.

DA COSTA F. A. MBE. Born 5/10/39. Commd 28/1/58. Sqn Ldr 1/1/85. Retd GD 5/10/01.
DALBY A. P. MBA MSc MHSM MCMI DipHSM. Born 18/8/58. Commd 25/4/82. Sqn Ldr 1/7/95.
    Retd MED SPT 3/4/02.
DALTON R. A. BSc. Born 28/5/63. Commd 29/4/83. Sqn Ldr 1/1/98. Retd GD 28/2/02.
DAULBY K. J. BSc. Born 23/10/63. Commd 29/9/85. Flt Lt 29/3/88. Retd GD 23/10/01.
DAVIDSON W. A. IEng FIIE. Born 6/2/47. Commd 5/1/78. Sqn Ldr 1/1/86. Retd ENG 6/2/02.
DAVIES A. T. Born 11/5/52. Commd 29/3/90. Flt Lt 29/3/94. Retd ENG 26/10/01.
DAVIES H. E. J. BSc. Born 13/7/51. Commd 15/9/69. Sqn Ldr 1/7/85. Retd ENG 1/1/02.
DAVIES M. J. MSc. Born 20/2/47. Commd 4/1/83. Sqn Ldr 1/7/94. Retd ENG 2/7/01.
DAVISON C. MBE FCMI DPhysEd. Born 26/09/47. Commd 11/8/69. AVM 1/7/00.
    Retd ADMIN 28/6/01.
DAWSON P. Born 27/8/79. Commd 1/4/99. Plt Offr 1/10/99. Retd OPS SPT 31/1/02.
DE SOYZA K. W. MSc BSc. Born 19/1/62. Commd 30/8/81. Sqn Ldr 1/7/95. Retd ENG 15/1/02.
DENNIS G. J. Born 8/12/46. Commd 11/4/85. Sqn Ldr 1/1/98. Retd ENG 4/3/02.
DIAMOND P. A. BEng CEng MIEE. Born 15/9/63. Commd 7/8/87. Sqn Ldr 1/7/87.
    Retd ENG 15/12/01.
DIQUE M. J. A. BEng. Born 25/9/61. Commd 7/8/87. Flt Lt 7/1/93. Retd ENG 23/7/01.
DIXON P. M. Born 29/8/46. Commd 22/12/67. Sqn Ldr 1/1/83. Retd GD 29/8/01.
DIXON P. S. AFC. Born 18/5/46. Commd 28/9/64. Sqn Ldr 1/1/85. Retd GD 28/1/02.
DOGGETT B. P. Born 15/5/49. Commd 12/7/68. A Cdre 1/7/99. Retd GD 30/9/01.
DONNELLY J. AFM*. Born 19/3/44. Commd 19/3/81. Flt Lt 19/3/84. Retd GD 19/9/01.
DUGUID M. Born 10/4/48. Commd 22/9/69. Wg Cdr 1/7/93. Retd ENG 27/10/01.
DYER-PERRY A. H. C. BSc MRAeS. Born 15/2/45. Commd 23/2/68. Wg Cdr 1/1/88.
    Retd GD 15/2/02.

EARLE P. J. BSc. Born 9/6/52. Commd 16/2/86. Flt Lt 16/2/88. Retd ADMIN 16/2/02.
EARNDEN K. C. BA CEng MRAeS. Born 18/2/56. Commd 5/4/79. Wg Cdr 1/7/97.
  Retd ENG 7/2/02.
ECKERSLEY A. M. Born 1/5/63. Commd 4/11/82. Sqn Ldr 1/1/95. Retd GD 1/2/02.
EDMONDS A. J. Born 13/4/44. Commd 24/11/67. Flt Lt 24/5/73. Retd GD 13/6/01.
EDWARDS D. Born 8/8/51. Commd 16/3/73. Flt Lt 16/3/74. Retd GD 18/9/01.
EIGHTEEN D. E. OBE. Born 14/6/46. Commd 16/9/76. Wg Cdr 1/7/96. Retd ENG 16/6/01.
ELLIOTT J. G. MBE. Born 24/11/46. Commd 1/3/68. Wg Cdr 1/7/96. Retd GD 24/11/01.
ELLIOTT R. P. Born 15/3/53. Commd 2/9/73. Wg Cdr 1/1/94. Retd SUP 1/10/01.
ELLIS R. M. H. Born 17/5/47. Commd 17/7/70. Wg Cdr 1/1/95. Retd GD 17/5/02.
ELTON E. A. BA. Born 7/11/44. Commd 28/9/64. Sqn Ldr 1/7/75. Retd GD 3/5/02.
EMMETT P. C. PhD MSc BSc CEng MIEE. Born 2/6/51. Commd 29/9/85. Sqn Ldr 1/7/95.
  Retd ENG 29/9/01.
ENGWELL M. J. OBE. Born 9/9/44. Commd 31/8/62. Wg Cdr 1/1/83. Retd GD 9/9/01.
ETHERIDGE J. Born 28/5/58. Commd 8/5/86. Wg Cdr 1/1/99. Retd ENG 28/5/02.
EVANS D. J. Born 18/7/50. Commd 19/12/85. Sqn Ldr 1/7/96. Retd SUP 13/8/01.
EVANS P. MEd BA. Born 6/3/62. Commd 20/1/85. Sqn Ldr 1/7/94. Retd ADMIN 20/1/02.
EVANS R. A. Born 21/8/43. Commd 39/6/72. Flt Lt 29/6/74. Retd GD 12/12/01.

FARMER M. K. Born 20/1/48. Commd 24/11/67. Sqn Ldr 1/7/88. Retd GD 1/5/02.
FARRER G. B. J. BSc. Born 31/8/61. Commd 11/12/83. Sqn Ldr 1/7/98. Retd SUP 1/7/01.
FENTON T. J. Born 20/4/62. Commd 8/10/87. Sqn Ldr 1/1/98. Retd ADMIN 1/8/01.
FERRAR D. CertEd. Born 21/4/44. Commd 29/4/71. Wg Cdr 1/7/96. Retd ADMIN 21/8/01.
FISH M. MA BA. Born 5/11/60. Commd 14/4/85. Sqn Ldr 1/7/95. Retd ADMIN 30/9/01.
FITNESS J. H. Born 26/10/63. Commd 12/3/87. Sqn Ldr 1/7/97. Retd OPS SPT 27/2/02.
FIXTER M. R. Born 25/9/63. Commd 8/9/83. Sqn Ldr 1/1/97. Retd OPS SPT 25/9/01.
FLETCHER A. K. Born 14/7/46. Commd 28/4/65. Sqn Ldr 1/1/84. Retd GD 14/7/01.
FORD E. A. BSc. Born 30/6/51. Commd 25/2/72. Sqn Ldr 1/1/89. Retd ENG 6/8/01.
FOSTER E. C. Born 6/6/50. Commd 19/6/70. Gp Capt 1/1/99. Retd ADMIN 7/6/01.
FOX P. N. Born 25/7/49. Commd 16/8/68. Sqn Ldr 1/1/96. Retd GD 9/4/02.
FOZARD M. J. CEng MRAeS. Born 12/12/46. Commd 2/8/68. Wg Cdr 1/7/87. Retd ENG 12/12/01.
FROST M. Born 28/9/63. Commd 19/6/86. Flt Lt 19/12/91. Retd GD 17/2/02.
FURR R. D. Born 29/4/44. Commd 1/11/63. Flt Lt 1/7/69. Retd GD 22/5/02.

GALLAUGHER R. A. MBE. Born 30/7/46. Commd 1/3/68. Sqn Ldr 1/1/88. Retd SUP 30/7/01.
GARDEN E. R. BSc(Eng) CEng MIMechE MRAeS. Born 1/7/45. Commd 22/9/63. Sqn Ldr 1/1/75.
  Retd ENG 1/7/83. Re-entered 2/6/86. Sqn Ldr 2/12/77. Retd ENG 1/7/01.
GARRATT W. H. Born 19/6/63. Commd 8/5/86. Flt Lt 25/2/89. Retd GD 19/6/01.
GARROD M. D. Born 23/8/64. Commd 22/11/84. Flt Lt 22/5/90. Retd GD 4/12/01.
GAULT R. K. OBE. Born 5/11/52. Commd 29/6/72. Wg Cdr 1/7/90. Retd GD 27/4/02.
GIBB P. H. Born 17/10/59. Commd 6/11/80. Sqn Ldr 1/1/96. Retd OPS SPT 5/6/01.
GIBSON M. BEng CEng MIMechE. Born 19/6/63. Commd 2/9/84. Sqn Ldr 1/1/96.
  Retd ENG 19/6/01.
GILBERT A. I. Born 10/5/51. Commd 24/7/81. Sqn Ldr 1/1/93. Retd ADMIN 15/11/01.
GILBERT M. P. BSc CEng MIEE. Born 30/10/59. Commd 30/3/86. Sqn Ldr 1/7/93.
  Retd ENG 30/4/02.
GILBERT R. L. MBE BSc CEng MBCS. Born 9/11/46. Commd 2/4/65. Sqn Ldr 1/7/85.
  Retd ADMIN 9/11/01.
GILES P. W. OBE PhD MA. Born 14/12/45. Commd 15/9/69. A Cdre 1/1/97. Retd ENG 11/3/02.
GLYDE P. L. Born 8/5/47. Commd 23/3/67. Flt Lt 23/9/72. Retd GD 8/5/02.
GOODMAN G. J. OBE MRIN. Born 30/12/46. Commd 2/8/68. Wg Cdr 1/7/88. Retd GD 30/12/01.
GOOLD I. G. BA. Born 11/3/66. Commd 14/2/88. Flt Lt 14/8/90. Retd GD 14/7/01.
GOULD J. C. MBE. Born 19/5/61. Commd 17/1/85. Sqn Ldr 1/1/99. Retd SUP 1/1/02.

GRAY-WALLIS H. F. Born 1/8/50. Commd 1/8/69. Wg Cdr 1/7/92. Retd OPS SPT 3/8/01.
GREEN G. N. Born 17/5/47. Commd 2/8/68. Sqn Ldr 1/7/89. Retd ENG 17/3/02.
GREEN S. C. MSc MCGI MRAeS. Born 4/6/63. Commd 28/2/85. Flt Lt 28/8/90. Retd GD 4/6/01.
GREGORY R. J. Born 23/4/63. Commd 20/10/83. Flt Lt 20/4/89. Retd GD 1/9/01.
GRISDALE J. N. J. MBE. Born 4/1/47. Commd 13/4/66. Gp Capt 1/7/94. Retd GD 4/1/02.
GRITTEN A. J. MBE. Born 28/3/47. Commd 2/8/68. Wg Cdr 1/7/86. Retd OPS SPT 28/3/02.
GROSE L. A. Born 24/1/42. Commd 1/10/65. Flt Lt 1/4/71. Retd GD 21/9/82. Re-entered 23/4/86.
    Sqn Ldr 1/7/99. Retd GD 24/1/02.
GROVE A. D. W. Born 17/1/47. Commd 3/6/65. Sqn Ldr 1/1/84. Retd OPS SPT 17/1/02.
GURDEN M. BEng. Born 27/1/64. Commd 2/8/85. Flt Lt 21/8/91. Retd ENG 27/1/02.

HAGAN J. G. BSc. Born 10/5/56. Commd 21/11/82. Sqn Ldr 1/1/90. Retd OPS SPT 1/8/01.
HAINES J. H. OBE. Born 17/10/45. Commd 8/1/65. A Cdre 1/1/96. Retd GD 1/2/02.
HALFTER P. N. BA. Born 14/2/50. Commd 16/1/72. Wg Cdr 1/7/90. Retd ADMIN 6/4/02.
HAMILTON D. A. BTech. Born 23/12/50. Commd 13/11/72. Wg Cdr 1/1/00. Retd GD 1/1/02.
HAMILTON I. P. Born 17/6/47. Commd 2/7/72. Wg Cdr 1/7/95. Retd ENG 1/11/01.
HAMLYN G. M. Born 9/12/46. Commd 15/12/67. Flt Lt 15/3/73. Retd GD 9/12/01.
HAMPSON-JONES C. BEng. Born 5/6/63. Commd 3/8/88. Sqn Ldr 1/1/99. Retd ENG 5/6/01.
HANCOCK J. L. MDA BSc CEng MRAeS. Born 24/11/55. Commd 14/3/77. Wg Cdr 1/7/93.
    Retd ENG 31/1/02.
HANNABY A. R. BSc CEng MRAeS. Born 16/4/58. Commd 5/9/76. Wg Cdr 1/7/97.
    Retd ENG 16/4/02.
HANSLOW M. G. Born 18/9/46. Commd 24/3/83. Sqn Ldr 1/7/94. Retd ENG 18/9/01.
HARDY N. J. Born 14/6/63. Commd 1/7/82. Flt Lt 1/1/88. Retd GD 14/6/01.
HARKER G. S. MDA FRAeS. Born 4/05/50. Commd 15/9/69. Gp Capt 1/7/97. Retd ENG 31/5/02.
HARPER I. F. MBE. Born 3/6/49. Commd 29/3/68. Wg Cdr 1/7/93. Retd GD 10/8/01.
HARRIS P. V. AFC FRAeS. Born 4/03/49. Commd 27/2/70. AVM 1/7/99. Retd GD 30/4/02.
HARRISON R. L. DPhysEd. Born 1/5/47. Commd 16/8/70. Sqn Ldr 1/1/86. Retd ADMIN 1/5/02.
HART M. C. BSc. Born 1/10/62. Commd 14/4/85. Flt Lt 14/10/87. Retd GD 14/10/01.
HARWELL G. G. M. BSc. Born 29/8/63. Commd 30/8/81. Flt Lt 15/10/85. Retd GD 29/8/01.
HASLAM A. S. MSc BSc CEng MRAeS. Born 13/2/47. Commd 17/1/82. Sqn Ldr 1/1/89.
    Retd ADMIN 13/2/02.
HASTINGS J. B. BA. Born 11/6/46. Commd 17/7/75. Wg Cdr 1/7/88. Retd ENG 11/6/01.
HAY J. C. BA. Born 17/9/46. Commd 29/6/72. Wg Cdr 1/7/99. Retd ENG 17/9/01.
HAYNES A. R. BSc. Born 7/2/47. Commd 26/5/67. Sqn Ldr 1/7/79. Retd ENG 7/2/02.
HEATON M. R. BSc. Born 22/2/64. Commd 18/8/85. Flt Lt 18/2/88. Retd GD 1/9/01.
HEELEY J. M. Born 24/9/57. Commd 18/10/79. Flt Lt 5/10/83. Retd OPS SPT 24/9/01.
HENDERSON J. M. AMBCS. Born 8/11/46. Commd 9/3/66. Wg Cdr 1/1/91. Retd SUP 11/9/01.
HENDERSON S. K. Born 13/3/63. Commd 10/5/87. Flt Lt 5/9/91. Retd OPS SPT 24/1/02.
HENRY B. L. MBE. Born 23/10/44. Commd 4/12/64. Sqn Ldr 1/7/86. Retd GD 23/10/01.
HEROD J. R. MBE. Born 21/3/63. Commd 8/12/83. Flt Lt 1/1/97. Retd GD 21/9/01.
HIGGS S. M. Born 9/1/61. Commd 28/2/80. Flt Lt 28/8/86. Retd OPS SPT 1/1/01.
HILL A. K. Born 11/2/47. Commd 21/1/86. Sqn Ldr 1/7/97. Retd GD 11/2/02.
HILLIER P. S. BSc CEng MRAeS. Born 17/7/46. Commd 3/2/69. Wg Cdr 1/7/90. Retd ENG 17/7/01.
HILLS P. L. MSc BSc CEng MIEE. Born 29/7/43. Commd 15/7/65. Sqn Ldr 1/7/77.
    Retd ENG 26/7/01.
HODGSON D. C. Born 10/3/63. Commd 1/7/82. Sqn Ldr 1/7/98. Retd GD 1/7/01.
HOGG J. K. Born 23/4/63. Commd 13/8/82. Sqn Ldr 1/7/96. Retd GD 1/1/02.
HOLDER S. BSc. Born 12/3/63. Commd 11/10/83. Wg Cdr 1/1/99. Retd ENG 1/1/02.
HOLLEY B. J. PhD MSc BSc CEng CPhys MInstP CertEd. Born 6/2/53. Commd 16/2/86.
    Sqn Ldr 1/7/94. Retd ADMIN 16/5/02.
HONEY N. J. MSc BSc CEng. Born 4/5/55. Commd 28/2/82. Sqn Ldr 1/7/89. Retd ENG 31/3/02.

HOOPER R. W. MBE MSc BSc(Eng) CEng FRAeS. Born 20/11/46. Commd 2/8/68.
 Gp Capt 1/7/94. Retd ENG 20/11/01.
HORLOCK N. J. Born 7/10/63. Commd 19/12/85. Flt Lt 19/6/91. Retd GD 7/10/01.
HORNE B. P. BA IEng FIIE AMRAeS. Born 14/8/53. Commd 15/8/85. Sqn Ldr 1/7/97.
 Retd ENG 30/9/01.
HORROCKS P. A. BSc CEng MIEE. Born 3/9/44. Commd 4/6/72. Sqn Ldr 1/1/86. Retd ENG 3/9/01.
HUDSON D. J. Born 12/4/58. Commd 9/8/79. Sqn Ldr 1/7/91. Retd GD 30/6/01.
HUDSON M. J. Born 3/9/63. Commd 19/7/84. Sqn Ldr 1/7/97. Retd GD 3/9/01.
HUGHES J. T. BA. Born 3/8/55. Commd 20/11/78. Wg Cdr 1/7/97. Retd OPS SPT 6/4/02.
HUGHES P. B. Born 1/8/46. Commd 28/4/65. Sqn Ldr 1/7/87. Retd ADMIN 1/8/01.
HUKE C. W. N. BA. Born 26/5/64. Commd 30/5/86. Flt Lt 30/9/88. Retd GD 26/5/02.
HUMPHREY M. H. Born 29/12/46. Commd 28/6/79. Sqn Ldr 1/7/95. Retd GD 29/12/01.
HURLEY D. J. MBE. Born 13/3/50. Commd 25/3/69. Wg Cdr 1/1/91. Retd GD 3/12/01.
HYDE D. C. MSc MSc BSc. Born 30/3/43. Commd 22/8/71. Wg Cdr 1/1/87. Retd ENG 30/9/01.

IDDENDEN P. Born 29/4/47. Commd 24/3/83. Sqn Ldr 1/1/95. Retd ENG 29/4/02.
IZATT G. N. AIB. Born 26/1/47. Commd 16/8/68. Flt Lt 16/2/74. Retd GD 26/1/02.

JACKMAN S. M. Born 20/9/59. Commd 27/8/87. Sqn Ldr 1/1/97. Retd ADMIN 1/8/01.
JACKSON D. Born 24/10/49. Commd 15/8/85. Flt Lt 15/8/89. Retd ENG 1/8/01.
JACKSON M. R. Born 14/4/48. Commd 16/12/66. Sqn Ldr 1/7/84. Retd OPS SPT 2/7/01.
JARVIS J. A. MBE MHSM RMN. Born 13/7/46. Commd 12/10/78. Sqn Ldr 1/1/86.
 Retd MED SPT 31/8/01.
JEFFERIES I. S. Born 15/11/43. Commd 24/6/76. Sqn Ldr 1/1/93. Retd GD 15/5/02.
JEFFERS P. Born 23/1/46. Commd 18/8/67. A Cdre 1/1/96. Retd GD 11/5/02.
JENKINS I. P. Born 8/2/58. Commd 1/12/77. Wg Cdr 1/7/96. Retd OPS SPT 7/2/02.
JENNINGS P. T. Born 22/3/42. Commd 28/10/66. Flt Lt 28/4/72. Retd GD 22/3/02.
JOHNSTON D. C. Born 30/8/61. Commd 30/4/81. Sqn Ldr 1/7/96. Retd OPS SPT 8/1/02.
JONES G. Born 27/2/62. Commd 19/3/81. Sqn Ldr 1/1/99. Retd OPS SPT 1/1/02.
JONES P. Born 20/1/48. Commd 2/11/88. Sqn Ldr 1/7/97. Retd ENG 19/9/01.
JONES R. L. MBE. Born 13/8/49. Commd 25/2/88. Flt Lt 25/2/90. Retd GD 29/1/02.
JONES R. P. Born 5/3/63. Commd 13/4/86. Sqn Ldr 1/7/96. Retd GD 13/4/02.
JONES R. R. Born 7/8/62. Commd 15/3/84. Flt Lt 15/9/89. Retd GD 1/7/01.
JONES S. A. Born 8/3/52. Commd 21/12/89. Flt Lt 21/12/93. Retd ENG 19/4/02.
JUDD D. G. M. MSc MSc BSc. Born 12/1/62. Commd 30/10/83. Sqn Ldr 1/7/95.
 Retd ENG 15/1/02.

KAYE P. M. Born 29/4/59. Commd 11/1/79. Wg Cdr 1/1/97. Retd OPS SPT 8/4/02.
KEEP D. J. MA MSc BSc CEng MIEE. Born 22/11/61. Commd 31/8/80. Wg Cdr 1/1/99.
 Retd ENG 1/1/02.
KELLARD C. A. MCSP. Born 15/12/51. Commd 30/3/89. Flt Lt 30/3/93. Retd OPS SPT 1/5/02.
KERSHAW J. Born 22/6/46. Commd 20/8/69. Wg Cdr 1/1/92. Retd GD 22/6/01.
KIMBER C. J. BEd. Born 19/10/61. Commd 30/3/86. Flt Lt 30/9/89. Retd OPS SPT 30/3/02.
KING P. M. BSc. Born 26/2/56. Commd 1/8/76. Wg Cdr 1/7/93. Retd SUP 26/2/02.
KINGWILL P. M. Born 14/8/46. Commd 23/3/66. Sqn Ldr 1/7/79. Retd SUP 14/8/84.
 Re-entered 1/3/88. Sqn Ldr 17/1/83. Retd SUP 14/8/01.
KIRKHOPE T. BSc. Born 9/10/49. Commd 17/10/71. Wg Cdr 1/7/94. Retd GD 4/8/01.
KIRKUP A. P. J. Born 21/6/51. Commd 16/3/73. Flt Lt 16/3/76. Retd GD 1/7/01.
KNIGHT P. Born 30/11/62. Commd 20/10/83. Flt Lt 20/4/89. Retd GD 3/11/01.

LACEY T. A. BSc. Born 20/9/48. Commd 25/2/88. Flt Lt 25/2/92. Retd ENG 31/1/02.
LAKE A. R. Born 19/7/63. Commd 17/1/85. Flt Lt 17/7/90. Retd GD 19/7/01.
LAMBIE P. S. BTech MCMI. Born 26/6/46. Commd 24/4/77. Sqn Ldr 1/7/88. Retd ENG 26/6/01.

LAWRENCE N. J. BSc. Born 27/6/59. Commd 30/3/86. Flt Lt 30/9/89. Retd OPS SPT 30/3/02.
LE GALLOUDEC S. J. Born 25/9/58. Commd 26/9/70. Flt Lt 26/9/92. Retd ENG 10/10/01.
LEACH P. W. BSc. Born 10/12/62. Commd 16/11/83. Flt Lt 15/1/87. Retd GD 15/7/01.
LEE R. R. G. Born 31/3/47. Commd 20/9/79. Flt Lt 20/9/81. Retd OPS SPT 31/3/02.
LEES M. N. Born 3/12/50. Commd 5/11/70. Gp Capt 1/1/95. Retd GD 14/12/01.
LEFFLER T. Born 25/9/63. Commd 2/5/84. Flt Lt 2/8/90. Retd OPS SPT 25/9/01.
LEIGH R. G. Born 27/1/44. Commd 14/6/63. Flt Lt 14/12/68. Retd GD 27/1/02.
LEWIS I. V. Born 21/5/46. Commd 8/8/74. Sqn Ldr 1/1/85. Retd ENG 15/8/01.
LEWIS-MORRIS M. J. MSc BSc. Born 1/2/46. Commd 29/4/84. Sqn Ldr 1/1/92.
    Retd ADMIN 1/5/02.
LIMBERT J. J. Born 5/4/53. Commd 2/8/90. Flt Lt 2/8/94. Retd ADMIN 15/4/02.
LINES P. J. Born 1/3/64. Commd 24/3/83. Sqn Ldr 1/1/98. Retd GD 24/6/01.
LOGAN K. A. MSc FISM FCIPD. Born 6/5/58. Commd 20/8/90. Sqn Ldr 1/7/98.
    Retd ADMIN 3/4/02.
LOOKER I. MSc BSc. Born 14/8/60. Commd 29/4/84. Sqn Ldr 1/7/96. Retd ENG 10/1/02.
LUDLOW S. Born 11/2/62. Commd 23/5/85. Flt Lt 23/11/90. Retd GD 24/11/01.
LYDIATE D. MSc FCIPD CertEd. Born 2/6/51. Commd 5/1/86. Sqn Ldr 1/7/94.
    Retd ADMIN 5/1/02.
LYSTER J. M. MCIPD. Born 22/10/46. Commd 6/1/96. Wg Cdr 1/7/98. Retd ADMIN 22/10/01.

MACDONALD G. B. Born 5/12/47. Commd 23/8/87. Flt Lt 23/4/91. Retd ENG 31/7/01.
MACDONALD G. W. B. MSc FICD. Born 16/11/51. Commd 28/7/88. Sqn Ldr 1/1/98.
    Retd MED SPT 16/11/01.
MACKENZIE M. R. BSc. Born 15/12/45. Commd 13/9/71. Sqn Ldr 1/1/87. Retd ADMIN 19/11/01.
MANN C. F. MSc BSc CPhys CEng. Born 26/2/51. Commd 14/6/81. Sqn Ldr 1/1/88.
    Retd ADMIN 30/11/01.
MANNION D. T. Born 13/9/63. Commd 4/12/86. Flt Lt 17/11/90. Retd GD 13/9/01.
MARKS P. J. Born 16/7/44. Commd 22/2/63. Flt Lt 22/8/68. Retd GD 16/7/01.
MARSHALL R. J. Born 28/5/54. Commd 14/1/88. Flt Lt 14/1/90. Retd ENG 14/1/02.
MASON G. Born 20/7/63. Commd 15/10/81. Sqn Ldr 1/1/98. Retd GD 20/7/01.
MASTERS C. W. Born 3/5/56. Commd 2/8/90. Sqn Ldr 1/7/98. Retd SUP 3/7/01.
MAY J. E. BSc(Eng). Born 17/6/63. Commd 29/9/85. Flt Lt 29/3/88. Retd GD 23/4/02.
MCALL D. MDA. Born 8/5/59. Commd 11/6/81. Wg Cdr 1/1/97. Retd ADMIN 2/7/01.
MCCARTHY M. B. Born 27/8/46. Commd 21/4/77. Sqn Ldr 1/1/90. Retd ENG 27/8/01.
MCCAY D. D. Born 24/9/49. Commd 9/11/89. Sqn Ldr 1/1/00. Retd MED SPT 3/4/02.
MCCONNELL R. BA. Born 12/11/48. Commd 3/1/69. A Cdre 1/1/99. Retd ADMIN 5/4/02.
MCCOWAN N. C. Born 30/12/63. Commd 19/12/85. Flt Lt 19/6/91. Retd GD 30/12/01.
MCDONALD I. J. MA. Born 19/9/47. Commd 11/9/77. Sqn Ldr 1/7/88. Retd ADMIN 1/10/01.
MCFADYEN A. G. BA. Born 18/11/55. Commd 29/11/81. Sqn Ldr 1/1/91. Retd OPS SPT 27/11/01.
MCGLARY S. Born 9/11/53. Commd 14/1/88. Sqn Ldr 1/7/97. Retd ENG 14/1/02.
MCGRATH J. G. BSc. Born 1/11/60. Commd 14/10/84. Flt Lt 14/4/86. Retd GD 28/8/01.
MCGUIRE K. Born 21/11/47. Commd 31/7/70. Sqn Ldr 1/1/96. Retd GD 23/9/01.
MCKENNA M. J. MBE. Born 26/4/46. Commd 23/2/68. Sqn Ldr 1/7/87. Retd GD 26/8/01.
MCLAREN B. G. MSc MBA MCMI. Born 3/11/47. Commd 27/2/75. Gp Capt 1/1/96.
    Retd GD 24/8/01.
MCLAUGHLIN A. N. MA BSc. Born 20/3/62. Commd 14/9/80. Wg Cdr 1/7/98. Retd GD 19/11/01.
MCLOUGHLIN K. H. MB BCh BAO FFARCS(Ire). Born 5/3/55. Commd 13/10/85. Wg Cdr 1/8/93.
    Retd MED 14/5/02.
MCNEIL J. J. Born 3/7/46. Commd 10/1/69. Sqn Ldr 1/1/87. Retd GD 1/7/01.
MIDDLETON J. Born 21/09/48. Commd 31/7/70. Gp Capt 1/1/98. Retd GD 30/7/01.
MILLER A. S. Born 25/12/48. Commd 31/7/70. Flt Lt 31/7/73. Retd GD 5/7/01.
MILNES J. P. BEd. Born 22/11/46. Commd 30/7/72. Wg Cdr 1/7/91. Retd ADMIN 26/9/01.
MITCHELL A. N. MBE. Born 2/9/48. Commd 27/2/70. Wg Cdr 1/7/90. Retd GD 16/2/02.

MITCHELL J. I. Born 5/3/56. Commd 29/1/87. Flt Lt 29/1/89. Retd GD 1/2/02.
MITCHELL M. BDS. Born 21/1/63. Commd 19/1/86. Wg Cdr 19/7/98. Retd DEL 19/1/02.
MITCHELL R. A. Born 29/11/45. Commd 5/6/67. Sqn Ldr 1/7/94. Retd ADMIN 30/11/01.
MITCHELL S. A. DFC. Born 14/7/61. Commd 5/1/83. Sqn Ldr 1/1/98. Retd GD 1/2/02.
MOGFORD F. L. Born 8/11/46. Commd 28/4/67. Wg Cdr 1/7/90. Retd GD 8/11/01.
MOON S. Born 17/12/52. Commd 10/5/90. Flt Lt 10/5/94. Retd OPS SPT 31/12/01.
MOORE M. L. BSc. Born 21/7/61. Commd 11/12/83. Flt Lt 11/6/86. Retd GD 19/4/02.
MORFFEW C. G. Born 27/9/47. Commd 30/5/69. Wg Cdr 1/7/90. Retd GD 11/3/02.
MORGAN C. R. Born 26/1/47. Commd 24/3/83. Sqn Ldr 1/1/92. Retd ENG 17/9/01.
MORGAN D. Born 15/4/47. Commd 29/7/83. Sqn Ldr 1/7/92. Retd ADMIN 15/4/02.
MORGAN J. R. MHCIMA. Born 13/10/50. Commd 19/9/71. Wg Cdr 1/1/89. Retd ADMIN 21/2/02.
MORLEY E. MBE. Born 27/3/45. Commd 8/9/77. Sqn Ldr 1/1/89. Retd ENG 27/3/02.
MORRIS A. J. S. BSc. Born 26/3/67. Commd 24/10/85. Flt Lt 15/1/93. Retd ENG 15/7/01.
MORRIS A. M. D. MSc. Born 12/9/46. Commd 21/5/65. Gp Capt 1/1/94. Retd GD 12/9/01.
MORRIS R. V. CBE AFC. Born 24/9/49. Commd 14/2/69. AVM 1/1/01. Retd GD 30/4/02.
MORRIS S. C. Born 22/2/64. Commd 13/2/86. Flt Lt 2/3/90. Retd GD 22/2/02.
MORRISON G. J. Born 6/3/49. Commd 8/1/76. Sqn Ldr 1/7/84. Retd ENG 3/12/01.
MOSS A. S. Born 4/4/65. Commd 2/8/90. Sqn Ldr 1/1/00. Retd ENG 5/4/02.
MUMME I. G. T. Born 18/1/46. Commd 18/11/66. Flt Lt 18/3/73. Retd SUP 18/11/01.
MURKIN S. D. AFC. Born 9/12/52. Commd 21/4/77. Sqn Ldr 1/7/89. Retd GD 8/12/96.
    Re-entered 4/11/97. Wg Cdr 1/1/00. Retd GD 12/4/02.
MUSKETT A. J. MBE. Born 26/8/63. Commd 14/1/82. Sqn Ldr 1/1/96. Retd GD 26/8/01.

NASH A. J. MA. Born 31/12/59. Commd 9/8/79. Wg Cdr 1/1/99. Retd GD 5/4/02.
NEGUS T. W. OBE BDS FDSRCSEd LDSRCS. Born 10/1/43. Commd 29/12/63. A Cdre 1/1/94.
    Retd DEL 2/4/02.
NETHAWAY M. F. J. MInstD. Born 28/8/46. Commd 10/5/73. Wg Cdr 1/7/94. Retd ENG 28/8/01.
NEWCOMBE A. M. MBE. Born 27/12/48. Commd 4/7/69. Sqn Ldr 1/7/86. Retd ADMIN 7/1/02.
NEWTON R. T. BEng. Born 15/3/64. Commd 18/8/85. Sqn Ldr 1/7/96. Retd GD 12/4/02.
NICHOLL S. M. CB CBE AFC BA FRAeS. Born 15/11/46. Commd 22/9/65. AVM 1/7/98.
    Retd GD 15/11/01.
NORRIS P. G. Born 28/11/45. Commd 15/7/66. Sqn Ldr 1/7/76. Retd ENG 28/11/83.
    Re-entered 13/9/85. Sqn Ldr 8/4/78. Retd ENG 28/11/01.
NORTON J. R. Born 5/6/55. Commd 5/1/78. Sqn Ldr 1/1/94. Retd GD 3/11/01.

O'CONNELL P. M. MCMI. Born 18/5/53. Commd 11/9/86. Sqn Ldr 1/7/94. Retd ENG 17/11/01.
O'DELL P. M. H. Born 20/1/64. Commd 11/10/84. Sqn Ldr 1/7/97. Retd GD 20/1/02.
O'DONNELL J. J. BDS LDSRCS. Born 18/4/60. Commd 1/9/85. Wg Cdr 3/3/97. Retd DEL 1/9/01.
OLIVER S. W. STJ. BSc. Born 26/12/51. Commd 30/5/76. Wg Cdr 1/7/90. Retd ENG 31/5/02.
ORDISH G. A. Born 15/4/47. Commd 29/7/65. Wg Cdr 1/1/92. Retd OPS SPT 19/1/02.

PAISH S. C. BA. Born 29/12/61. Commd 29/9/85. Flt Lt 29/3/87. Retd GD 29/9/01.
PARNELL-HOPKINSON The Rev C. Born 1/8/46. Commd 19/2/84. Retd 1/8/01. Wg Cdr.
PARSONS G. A. BA. Born 23/10/62. Commd 16/2/86. Flt Lt 16/8/89. Retd OPS SPT 4/4/02.
PATTENDEN G. E. P. LLB FCIS. Born 31/12/47. Commd 22/7/71. Wg Cdr 1/7/99.
    Retd ADMIN 30/9/01.
PEARCE N. G. MSc BSc. Born 22/9/59. Commd 18/8/85. Sqn Ldr 1/1/95. Retd SUP 18/8/01.
PEARSON N. F. BSc CEng MRAeS. Born 21/12/61. Commd 2/2/84. Sqn Ldr 1/1/97.
    Retd ENG 3/1/02.
PEARSON N. J. FRAeS FCMI. Born 17/2/46. Commd 4/7/69. Gp Capt 1/1/96.
    Retd OPS SPT 1/7/01.
PEARSON S. J. MCIPS MILogDip. Born 25/6/58. Commd 25/2/88. Sqn Ldr 1/1/96.
    Retd SUP 1/2/02.

PEDLEY M. Born 30/9/46. Commd 5/2/65. Flt Lt 5/8/70. Retd GD 30/9/01.
PHILLIPS P. L. BSc CEng MRAeS. Born 7/10/40. Commd 15/8/82. Sqn Ldr 1/7/89.
    Retd ENG 4/1/02.
PHILLIPS R. C. MB ChB MRCGP DRCOG. Born 6/12/55. Commd 9/6/85. Wg Cdr 8/1/95.
    Retd MED 9/6/01.
PHYSICK M. D. BSc. Born 24/6/63. Commd 18/8/85. Flt Lt 18/2/87. Retd GD 18/8/01.
PILLING J. A. BSc. Born 28/6/63. Commd 13/9/81. Sqn Ldr 1/1/98. Retd GD 28/6/01.
PIM R. S. BSc. Born 6/6/58. Commd 29/9/85. Flt Lt 29/3/86. Retd ADMIN 29/9/01.
PLATT J. C. BA. Born 2/4/47. Commd 22/9/68. Gp Capt 1/1/96. Retd GD 2/4/02.
POLLINGTON D. AFC. Born 26/12/46. Commd 1/3/68. Gp Capt 1/1/00. Retd GD 3/1/02.
POTTS D. S. Born 16/4/64. Commd 24/9/92. Flt Lt 14/6/95. Retd SUP 16/4/02.
POULTON S. BSc. Born 22/11/46. Commd 22/10/72. Sqn Ldr 1/1/89. Retd ENG 22/11/01.
POWELL L. R. Born 25/7/47. Commd 10/12/65. Wg Cdr 1/7/94. Retd GD 2/11/01.
POWELL M. B. BTech. Born 27/12/62. Commd 5/1/86. Flt Lt 5/7/87. Retd OPS SPT 5/1/02.
PRESTON M. MA. Born 9/2/63. Commd 29/9/85. Sqn Ldr 1/7/96. Retd GD 29/12/01.
PRICE R. G. Born 21/4/64. Commd 4/12/86. Flt Lt 11/5/90. Retd GD 21/4/02.
PRISSICK M. CBE. Born 11/6/49. Commd 25/2/72. A Cdre 1/7/99. Retd GD 11/7/01.

QUICK P. E. Born 18/7/54. Commd 16/9/76. Flt Lt 1/3/81. Retd GD 31/1/02.

REED S. C. MSc BSc. Born 29/12/63. Commd 5/9/82. Sqn Ldr 1/1/95. Retd ENG 29/12/01.
REEVE N. P. Born 14/9/44. Commd 7/6/73. Sqn Ldr 1/7/91. Retd OPS SPT 11/7/01.
RENSHAW A. Born 29/11/47. Commd 3/12/70. Wg Cdr 1/7/92. Retd ENG 1/11/01.
RICE W. OBE. Born 1/8/46. Commd 22/7/66. Wg Cdr 1/7/91. Retd ADMIN 1/8/01.
RITCH D. N. S. BSc. Born 11/6/63. Commd 1/4/85. Flt Lt 15/1/88. Retd GD 11/6/01.
RITCHIE J. M. B. Born 27/1/47. Commd 6/5/66. Sqn Ldr 1/1/84. Retd GD 27/1/02.
ROBERTS P. A. BSc. Born 20/3/56. Commd 1/7/79. Sqn Ldr 1/7/91. Retd OPS SPT 1/7/01.
ROBINSON D. F. BSc. Born 17/1/49. Commd 28/2/82. Sqn Ldr 1/1/88. Retd ENG 27/7/01.
ROSIE K. S. Born 26/4/62. Commd 5/2/81. Flt Lt 5/8/87. Retd OPS SPT 31/12/01.
ROWLEY-BROOKE P. S. J. BA. Born 9/6/46. Commd 1/3/68. Sqn Ldr 1/1/82. Retd ENG 9/6/01.
ROYCE M. J. Born 21/8/63. Commd 25/2/82. Sqn Ldr 1/7/98. Retd GD 21/8/01.
RUDD M. J. Born 20/8/51. Commd 16/3/73. Sqn Ldr 1/7/94. Retd ADMIN 1/10/01.
RUSSELL J. R. Born 22/8/46. Commd 21/4/67. Flt Lt 29/7/73. Retd OPS SPT 22/8/01.
RUTHERDALE R. J. Born 9/1/53. Commd 27/7/89. Flt Lt 27/7/93. Retd OPS SPT 1/10/01.
RYALL F. D. Born 14/9/56. Commd 5/8/76. Wg Cdr 1/1/96. Retd GD 14/9/01.
RYCROFT A. S. BSc(Eng). Born 30/5/61. Commd 1/5/80. Sqn Ldr 1/7/98. Retd GD 1/7/01.

SAINSBURY D. J. MSc BEd. Born 5/5/53. Commd 25/5/80. Wg Cdr 1/1/99.
    Retd ADMIN 25/5/02.
SAUNDERS A. E. J. BA. Born 11/4/62. Commd 30/3/86. Flt Lt 30/9/88. Retd OPS SPT 30/3/02.
SAUNDERS M. B. MSc BDS MGDSRCS(Eng). Born 26/2/63. Commd 19/1/86. Wg Cdr 11/7/98.
    Retd DEL 19/1/02.
SCANNELL K. H. E. BSc. Born 2/6/55. Commd 5/2/84. Sqn Ldr 1/7/94. Retd ENG 23/2/02.
SCULLY J. M. Born 1/10/46. Commd 9/8/79. Sqn Ldr 1/1/89. Retd ENG 1/10/01.
SHARPLES C. J. QHP MSc FFOM MRCS(Eng) LRCP DAvMed MRAeS. Born 9/4/42.
    Commd 23/9/63. AVM 1/7/97. Retd MED 9/4/02.
SHEPPARD P. R. BEM. Born 17/8/49. Commd 5/5/88. Sqn Ldr 1/7/99. Retd ENG 27/5/02.
SHIELDS R. Born 22/5/58. Commd 26/2/79. Wg Cdr 1/1/96. Retd ADMIN 22/5/02.
SHILLITO P. MSc BSc CEng MIEE. Born 6/1/61. Commd 18/3/84. Sqn Ldr 1/1/92.
    Retd ENG 18/6/01.
SIMPSON A. C. Born 25/8/44. Commd 19/8/66. Flt Lt 17/3/71. Retd GD 13/11/82. Re-entered
    5/1/90. Flt Lt 5/1/87. Retd GD 25/8/01.

SIMPSON R. MSc BSc CEng MIEE. Born 13/7/63. Commd 5/9/82. Sqn Ldr 1/1/93. Retd ENG 14/9/01.
SMAILES M. S. Born 4/9/58. Commd 11/5/78. Sqn Ldr 1/7/94. Retd OPS SPT 1/1/02.
SMALE M. J. IEng MIIE. Born 21/5/55. Commd 8/5/86. Flt Lt 8/5/88. Retd ENG 20/8/01.
SMITH C. J. BSc. Born 17/10/63. Commd 26/5/85. Flt Lt 26/11/87. Retd GD 17/10/01.
SMITH G. P. Born 7/3/46. Commd 1/3/68. Wg Cdr 1/1/87. Retd GD 10/6/01.
SNELDERS F. M. Born 20/7/45. Commd 27/3/70. Sqn Ldr 1/1/84. Retd GD 20/7/01.
SOMERVILLE A. D. Born 6/7/62. Commd 8/9/83. Sqn Ldr 1/7/98. Retd GD 1/7/01.
SPARKS J. C. BA CertEd. Born 11/12/52. Commd 30/3/86. Sqn Ldr 1/1/94. Retd ADMIN 30/3/02.
STAINCLIFFE C. D. Born 31/5/49. Commd 8/10/70. Sqn Ldr 1/1/89. Retd ADMIN 15/7/01.
STAMP R. J. Born 19/2/59. Commd 20/12/90. Flt Lt 20/12/92. Retd GD 1/8/01.
STEVENSON J. Born 5/1/47. Commd 29/3/68. Sqn Ldr 1/1/88. Retd GD 5/1/02.
STEWART J. W. Born 8/10/46. Commd 26/5/67. Gp Capt 1/1/97. Retd ENG 8/10/01.
STOBART G. Born 14/10/63. Commd 8/12/83. Sqn Ldr 1/1/00. Retd GD 14/10/01.
STOBART R. H. MILT. Born 20/5/64. Commd 13/2/86. Sqn Ldr 1/7/97. Retd SUP 20/5/02.
STOCK I. M. BSc. Born 25/1/51. Commd 11/12/83. Sqn Ldr 1/1/99. Retd ADMIN 1/1/02.
STOUT T. A. BSc. Born 15/11/63. Commd 10/11/85. Sqn Ldr 1/1/99. Retd GD 1/1/02.
STRANG A. J. M. BA BSc. Born 14/1/47. Commd 13/2/72. Sqn Ldr 1/1/82. Retd GD 14/4/02.
STURMAN R. J. Born 4/11/46. Commd 23/6/67. Gp Capt 1/1/94. Retd OPS SPT 6/4/02.
SUTTON M. C. Born 7/12/63. Commd 15/6/83. Sqn Ldr 1/1/96. Retd GD 7/12/01.
SZYMANSKI A. R. Born 12/6/67. Commd 9/11/89. Flt Lt 9/5/95. Retd GD 16/1/02.

TANDY R. MSc BSc CEng MIEE. Born 12/1/64. Commd 11/11/82. Sqn Ldr 1/1/98. Retd ENG 12/1/02.
TANK J. S. R. BSc. Born 25/3/63. Commd 22/7/84. Sqn Ldr 1/7/98. Retd GD 1/7/01.
TAYLOR A. H. BSc. Born 16/5/63. Commd 25/11/84. Flt Lt 25/5/87. Retd GD 16/11/01.
TAYLOR N. E. BSc FRAeS. Born 6/12/47. Commd 9/8/71. A Cdre 1/1/98. Retd GD 13/5/02.
TAYLOR P. Born 8/1/64. Commd 24/3/83. Sqn Ldr 1/7/94. Retd GD 25/9/01.
TAYLOR P. F. Born 14/6/46. Commd 7/7/67. Flt Lt 7/1/73. Retd GD 14/6/01.
TAYLOR S. J. Born 15/9/51. Commd 15/3/79. Flt Lt 17/2/86. Retd GD 18/7/01.
TELFORD G. M. BSc. Born 21/4/54. Commd 17/9/72. Wg Cdr 1/1/94. Retd GD 28/9/01.
THOMAS P. D. BSc. Born 5/1/63. Commd 18/8/85. Flt Lt 18/2/89. Retd ENG 18/8/01.
THOMPSON G. J. BA. Born 6/11/53. Commd 7/3/74. Sqn Ldr 1/7/98. Retd SUP 31/8/01.
THOMPSON M. H. Born 2/2/47. Commd 20/12/90. Flt Lt 20/12/94. Retd ENG 2/2/02.
THOMSON C. G. A. Born 5/3/64. Commd 9/11/89. Flt Lt 7/2/93. Retd ADMIN 5/3/02.
THORPE A. J. Born 13/9/46. Commd 28/4/65. Wg Cdr 1/7/87. Retd GD 13/9/01.
THOW D. P. BSc CEng MRAeS MIMechE MCMI. Born 10/12/50. Commd 15/9/69. Wg Cdr 1/1/90. Retd ENG 6/12/01.
THURTLE I. C. Born 22/8/63. Commd 20/6/91. Flt Lt 20/6/93. Retd GD 22/8/01.
TIMBERS H. A. Born 17/7/46. Commd 2/12/66. Flt Lt 4/5/72. Retd GD 17/7/01.
TOFI P. M. Born 13/9/57. Commd 1/7/82. Sqn Ldr 1/7/95. Retd ADMIN 1/12/01.
TRACE M. R. OBE MA FRAeS. Born 11/9/47. Commd 23/9/68. Gp Capt 1/1/94. Retd GD 5/7/01.
TREDRAY N. P. K. Born 9/8/47. Commd 23/2/68. Sqn Ldr 1/1/99. Retd GD 10/8/01.
TROTT D. T. BSc. Born 5/3/63. Commd 14/10/84. Flt Lt 14/4/87. Retd GD 5/7/01.
TURBITT D. BSc. Born 11/10/49. Commd 15/9/69. Flt Lt 15/10/73. Retd GD 19/4/02.
TURNER G. J. Born 19/3/59. Commd 15/3/84. Flt Lt 15/9/90. Retd OPS SPT 31/10/01.

UNDERWOOD R. Born 19/6/63. Commd 15/6/83. Flt Lt 15/12/88. Retd GD 19/6/01.
UPHAM J. A. MSc BSc CEng FCIPD MIEE MBCS DIC CDipAF. Born 17/3/46. Commd 19/9/71. Gp Capt 1/1/99. Retd ADMIN 31/7/01.

VASS A. Born 9/4/45. Commd 19/10/72. Sqn Ldr 1/7/83. Retd OPS SPT 9/4/02.

VASS D. C. MBE FRAes FCMI MCIPD. Born 7/3/50. Commd 4/7/69. A Cdre 1/1/00.
Retd GD 12/1/02.
VERNAL J. Born 6/9/45. Commd 21/4/67. Sqn Ldr 1/7/83. Retd OPS SPT 1/10/01.
VOLTZENLOGEL P. N. MCIT MILT. Born 3/3/58. Commd 21/4/77. Wg Cdr 1/7/97.
Retd SUP 3/3/02.
WALKER C. G. Born 8/7/52. Commd 10/2/72. Sqn Ldr 1/1/89. Retd OPS SPT 8/5/02.
WALKER E. S. Born 7/12/41. Commd 19/12/85. Flt Lt 19/12/87. Retd GD 7/12/01.
WALKER K. J. BSc CEng MIMechE. Born 18/2/47. Commd 30/3/75. Sqn Ldr 1/7/83.
Retd ENG 1/4/02.
WALKER S. A. Born 22/11/63. Commd 2/11/88. Flt Lt 4/9/91. Retd OPS SPT 22/11/01.
WALLER C. J. N. IEng FIIE AMRAeS. Born 14/4/45. Commd 23/11/78. Sqn Ldr 1/1/91.
Retd ENG 14/4/02.
WALSH L. M. P. BSc. Born 21/4/49. Commd 22/9/71. Gp Capt 1/7/99. Retd ENG 17/2/02.
WALTERS R. J. BSc. Born 17/10/46. Commd 11/5/71. Sqn Ldr 1/7/84. Retd GD 17/10/01.
WARBURTON G. R. Born 28/12/46. Commd 1/10/65. Wg Cdr 1/1/95. Retd GD 15/5/02.
WARREN M. D. BSc. Born 7/5/64. Commd 29/9/85. Sqn Ldr 1/1/99. Retd GD 7/5/02.
WATKIN J. S. BEng CEng MRAeS. Born 30/11/70. Commd 17/9/89. Flt Lt 15/1/96.
Retd ENG 17/9/01.
WEBSTER E. E. Born 15/3/51. Commd 1/4/76. Wg Cdr 1/7/00. Retd OPS SPT 18/5/02.
WEEKS R. M. H. Born 4/4/64. Commd 27/3/86. Flt Lt 27/9/91. Retd GD 4/4/02.
WEIGHT P. E. Born 8/9/46. Commd 1/3/68. Sqn Ldr 1/1/82. Retd ENG 8/9/01.
WESLEY D. M. OBE FInstPet. Born 29/9/46. Commd 24/2/67. Gp Capt 1/7/93. Retd SUP 29/9/01.
WESTERN G. R. Born 1/5/52. Commd 25/2/88. Sqn Ldr 1/7/01. Retd ADMIN 29/12/01.
WESTWOOD M. P. OBE. Born 29/8/44. Commd 19/4/63. Wg Cdr 1/1/91. Retd GD 29/8/01.
WHITE M. G. F. OBE. Born 18/11/52. Commd 9/3/72. A Cdre 1/1/97. Retd GD 15/8/01.
WHITTINGHAM R. J. FRAeS FCMI. Born 16/02/44. Commd 15/7/65. Gp Capt 1/7/91.
Retd ENG 10/6/01.
WILKINS M. J. BSc CEng MRAeS. Born 31/12/43. Commd 14/4/69. Wg Cdr 1/7/87.
Retd ENG 30/11/01.
WILKINSON M. BA PGCE MIL. Born 15/8/53. Commd 29/9/85. Sqn Ldr 1/7/94.
Retd ADMIN 29/9/01.
WILLERTON A. Born 9/3/60. Commd 28/7/88. Sqn Ldr 1/1/97. Retd ADMIN 31/10/01.
WILLIAMS A. H. BSc MCMI. Born 8/6/46. Commd 4/6/72. Sqn Ldr 1/7/83. Retd GD 8/6/01.
WILLIAMS I. R. Born 24/7/57. Commd 22/2/79. Sqn Ldr 1/7/89. Retd GD 24/7/01.
WILLIAMS S. C. BSc. Born 24/5/64. Commd 18/8/85. Sqn Ldr 1/1/99. Retd GD 24/5/02.
WILLIAMS V. J. MBE BSc. Born 15/1/48. Commd 5/1/70. Sqn Ldr 1/1/89. Retd OPS SPT 22/4/02.
WILLIAMSON N. P. Born 7/4/60. Commd 11/5/86. Sqn Ldr 1/1/99. Retd ENG 11/5/02.
WILSON D. J. BSc. Born 4/9/62. Commd 18/10/83. Sqn Ldr 1/7/95. Retd ENG 1/3/02.
WILSON G. BSc. Born 6/12/63. Commd 29/9/85. Sqn Ldr 1/7/96. Retd ADMIN 24/3/02.
WILSON G. A. BEM. Born 28/12/46. Commd 24/4/84. Sqn Ldr 1/7/94. Retd ENG 18/6/01.
WILSON J. R. Born 21/8/48. Commd 11/8/77. Sqn Ldr 1/1/89. Retd ADMIN 1/5/02.
WINGHAM A. MB BS DRCOG. Born 13/12/58. Commd 13/2/80. Wg Cdr 3/8/97.
Retd MED 1/9/01.
WINKLES A. R. C. Born 17/2/45. Commd 28/2/64. Wg Cdr 1/7/83. Retd GD 1/7/01.
WINTERMEYER M. J. BSc. Born 5/3/63. Commd 18/8/85. Flt Lt 18/2/88. Retd GD 18/8/01.
WITHERS B. R. MBE AFC. Born 12/9/46. Commd 25/2/66. Sqn Ldr 1/1/88. Retd GD 12/9/01.
WOOD D. M. Born 10/8/57. Commd 5/8/76. Wg Cdr 1/1/97. Retd GD 10/8/01.
WOOD P. M. Born 8/5/58. Commd 21/4/77. Wg Cdr 1/7/96. Retd OPS SPT 8/5/02.
WOOD T. J. Born 16/10/48. Commd 31/7/70. Gp Capt 1/1/98. Retd GD 27/2/02.
WOODROFFE R. J. MBE. Born 12/6/50. Commd 19/8/71. Wg Cdr 1/7/89. Retd ADMIN 2/11/01.
WOODS T. J. A. Born 1/3/63. Commd 8/4/82. Sqn Ldr 1/7/98. Retd GD 1/7/01.
WOOLLACOTT R. N. MBE. Born 4/9/43. Commd 28/7/64. Wg Cdr 1/1/89. Retd GD 26/6/01.
WRAY H. L. BSc. Born 23/5/67. Commd 6/11/88. Sqn Ldr 1/1/96. Retd ENG 10/9/01.

WRIGLEY D. A. Born 17/12/47. Commd 2/8/68. Sqn Ldr 1/1/92. Retd ENG 12/6/01.

YORKE D. J. FBIFM. Born 5/6/47. Commd 19/7/84. Sqn Ldr 1/1/96. Retd ADMIN 3/8/01.
YOUNG D. J. MSc BSc CEng MIMechE. Born 29/7/57. Commd 3/5/81. Sqn Ldr 1/1/91. Retd ENG 27/7/01.
YOUNG N. F. Born 7/12/60. Commd 11/4/85. Flt Lt 19/7/88. Retd GD 22/8/01.
YOUNG S. MA CEng MIEE CertEd. Born 14/11/54. Commd 16/12/79. Sqn Ldr 1/1/90. Retd ENG 16/12/01.
YOUNG S. J. Born 12/3/62. Commd 11/6/81. Wg Cdr 1/7/99. Retd GD 31/10/01.
YOUNGMAN M. A. Born 27/8/61. Commd 24/7/81. Sqn Ldr 1/7/98. Retd GD 20/1/02.

LIST OF RETIRED OFFICERS OF
THE PRINCESS MARY'S ROYAL AIR FORCE
NURSING SERVICE

WILLIAMS R. H. RRC. Born 13/10/44. A Cdre 1/7/99. Retd 2/7/01.

OBITUARY

RETIRED LIST

Retired Officers
whose deaths have been reported since July 2001

Rank and Name	Date of Death	Rank and Name	Date of Death
ABLETT S. G. Flt Lt	2.3.02	BICKERSTAFF G. G. F. DFC Flt Lt	14.6.01
ABROOK R. H. BEM Wg Cdr ...	2.9.01	BIRD-WILSON H. A. C. CBE DSO	
ACKERS J. R. Wg Cdr	21.8.01	DFC* AFC* AVM	27.12.00
ADAMSON D. E. MA Wg Cdr ...	20.8.01	BIRSE R. C. G. BSc Flt Lt ...	4.6.01
ADDINGTON F. F. DFC Wg Cdr...	15.2.02	BLACK F. A. Sqn Ldr	25.4.01
AEDY K. J. Sqn Ldr	16.11.01	BLACKBURN G. J. MBE Sqn Ldr	20.1.02
ALDRICH E. W. Flt Lt	30.5.02	BLACKLAW J. Sqn Ldr	26.3.02
ALDRIDGE H. V. Sqn Ldr	4.10.01	BLAKE B. J. Sqn Ldr	6.5.02
ALLAMBY W. L. R. Flt Lt	11.6.02	BLAKELEY J. B. OBE Gp Capt	27.4.02
ALLISON H. MC Flt Lt	13.7.01	BLENCOE The Rev C. D. BA	
APPLEGARTH G. F. Flt Lt	2.12.01	Wg Cdr	30.5.01
APPLETON W. A. OBE Wg Cdr...	4.12.01	BLEW D. Flt Lt...	1.5.02
ARMIGER B. OBE Wg Cdr... ...	3.5.02	BLOXAM J. R. OBE DFC Wg Cdr	22.11.01
ASHBY D. W. Sqn Ldr	16.11.01	BOALCH C. J. Sqn Ldr	8.8.01
ASPY J. T. Flt Lt	25.8.01	BOOTLE C. H. Sqn Ldr	8.8.01
ASTLE J. Sqn Ldr	16.9.01	BOWEN N. E. Wg Cdr	9.5.02
ATTERWILL H. G. Sqn Ldr... ...	28.3.02	BOWEN-EASLEY F. OBE FCMI	
AYLETT G. J. CBE CEng FCMI		Gp Capt	12.11.01
MRAeS Gp Capt	22.11.01	BOWER A. W. OBE DFC Wg Cdr	5.11.01
BAILEY G. M. AFC Sqn Ldr ...	9.8.01	BOWMAN D. W. MBE Sqn Ldr	20.12.01
BAKER F. T. BEM Sqn Ldr ...	18.1.02	BRADFORD G. Flt Lt	21.1.02
BAKER H. G. Sqn Ldr...	21.10.01	BRAIN A. S. Flt Lt	24.4.02
BALDWIN C. F. DFM Flt Lt... ...	6.3.01	BRICKWOOD R. MBE MIEE Sqn Ldr	
BARLOW J. R. Flt Lt	12.2.02		7.12.01
BARNES-MOSS J. D. Sqn Ldr ...	31.12.01	BRITTAIN R. E. G. Gp Capt ...	11.11.01
BATTEN J. Flt Lt	11.2.02	BRITTON R. T. Sqn Ldr	21.2.02
BEATTIE A. C. Flt Lt	11.1.02	BROOKS F. J. T. DFC DFM Flt Lt	11.12.01
BEEBE A. S. MBE Sqn Ldr ...	19.8.01	BROOKS M. A. Sqn Ldr ...	31.10.01
BEENY R. E. OBE Gp Capt ...	7.11.01	BROWN A. Wg Cdr	20.5.02
BEILL A. CB AVM	14.11.01	BROWN C. J. T. MCMI Flt Lt	27.9.01
BELDING V. C. MBE Sqn Ldr ...	7.10.01	BROWN J. R. Sqn Ldr	22.7.01
BELL A. MacD. BSc CEng MIEE		BROWN J. S. Sqn Ldr	27.1.02
MCMI Sqn Ldr	29.9.01	BROWN L. G. Fg Offr	13.2.02
BELL G. B. M. OBE Gp Capt ...	1.7.01	BROWN R. A. CEng MIEE MRAeS	
BELL J. H. CEng MRAeS MCMI,		MCMI Wg Cdr	30.8.01
Born 5/2/22 Sqn Ldr	14.4.02	BUDD A. W. Flt Lt	25.11.01
BENJAMIN C. Flt Lt	24.12.01	BUIST L. J. Sqn Ldr	11.4.02
BENTLEY A. C. Flt Lt	18.5.02	BULLIVENT A. E. Sqn Ldr ...	12.12.01
BENTLEY W. H. OBE FCMI Wg Cdr	1.4.02	BUNKHALL E. W. CDipAF Wg Cdr	5.5.02
BERRY L. G. DFC MCMI Sqn Ldr	1.11.01	BURNS R. E. CBE DFC* BSc CEng	
BERTRAM J. S. Flt Lt...	26.6.01	MRAeS Gp Capt	19.9.01

331

Rank and Name	Date of Death	Rank and Name	Date of Death
BURT A. G. Sqn Ldr	6.6.02	CRAVEN J. K. Wg Cdr	25.9.01
BUSHELL C. T. Flt Lt	29.7.01	CRAWFORD C. W. AFC Flt Lt	11.1.02
BUTLAND J. E. Sqn Ldr	30.11.01	CROMWELL O. Sqn Ldr ...	9.5.02
BYRNE J. T. C. CEng MIMechE		CROWE J. B. MA MB BChir DMRD	
Sqn Ldr	6.9.01	FFSR Wg Cdr	6.11.01
CALVERT C. J. DFC Flt Lt	21.6.01	CROWHURST T. Sqn Ldr ...	10.10.01
CAMPBELL I. R. CB CBE AFC AVM	18.10.01	CRUICKSHANK L. W. Sqn Ldr	23.10.01
CARLSON I. O. B. Wg Cdr... ...	10.8.01	CULLEN J. J. Sqn Ldr	14.6.02
CARNERIS L. Flt Lt	11.4.02	CURRASS A. E. Flt Lt	28.7.01
CARR W. Fg Offr	22.11.01	CURTIS D. J. MBE Sqn Ldr ...	26.3.02
CARTER C. L. MHCIMA Sqn Ldr	28.5.02	DACE P. A. Sqn Ldr	2.12.01
CARTER G. R. Flt Lt	26.10.01	DALE R. M. Flt Lt	27.9.01
CATER K. P. MBE CEng MRAeS		DALY R. J. Sqn Ldr	23.12.01
Sqn Ldr	3.4.02	DANDY G. T. Sqn Ldr	14.4.02
CHAMBERS R. Sqn Ldr	25.1.01	DANIEL J. M. DFC Gp Capt ...	17.10.01
CHAPMAN G. H. Flt Lt	26.12.01	DARWENT W. Flt Lt	18.10.01
CHAPMAN R. C. DFC MRAeS		DAVIDSON C. A. DFM Flt Lt ...	23.10.01
Sqn Ldr	24.7.01	DAVIES S. R. Flt Lt	21.10.01
CHAPMAN T. W. DFC MIMgt		DAW F. G. DFC AFC Wg Cdr...	2.7.01
Sqn Ldr	8.1.02	DE LAURIER D. R. P. Sqn Ldr	28.2.02
CHILCOTT C. J. M. BEM Sqn Ldr	23.12.01	DENNEHEY R. T. M. MBE Sqn Ldr	5.8.01
CHRISTIE D. Flt Lt	13.5.02	DENT F. T. MSc CEng MIMechE	
CHURCH F. W. MBE Sqn Ldr ...	8.11.01	Wg Cdr	24.2.02
CLAPPERTON W. T. Sqn Ldr ...	23.7.01	DICKINSON H. E. Sq Ldr ...	9.10.01
CLARK E. BEM Sqn Ldr	18.12.01	DISBREY W. D. CB CBE AFC CEng	
CLARK J. Sqn Ldr	7.3.02	FIMechE FRAeS AVM ...	26.6.01
CLARKE C. J. V. Flt Lt...	12.2.02	DODGSON H. J. Sqn Ldr ...	30.12.01
CLINCH C. W. Sqn Ldr	4.10.01	DONNELLY D. V. Flt Lt	7.1.02
CLOUGH D. B. Flt Lt	8.7.01	DONNELLY W. D. BSc Sqn Ldr	27.7.01
COATES A. Sqn Ldr	6.3.02	DORRINGTON B. Flt Lt	12.8.01
COBB F. Sqn Ldr	7.4.02	DOUGLAS J. C. DFC Wg Cdr	12.3.02
COHEN G. A. Flt Lt	18.6.02	DRING G. Sqn Ldr	23.10.01
COLL J. G. M. Flt Lt	28.9.01	DRIVER W. F. Flt Lt...	4.4.02
COOK F. A. Flt Lt...	23.3.02	DUCKWORTH C. CEng MRAeS	
COOK J. A. Flt Lt...	10.4.02	MCMI Sqn Ldr	23.2.02
COOK J. R. Sqn Ldr	24.5.02	DUNCAN E. C. D. BSc CEng	
COOKSEY J. R. Sqn Ldr	12.7.01	MRAeS Flt Lt	16.2.02
COOKSLEY A. G. Flt Lt	17.12.01	DWELLY J. F. Flt Lt...	24.6.02
COOPER E. W. Sqn Ldr	19.6.02	DYKE Rev. K. A. Wg Cdr ...	12.5.02
COOPER I. R. Gp Capt	11.11.01	EARNSHAW E. OBE AMInstMunE	
COOPER J. W. Flt Lt	4.12.01	Gp Capt	9.6.01
COOPER R. S. Flt Lt	20.2.02	EASTWOOD E. S. MA Wg Cdr	30.3.02
CORDERY J. V. MBE AFC BA Flt Lt	17.12.01	EDWARDS D. M. MCIPS MCMI	
COTTEW T. F. Sqn Ldr	16.2.02	Gp Capt	2.8.01
COULSON P. G. MBE AFC Wg Cdr	25.10.01	ELLIS A. I. Flt Lt	12.1.02
COULSON T. M. Sqn Ldr	17.5.02	ELLIS J. CBE DFC* Gp Capt ...	19.11.01
COUPER J. L. Flt Lt	24.7.01	EMANUEL M. H. MCMI Sqn Ldr	6.3.02
COURSE R. H. Sqn Ldr	27.9.01	EMMITT R. Flt Lt	27.9.01
CRAVEN A. H. PhD MSc DCAe		EVANS J. C. Sqn Ldr	27.4.02
Sqn Ldr	21.9.01	EYRE T. Flt Lt	23.3.02

Rank and Name	Date of Death	Rank and Name	Date of Death
FAIRBROTHER E. A. Flt Lt	19.4.02	GRINDON J. E. CVO DSO AFC	
FELL H. Sqn Ldr	19.2.02	Gp Capt	11.11.01
FELSTEAD L. S. Flt Offr	4.10.01	GRUNDY W. L. Sqn Ldr ...	29.9.01
FIELD D. MA PhD Gp Capt ...	11.1.01	HAMILTON-BROWN T. H. Sqn Ldr	19.2.02
FINLAY D. CBE A Cdre	18.10.01	HAMPTON A. A. Flt Lt	11.8.01
FISHBURN A. Flt Lt	17.1.02	HARDCASTLE H. CEng MRAeS	
FISK D. C. Flt Lt	13.4.02	Wg Cdr	11.7.01
FORSTER A. D. DFC Wg Cdr ...	24.10.01	HARPER N. B. Flt Lt	20.5.02
FOSTER L. B. P. Sqn Ldr	17.1.02	HARPER P. J. C. DFC Sqn Ldr	4.7.01
FOSTER W. R. Flt Lt	1.2.02	HARRIS A. D. Flt Lt	8.8.01
FRANCE L. K. PhD BSc CEng MIM		HARRISON J. B. Sqn Ldr ...	25.2.02
MIEE Wg Cdr	8.8.01	HARRISON R. Flt Lt	24.1.02
FRANK A. D. CB CBE DSO DFC BA		HARVATT B. E. Sqn Ldr... ...	29.8.01
AVM	6.10.01	HAWKEN A. V. B. AFC	28.11.01
FRANKLIN H. J. AFC Sqn Ldr ...	10.11.01	HAWORTH T. D. Flt Lt	15.2.02
FRASER J. J. S. Flt Lt...	27.7.01	HAWRYLOWICZ A. S. Sqn Ldr	9.5.02
FRASER Sir Paterson KBE CB AFC		HAYES N. C. AFM Sqn Ldr ...	14.6.01
BA FRAeS AM	4.8.01	HAYTER F. E. G. Flt Lt	29.5.02
FROUD T. R. W. Sqn Ldr	5.4.02	HEAL H. J. DFC* Wg Cdr ...	27.6.01
FUSSELL A. L. BSc CEng MIEE		HEATH-SMITH G. M. MBE Wg Cdr	17.10.01
MRAeS Wg Cdr	23.2.02	HEAVERY F. C. AFC DFM Flt Lt	17.1.02
GALLOP G. A. M. DFC Sqn Ldr	11.1.02	HEAVISIDE W. Sqn Ldr	5.11.01
GARDINER R. J. MCMI Sqn Ldr	17.5.02	HEMSLEY W. A. C. Sqn Ldr ...	26.4.02
GELBHAUER M. DFC Flt Lt ...	22.4.02	HENSON W. J. Flt Lt	15.8.01
GIBBON Rev E. H. M. BA Wg Cdr	15.5.02	HERMAN J. E. Flt Lt	26.8.01
GILL W. G. LDSRCS Wg Cdr ...	12.9.01	HERSEY G. H. Flt Lt	10.6.02
GILLATT D. G. Flt Lt	3.9.01	HODGSON T. G. Sqn Ldr ...	26.7.01
GLEN J. G. OBE Gp Capt	14.2.02	HOLLAND N. T. H. Sqn Ldr ...	3.11.01
GOLDTHORPE S. D. Flt Lt	10.10.01	HOLMES J. W. Sqn Ldr... ...	12.9.01
GOOD R. J. A. Sqn Ldr	23.11.01	HOLMES W. G. AFC Flt Lt ...	12.12.01
GOODWIN B. E. Wg Cdr	2.10.01	HOPKINS A. F. Sqn Ldr... ...	29.6.02
GORDON S. L. CEng MIEE MCMI		HORDLEY W. G. J. Sqn Ldr ...	12.2.02
Gp Capt	13.4.02	HORE C. Flt Lt...	2.6.02
GOREY S. N. BEng Flt Lt	19.4.02	HORSLEY Sir Peter KCB CBE MVO	
GOWANS J. W. Sqn Ldr	7.9.01	AFC AM	20.12.01
GRACE T. DFC Sqn Ldr	17.6.01	HOUGHTON P. F. Flt Lt	14.12.01
GRAHAM-WILSON E. B. Flt Offr	9.7.01	HOW A. J. Flt Lt	23.12.01
GRANT T. A. Flt Lt	20.1.02	HOWES H. L. Sqn Ldr	8.9.01
GRANT-DAVIE R. H. Flt Lt	22.11.01	HOYLAND P. Sqn Ldr	9.12.01
GRATTON L. G. Sqn Ldr	11.4.02	HUBBARD W. Flt Lt	11.2.02
GRAY W. G. Flt Lt	17.8.01	HUDGELL P. H. MBE Sqn Ldr	31.7.01
GRAYSON S. Flt Lt	4.10.01	HUDSON F. B. Flt Lt	7.1.02
GREEN R. J. Sqn Ldr	9.8.01	HUGHES G. G. Flt Lt	17.8.01
GREENALL P. MBE MMAR MCMI		HUGHES R. W. A. Sqn Ldr ...	20.12.01
Wg Cdr	3.11.01	HUGHES W. D. Flt Lt	11.6.01
GREENHALGH J. S. BA MIRTE		HUME J. W. OBE CEng MRAeS	
MCMI Sqn Ldr	4.2.02	Gp Capt	21.4.02
GREGORY W. J. DSO DFC* DFM		HUNT J. L. Flt Lt	12.7.01
Wg Cdr	28.9.01	HUNTER W. J. MCMI Wg Cdr	28.2.02
GREW P. E. Sqn Ldr	25.2.02	HURLEY W. J. OBE FCMI Gp Capt	9.8.01

Rank and Name	Date of Death
HUTCHINS M. B. Wg Cdr	25.8.01
HYNDS H. A. AFC Sqn Ldr ...	17.9.01
HYSLOP J. S. D. Sqn Ldr	5.11.01
ILES R. G. AFC Sqn Ldr	25.11.01
ILES W. A. J. Wg Cdr	3.2.02
ISAAC P. N. Wg Cdr	27.8.01
JACKSON C. F. Flt Lt	7.8.01
JACKSON G. AFM Flt Lt	21.4.02
JACKSON H. McL. M. Flt Lt ...	1.6.02
JARVIS W. D. AFC Flt Lt	5.5.02
JASKE J. A. Sqn Ldr	20.6.01
JEFFRIES R. K. OBE Gp Capt ...	15.2.02
JENNINGS D. C. Sqn Ldr	3.5.02
JESSIMAN W. Flt Lt	3.4.02
JOHNSON A. MBE Flt Lt	5.2.02
JOHNSTON E. A. OBE Gp Capt	3.6.02
JOLL W. I. Sqn Ldr	13.5.02
JONES A. E. Fg Offr	3.1.01
JONES D. G. Flt Lt	22.2.02
JORDAN C. CEng MIEE MCMI Sqn Ldr	17.3.02
JUKES G. AFC Sqn Ldr	29.7.01
KEARN S. C. CEng MRAeS Wg Cdr	19.4.02
KEECH J. E. Flt Lt	4.6.01
KELLY W. W. DFC Flt Lt	24.6.01
KIMBREY C. G. Wg Cdr	21.7.01
KINDER C. T. Flt Lt	27.6.01
KING F. G. H. Flt Lt	6.1.02
KIRKWOOD A. S. MA Sqn Ldr ...	11.1.02
KLIDJIAN A. MB BS FRCS FRCP A Cdre	30.7.01
KNIGHT D. E. Flt Lt	31.12.01
LANNING G. E. Flt Lt	25.5.02
LATTER B. Wg Cdr	6.6.02
LATTIMER D. N. MBE Wg Cdr ...	4.8.01
LATTON K. B. BA FRAeS A Cdre	19.10.01
LAWSON A. J. MBE ChB Wg Cdr	12.8.01
LAYCOCK F. Flt Lt	15.2.02
LEE J. F. Flt Lt	22.1.02
LEWIS B. D. B. DFM AFM Flt Lt	24.5.02
LEWIS D. G. DFC A Cdre	21.7.01
LITTLE T. W. BSc ACGI Sqn Ldr	8.4.02
LLOYD R. A. Flt Lt	29.11.01
LLOYD W. F. Sqn Ldr	22.8.01
LOGAN J. J. F. M. AFM Flt Lt ...	24.9.01
LONGDEN E. J. AFC Sqn Ldr ...	13.6.01
LOWE H. H. Sqn Ldr	21.10.01
LUND C. B. Sqn Ldr	19.4.02
LYDON B. B. DFC Flt Lt	19.5.02
LYNCH P. A. Sqn Ldr	8.11.01
Le ROUGETEL S. Wg Cdr ...	3.4.02
MacDONALD C. S. MCMI Wg Cdr	20.3.02
MacDONALD D. A. F. Sqn Ldr	5.6.01
MacDONALD J. DFC MBE Wg Cdr	16.7.01
MACKENZIE R. M. DSO DFC AFC Wg Cdr	5.6.02
MacFARLANE G. N. W. BA CEng MIEE Sqn Ldr	3.5.02
MacLEOD W. DFM Flt Lt ...	29.5.02
MACKEY P. E. A. Sqn Ldr ...	29.3.02
MACMASTER J. Flt Lt	24.3.02
MANFIELD S. L. Sqn Ldr ...	27.8.01
MANN J. Flt Lt	23.3.02
MARCHANT D. W. BDS A Cdre	7.2.02
MARGETTS D. Flt Lt	25.6.01
MARSH A. J. Flt Lt	30.7.01
MARSH J. S. Sqn Ldr	18.6.01
MARSHALL L. H. Flt Lt	22.4.02
MARSHALL R. J. Flt Lt	12.7.01
MARTIN H. W. DFM Sqn Ldr	16.4.02
MATHESON J. A. Flt Lt	20.1.02
MATTHEWS G. C. Sqn Ldr ...	11.11.01
MAY A. J. MBE Flt Lt	20.6.02
MCALLISTER C. MBE LHA FCMI Gp Capt	5.8.01
McCALLUM D. F. Sqn Ldr ...	24.10.01
McCOMBIE I. L. Wg Cdr ...	26.2.02
McGRAIL R. Flt Lt	21.6.02
McKENNA J. R. Flt Lt	5.2.02
McKINLEY D. C. CB CBE DFC AFC* AVM	23.4.02
McLOUGHLIN G. A. BEM Flt Lt	27.3.02
McMAHON G. F. DFM Wg Cdr	11.9.01
McNAIR I. S. Flt Lt	8.2.02
McRORY J. P. MB BCh BAO DPH Wg Cdr	29.5.02
MEES W. C. Sqn Ldr	11.6.02
MERCER I. H. LMSSA MFCH DPH Gp Capt	16.5.02
MIDDLETON A. R. DSO DFC Sqn Ldr	18.4.01
MIDDLETON J. S. DFC Flt Lt	29.3.02
MILLIS O. J. MBE Flt Lt	27.7.01
MILLS R. T. Sq Ldr	17.5.02
MINETT R. W. Sqn Ldr	9.8.01
MITCHELL C. H. A. Sqn Ldr ...	3.4.02
MOLLOY M. H. T. MBE Sqn Ldr	9.1.02
MOORE T. DFC Sqn Ldr ...	19.4.02
MORGAN A. P. DFC Wg Cdr...	1.10.01
MORGAN R. Sqn Ldr	14.6.02

Rank and Name	Date of Death	Rank and Name	Date of Death
MORGAN W. G. CB CBE FCCA ACMA AVM	12.1.02	PHILLIPS E. DFC Flt Lt	25.2.02
MORLEY J. H. Sqn Ldr	4.2.02	PHILLIPS J. W. Flt Lt	1.8.01
MORTIMER E. L. Flt Lt	23.10.01	PHILLIPS R. Flt Lt	15.12.01
MORTIMER K. Flt LT	22.5.01	PIGOTT D. F. St J. Sqn Ldr ...	26.2.02
MORTON R. M. CEng MRAeS MCMI Wg Cdr	10.4.02	PLAYER B. C. CBE A Cdre ...	16.1.02
		PLOWMAN W. A. Sqn Ldr ...	27.8.01
MOTT A. J. MBE Sqn Ldr	9.5.02	POLLARD N. J. MCIPS Sqn Ldr	8.2.02
MOTTERSHEAD J. K. Flt Lt ...	6.11.01	POMFORD J. A. Flt Lt	5.6.02
MUNCASTER G. S. Flt Lt	29.6.01	POOK H. A. Sqn Ldr	8.1.02
MURPHY F. E. MBE Sqn Ldr ...	6.12.01	POTTER M. A. G. Sqn Offr ...	19.4.02
MURPHY G. MCMI Sqn Ldr ...	17.12.01	POVEY C. F. Sqn Ldr	5.7.01
MURPHY W. Sqn Ldr	14.4.02	POWELL A. G. CEng MIEE A Cdre	22.12.01
NANCE C. T. OBE MA CEng MIMechE MRAeS A Cdre ...	23.1.02	POWELL A. OBE Wg Cdr ...	29.12.01
		POWELL F. W. Sqn Ldr	25.11.01
NELSON Sir Richard KCB OBE MD AM	5.11.01	PRINGLE H. J. AFC Gp Capt...	23.11.01
		PRITCHETT P. N. B. Flt Lt ...	2.7.01
NEVILLE R. E. AFC Flt Lt	3.8.01	PYE K. A. Flt Lt	25.4.02
NEWBROOK J. C. Flt Lt	11.12.01	QUINN J. DFC* Gp Capt ...	26.12.01
NEWBURY D. J. Wg Cdr	4.7.01	RAMSAY N. H. D. DFC Flt Lt	26.5.02
NEWMAN C. W. McN. OBE DFC* Wg Cdr	11.11.01	RANSLEY R. A. Flt Lt	26.2.02
		REEP T. C. ACA Wg Cdr ...	3.2.02
NICHOLAS R. J. K. Flt Lt	19.4.02	RICHARDSON K. E. OBE Gp Capt	29.3.02
NOAKES J. Sqn Ldr	7.4.02	RICKETS P. M. MBE Sqn Ldr	19.6.02
NORTHMORE L. N. Sqn Ldr ...	8.10.01	RIGGS G. Flt Lt	17.10.01
NOYCE P. K. Sqn Ldr	31.8.01	RITCHLEY K. CBE AFC Gp Capt	27.6.01
O'TOOLE E. H. MBE MCMI Wg Cdr	21.8.01	ROBERTS E. S. MCMI Sqn Ldr	28.8.01
OGILVIE H. AFC Sqn Ldr	25.2.02	ROBERTSON F. H. Flt Lt ...	15.4.02
OLD L. R. Wg Cdr	9.10.01	ROBINSON B. N. MIPM MCMI Sqn Ldr	22.1.02
OLLIFFE A. I. Flt Lt	23.11.01		
ORR J. S. OBE Wg Cdr	9.7.01	ROBINSON C. Flt Lt	2.10.01
OWEN W. R. DFC Sqn Ldr... ...	25.5.01	ROBINSON J. Sqn Ldr	23.12.01
PACKMAN R. E. E. Flt Lt	26.12.01	ROBINSON T. B. Sqn Ldr ...	6.3.02
PAIN R. C. Sqn Ldr	15.4.02	ROBSON F. Flt Lt	16.9.01
PALMER J. H. Wg Cdr	22.11.01	ROBSON N. Sqn Ldr	3.10.01
PALMER S. J. J. MCMI Sqn Ldr	20.4.02	ROGERS V. Flt Lt	9.2.02
PARKER H. J. OBE DFM MRAeS Wg Cdr	23.1.02	ROSCOE G. R. DFM Wg Cdr	1.4.02
		ROSS H. J. Flt Lt	24.11.01
PARKER J. F. Flt Lt	24.6.02	ROSS J. A. G. MVO Sqn Ldr	15.11.01
PARNABY G. S. A. OBE Gp Capt	6.3.02	ROWE C. G. Flt Lt	8.4.02
PATTEN D. A. R. Sqn Ldr	15.3.02	ROWLAND D. M. Flt Lt	22.8.01
PAYNE S. G. E. Flt Lt	21.3.02	ROWLEY R. L. Flt Lt	7.9.01
PEDEN W. Flt Lt	11.5.02	RUMBLE H. DFC Flt Lt	7.3.02
PERRETT G. E. CEng MRAeS Sqn Ldr	13.4.02	RUSHFORTH G. W. Sqn Ldr...	1.6.02
		RUSSELL B. E. Sqn Ldr... ...	30.6.01
PETERS J. P. E. Sqn Ldr	11.3.02	RUSSELL F. T. MBE Gp Capt	17.8.01
PETHICK A. F. DFC Flt Lt	28.3.02	RUXTON T. E. Flt Lt	25.10.01
PETR F. Flt Lt	25.2.02	SADLER W. R. Gp Capt... ...	21.8.01
PHILLIPS C. J. Gp Capt	21.6.01	SANFORD F. Sqn Ldr	20.7.01
PHILLIPS D. L. MM Flt Lt	21.12.01	SANSOM A. C. StQ. MBE Flt Lt	13.7.01
		SAUNDERS F. E. Flt Lt	15.12.01

Rank and Name	Date of Death	Rank and Name	Date of Death
SAWYER J. S. Sqn Ldr	16.7.01	STRANGE G. MCMI Wg Cdr	31.1.02
SAXBY G. Flt Lt	28.11.01	STRATTON G. J. Flt Lt	11.8.01
SAYER M. R. Fg Offr	1.8.01	SYMONDS E. J. G. Sqn Ldr ...	15.2.02
SCATES R. W. Sqn Ldr	2.6.02	TAGGESELL C. W. Sqn Ldr ...	18.8.01
SCHOFIELD A. E. CEng MIEE		TAIT T. R. V. Sqn Ldr	8.11.01
MCMI Gp Capt	10.7.01	TALBOT E. W. DFC* Wg Cdr	22.3.02
SCHOFIELD The Rev E. P. MA BD		TANNER D. W. DFC Sqn Ldr	8.2.02
Wg Cdr	20.8.01	TASWELL H. OBE MCMI Wg Cdr	16.8.01
SCOTT L. J. Flt Lt	6.4.02	TAYLOR D. A. DFC* Sqn Ldr	30.7.01
SERGEANT R. H. AE MCMI		TAYLOR D. Wg Cdr	26.5.01
Sqn Ldr	13.10.01	TAYLOR D. M. Sqn Ldr	18.6.02
SHARP C. G. FCA Gp Capt ...	28.7.01	TAYLOR H. L. CEng MIMechE	
SHARPE P. Flt Lt	6.11.01	Wg Cdr	21.5.02
SHARPLES A. O. MBE Flt Lt ...	30.4.02	TAYLOR J. V. MBE Gp Capt ...	15.3.02
SHAW M. J. A. DSO FCMI Gp Capt	31.1.02	TELFORD J. K. Flt Lt	31.12.01
SHEEN T. A. DFC Flt Lt	19.12.01	THOMAS D. L. BSc Sqn Ldr ...	18.3.02
SHINNIE G. M. DFC Wg Cdr ...	4.3.02	THOMAS F. M. Wg Cdr	18.9.01
SHIPLEY E. MA MRAeS Gp Capt	20.9.01	THOMAS M. P. BSc CEng MRAeS	
SHOTTON J. Wg Cdr	15.10.01	Sqn Ldr	8.2.02
SIM J. W. GM MA Gp Capt ...	2.4.02	THOMAS The Rev W. A. BA	
SIMCOCK S. W. Flt Lt...	31.1.02	Gp Capt	11.6.02
SIMMONS D. R. Flt Lt	27.2.02	THOMAS W. J. BSc Sqn Ldr	25.5.01
SINCLAIR J. Flt Lt	5.9.01	THOMPSON D. W. Sqn Ldr ...	17.10.01
GC SINCLAIR Sir Laurence KCB		THOMPSON R. W. P. CEng MRAeS	
CBE DSO* AVM	14.5.02	MCMI Sqn Ldr	12.8.01
SKINNER D. Flt Lt	17.10.01	THOMSON A. D. DFC Flt Lt ...	17.3.02
SLEDGE D. J. BSc CEng MIMechE		THOMSON J. A. Wg Cdr ...	30.10.01
MRAeS Gp Capt	22.8.01	THORNLEY G. A. Sqn Ldr ...	20.12.01
SMEATON L. W. Flt Lt	4.4.02	TIMEWELL G. C. Flt Lt	11.2.02
SMITH A. D. B. Sqn Ldr	5.3.02	TOPHAM D. O. Flt Lt	2.11.01
SMITH B. D. BSc CEng ARIC		TOPP R. A. Sqn Ldr	29.1.02
MRAeS Wg Cdr	22.6.01	TRELOAR G. H. L. CEng MRAeS	
SMITH C. J. MBE Flt Lt	10.11.01	Wg Cdr	10.4.02
SMITH G. C. OBE AFC Gp Capt	21.5.02	TRICE K. M. Sqn Ldr	23.3.02
SMITH I. R. G. Sqn Ldr	7.3.02	TROTTER P. I. W. Flt Lt	21.11.01
SMYTH P. A. Sqn Ldr	18.11.01	TUDOR H. M. H. DFC AFC Gp Capt	8.1.02
SMYTHE D. W. Gp Capt	1.1.02	TURNER E. C. MRAeS Sqn Ldr	26.9.01
SNEE J. J. Flt Lt	3.6.02	TURNER E. DSC Flt Lt	21.10.01
SOWDEN E. H. MBE MCMI		TYNDALL F. E. CBE A Cdre ...	27.7.01
Wg Cdr	8.1.02	UNWIN R. F. B. Fg Offr	4.2.02
SOWMAN P. N. Wg Cdr	28.11.01	VALE N. Sqn Ldr	18.4.02
SPINKS S. J. Sqn Ldr...	13.2.02	VERITY H. B. DSO* DFC MA	
SPOTTISWOOD J. Fg Offr... ...	27.1.02	Gp Capt	14.11.01
STALLWORTHY H. E. MBE Flt Lt	20.11.01	VESELY V. DFC AFC Sqn Ldr	12.12.01
STANDING P. A. Sqn Ldr	15.4.02	VIDOT C. C. MRCS LRCP DPH	
STANNARD J. H. AFC Sqn Ldr...	25.9.01	Wg Cdr	18.10.01
STEELE J. C. Sqn Ldr...	16.12.01	WADDELL R. G. Sqn Ldr ...	6.5.02
STEPHENS E. L. Sqn Ldr	26.8.01	WADDICOR A. E. DFC DFM Flt Lt	28.5.02
STEPHENSON G. DFC AFC Flt Lt	29.11.01	WADE Sir Ruthven KCB DFC ACM	24.9.01
STEVENS F. J. W. Sqn Ldr ...	18.6.02		

Rank and Name	Date of Death	Rank and Name	Date of Death
WADLEY M. E. BA MCMI CertEd Wg Cdr	5.3.02	WILLIAMS D. B. DFC Flt Lt ...	7.9.01
WAINWRIGHT J. A. DSO Flt Lt...	14.4.02	WILLIAMS E. I. Sqn Ldr ...	12.6.02
WAITING J. E. Flt Lt	31.3.02	WILLIAMS H. R. Gp Capt ...	23.8.01
WAKEFIELD W. J. N. Sqn Ldr ...	24.10.01	WILLIAMS J. E. F. CBE MMAR Gp Capt	29.12.01
WALES W. H. N. Flt Lt	20.6.02	WILLIAMS J. R. Flt Lt	9.9.01
WALKER A. C. BEM Sqn Ldr ...	27.3.02	WILLIAMS T. W. Flt Lt	14.11.01
WALKER E. E. Sqn Ldr	18.9.01	WILLIAMS The Rev G. Wg Cdr	15.11.01
WARD C. W. Sqn Ldr	16.5.02	WILLIS A. S. CEng MRAeS Wg Cdr	4.10.01
WARDEN K. E. Flt Lt	10.8.01	WILLSON J. D. MBE BSc MICE Sqn Ldr	12.6.01
WARDROP R. E. FINucE Sqn Ldr	14.11.01	WILSON J. W. MBE Sqn Ldr	20.2.02
WARREN D. E. BA MCMI Wg Cdr	12.2.02	WILSON P. M. Sqn Ldr	26.1.02
WARREN G. G. Flt Lt	19.1.02	WILTON A. E. Wg Cdr	2.12.01
WATSON G. C. MBE BEM Sqn Ldr	21.6.01	WINDER K. J. Sqn Ldr	24.3.02
WATSON R. W. Wg Cdr	15.10.01	WINTER T. J. Sqn Ldr	21.8.01
WATT J. R. DFC Sqn Ldr	15.3.02	WOOD D. Sqn Ldr	8.10.01
WEBBER L. B. Sq Ldr...	15.5.02	WOOD F. J. H. MBE Sqn Ldr	19.11.01
WEBSTER A. H. DFM Sqn Ldr ...	26.1.02	WOOD K. E. Sqn Ldr	10.11.01
WELFARE D. DFC* Flt Lt	24.8.01	WOOD P. D. J. DFC Wg Cdr ...	23.9.01
WESTERMAN A. G. Flt Lt	25.10.01	WOOD R. F. Flt Lt	21.12.01
WEVILL P. MMar Wg Cdr	21.1.02	WOODS P. R. ACIS Sqn Ldr ...	21.5.02
WHITAKER P. L. DFC Sqn Ldr ...	28.3.02	WOODWARD P. MBE Flt Lt ...	12.11.01
WHITE G. E. MCMI Flt Lt	29.5.02	WOODYATT A. P. Sqn Ldr ...	6.10.01
WHITFIELD E. J. Flt Lt	1.3.02	WRIGHT D. G. M. AFC Sqn Ldr	2.2.02
WHITLOCK J. E. OBE DFC Wg Cdr	12.3.02	WRIGHT K. W. MBE DFM Flt Lt	9.7.01
WHITNEY G. D. Wg Cdr	3.12.01	WRIGHT R. E. Fg Offr	26.9.01
WHITTLE P. S. Flt Lt	23.3.02	YATES P. M. Sqn Ldr	26.7.01
WICKS F. F. CBE DFC Gp Capt ...	13.11.01		
WIGLEY A. E. L. Sqn Ldr	31.10.01		
WILCOCK A. H. Flt Lt	20.1.02		
WILCOCK J. R. AFC Sqn Ldr ...	16.4.02	**Princess Mary's Royal Air Force**	
WILDIN B. A. Flt Lt	13.4.02	**Nursing Service**	
WILKINSON C. E. BSc Wg Cdr ...	22.9.01		
WILKINSON C. J. Flt Lt	15.5.02	CAYGILL M. RRC SRN SCM Gp Offr	5.11.01
WILKINSON J. H. Sqn Ldr... ...	17.9.01	O'REGAN T. S. SRN Sqn Offr	23.6.01
WILKINSON W. H. G. Sqn Ldr ...	29.10.71		
WILLCOX L. G. MCMI Sqn Ldr ...	15.5.02		

INDEX

INDEX

INDEX

INDEX

353

INDEX

INDEX

INDEX

INDEX

INDEX

INDEX

M

INDEX

INDEX

N

INDEX

INDEX

INDEX

INDEX

INDEX

INDEX

INDEX

INDEX

INDEX

INDEX

INDEX

INDEX

Honorary Agents to the Royal Air Force

The Agent's role is to provide a service of personal financial advice to all members of the Royal Air Force no matter whether they bank with the Agents Banks or elsewhere. The advice is unbiased and free of charge and may range from the simplicity of opening an account to constructive advice on commutation and investment at the time of resettlement. The Agents also specialise in dealing with technical financial matters relating to Units and formations.

The Royal Air Force Agents are:

Cox's & King's
PO Box 1190
7 Pall Mall
London SW1Y 5NA
Freephone: 0800 317053

Cox's & King's is a branch of Lloyds TSB which specialises in military business. Advice given is impartial and tailored to each individual. The branch has access to a very broad range of specialists within Lloyds TSB Group.

Holt's Branch, The Royal Bank of Scotland plc
Lawrie House
Victoria Road
Farnborough
Hampshire
GU14 7NR

Telephone: 01252 515841
Facsimile: 01252 377368

Attn RODERICK READING MILITARY BANKING MANAGER or BRIAN HARRIS MILITARY BANKING ADVISER
Holt's Farnborough is the Branch of the Royal Bank of Scotland which specialises in military business. The military banking team have access to a very broad range of specialists. Advice given is impartial and tailored to each individual.

LADY GROVER'S HOSPITAL FUND
FOR OFFICERS' FAMILIES

Registered under the Friendly Societies Acts 1974 and 1992

Registered No. 474F

The OBJECT OF THE Fund is to help Officers to defray expenses incurred **by the illness of their dependants**. Officer subscribers are NOT THEMSELVES eligible for benefit.

Membership is open to:
Any Officer, male or female, of the three Services, who holds or has held a regular commission for a minimum of five years.

Membership is also open to:
Widows or widowers of Officers, divorced wives or husbands of Officers, for their own benefit or that of their children, and for descendant carers of Officers (all within certain criteria).

RATES OF BENEFITS

GRANTS. The amount of each grant is assessed on the basis of the actual expenses incurred, with maximum rates as follows: –

(a)	For the expenses of temporary residence in a hospital or nursing home	£1,050 weekly
(b)	For the expenses of a temporary privately employed nurse	£280 weekly
(c)	For convalescence away from home	£280 weekly
(d)	For the expenses of a temporary Home Help	£175 weekly
(e)	In special cases, at the Committee's discretion, ex-Gratia payments	

The maximum period for which benefit is payable in any period of twelve months is EIGHT weeks TWELVE weeks for Home Help ONLY

ANNUAL SUBSCRIPTION RATE: – SCALE 'Y'—£30
For particulars apply to: –

The Administrator, Lady Grover's Hospital Fund for Officers' Families
48 Pall Mall, London SE1Y 5JY

Ladyg@oaed.org.uk.

(enclose 30p to include postage, for Book of Rules)

452

REGULAR FORCES EMPLOYMENT ASSOCIATION
FINDING JOBS FOR EX FORCES PERSONNEL
RFEA LIMITED

49 PALL MALL,
LONDON, SW1Y 5JG

Telephone: 020 7321 2011
Fax: 020 7839 0970
E-Mail: ghall@ctp.org.uk
www.rfea.org.uk

Patron
H.M. THE QUEEN

Chairman: Lieutenant General Sir RODERICK CORDY-SIMPSON, KBE CB
Vice-Chairman: (RAF) Air Vice-Marshal M SMART, BA FIPD
Chief Executive: Air Commodore P G JOHNSON, OBE

"The Association operates a network of Branches throughout the UK and exists for the express purpose of assisting men and women to find employment and return to civilian life when they leave the Regular Forces. They may register, as often as they wish, up to the national retirement age, provided they served for a minimum of three years (or if medically discharged regardless of length of service). RFEA is part of the Career Transition Partnership."

NATIONAL BRANCH NETWORK

ABERDEEN	LIVERPOOL
BEDFORD	LONDON (INNER)
BELFAST	LONDON (OUTER)
BIRMINGHAM	MAIDSTONE
BRISTOL	MANCHESTER
BURY ST EDMUNDS	NEWCASTLE-UPON-TYNE
CARDIFF	NORTHAMPTON
CHELMSFORD	NORWICH
CHELTENHAM	PLYMOUTH
CHESTER	PORTSMOUTH
DARLINGTON	PRESTON
DERBY	READING
EDINBURGH	SALISBURY
EXETER	SHEFFIELD
GLASGOW	SHREWSBURY
LEEDS	SWANSEA
LINCOLN	

"For contact details see Yellow Pages and local directories or contact head office"

Established 1885.   Registered under the Charities Act 1960:   Registered No: 1061212
Company Registration No: 3270369

THE
ROYAL PATRIOTIC FUND CORPORATION

FOUNDED 1854

REORGANISED UNDER THE PATRIOTIC FUND REORGANISATION ACT 1903,

AND THE ROYAL PATRIOTIC FUND CORPORATION ACT, 1950

President: H.R.H. Prince MICHAEL of KENT, KCVO

Vice-President: General Sir ROBERT PASCOE, KCB MBE

Secretary: BRIGADIER T. G. WILLIAMS, CBE

The Corporation administers a number of Funds for the benefit of widows, children and dependants of deceased officers and other ranks of the Naval, Military and Air Forces of the Crown.

Over £325,000 is distributed annually in allowances and grants.

Regular allowances are paid to widows of officers and other ranks where need exists.

Television sets and/or licences are provided for widows of former members of the Armed Services.

Grants are made to meet particular requirements.

In addition educational grants are available to children of deceased servicemen to assist with school fees where need exists.

Applications for assistance should be made through local branches of SSAFA/FH, RAFA or the War Pensions Agency.

Further information may be obtained from the Secretary, Royal Patriotic Fund Corporation, 40 Queen Anne's Gate, London, SW1H 9AP. Telephone 020-7233 1894. Fax 020-7233 1799.

THE ROYAL AIR FORCES ASSOCIATION

(Incorporated by Royal Charter)

MOVING WITH THE TIMES

RAFA, the Royal Air Forces Association, is a unique membership organisation with over 100,000 'RAF family' members worldwide. As a charity we provide support to all serving and retired RAF personnel and their dependants through our worldwide network of Branches. We help over 50,000 individuals each year and provide a range of services—from resettlement and war pensions advice to family apartments available for short breaks.

- We provide support and resettlement advice for RAF leavers and their families to help ease the transition into civilian life.

- We have a family unit at Rothbury, near Newcastle upon Tyne, available for short breaks.

- We have three convalescent and respite care homes—at Lytham St Annes, at Rothbury near Newcastle upon Tyne and at Weston super Mare.

- We run sheltered and supportive housing schemes.

- We provide 24 hour nursing care at Sussexdown, our nursing home near Storrington in West Sussex.

- We run a scheme enabling those in need of residential care to be treated close to their own home.

- Trained volunteer Welfare Officers offer free advice and assistance to those in need.

- RAFA Liaison Officers (RAFALOs) on stations act as a link between the Association and serving RAF personnel.

If you would like further information please contact your RAFALO on station or

The Royal Air Forces Association at
43 Grove Park Road
London
W4 3RX
Tel: 020 8994 8504

Membership is only £8.00 per year (£9.50 in the first year)

Charity Registration Number 226686

QUEEN VICTORIA SCHOOL

DUNBLANE, PERTHSHIRE, FK15 0JY

Patron: HRH THE DUKE OF EDINBURGH, KG, KT, OM, GBE

The School provides boarding school education for the children of Scottish servicemen and women and those who have served in Scotland. Quality education, including school clothing is provided at a low cost of under £300 per term. Set in 45 acres of beautiful Perthshire countryside, QVS is easily accessible by road, rail or air.

Pupils may be registered for entry from the age of 7 but the main entry is at Primary 7 (i.e. age 10.5/11 years). Applications must reach the School by 30 November so that they may be considered for the Admissions Board which convenes in February. However, consideration will also be given, in particular circumstances, to applications made after these dates, but only in exceptional circumstances.

The School offers a wide and balanced curriculum following the Scottish educational system, leading to Standard Grade, Intermediate 2, Higher and Advanced Higher. The majority of pupils move on to Higher or Further Education but careers links with the services remain strong. Pastoral care is afforded a very high priority along with Careers Guidance and Personal and Social Education.

Queen Victoria School is a unique boarding school and, as such, looks to achieve, the best that is possible academically for all its pupils. The School prides itself also on developing the pupil in the widest possible sense and, as well as academically, aims to achieve success in activities such as sport, music, drama and many other extra-curricular areas. The traditional ceremonial side adds a very special and unique dimension.

For further information, write to
The Headmaster
Queen Victoria School
Dunblane
Perthshire FK15 0JY

Telephone: 01786 822288 (Exchange)
0131 3102901 (Direct Line to HM's Secretary)
Fax No: 0131 310 2955

THE OFFICERS' ASSOCIATION

PATRON
HM THE QUEEN

PRESIDENTS
Admiral of the Fleet Sir Julian Oswald, GCB
General Sir John Waters, GCB CBE DL JP
Air Chief Marshal Sir Michael Graydon, GCB CBE FRAeS

The Officers' Association provides services to ex-officers of the Royal Navy (including Royal Marines), the Army and the Royal Air Force, and their widows and dependants, including those who held Commissions in the Womens' Services.

Services include:

- **EMPLOYMENT** – vacancies, advice and contacts to assist ex-officers of all ages and ranks to find suitable employment, both those just leaving the Services and those who are changing their civilian jobs. Many hundreds of ex-officers are found jobs every year, nationwide and in popular areas overseas, over a wide salary range.

- **BENEVOLENCE** – financial assistance is given in the form of allowances and grants towards specific household/disability related expenses to those in their own homes in financial distress. Help is also available to third party contributions towards Care Home fee shortfalls.

- **HOMES ADVICE** – advice and information on Independent Sector Homes, and Homes run by Service charities and other voluntary organisations; sheltered accommodation for the elderly, convalescence homes; advice on financial assistance towards Homes fees.

- **A HOME AND COUNTRY HOUSE** – management of "Huntly" a delightful country house at Bishopsteignton, South Devon, which affords comfort and security for ex-officers at or over the age of 65, both male and female, who do not need special nursing care. Selection is made with due regard to need.

- **BUNGALOWS** – management of 12 bungalow estate at Leavesden, Herts, for disabled ex-officers and their families.

The Association has offices in London and Dublin. The Officers' Association (Scotland) has offices in Glasgow and Edinburgh.

All enquiries should be made to the General Secretary, The Officers' Association, 48 Pall Mall, London SW1Y 5JY. (Tel: 020 7389 5204).

THE ROYAL AIR FORCE BENEVOLENT FUND

67, PORTLAND PLACE, LONDON W1B 1AR

Telephone: 0207-580 8343

Fax: 0207-636 7005

www.rafbf.org.uk

Patron: HER MAJESTY THE QUEEN

President: H.R.H. THE DUKE OF KENT, KG GCMG GCVO ADC

Chairman of Council: SIR RICHARD GEORGE, CVO

Controller: AIR CHIEF MARSHAL SIR DAVID COUSINS, KCB AFC BA

★　　★　　★

Purpose of the Fund. The Benevolent Fund exists to provide assistance to those of the extended Royal Air Force family who need support as a consequence of sickness, disability, accident, infirmity, poverty or other adversity. This extended family embraces all ranks, male and female, who are serving, or who have served, in the Royal Air Force or its associated Air Forces, and their dependants.

Welfare. The Fund's Welfare work can be divided into 4 areas:

Housing – where death or severe disablement has occurred in service the Fund may assist with the provision of housing. Help may take the form of a secured loan to provide the balance needed for house purchase, or possibly the use of a Fund-owned property.

Education – where a parent's death or severe disablement has occurred whilst serving, the Fund may assist with the costs of education until the completion of 'A' levels and exceptionally, to first degree level. Such children, known as Foundationers, may attend a boarding school of choice at both the preparatory and secondary stages of education; Fund help is based on need and limited to a maximum of the fees at appropriate benchmark schools.

Homes – the Fund has two Homes of its own, Alastrean House in Tarland, Scotland, providing residential and nursing accommodation and Princess Marina House on the Sussex coast, providing residential and respite care. The Fund also shares three other homes, Rothbury House in Northumberland, Richard Peck House at Lytham St Annes and Flowerdown House at Weston-Super-Mare, with the Royal Air Forces Association. Where nursing home care, or an alternative form of residential care is needed, the Fund may be able to assist in cases where the statutory provision is inadequate.

General Needs – this category forms the bulk of the Fund's welfare work and embraces circumstances which fall within the Fund's scope but not covered above. One-off help is normally by grant, except where the help is property-related, when a loan is considered more appropriate. Loans attract interest at the Fund's current rate, but repayment may be deferred. Help may be by the provision of wheelchairs or specialist furniture. For pensioners in need, a small regular addition to income may be provided.

Measure of the Assistance. Expenditure on all forms of relief continues to rise, year on year, and is currently above £24 million per annum.

How to Help. The Chairman and Council hope that the Service and general public will continue to respond generously and so enable the Fund to meet all its commitments. Donations, preferably under the "Gift-Aid" Scheme, or leaving something in a Will are all valued ways of helping the Fund.

Those who may be in need of assistance. Should you, as a member of the RAF family, be in need of our help, please contact us. Equally, if you know someone else who is, please encourage them to get in touch through the RAFBF freefone 0800-169-2942.

The Royal Air Force Benevolent Fund
Helping colleagues who need a brighter future

COMBAT STRESS

EX-SERVICES MENTAL WELFARE SOCIETY

Tyrwhitt House, Oaklawn Road, Leatherhead, Surrey KT22 0BX
Tel: 01372 841600   Fax: 01372 841601

Founded in 1919 the Ex-Services Mental Welfare Society, also known as COMBAT STRESS is the only charity to specialise in helping those of all ranks of the Armed Forces and Merchant Navy who are suffering from varying degrees of psychological injury, such as Post Traumatic Stress Disorder (PTSD), caused by the traumatic events they have experienced in service. To date we have provided some 75,000 veterans with a unique lifeline, our youngest client is 19 years old and one of 6,000 currently on the books. Our commitment to clients is for life.

Care is offered at the COMBAT STRESS treatment centres in Surrey, Ayrshire and Shropshire, which between them help over 2,500 veterans each year. Twelve regional Welfare Officers also cover the whole of the British Isles and Ireland to support clients in their homes.

Our Society is still acquiring new clients at the rate of about 600 each year, which reflects the ongoing casualties from the more recent campaigns, for example Northern Ireland and the Balkans. This means that the demand for our treatment shows no signs of abating for the foreseeable future. As our elderly veterans from the Second World War decrease in number and others are rehabilitated successfully, more present themselves in need of our help.

For further information:
Telephone: 01372 841600 or visit our website on www.combatstress.com

BLESMA

Tel: 020 8590 1124/Fax: 020 8599 2932/email: blesma@btconnect.com/website:www.blesma.org

The British Limbless Ex-Service Men's Association are providing for and supporting those who have suffered the loss of limb(s) in the service of their country. Even today the casualties of peacetime are producing more individuals eligible for our help and support. We also accept responsibility for their dependants and, in particular, their Widows.

Through our welfare system we ensure that they receive a counselling service both pre and post amputation, advice on pensions and allowances and, where necessary, represent them at Pensions Appeals Tribunals. Our two nursing homes provide permanent residential and convalescent care for Members and dependants alike.

All this costs money, a large amount of money. We receive no Government Grants and rely wholly on the generosity of the public, especially Armed Forces Personnel, who undertake and organise many fundraising events on our behalf.

Please help us to continue our work and consider making a donation, however small, to: **BLESMA, 185–187 High Road, Chadwell Heath, Romford, Essex RM6 6NA**

Shipwrecked
Fishermen and Mariners'
Royal Benevolent Society

Reg. Charity No. 212034   Patron: HRH The Princess Royal

Tragedy at sea hits the headlines—for a while . . . But it can be a life sentence for the families left behind—and they will need our help.

The Fishermen and Mariners' Royal Benevolent Society, through its country-wide network of Honorary Agents, will give financial assistance **without delay** at such times of loss and, if necessary, will continue to help on a regular basis.

The Society also makes grants to the elderly, chronically sick and disabled amongst the seafaring community and gives immediate practical and financial aid to all seamen shipwrecked on our coasts.

Please support our work with a donation or legacy, or if you know someone who might need our help contact us at:

Dpt.AFL, Shipwrecked Mariners' Society
1 North Pallant, Chichester, West Sussex PO19 1TL
Tel: 01243 789329   Fax: 01243 530853
E-mail: general@shipwreckedmariners.org.uk
Web: www.shipwreckedmariners.org.uk

ALEXANDRA HOUSE

(Royal United Services Short Stay Residence for Service Children)
20 Crownhill Fort Road, Crownhill, Plymouth PL6 5BX
Telephone: Plymouth 01752 781888
Patron: H.R.H. Princess Alexandra, the Hon. Lady Ogilvy GCVO
President: Naval Base Commander, HM Naval Base Devonport

The Foundation (formerly based at Newquay) has since 1839 looked after children of men and women in the Armed Services. Its short stay home is now established in a modern house to meet the immediate temporary need that arises when a family crisis occurs, such as injury to the father serving abroad, sudden departure of the mother to join him, and lack of relatives or friends to care for the children. The problem is met AT ONCE, at any hour of the day or night, and the children are cared for, placed in schools and by arrangement given whatever support they need, while family affairs are settled.

The House is run as a family home, not as an institution, and the manager has long experience in child care. It is supported by voluntary contributions and by a modest scale of payments by the parents.

Grants, covenants, donations and legacies are especially valuable to the Foundation as a Charity under current law, and an outline of the tax advantages to the donor or his estate may be obtained from the Comptroller by interested parties.

Urgent and emergency inquiries should be made by telephone as above. Routine correspondence should be addressed to the Comptroller.

THE ROYAL AIR FORCE MUSEUM

The Royal Air Force Museum exists to promote the public's understanding of the history and traditions of the Royal Air Force and aviation generally. The Museum operates two publicly accessible sites at Hendon, North London and at Cosford in the West Midlands. Both sites display world-class collections of aircraft as well as uniforms, flying clothing, personal relics, equipment and important documents. The interactive *fun 'n' flight* galleries at both Hendon and Cosford enable visitors to explore the science behind aviation by operating hands-on exhibits for themselves. Popular with visitors of all ages, *fun 'n' flight* is educational, interesting and a lot of fun! Both museums have restaurant facilities and the souvenir shops offer an extensive range of gifts, clothing, books, models and videos.

RAF MUSEUM, HENDON

Occupying fifteen acres of the former historic Hendon Aerodrome, the museum's collection of aircraft is housed in three gigantic halls. The Main Aircraft Hall, consisting of two First World War hangars, displays aircraft from the early days of aviation to the Tornado GR1. Life in the past and present RAF is covered and a dramatic simulation of a mission in the Eurofighter gives a glimpse into the future.

The Battle of Britain Hall focuses on the epic struggle of 1940. Apart from the unique collection of British, German and Italian aircraft, the museum has recently commissioned 'Our Finest Hour', a lively and stimulating interpretation of the Battle of Britain. This multi-media approach neither trivialises the events of the Battle nor endows them with false glamour, but it aims to attract and educate an audience for whom the Second World War is not recent history. Visitors may see a V1 flying bomb and a V2 rocket and walk through the mighty Sunderland flying boat.

Among the aircraft within the Bomber Command Hall are the Lancaster, Halifax, Wellington and Flying Fortress of the Second World War, the diminutive Sopwith Tabloid and DH9A of earlier days and the Vulcan and Valiant of the Cold War era. A special exhibition chronicles the events of the heroic 'Dambusters' Raid, making use of archive film footage and artefacts associated with the people involved.

Currently the Museum is undertaking its largest expansion since it opened in 1972. Construction has begun on a major new 'landmark' building to act as a new focal point for the whole Hendon site This barrel-vaulted stainless steel building, supported by funding from the Heritage Lottery Fund, will celebrate 100 years of aviation and the significant part played by British industry and the Royal Air Force. The exhibition "Milestones of Flight" will trace the history from the earliest gliders and kites to the Eurofighter of the future. The overall development also includes the relocation of the historic 1917 Grahame-White Aircraft Factory into which will be placed the oldest aircraft in the collection. On 17th December 2003 (100 years ago to the day, when Orville Wright flew 120' in a powered aircraft) this massive new development will be opened to the public.

RAF MUSEUM, COSFORD

Based on an active airfield the RAF Museum at Cosford is home to many huge retired British Airways airliners and Royal Air Force Transport aircraft telling the fascinating story of passenger and freight carriage by air from the early days of flying.

The unique and exotic aircraft in the Museum's Research and Development Collection demonstrate the dramatic strides in the advancement of aviation technology from the early days in 1941 when the first British jet aircraft made its maiden flight through the thrilling post-war period when jet airliners revolutionised world travel.

British, American, German, Argentinian and Japanese aircraft of the Second World War are found in the Warplane Collection, along with more modern military aircraft such as the Buccaneer, Venom and Jaguar.

Cosford is also home to one of the finest collections of aero engines in Britain. Power plants from early piston engined aircraft to modern jets are on show, some being sectioned to display the working parts.

The history and development of the guided missile is covered with a remarkable assembly of over 40 rockets and missiles ranging from wood and concrete experimental types to state-of-the-art technology.

Both the Hendon and Cosford sites of the Royal Air Force Museum are open from 10.00 to 18.00 hours every day with the exception of Christmas Eve, Christmas Day, Boxing Day and New Year's Day. Serving RAF personnel and their immediate families are admitted free on production of RAF form 1250. Accompanied children and senior citizens are also eligible for free entry. For details of admission prices, special events and for other information please concact:

Hendon
RAF Museum
Grahame Park Way
London
NW9 5LL

020 8205 2266

Visit our website at www.rafmuseum.org.uk

Cosford
RAF Museum
Cosford
Shifnal
TF11 8UP

01902 376200

Scottish Veterans' Residences

WHITEFOORD HOUSE
53 Canongate
EDINBURGH
EH8 8BS
0131-556 6827

THE MURRAY HOME
470 Gilmerton Road
EDINBURGH EH17 7SA
0131-664 3037

ROSENDAEL
3 Victoria Road
BROUGHTY FERRY
DUNDEE DD5 1BE
01382 477078

REGISTERED OFFICE
53 Canongate
EDINBURGH EH8 8BS
0131-556 0091

Patron-in-Chief
Her Royal Highness Princess Alice
Duchess of Gloucester
GCB, CI, GCVO, GBE

Charity No. SCO 15260

Chairman
Major General M.J. Strudwick, CBE

WHITEFOORD HOUSE and ROSENDAEL can accommodate up to 160 former members of the Armed Forces of the Crown in warm, comfortable surroundings. Both residences have first class communal facilities including TV rooms, games rooms and bowling greens. A high standard of full board catering is inclusive with the accommodation charge which is kept within DSS approved rates. No application need ever be turned away for financial reasons. **THE MURRAY HOME** accommodates a further 36 ex-servicemen in need of medical care and provides 24 hour cover in a more sheltered environment, as well as short term Respite Care. All residents are accommodated in fully furnished single rooms.

For details of the currently available accommodation contact the appropriate Manager. Please bring the above information to the attention of those who could benefit. We exist to serve their needs.

If, on the other hand, you are able to offer financial assistance with maintaining these facilities, donations should be sent to the General Secretary at the office address or else contact him for information about covenants or legacies.

SSAFA Forces Help is the national caseworking charity helping serving and ex-Service men and women and their families, in need. It is the only charity which provides such a breadth of support to the serving and ex-Service communities both in the UK and around the world.

- **In the serving community overseas** we offer: a professional, comprehensive, confidential and cost-effective range of welfare support services, including a social work and adoption service, to Armed Forces personnel and their families. This is available in Western Europe, Gibraltar and Cyprus

  - We employ midwives, health visitors, community psychiatric nurses, practice nurses, practice managers and pharmacists within the BFG Health Service.

- **In the serving community in the UK,** SSAFA Forces Help social workers advise and assist with welfare support within RAF Command. Our Community Volunteers, who are selected and trained Service personnel and family members, offer friendship and support

- **In the ex-Service community,** we offer: practical and personal welfare support; financial advice and support; training; residential care; short-stay accommodation and a Housing Advisory Service

- We have over 7,500 trained volunteers in the UK and overseas, based in branches and in-Service Committees helping more than 75,000 people annually

- More than 14 million people are estimated to be eligible for our help and their need is expected to grow into the next century

For more information please contact:

THE SOLDIERS, SAILORS, AIRMEN AND FAMILIES ASSOCIATION – FORCES HELP
19 Queen Elizabeth Street London SE1 2LP Telephone: 020 7403 8783 Facsimile: 020 7403 8815

E-Mail: info@ssafa.org.uk
www.ssafa.org.uk

THE ROYAL HOMES FOR OFFICERS' WIDOWS AND DAUGHTERS

Queen Alexandra's Court, Wimbledon
(A branch of SSAFA – Forces Help)
Chairman: Mr Tim Stranack BA, Solicitor

The accommodation comprises unfurnished self-contained flats for the widows, divorcees or unmarried daughters of Officers or Warrant Officers and women who are retired Officers or Warrant Officers of the Royal Navy, Army and Royal Air Force.

For full particulars application should be made in writing to:

The Manager, Queen Alexandra's Court, St. Mary's Road, Wimbledon SW19 7DE. Tel: (020) 8946 5182.

ROYAL UNITED SERVICES INSTITUTE FOR DEFENCE STUDIES

Whitehall, London SW1A 2ET

Tel: 020-7930 5854. Fax: 020 7321 0943. Web-site: *www.rusi.org*

The Aim of the RUSI

- keep you informed and up-to-the minute on both current and developing defence issues;

- provide depth and breadth to your interests, knowledge and expertise

- act as neutral ground for and encourage the exchange of opinions and ideas, both in person and in print.

The RUSI is independent of government and other political affiliations. We are and have been since 1831, dedicated to the study and vigorous debate of all issues of defence and international security, focusing particularly on Britain's interests, but set in a wide international context. We aim to develop fresh thinking and to develop options with an analysis of their implications. Our work ranges from defence procurement, technology and management, through the military sciences and strategic studies, to the causes, prevention and resolution of conflicts. We aim to make a difference.

Individual Membership is open to those serving in the armed forces and to members of the public who have a responsibility or simpy an interest in defence and security matters.

The fees to be a **'Member'** for a year are **£56.00** and include receipt of the bi-monthly RUSI journal, the bi-annual World Defence Systems, use of the Library, Reading Room and access to Lectures.

The fees to be a **'Full Member'** for a year are **£105.00** and include the above publications, plus receipt of the monthly RUSI Newsbrief and occasional Whitehall Papers.

A **40% discount** is given for the first year of Individual Membership and thereafter for those aged 30 or under.

Mess Membership offers the flexibility needed by a UK-based mess or unit, who wish its personnel to use the Institute. Mess members receive 1 full set of RUSI publications and access to the building as well as lectures for up to 5 members of the mess or unit per visit. The fees begin at £285.00 per year.

For further details, please contact the Membership Secretary by Post, Fax, E-mail: membership@rusi.org or log on to our Web-site: www.rusi.org

Founded in 1831   Patron: Her Majesty Queen Elizabeth   Charity No 21063

Providing
world class
services . . .

Naafi, in partnership with leading
commercial companies, provides a range of
services supporting the Armed Forces and
their families all over the world.

All our profits are either reinvested in our
shops and clubs to improve the quality of
facilities and services or returned in the form
of a dividend.

for the
British Armed Forces

Serving the Services Worldwide

Forces Pension Society—Your Pension Is Not Complete Without It

Since 1946 the Society has been *Fighting Your Corner* by planning strategy, directing operations and going into action on behalf of all ranks, their widows and dependants. At the FPS we aim to procure, where equitable, improvements in the AFPS for members of the Society, their widows, widowers and dependants, and to advise and assist them on Service Retired Pay and Service pension problems. We endeavour to promote these aims, in co-operation with other Service and civilian organisations, for all past, present and future members of the Armed Forces. *Independence from the Ministry of Defence* allows the FPS to campaign vigorously with Parliament, Ministers and the MoD to ensure that the AFPS is as good as it can be, and to have injustices and anomalies corrected. Examples of this are our War and Service Widows' campaigns in 1989 and 1995 which secured important changes in legislation.

All ranks can, and are encouraged, to become members of the Society for less than a pint of beer a month (£1.75 a month, or £20 a year (£9.00 for widows)). You may be tempted to ask *"What's in it for me"?* To begin with we have negotiated exclusively with the MoD that our members will have complete access to all benefits currently available to serving members of the Armed Forces, via the 'Forces Discount Brochure'. And even if our work doesn't affect you right now, there may well come a time when it will. More importantly, shouldn't we all feel a sense of duty to our fellow servicemen and women, their spouses and dependants, to present a united front?

Membership Secretary
Forces Pension Society
68 South Lambeth Road
Vauxhall
LONDON
SW8 1RL

Tel: 020 7820 9988
Fax: 020 7820 7583
Email: memsec@forpen.co.uk